Textbooks in Applied Mathematics

C. C. Lin, Editor

Linear Analysis and Differential Equations

Richard C. MacCamy
Victor J. Mizel
Carnegie-Mellon University

Linear Analysis and Differential Equations

The Macmillan Company
Collier-Macmillan Limited, London

To Fae and Phyllis

First Printing

Library of Congress catalog card number: 69-11796

THE MACMILLAN COMPANY
COLLIER-MACMILLAN CANADA, LTD., TORONTO, ONTARIO

Printed in the United States of Amerca

Preface

This book is designed to serve as an introduction to the subjects of differential equations and linear algebra. More specifically, it is designed to bring out the connections between the two subjects. It seems to the authors that the traditional separation of these areas into different courses has resulted in a loss to both. Furthermore, it appears that there has been an increasing tendency in scientific literature, at the research level, to draw upon the intimate connections between these two subjects. Therefore, it seems desirable to try to stimulate students, *at an early level*, to think in terms of linear analysis.

In addition to attempting to connect differential equations and linear algebra, we have also made an effort in this book to relate both subjects to physical principles. For instance, we have attempted to motivate mathematical ideas such as linearity, existence, and uniqueness, through associated physical concepts.

The course from which this book derives has been given to all sophomore engineering and science students at Carnegie-Mellon University. These students have all had a full-year course in calculus including an introduction to functions of several variables. However, a short review of this last topic as well as a few remarks about infinite sequences and series is included in Chapter 0.

It is our opinion that the book offers a certain flexibility in the design of courses. In a one-year course, students who have had adequate preparation in calculus should be able to complete the book. Such students would then have most of the work necessary in order to proceed into such courses as fluid mechanics or electricity and magnetism. They would also have a basis for further work in traditional upper-division mathematics courses. It is our opinion that *in either case* the necessity for the usual junior-level work in "mathematics for engineers and physicists" would be precluded.

It is also possible to develop a one-semester course more narrowly focused on ordinary differential equations and linear algebra. This could be done by utilizing only Chapters 1, 4, 5, 8, 9, and 10.

Various possibilities exist for pruning material in the book to accommodate either the one-semester or full-year courses outlined above. We have marked with an asterisk material both in problems and in the text that seems to us to be of a somewhat greater level of difficulty than the rest and that could be omitted. In addition, the following synopses should help in making a choice of material to be omitted: Chapter 2 is concerned with providing a technical basis for certain arguments in later chapters, in particular in Chapters 9 and 10, but can be skimmed lightly or even omitted altogether. Chapter 3 is devoted to a discussion of particle mechanics and can be omitted without formal loss of continuity; however, we feel that it does provide motivation for what follows. Chapter 7 applies the development of Fourier series in Chapter 6 to the study of boundary value problems (in one space dimension) for partial differential equations. Chapter 10 extends the study of systems of ordinary differential equations (Chapter 9) to include systems with complex eigenvalues, and it can thus be omitted if the consequent reduction of generality is acceptable. Chapters 11 and 12 concern integral theorems of vector analysis and their application to the derivation and treatment of boundary value problems (in three space dimensions) for partial differential equations. Because of the topics covered in earlier chapters, we feel that it has been possible to present the subject matter of Chapters 11 and 12 in a more unified way than is ordinarily encountered at this level.

Some remarks are in order in regard to things which have been left out of the text. To begin with, an effort has been made to minimize proofs which involve technical details. Rather, the goal has been to give the important theorems, often with no proof at all, and then to bring out their meaning through applications. With only a few exceptions, those proofs that have been included are both easy and illustrative of some point of special importance. In this connection, we have adopted the policy of reserving the title "theorem" for results of exceptional importance and designating other results by the term "proposition."

Many specific subjects could have been included and were not. In part this was in the interest of brevity, but in larger part these omissions reflect the authors' personal preferences. There is no mention of series solutions of ordinary differential equations or of the related topic of special functions. There is almost no discussion of matrix computation. There is no discussion of the Laplace transform. As to this last omission, however, the authors believe that most of the results obtainable by elementary transform techniques are already included, in a conceptually simpler fashion, in Chapters 9 and 10. In addition, a *proper* formulation of the Laplace transformation within the framework of linear analysis is rather difficult.

We have received generous help and stimulating encouragement from our colleague David Moskovitz. He was with the project from the very beginning and, as with everything affected by his wisdom and concern, this book has benefited greatly from his constructive and patient criticism. We also owe thanks to our colleagues James Greenberg and William Williams for their help in teaching from this material and improving the notes from which this book has developed.

Benjamin Haytock and Nathaniel Withers were very helpful in spotting errors and in recommending improvements. To them and to the other students who participated in this experiment, whether as "givers" or as "takers," our sincere thanks.

Our appreciation goes to Mrs. Lister McIver, Mrs. Carol Rumble, and Mrs. Joyce Smith for typing various drafts of the manuscript and to Miss Lois Croco for her valuable overall assistance.

R. C. MacCamy
V. J. Mizel

Pittsburgh

To the Student

This book is designed to introduce two areas of mathematics, *linear algebra* and *differential equations*. It would be difficult to overstate the importance of these areas, both in mathematics itself and in its applications to physics. Nearly all mathematical models of physical situations draw upon one or both of these disciplines.

Mathematics plays a major role in the study of many physical situations. This role might be called the process of generalization. The essential idea is to search for general mathematical principles which are applicable to a large variety of physical problems. Historically, people working in diverse fields such as mechanics and electricity painstakingly developed special mathematical tools designed to fit their specific problems. Only very slowly was it realized that many of the things which were being done over and over by different people were all special cases of general mathematical principles and thus could be done once and for all.

The idea of generalization is not an easy one to accept. It is often a great strain on one's patience to absorb a seemingly large amount of formal structure. Indeed, the reader will no doubt find places in this text in which it seems that the machinery is much too complicated for the problem to which it is applied. Here he will be in good historical company. The authors can only offer the assurance that an investment of time in the study of this machinery will eventually be of great value and that, in fact, without a mastery of these ideas, progress in contemporary mathematics and science is impossible.

To the Student

Contents

4
Ordinary Differential Equations 100

5
Bases, Coordinates, and Linear Differential Equations 144

6
Orthonormal Bases, Least Squares, and Fourier Series 192

7
Partial Differential Equations—I 250

0

Review of Calculus

1. Partial Derivatives

This preliminary chapter is intended to give a brief summary of three aspects of the usual courses in calculus. We do not provide proofs but simply state certain facts. If the ideas are not familiar to the reader or if he wishes to try his hand at exercises involving this material, he should consult any calculus textbook.

The first idea is that of the partial derivative. Here we consider functions of two variables.† We denote the two variables by x and t. If f is the function in question we write $f(x, t)$ for its value at the pair (x, t). The *partial derivative of f with respect to x at* (x, t) is then obtained by simply keeping t fixed, that is, treating t as if it were a constant, and calculating the ordinary derivative with respect to x. If this quantity exists, we denote it by the symbol $f_x(x, t)$ [it is also written $\frac{\partial f}{\partial x}(x, t)$]. *The partial derivative with respect to t at* (x, t), denoted by $f_t(x, t)$ or $\frac{\partial f(x, t)}{\partial t}$, is similarly obtained by considering x as a constant and calculating the ordinary derivative with respect to t.

†Precisely similar comments apply to functions of three variables, or indeed to any number of variables exceeding one.

(1.1) Examples. *f_x and f_t.*

(a) $f(x, t) = xt$: $f_x(x, t) = t$, $f_t(x, t) = x$

(b) $f(x, t) = xt^2$: $f_x(x, t) = t^2$, $f_t(x, t) = 2tx$

(c) $f(x, t) = x^3t^3$: $f_x(x, t) = 3x^2t^3$, $f_t(x, t) = 3x^3t^2$

(d) $f(x, t) = e^{xt}$: $f_x(x, t) = te^{xt}$, $f_t(x, t) = xe^{xt}$

(e) $f(x, t) = \sin(2x^2t)$: $f_x(x, t) = 4xt\cos(2x^2t)$, $f_t(x, t) = 2x^2\cos(2x^2t)$.

One can also calculate partial derivatives of higher order. Thus, if f is a function of x and t which has a partial derivative with respect to x for all (x, t) in some region of the x–t plane, then this partial derivative defines a new function in that region. We call this new function f_x; its value at the point (x, t) is $f_x(x, t)$. It makes sense then to ask whether this new function has a partial derivative with respect to x. If it does we denote this derivative by $f_{xx}(x, t)$. We could also ask whether f_x has a derivative with respect to t at (x, t). If it does we write this derivative $f_{xt}(x, t)$.

We observe that f_t, wherever it exists, also defines a function of x and t. Here again we could ask whether this function has partial derivatives with respect to x or t at a point (x, t). If it has a derivative with respect to x we write this $f_{tx}(x, t)$, and if it has a derivative with respect to t we write this $f_{tt}(x, t)$. We note the following theorem:

(1.2) Theorem. *If f_{xt} and f_{tx} both exist and are continuous in a region, then $f_{xt} = f_{tx}$ in that region.*

(1.3) Examples. Second Derivatives.

(a) $f(x, t) = xt^2$: $f_{xx}(x, t) = 0$, $f_{xt}(x, t) = 2t$
$f_{tx}(x, t) = 2t$, $f_{tt}(x, t) = 2x$

(b) $f(x, t) = e^{xt}$: $f_{xx}(x, t) = t^2e^{xt}$, $f_{xt}(x, t) = e^{xt} + xte^{xt}$
$f_{tx}(x, t) = e^{xt} + xte^{xt}$, $f_{tt}(x, t) = x^2e^{xt}$.

It should be clear that one can proceed to calculate higher-order partial derivatives. Thus f_{xxt} and f_{xtx} would denote the partial derivative of f_{xx} with respect to t and the partial derivative of f_{xt} with respect to x. These calculations are facilitated by the fact that once again it is true in most circumstances that the order of the subscripts is immaterial. Thus, for example, $f_{xxt} = f_{xtx}$ and $f_{xtt} = f_{ttx}$.

There exists a number of formulas called *chain rules* for calculating partial derivatives. We give one of these.

(1.4) A Chain Rule. *Suppose g is a function of a single variable z and let g' denote its derivative with respect to z. Let h be a function of x and t with partial derivatives h_x and h_t. Let f be the function of x and t obtained by substituting h into g. That is, f is defined by*

$$f(x, t) = g\big(h(x, t)\big).$$

Then

(i) $f_x(x, t) = g'\big(h(x, t)\big)h_x(x, t)$,
(ii) $f_t(x, t) = g'\big(h(x, t)\big)h_t(x, t)$.

We shall not give precise conditions under which this theorem is true. It suffices to say that essentially it is true whenever it makes sense; that is, one must be able to calculate the derivatives in question. For example, it would *not* make sense if $g(z) = \sqrt{z}$ and $h(x, t) = -x^2$. For then $g'(z) = 1/2\sqrt{z}$ and the formulas would require that we calculate $\sqrt{-x^2}$, which does not exist.

It is important to study the notation in (i) and (ii) carefully. Note that $g'\big(h(x, t)\big)$ means that one *first* calculates $g'(z)$, as a function of z, and *then* replaces z by $h(x, t)$. An example of the chain rule is provided by (e) of examples (1.1). There we have $g(z) = \sin z$, so that $g'(z) = \cos z$, and $h(x, t) = 2x^2t$, so that $h_x(x, t) = 4xt$ and $h_t(x, t) = 2x^2$. It is easy to check that the given g and h do lead to the desired f:

$$f(x, t) = g\big(h(x, t)\big) = \sin(2x^2t).$$

Thus (i) yields

$$f_x(x, t) = g'\big(h(x, t)\big)h_x(x, t) = \cos(2x^2t)4xt.$$

This agrees with the formula we obtained in example (1.1e) without use of a chain rule.

There exists a law of the mean for partial derivatives which we state now.

(1.5) Law of the Mean for Partial Derivatives. *Suppose f has continuous partial derivatives f_x and f_t in some region R. Let (x, t) and (x', t') be two points in R and suppose that the line segment joining (x, t) and (x', t') lies entirely in R (see Figure 0.1). Then there exists a point (ξ, τ) on this line segment such that*

$$f(x', t') = f(x, t) + f_x(\xi, \tau)(x' - x) + f_t(\xi, \tau)(t' - t).$$

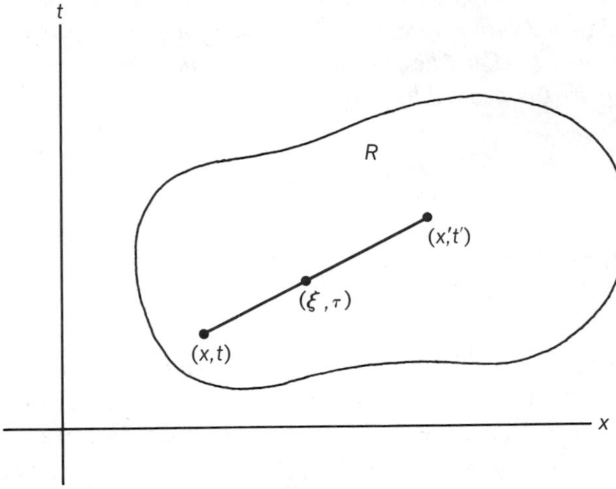

Figure 0.1

2. Double Integrals

In this section we discuss the integrals of functions of two variables in a special situation. Suppose that f is a function defined on a region R of the type shown in Figure 0.2. The distinguishing feature of the regions we want to consider is that any vertical or horizontal line intersects the boundary of

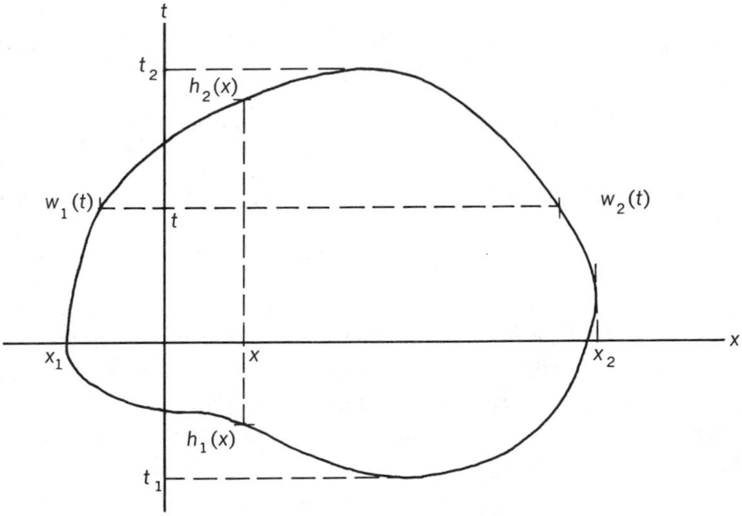

Figure 0.2

the region exactly twice. At a fixed value of x we denote by $h_1(x)$ and $h_2(x)$, respectively, the values of t at the lower and upper intersections of the vertical line at position x with the boundary. Similarly, $w_1(t)$ and $w_2(t)$ are, respectively, the values of x at the left and right intersections of the horizontal line at position t with the boundary. We let x_1 and x_2 denote the smallest and largest values of x in R and we let t_1 and t_2 denote the smallest and largest values of t in R.

Now let f be a function defined and continuous on R. For a fixed x consider the integral

$$\int_{h_1(x)}^{h_2(x)} f(x, t)\, dt.$$

This is an ordinary integral with respect to t. The result, however, varies with x; hence the integral defines a function of x. We integrate this function of x from x_1 to x_2 obtaining the quantity I_1; that is,

$$I_1 = \int_{x_1}^{x_2} \left(\int_{h_1(x)}^{h_2(x)} f(x, t)\, dt \right) dx. \tag{2.1}$$

We can also proceed the other way. For a fixed t consider the integral

$$\int_{w_1(t)}^{w_2(t)} f(x, t)\, dx.$$

This yields a function of t. We integrate that function from t_1 to t_2 obtaining the quantity I_2:

$$I_2 = \int_{t_1}^{t_2} \left(\int_{w_1(t)}^{w_2(t)} f(x, t)\, dx \right) dt. \tag{2.2}$$

The quantities I_1 and I_2 are called *iterated integrals* of f. It is a theorem that if f is continuous they both exist and are equal; that is, $I_1 = I_2$. Their common value is called the *integral of f over R* and is written

$$I_1 = I_2 = \iint_R f\, dA \qquad \left(\text{sometimes, } \iint_R f\, dx\, dt\right). \tag{2.3}$$

The reason for the symbol dA in (2.3) is that if one chooses f as the special function $f(x, t) \equiv 1$, then the resulting integral is called the *area of R*.

(2.4) Example. Double Integrals. We consider a very simple example of a double integral. Let R denote the rectangle $a \leq x \leq b$, $c \leq t \leq d$ (Figure 0.3). It is clear that for this region $x_1 = a$, $x_2 = b$, $t_1 = c$, and $t_2 = d$. Moreover, we have $h_1(x) = c$, $h_2(x) = d$ for $a \leq x \leq b$ and $w_1(t) = a$, $w_2(t) = b$ for $c \leq t \leq d$.

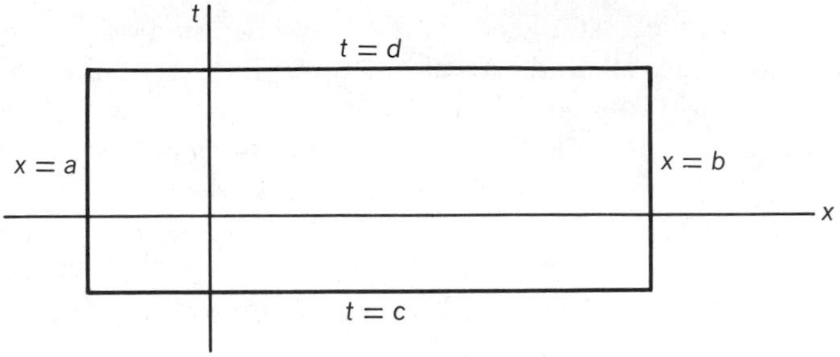

Figure 0.3

Now consider the function f defined by $f(x, t) = x^2t$. Formula (2.1) becomes

$$I_1 = \int_a^b \left(\int_c^d x^2t\,dt\right) dx = \int_a^b x^2 \left[\frac{t^2}{2}\right]_c^d dx = \int_a^b x^2\left(\frac{d^2}{2} - \frac{c^2}{2}\right) dx$$
$$= \left(\frac{d^2}{2} - \frac{c^2}{2}\right)\left[\frac{x^3}{3}\right]_a^b = \left(\frac{d^2}{2} - \frac{c^2}{2}\right)\left(\frac{b^3}{3} - \frac{a^3}{3}\right).$$

On the other hand, (2.2) yields

$$I_2 = \int_c^d \left(\int_a^b x^2t\,dx\right) dt = \int_c^d t\left[\frac{x^3}{3}\right]_a^b dt = \int_c^d t\left(\frac{b^3}{3} - \frac{a^3}{3}\right) dt$$
$$= \left(\frac{b^3}{3} - \frac{a^3}{3}\right)\left[\frac{t^2}{2}\right]_c^d = \left(\frac{b^3}{3} - \frac{a^3}{3}\right)\left(\frac{d^2}{2} - \frac{c^2}{2}\right).$$

3. Infinite Sequences

Let t be a number between 0 and 1 and consider the quantity $1/(1 - t)$. If one divides 1 by $1 - t$, one finds easily the formulas

$$(3.1)\qquad \frac{1}{1-t} = 1 + t + \cdots + t^n + \frac{t^{n+1}}{1-t}, \qquad n = 0, 1, 2, 3, \ldots.$$

For a fixed t let $a_n(t)$ for $n = 0, 1, 2, \ldots$ denote the numbers

$$a_0(t) = 1, \quad a_1(t) = 1 + t, \quad a_2(t) = 1 + t + t^2, \ldots,$$
$$a_n(t) = 1 + t + \cdots + t^n, \ldots$$

Since we can choose n arbitrarily large, there is an unending list of these numbers $a_n(t)$. We call such an unending list of numbers an *infinite sequence* and designate it by $\{a_n(t)\}$.

Observe that (3.1) yields the relations

$$(3.2)\qquad \left|\frac{1}{1-t} - a_n(t)\right| = \left|\frac{1}{1-t} - (1 + t + \cdots + t^n)\right| = \left|\frac{t^{n+1}}{1-t}\right|, \qquad n = 1, 2, \ldots .$$

Now, for any fixed t which is between 0 and 1 we note that the right side of (3.2) gets smaller and smaller as n gets larger. For example, if $t = \frac{1}{2}$, then the right side is $(\frac{1}{2})^n$. We note further that if we specify any number $\varepsilon > 0$, no matter how small, we can always choose n large enough so that the right side of (3.2), for $t = \frac{1}{2}$, is less than ε. For example, if $\varepsilon = \frac{1}{10}$, then for $n = 4$ we have

$$(\tfrac{1}{2})^n = (\tfrac{1}{2})^4 = \tfrac{1}{16} < \tfrac{1}{10}.$$

More than this, though, not only is $(\frac{1}{2})^n < \frac{1}{10}$ for $n = 4$ but also $(\frac{1}{2})^n < \frac{1}{10}$ for all n greater than or equal to 4.

We say in the above situation that the infinite sequence $\{a_n(\frac{1}{2})\}$ *converges* to the number $1/(1 - \frac{1}{2}) = 2$. More generally, we make the following definition:

(3.3) Definition. The infinite sequence $\{a_n\}$ of numbers **converges** to a if given any number $\varepsilon > 0$ there exists an integer N such that for *all* $n \geq N$ one has the inequality

$$|a - a_n| < \varepsilon.$$

If $\{a_n\}$ converges to a, we write $a_n \to a$ or $\lim_{n\to\infty} a_n = a$.

In the above example with $\varepsilon = \frac{1}{10}$ we could take N to be 4. Observe that had we taken ε smaller in the example then we would have had to take N larger. For example, if $\varepsilon = \frac{1}{100}$, then

$$(\tfrac{1}{2})^n \leq \tfrac{1}{100} \qquad \text{if } n \geq 7;$$

hence we would take $N \geq 7$. Observe also that had we taken a different value of t, then for the same value of ε, N might have to be changed. For example, if we took $t = \frac{3}{4}$, then the right side of (3.2) would be $(\frac{3}{4})^{n+1}/\frac{1}{4} = 3^{n+1}/4^n$. If we want this to be less than say $\varepsilon = \frac{1}{10}$, then we must make $n \geq 13$; hence here we have to take $N \geq 13$.

The idea of convergence of sequences is of fundamental importance in mathematics. We point out that it is the basis for much of arithmetic. If one wishes to compute things, then he must do all his calculations with rational numbers, that is, fractions. On the other hand, one does wish to compute quantities such as $\sqrt{2}$ which are *not* rational numbers. What is done in practice is to calculate a number of *rational* numbers $a_1, a_2, \ldots, a_n$ which, one hopes, get closer and closer to $\sqrt{2}$. The underlying idea here is that there is actually an infinite sequence $\{a_n\}$ of rational numbers which converges to $\sqrt{2}$, of which $a_1, \ldots, a_n$ are the first n terms.

From the formula (3.2) we were able to determine explicitly the number to which the $a_n(t)$'s converged. It usually happens that one is presented with a more difficult situation. One has an infinite sequence $\{a_n\}$ and one suspects that there is some a to which it converges but the value of that a is not known. It is important in this connection to have tests which can be applied directly to the sequence and which will enable one to determine whether or not there is some a to which it converges. There are such tests. The first one we mention is of fundamental theoretical importance and is called the *Cauchy criterion.*

(3.4) Theorem. *An infinite sequence $\{a_n\}$ will converge to some number a if and only if given any $\varepsilon > 0$ there is an integer N such that for all integers m and n greater than or equal to N we have the inequality*

$$|a_n - a_m| < \varepsilon.$$

We emphasize that theorem (3.4) in no way tells how to calculate a; it merely gives conditions for some such a to exist or not exist.

Theorem (3.4) is usually hard to use in practice. There is a more specialized test which applies in the situations we shall encounter in this book. This test applies to a special class of sequences which arise from what are called *infinite series.* Suppose we have an infinite sequence $\{b_n\}$ made up of numbers $b_1, b_2, \ldots$. From these we form another sequence $\{a_n\}$ as follows. Set

$$\text{(3.5)} \qquad a_1 = b_1, \qquad a_2 = b_1 + b_2, \qquad a_3 = b_1 + b_2 + b_3, \ldots,$$
$$a_n = b_1 + b_2 + \cdots + b_n, \ldots.$$

Now we can give a very useful criterion for the convergence of the sequence $\{a_n\}$. This criterion is stated in terms of the b_n's. (It combines two well-known tests called the *comparison test* and the *ratio test.*)

(3.6) Theorem. *Let $\{a_n\}$ be the infinite sequence defined by formula* (3.5).

(i) *Suppose that $|b_n| \leq \beta_n$ for all n. Suppose further that there exists a number ρ, $0 < \rho < 1$, and an integer N such that*

$$(*) \qquad \frac{\beta_{n+1}}{\beta_n} \leq \rho \qquad \text{for all } n \geq N.$$

Then there exists an a *such that* $\lim_{n\to\infty} a_n = a$.

(ii) *Suppose that* $|b_n| \geq \beta_n$ *for all* n. *Suppose further that there exists a number* $\rho > 1$ *and an integer* N *such that*

$$(**) \qquad \frac{\beta_{n+1}}{\beta_n} \geq \rho \qquad \text{for all } n \geq N.$$

Then there is no a *such that* $\lim_{n\to\infty} a_n = a$. (In this case we say that the sequence $\{a_n\}$ *diverges.*)

Theorem (3.6) is particularly useful when the sequence in question has elements which depend on t. We give two examples.

(3.7) Examples

(a) We apply theorem (3.6) to the example we first considered, that is,

$$a_0(t) = 1,\ a_1(t) = 1 + t, \ldots, a_n(t) = 1 + t + \cdots + t^n, \ldots$$

This is (almost) of the form (3.5) with $b_0 = 1$, $b_1 = t, \ldots, b_n = t^n$. Suppose $|t| \leq \rho < 1$. Then we have $|b_n| \leq \beta_n = \rho^n$ and

$$\frac{\beta_{n+1}}{\beta_n} \leq \left|\frac{\rho^{n-1}}{\rho^n}\right| = \rho.$$

Thus (*) holds with $N = 1$ and we conclude that the sequence $\{a_n(t)\}$ converges to some $a(t)$ for any t with $|t| < 1$. [In fact, by (3.2) we know in this case that $a(t) = 1/(1 - t)$.]

(b) Let $\{a_n(t)\}$ be the sequence

$$\begin{aligned}
a_1(t) &= 1\\
a_2(t) &= 1 + t\\
a_3(t) &= 1 + t + (t^2/2)\\
a_4(t) &= 1 + t + (t^2/2) + (t^3/2 \cdot 3), \ldots\\
&\quad \cdot \qquad \cdot \qquad \cdot\\
a_n(t) &= 1 + t + (t^2/2) + (t^3/2 \cdot 3) + \cdots\\
&\quad + (t^{n-1}/2 \cdot 3 \cdot 4 \cdot \ldots \cdot (n-1)),\\
&\quad \cdot \qquad \cdot \qquad \cdot
\end{aligned}$$

This is of the form (3.5) with

$$b_n(t) = t^{n-1}/2 \cdot 3 \cdot 4 \cdot \ldots \cdot (n-1).$$

Suppose $|t| \leq T$. Then we have

$$|b_n(t)| \leq \beta_n = T^{n-1}/2 \cdot 3 \cdot 4 \cdot \ldots \cdot (n-1)$$

and

$$\text{(i)} \qquad \frac{\beta_{n+1}}{\beta_n} = \frac{T^n}{2 \cdot 3 \cdot 4 \cdot \ldots \cdot n} \frac{2 \cdot 3 \cdot \ldots \cdot (n-1)}{T^{n-1}} = \frac{T}{n}.$$

Choose an integer N so large that $T/N < \frac{1}{2}$. Then by (i) we have

$$\frac{\beta_{n+1}}{\beta_n} \leq \rho = \tfrac{1}{2} \qquad \text{for } n \geq N.$$

It follows that the sequence $\{a_n(t)\}$ converges to some $a(t)$ for *any* t. [The quantity $a(t)$ to which it converges is, in fact, e^t.]

1

Vectors and Vector Spaces

0. Introduction

Consider two particles, one moving and the other at rest at the point Q. If we observe the particles at some instant t_1, they will be located at points $P(t_1)$ and Q, respectively. The displacement from the stationary particle to the moving particle is then best represented by an arrow $\overline{QP}(t_1)$ whose tail is at Q and whose head is at $P(t_1)$ (Figure 1.1).

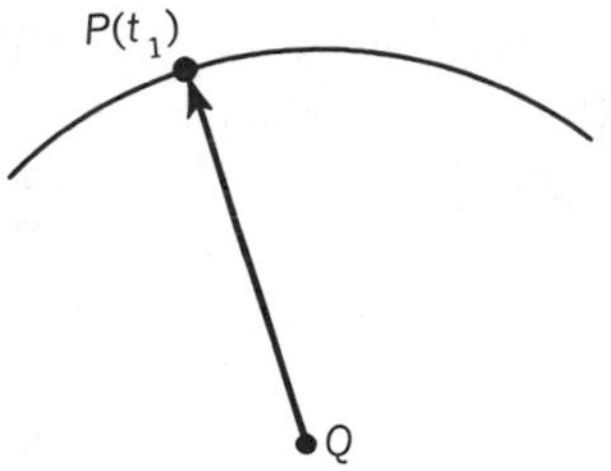

Figure 1.1

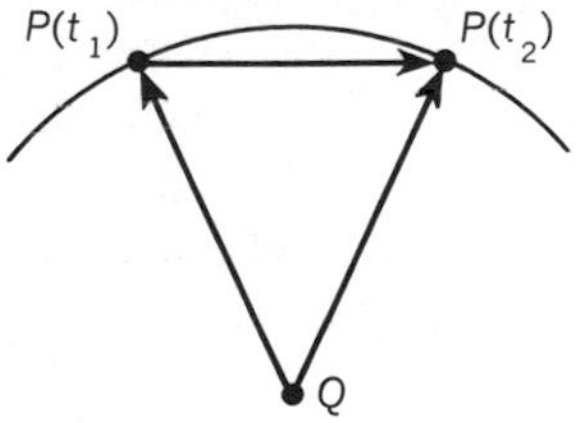

Figure 1.2

If we now observe these same particles at some later time t_2, then the moving particle occupies a new location $P(t_2)$ while the stationary particle remains at Q. The displacement undergone by the moving particle from time t_1 to time t_2 is represented by an arrow from $P(t_1)$ to $P(t_2)$, while the displacement at time t_2 from the stationary to the moving particle is given by $\overline{QP}(t_2)$ (Figure 1.2). It has been found useful in such situations to interpret the resultant displacement between the particles at time t_2 as the *sum* of the displacement between them at time t_1 and the displacement undergone by the moving particle from t_1 to t_2:

$$\overline{QP}(t_2) = \overline{QP}(t_1) + \overline{P(t_1)P(t_2)}. \tag{0.1}$$

Consider next the differential equation of a vibrating spring:

$$\frac{d^2x}{dt^2} + k^2x = 0. \tag{0.2}$$

It will be shown later that each solution of this equation can be put in the form

$$x(t) = A \sin(kt + B) \tag{0.3}$$

for an appropriate amplitude A and phase angle B. Now suppose x_1, x_2 denote solutions of (0.2). We can add the functions x_1 and x_2 to get a new *function* $x_1 + x_2$ (see Figure 1.3). This function is defined by specifying its value for each t; that is,

$$\begin{aligned} (x_1 + x_2)(t) &= x_1(t) + x_2(t) \\ &= A_1 \sin(kt + B_1) + A_2 \sin(kt + B_2). \end{aligned} \tag{0.4}$$

What is particularly important to note is that $x_1 + x_2$ is also a *solution of* (0.2) (see problem 1 of §1). That is, sums of solutions of (0.2) are themselves solutions of (0.2).

In this book we shall frequently deal with systems of mathematical objects for which an operation analogous to ordinary addition is available. As we have seen, two examples of such systems are (a) the class of all rectilinear displacements in space, and (b) the class of all functions which satisfy a certain differential equation. Superficially these two systems have no re-

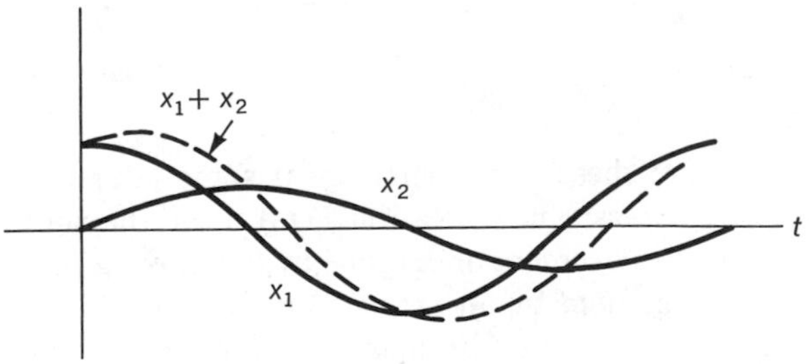

Figure 1.3

lationship to one another. Yet it has been discovered that because of the addition notions for these systems there is actually a profound analogy. This analogy suggests that we save time and mental effort by learning just *once* the basic facts common to these and other systems. Such an economy has been made possible because mathematicians have succeeded in distilling out of the various systems in which we are interested the important properties which they possess in common. The result has been the description of a mathematical structure called a *vector space*. It is defined by a list of properties (axioms) which are shared by many different mathematical systems. Any system having all properties in the list can be called a vector space.

1. Linear (Vector) Spaces

The axioms for a real vector space are given below. (The term *real* is only needed when contrasting with the *complex* vector spaces to be introduced in Chapter 10; hence this term will usually be omitted.)

(1.1) Definition. A (*real*) **vector space** consists of a set $\mathcal{V}$ of quantities $\boldsymbol{\alpha}$, $\boldsymbol{\beta}$, . . . called *vectors* for which two operations are prescribed. One operation assigns to each pair of vectors $\boldsymbol{\alpha}$, $\boldsymbol{\beta}$ a third vector called their *sum* and designated by $\boldsymbol{\alpha} + \boldsymbol{\beta}$. The other operation assigns to each real number c and each vector $\boldsymbol{\alpha}$ a second vector called the *c-multiple* of $\boldsymbol{\alpha}$ and designated by $c\boldsymbol{\alpha}$.

The operation of forming the sum of two vectors is called *addition*; the operation of forming the c-multiple of a vector is called *scalar multiplication*. It is required that addition and scalar multiplication have the following properties:

(A_1) Addition is commutative: $\boldsymbol{\alpha} + \boldsymbol{\beta} = \boldsymbol{\beta} + \boldsymbol{\alpha}$ for all $\boldsymbol{\alpha},\boldsymbol{\beta} \in \mathcal{V}$.†
(A_2) Addition is associative: $(\boldsymbol{\alpha} + \boldsymbol{\beta}) + \boldsymbol{\gamma} = \boldsymbol{\alpha} + (\boldsymbol{\beta} + \boldsymbol{\gamma})$ for all $\boldsymbol{\alpha},\boldsymbol{\beta},\boldsymbol{\gamma} \in \mathcal{V}$.
(A_3) $\mathcal{V}$ has a vector $\mathbf{0}$ called the *zero* or *null vector* for which $\boldsymbol{\alpha} + \mathbf{0} = \boldsymbol{\alpha}$ for all $\boldsymbol{\alpha} \in \mathcal{V}$.
(A_4) For each $\boldsymbol{\alpha} \in \mathcal{V}$ the equation $\mathbf{x} + \boldsymbol{\alpha} = \mathbf{0}$ has a unique solution for the vector $\mathbf{x}$. This vector is called the *negative* of $\boldsymbol{\alpha}$ and is denoted by $-\boldsymbol{\alpha}$.

We shall denote the quantity $\boldsymbol{\alpha} + (-\boldsymbol{\beta})$ simply as $\boldsymbol{\alpha} - \boldsymbol{\beta}$. This gives us a notion of *subtraction* of vectors.

---

†If S is a set of objects and x is some object, we write $x \in S$ if the object x belongs to the set S; and $x \in S$ is read "x belongs to S" or "x is a member of the set S."

(M_1) $1\boldsymbol{\alpha} = \boldsymbol{\alpha}$ for all $\boldsymbol{\alpha} \in \mathcal{V}$.
(M_2) Scalar multiplication is associative: $c_1(c_2\boldsymbol{\alpha}) = (c_1c_2)\boldsymbol{\alpha}$ for all $\boldsymbol{\alpha} \in \mathcal{V}$ and all numbers c_1, c_2.
(M_3) Scalar multiplication and addition are distributive:
(i) $c(\boldsymbol{\alpha} + \boldsymbol{\beta}) = c\boldsymbol{\alpha} + c\boldsymbol{\beta}$ for all $\boldsymbol{\alpha},\boldsymbol{\beta} \in \mathcal{V}$ and every number c.
(ii) $(c_1 + c_2)\boldsymbol{\alpha} = c_1\boldsymbol{\alpha} + c_2\boldsymbol{\alpha}$ for every $\boldsymbol{\alpha} \in \mathcal{V}$ and all numbers c_1, c_2.

The list of axioms for a vector space is long and many of the axioms are rather technical. The main things to keep in mind are the existence of the two operations and the fact that $\mathcal{V}$ is "closed" under these operations. That is, the sum of two vectors is always a vector in $\mathcal{V}$ and the c-multiple of a vector is always a vector in $\mathcal{V}$. We always use the symbol $+$ for the addition operation. We point out that in different vector spaces addition can mean entirely different things. Do not think because $+$ is used for addition in vector spaces that addition always has something to do with ordinary arithmetic. What *is* true, though, is that the very simplest example of a real vector space is just the set of real numbers in which we take both addition and scalar multiplication to have exactly the old meaning. The reader should verify this statement.

In the context of real vector spaces the word *scalar* is often used as a synonym for *real number*.

(1.2) Examples. Vector Spaces

(a) $\mathcal{R}^2$. Let S denote the set of all ordered pairs of numbers $\boldsymbol{\alpha} = (a_1, a_2)$, $\boldsymbol{\beta} = (b_1, b_2)$, $\boldsymbol{\gamma} = (c_1, c_2), \ldots$. Ordered means that one has to say which number is first. That is, (a, b) is not the same thing as (b, a). Define addition and scalar multiplication as follows:

$$\boldsymbol{\alpha} + \boldsymbol{\beta} = (a_1 + b_1, a_2 + b_2)$$
$$c\boldsymbol{\alpha} = (ca_1, ca_2),$$

where c is any scalar. S together with these rules of addition and scalar multiplication is a vector space which we denote by $\mathcal{R}^2$.

To prove that $\mathcal{R}^2$ is a vector space one must explicitly verify that with the above definitions each of the axioms in (1.1) holds. (That $\mathcal{R}^2$ is closed under addition and scalar multiplication is obvious.) To illustrate, the verification of the first four axioms goes as follows.

(A_1) $\boldsymbol{\alpha} + \boldsymbol{\beta} = (a_1 + b_1, a_2 + b_2)$, $\boldsymbol{\beta} + \boldsymbol{\alpha} = (b_1 + a_1, b_2 + a_2)$, so $\boldsymbol{\alpha} + \boldsymbol{\beta} = \boldsymbol{\beta} + \boldsymbol{\alpha}$.

(A_2)
$$\begin{aligned}(\boldsymbol{\alpha} + \boldsymbol{\beta}) + \boldsymbol{\gamma} &= (a_1 + b_1, a_2 + b_2) + (c_1, c_2)\\ &= \big((a_1 + b_1) + c_1, (a_2 + b_2) + c_2\big)\end{aligned}$$

$$\begin{aligned}\boldsymbol{\alpha} + (\boldsymbol{\beta} + \boldsymbol{\gamma}) &= (a_1, a_2) + (b_1 + c_1, b_2 + c_2) \\ &= (a_1 + (b_1 + c_1), a_2 + (b_2 + c_2)),\end{aligned}$$

so $(\boldsymbol{\alpha} + \boldsymbol{\beta}) + \boldsymbol{\gamma} = \boldsymbol{\alpha} + (\boldsymbol{\beta} + \boldsymbol{\gamma})$.

(A_3) A reasonable candidate for the null vector is $\mathbf{0} = (0, 0)$. Indeed, with this choice for $\mathbf{0}$,

$$\boldsymbol{\alpha} + \mathbf{0} = (a_1 + 0, a_2 + 0) = (a_1, a_2) = \boldsymbol{\alpha}.$$

(A_4) $\boldsymbol{\alpha} + \mathbf{x} = (a_1 + x_1, a_2 + x_2)$, so $\boldsymbol{\alpha} + \mathbf{x} = \mathbf{0}$ implies

$$a_1 + x_1 = 0, \qquad a_2 + x_2 = 0;$$

this gives for $\mathbf{x}$ the unique solution $\mathbf{x} = (-a_1, -a_2)$.

The reader should proceed in like manner to verify that the remaining three axioms hold for $\mathcal{R}^2$. In fact, it is important that he verify the validity of all seven axioms in *each* of the examples to follow.

(b) $\mathcal{R}^n$. Let n be a fixed positive integer; let S denote the set of all ordered n-tuples of real numbers $\boldsymbol{\alpha} = (a_1, \ldots, a_n)$, $\boldsymbol{\beta} = (b_1, \ldots, b_n), \ldots$. Define addition and scalar multiplication as follows:

$$\begin{aligned}\boldsymbol{\alpha} + \boldsymbol{\beta} &= (a_1 + b_1, \ldots, a_n + b_n) \\ c\boldsymbol{\alpha} &= (ca_1, \ldots, ca_n),\end{aligned}$$

where c is any scalar. S together with these rules of addition and scalar multiplication is a vector space which we denote by $\mathcal{R}^n$. A member of $\mathcal{R}^n$ is sometimes called an *n-vector.*

The reader is very likely familiar with the idea of displacements or arrows. However, we shall see that some subtlety is required to fit this idea into the general idea of a vector space.

(c) $\mathcal{A}$. Consider the set S'' of all rectilinear displacements $\overline{AB}$, $\overline{CD}, \ldots$ in space. Recall that these are just directed line segments starting at the first point indicated and ending at the second. We associate with the displacement $\overline{AB}$ a quantity $\boldsymbol{\alpha}$ which represents not only $\overline{AB}$ but all displacements $\overline{CD}$ which are related to $\overline{AB}$ in the following manner (see Figure 1.4):

(1) $\overline{CD}$ is parallel to $\overline{AB}$.
(2) $\overline{CD}$ has the same sense (orientation) as $\overline{AB}$.
(3) $\overline{CD}$ has the same length as $\overline{AB}$.

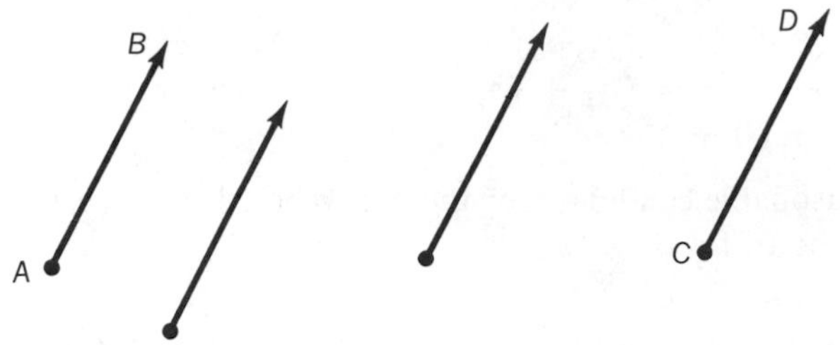

Figure 1.4

The quantity $\boldsymbol{\alpha}$ will be called an *arrow*, the arrow determined by $\overline{AB}$. Thus an arrow is a class of displacements having certain features in common, namely, properties (1), (2), and (3). Two displacements determining the same arrow are said to be *equivalent*. Thus the $\overline{AB}$ and $\overline{CD}$ pictured in Figure 1.4 are equivalent to each other. $\overline{AB}$ and $\overline{CD}$ are called *representatives* of $\boldsymbol{\alpha}$.

Let S' denote the collection of all arrows. We emphasize the difference between S' and the original set S''. The notion of collecting parallel displacements together may be familiar to the reader from physics, since in parts of mechanics all that matters is the magnitude and direction of a force, *not* the point at which it is applied.

Let $\boldsymbol{\alpha}$ and $\boldsymbol{\beta}$ be a pair of arrows. Their *sum*, which is an arrow to be denoted by $\boldsymbol{\alpha} + \boldsymbol{\beta}$, is defined as follows. Let $\overline{AB}$ be a representative of the arrow $\boldsymbol{\alpha}$. Choose a displacement $\overline{CD}$ which determines $\boldsymbol{\beta}$ and has $C = B$. Then $\boldsymbol{\alpha} + \boldsymbol{\beta}$ is defined to be the arrow determined by the displacement $\overline{AD}$ (Figure 1.5). Note that in certain exceptional cases this prescription fails to produce an arrow: If $D = A$, then the displacement $\overline{AD}$ is undefined.

Let c be a scalar and let $\boldsymbol{\alpha}$ be an arrow. The *c-multiple* of $\boldsymbol{\alpha}$, which is an arrow to be denoted by $c\boldsymbol{\alpha}$, is defined as follows.

CASE 1, $c > 0$. Let $\overline{AB}$ be a representative of $\boldsymbol{\alpha}$. Choose the point D so that $\overline{AD}$ has the same direction as $\overline{AB}$ but is c times as long as $\overline{AB}$. Then $c\boldsymbol{\alpha}$ is the arrow determined by the displacement $\overline{AD}$ (Figure 1.6a).

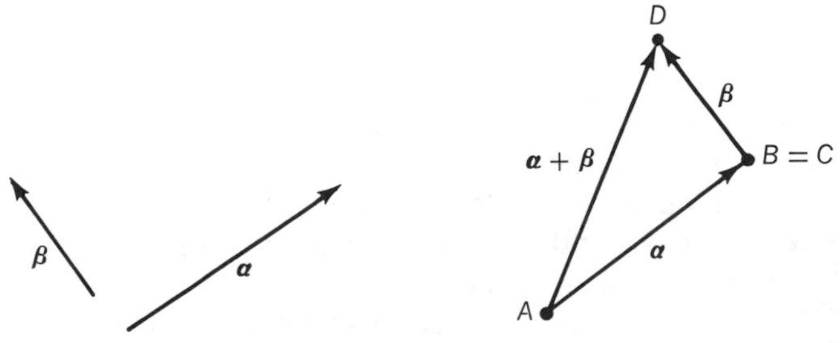

Figure 1.5

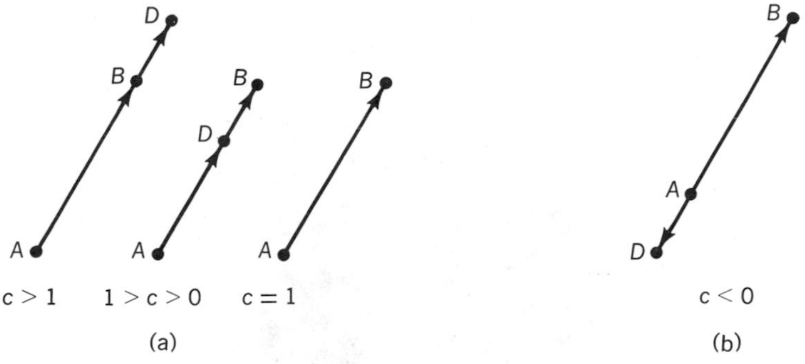

Figure 1.6

CASE 2, $c < 0$. Let $\overline{AB}$ be a representative of $\boldsymbol{\alpha}$. Choose the point D so that $\overline{AD}$ has the direction *opposite* to $\overline{AB}$ and is $|c|$ times as long as $\overline{AB}$. Then $c\boldsymbol{\alpha}$ is the arrow determined by the displacement $\overline{AD}$ (Figure 1.6b).

CASE 3, $c = 0$. Here there is no appropriate class of displacements for defining $0\boldsymbol{\alpha}$, but the desire for completeness compels us to introduce for this case an additional arrow $\mathbf{0}$ called the *zero* or *null arrow*. It corresponds to the exceptional "displacements" with coincident initial and end points encountered earlier. By agreement this arrow satisfies:

$$\mathbf{0} + \boldsymbol{\alpha} = \boldsymbol{\alpha} + \mathbf{0} = \boldsymbol{\alpha} \qquad \text{for all arrows } \boldsymbol{\alpha}$$
$$c\mathbf{0} = \mathbf{0} \qquad \text{for all scalars } c.$$

Using the above definitions, the set S consisting of S' *and* $\mathbf{0}$ is a vector space. We denote this vector space of arrows by $\mathcal{A}$. Axiom (A.4), that is, the existence of a solution of $\boldsymbol{\alpha} + \mathbf{x} = \mathbf{0}$, is satisfied by simply choosing $\mathbf{x}$ so that $\boldsymbol{\alpha}$ and $\mathbf{x}$ form an exceptional pair. That is one takes $\mathbf{x} = (-1)\boldsymbol{\alpha}$. The verification that S satisfies all the other axioms is a straightforward but rather tedious exercise in geometry and we omit it.

We want to connect the vector spaces $\mathcal{A}$ and $\mathcal{R}^3$. Let a point O be prescribed. Since an arrow has representatives at all possible initial points, we can depict every $\boldsymbol{\alpha} \in \mathcal{A}$ by that representative issuing from O. In this way each $\boldsymbol{\alpha}$ locates a definite point P in space by the requirement that $\overline{OP}$ represent $\boldsymbol{\alpha}$ (Figure 1.7). Now draw a set of three rectangular axes Ox^1, Ox^2, Ox^3. The point P is then determined by giving its coordinates (x^1, x^2, x^3) relative to these axes. Hence to each arrow $\boldsymbol{\alpha}$ corresponds a set of three numbers, the coordinates of P, and to each set of three numbers (x^1, x^2, x^3) corresponds an arrow $\boldsymbol{\alpha}$ determined by $\overline{OP}$, where P is the point with coordinates (x^1, x^2, x^3). Thus we have a one-to-one correspondence between arrows $\boldsymbol{\alpha}$ and triples (x^1, x^2, x^3). But more than this is true. Suppose that the arrows $\boldsymbol{\alpha}$ and

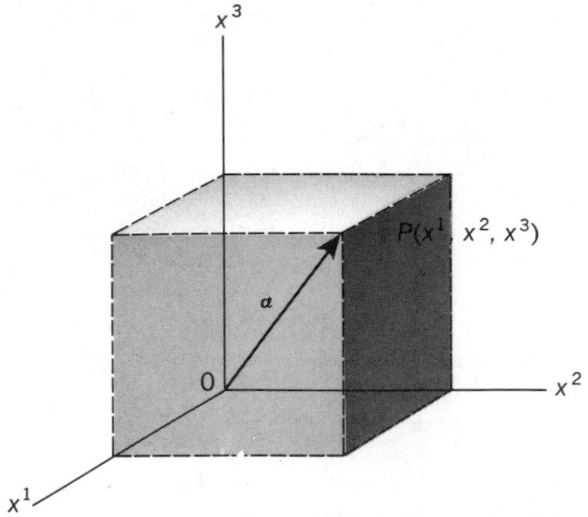

Figure 1.7

$\boldsymbol{\beta}$ correspond respectively to the triples (x^1, x^2, x^3) and $(\bar{x}^1, \bar{x}^2, \bar{x}^3)$. Then one can show, by some geometry, that the vector $\boldsymbol{\alpha} + \boldsymbol{\beta}$ will correspond in the same way to the triple $(x^1 + \bar{x}^1, x^2 + \bar{x}^2, x^3 + \bar{x}^3)$. Moreover, the vector $c\boldsymbol{\alpha}$ for any vector scalar c will correspond to the triple (cx^1, cx^2, cx^3).

Notation. Hereafter we shall denote the arrow $\boldsymbol{\alpha}$ represented by the displacement $\overline{PQ}$ by the symbol $\boldsymbol{\alpha} = \overrightarrow{PQ}$ whenever this is convenient.

(d) $\mathcal{C}[a, b]$. Let S denote the set of all continuous real-valued functions $f, g, \ldots$ defined on the interval $a \leq t \leq b$. Let $f + g$ denote the function in S whose value for each t is given by

$$(f + g)(t) = f(t) + g(t).$$

Observe this formula carefully. The $+$ on the left denotes addition in the vector sense in $\mathcal{C}[a, b]$, that is, addition of functions. The $+$ on the right means ordinary addition of the two numbers $f(t)$ and $g(t)$. Simlarly, for each number c, let cf denote the function whose value at t is given by

$$(cf)(t) = c\big(f(t)\big).$$

Note again that cf on the left does not mean the same thing as $cf(t)$ on the right. S, together with the above prescription for addition and scalar multiplication, is a vector space $\mathcal{C}[a, b]$, which is an example of what is sometimes called a *function space*.

A good way to think about the above space of functions is to visualize the functions by means of their graphs. Thus the whole graph of f as a function of t represents simply *one* vector in the space $\mathcal{C}[a, b]$. Two elements f and g and their sum $f + g$ as well as the function $-\frac{1}{2}f$ are represented in Figure 1.8.

(e) Let S denote again the set of all ordered pairs of real numbers $\boldsymbol{\alpha} = (a_1, a_2)$, $\boldsymbol{\beta} = (b_1, b_2)$, ... This time define addition and scalar multiplication as follows:

$$\boldsymbol{\alpha} + \boldsymbol{\beta} = ((a_1^3 + b_1^3)^{1/3}, (a_2^3 + b_2^3)^{1/3})$$
$$c\boldsymbol{\alpha} = (ca_1, ca_2).$$

The system S is *not* a vector space. The reader will find that it satisfies all axioms in (1.1) except the last. This example emphasizes the fact that the particular specifications of addition and scalar multiplication are as important as the set in the makeup of a vector space. A set S can be part of different vector spaces according to the specification of addition and scalar multiplication on S.

As an illustration of how strong the analogy is between the various mathematical systems which are vector spaces, we mention the following facts.

(1.3) Proposition. *Let $\mathcal{V}$ be any vector space. For any $\boldsymbol{\alpha} \in \mathcal{V}$ and any real number c we have*

(a) $0\boldsymbol{\alpha} = \mathbf{0}$.

(b) $c\mathbf{0} = \mathbf{0}$.

(c) $(-1)\boldsymbol{\alpha} = -\boldsymbol{\alpha}$.

If the product of a scalar and a vector is the zero vector, then either the scalar is the zero scalar or the vector is the zero vector:

$$c\boldsymbol{\alpha} = \mathbf{0}$$

implies that $c = 0$ or $\boldsymbol{\alpha} = 0$.

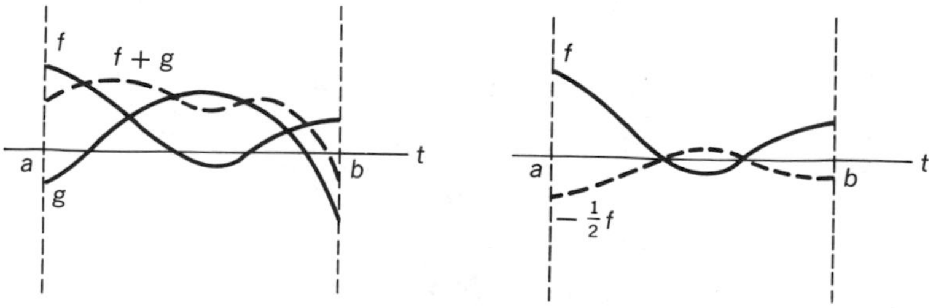

Figure 1.8

One's first impression of the formulas in the proposition is that they are obvious. This is quite wrong. For example, $0\boldsymbol{\alpha}$ is simply the product of the vector $\boldsymbol{\alpha}$ by the scalar 0. There is no reason at all that this need be the same as the $\mathbf{0}$ vector. That it is $\mathbf{0}$ is a theorem which has to be proved from the axioms given. We are not going to give proofs of these formulas, but we suggest that the reader try to construct them himself.

In Chapter 3 we shall show how the vector space of arrows can be used in the study of mechanics. Here we give an illustration of the use of arrows in the study of geometry.

(1.4) Examples. Arrows in Geometry

(a) Let P_0, P_1, P_2 denote three noncollinear points in space; let $\boldsymbol{\alpha}$ denote the arrow $\overrightarrow{P_0P_1}$ and $\boldsymbol{\beta}$ denote the arrow $\overrightarrow{P_0P_2}$. Let Q denote the point of $\overline{P_1P_2}$ whose distance from P_1 is r times the length of $\overrightarrow{P_1P_2}$, where r is an arbitrary real number satisfying $0 < r < 1$. We wish to express the arrow $\boldsymbol{\gamma} = \overrightarrow{P_0Q}$ in terms of $\boldsymbol{\alpha}$ and $\boldsymbol{\beta}$, as shown in Figure 1.9. We note that $\overrightarrow{P_0Q}$ is the sum of $\overrightarrow{P_0P_1}$ and $\overrightarrow{P_1Q}$, while $\overrightarrow{P_1Q} = r\overrightarrow{P_1P_2}$. Moreover, $\overrightarrow{P_1P_2}$ is the unique arrow $\mathbf{x}$ satisfying $\boldsymbol{\alpha} + \mathbf{x} = \boldsymbol{\beta}$; that is, $\overrightarrow{P_1P_2} = \boldsymbol{\beta} - \boldsymbol{\alpha}$. Thus $\boldsymbol{\gamma} = \boldsymbol{\alpha} + r(\boldsymbol{\beta} - \boldsymbol{\alpha})$. Simplifying we have

$$\boldsymbol{\gamma} = (1 - r)\boldsymbol{\alpha} + r\boldsymbol{\beta}. \tag{1.5}$$

(b) We prove that the medians of a triangle trisect one another. Let A, B, C denote the vertices of a triangle, and let P denote an arbitrary point chosen as "origin." Denote the arrow $\overrightarrow{PA}$ by $\boldsymbol{\alpha}$, $\overrightarrow{PB}$ by $\boldsymbol{\beta}$, and $\overrightarrow{PC}$ by $\boldsymbol{\gamma}$, as shown in Figure 1.10. Then by (1.5) the arrow from P to the midpoint Q_{AB} of $\overline{AB}$ is given as

$$\overrightarrow{PQ}_{AB} = \tfrac{1}{2}\boldsymbol{\alpha} + \tfrac{1}{2}\boldsymbol{\beta}.$$

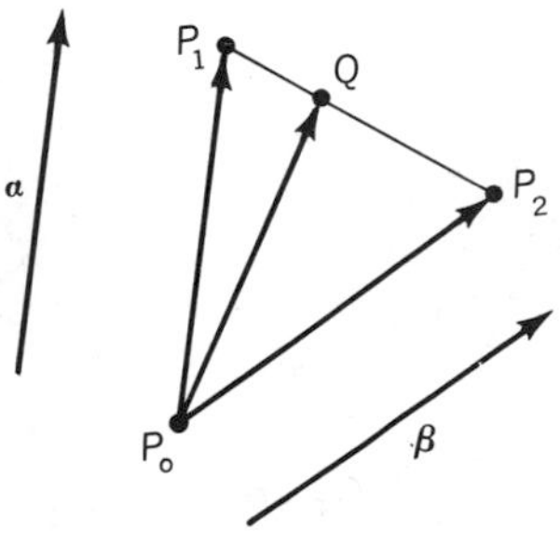

Figure 1.9

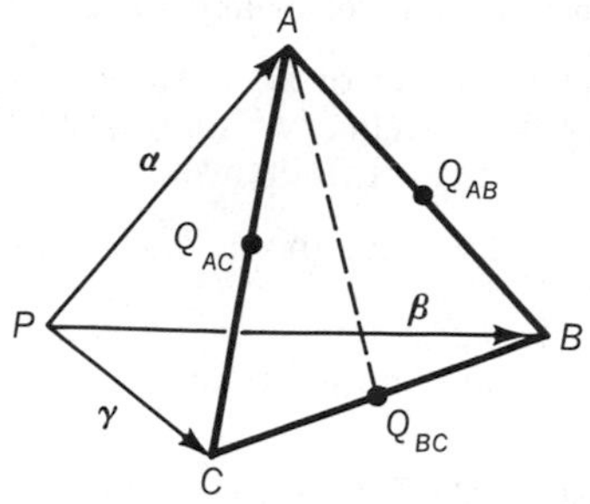

Figure 1.10

Similarly,

$$\overrightarrow{PQ}_{BC} = \tfrac{1}{2}\beta + \tfrac{1}{2}\gamma \qquad \overrightarrow{PQ}_{AC} = \tfrac{1}{2}\alpha + \tfrac{1}{2}\gamma.$$

Since we now know the arrows joining P to both end points of the median $\overline{AQ_{BC}}$ we can use (1.5) to obtain the arrow from P to any point of this median. In particular, the arrow from P to the point R which lies $\frac{2}{3}$ of the way from A to Q_{BC} is given by

$$\overrightarrow{PR} = \tfrac{1}{3}\alpha + \tfrac{2}{3}(\tfrac{1}{2}\beta + \tfrac{1}{2}\gamma).$$

Similarly, the arrows from point P to the point R' lying $\frac{2}{3}$ of the way from B to Q_{AC} and to the point R'' lying $\frac{2}{3}$ of the way from C to Q_{AB} are given by

$$\overrightarrow{PR'} = \tfrac{1}{3}\beta + \tfrac{2}{3}(\tfrac{1}{2}\alpha + \tfrac{1}{2}\gamma) \qquad \overrightarrow{PR''} = \tfrac{1}{3}\gamma + \tfrac{2}{3}(\tfrac{1}{2}\alpha + \tfrac{1}{2}\beta).$$

Since the arrows $\overrightarrow{PR}$, $\overrightarrow{PR'}$, $\overrightarrow{PR''}$ thereby turn out to be the same arrow, it follows that R, R', and R'' are the same point. This completes the argument.

PROBLEMS

1. In example (1.2a), verify axioms (M_1), (M_2), and (M_3).
2. Let $\alpha = (1, -1, 2, 0)$ and $\beta = (2, 6, 4, -3)$ be two vectors in $\mathcal{R}^4$. Compute the following vectors:

   (a) $\alpha + \beta$ (c) $\frac{1}{10}\alpha$

   (b) $10\alpha - 2\beta$ (d) $3\alpha - (t + 1)\beta$

3. Let $\alpha = (-1, 1)$ and $\beta = (2, 1)$ be two vectors in $\mathcal{R}^2$. Draw appropriate displacements in the plane for $\alpha, \beta, \alpha + \beta$, and $\alpha - \beta$.
4. For the vector space $\mathcal{A}$ draw pictures which illustrate the validity of axioms (A_1) and (M_3)-(i).

5. In example (1.2d), what is the $\mathbf{0}$ vector and what is the negative of a vector?

6. (a) Suppose we consider the set of all functions f in $\mathcal{C}[a, b]$ which have the property that $f(a) = 0$. Define addition and scalar multiplication as in example (1.2d). Show that one obtains a vector space in this way.

(b) What happens if one considers those f's in $\mathcal{C}[a, b]$ such that $f(a) = 1$?

7. Let $\mathcal{P}^n$ denote the set of all polynomials p of degree less than or equal to $n - 1$. Give a definition of addition and multiplication by a scalar which makes this into a vector space.

8. Let S denote the set of all ordered pairs of numbers $\boldsymbol{\alpha} = (a_1, a_2), \boldsymbol{\beta} = (b_1, b_2)$, ... Define addition and scalar multiplication on S in each of the following ways. In each case find out which of the axioms (1.1) is not satisfied.

(a) $\boldsymbol{\alpha} + \boldsymbol{\beta} = (a_1 - b_1, a_2 - b_2)$, $c\boldsymbol{\alpha} = (ca_1, ca_2)$

(b) $\boldsymbol{\alpha} + \boldsymbol{\beta} = (a_1b_1, a_2b_2)$, $c\boldsymbol{\alpha} = (ca_1, ca_2)$

(c) $\boldsymbol{\alpha} + \boldsymbol{\beta} = (2a_1 + 2b_1, 3a_2 + 3b_2)$, $c\boldsymbol{\alpha} = (ca_1, ca_2)$

(d) $\boldsymbol{\alpha} + \boldsymbol{\beta} = (0, 0)$ for all $\boldsymbol{\alpha},\boldsymbol{\beta} \in S$, $c\boldsymbol{\alpha} = (ca_1, ca_2)$

9. (a) Let S denote the set of all ordered pairs of *positive* numbers, $\boldsymbol{\alpha} = (a_1, a_2)$, $\boldsymbol{\beta} = (b_1, b_2)$, ... Define $\boldsymbol{\alpha} + \boldsymbol{\beta} = (a_1b_1, a_2b_2)$, $c\boldsymbol{\alpha} = (a_1^c, a_2^c)$. Is S together with this prescription for addition and scalar multiplication a vector space? (For this to be answered one must check *each* of the axioms.)

(b) Let S denote the set of all ordered pairs of numbers $\boldsymbol{\alpha} = (a_1, a_2)$, $\boldsymbol{\beta} = (b_1, b_2)$, ... with addition and scalar multiplication defined as follows:

$$\boldsymbol{\alpha} + \boldsymbol{\beta} = \left((a_1^3 + b_1^3)^{1/3}, (a_2^3 + b_2^3)^{1/3}\right), \qquad c\boldsymbol{\alpha} = (c^{1/3}a_1, c^{1/3}a_2).$$

Is this a vector space?

10. (a) Verify explicitly that all functions of the form (0.3) are solutions of (0.2).

(b) Let S denote the set of all functions of the form (0.3). Define addition and scalar multiplication as in example (1.2d). Show that this yields a vector space. State what the null vector and the negative of a vector are to be.

(c) Show that the function x defined by $x(t) = \cos kt$ can be written in the form (0.3); hence deduce that it is a solution of (0.2).

11. Let $\boldsymbol{\alpha}, \boldsymbol{\beta}, \boldsymbol{\gamma}, \boldsymbol{\delta}$ be four vectors in a vector space. Prove that

$$(\boldsymbol{\alpha} + \boldsymbol{\beta}) + (\boldsymbol{\gamma} + \boldsymbol{\delta}) = \left(\boldsymbol{\alpha} + (\boldsymbol{\beta} + \boldsymbol{\delta}) + \boldsymbol{\delta}\right).$$

12. Using the axioms (1.1), prove that the zero vector is unique, that is, if $\boldsymbol{\alpha}_0$ is a vector such that $\boldsymbol{\alpha} + \boldsymbol{\alpha}_0 = \boldsymbol{\alpha}$ for each vector $\boldsymbol{\alpha} \in V$, then necessarily $\boldsymbol{\alpha}_0 = 0$.

13. Prove part (a) of proposition (1.3). [*Hint:* By (M_1) and (M_3)–(ii) we have

$$\begin{aligned}\boldsymbol{\beta} + 0\boldsymbol{\alpha} = \boldsymbol{\beta} - \boldsymbol{\alpha} + \boldsymbol{\alpha} + 0\boldsymbol{\alpha} &= (\boldsymbol{\beta} - \boldsymbol{\alpha}) + 1 \cdot \boldsymbol{\alpha} + 0\boldsymbol{\alpha} \\ &= (\boldsymbol{\beta} - \boldsymbol{\alpha}) + (1 + 0)\boldsymbol{\alpha} = \boldsymbol{\beta} - \boldsymbol{\alpha} + \boldsymbol{\alpha}.]\end{aligned}$$

14. Using the technique of example (1.4b), prove that the diagonals of a parallelogram bisect each other.

15. (a) For any trapezoid with one base twice as long as the other, prove that the diagonals meet at a point which divides both diagonals in the same (fixed) ratio.

(b) Generalize this result to the case in which one base is c times as long as the other, for an arbitrary positive number c.

2. Inner Products

Let us return now to our earlier example of two particles in space. One quantity which we might wish to keep track of is the distance separating these particles. At time t_1 we would measure the distance between Q and $P(t_1)$. This distance, which is a nonnegative scalar, is equal to the length of the arrow $\overrightarrow{QP}(t_1)$ and we denote it by $\|\overrightarrow{QP}(t_1)\|$. Similarly, at time t_2 we would measure the quantity $\|\overrightarrow{QP}(t_2)\|$. A second quantity of interest would be the change in direction between the particles with the passage of time. For instance, at time t_2 we could measure the angle between the arrows $\overrightarrow{QP}(t_1)$ and $\overrightarrow{QP}(t_2)$ as indicated in Figure 1.11. This would be a certain real number θ in the interval $0 \leq \theta \leq \pi$.

This discussion makes it clear that much of the utility of the vector space $\mathcal{A}$ depends on the fact that arrows have more attributes than are involved in addition and scalar multiplication. Arrows also have length and angular separations from one another. In the sequel we shall systematically exploit these features to analyze motions of particles. But what of the other example discussed in the Introduction? For the differential equation

$$\frac{d^2x}{dt^2} + k^2x = 0, \tag{2.1}$$

is there any useful "length" to be associated with its solutions? Certainly one could think of various graphical quantities, for example, the arc length of the graph of x over some interval of time. However, this bears little analogy to the natural meaning of length for arrows. Therefore, it should come as a

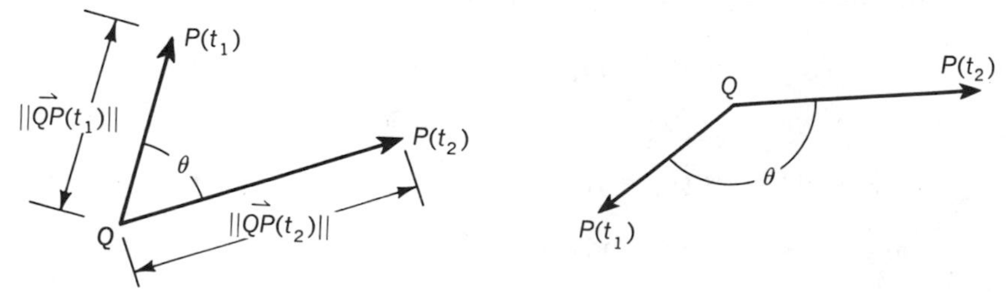

Figure 1.11

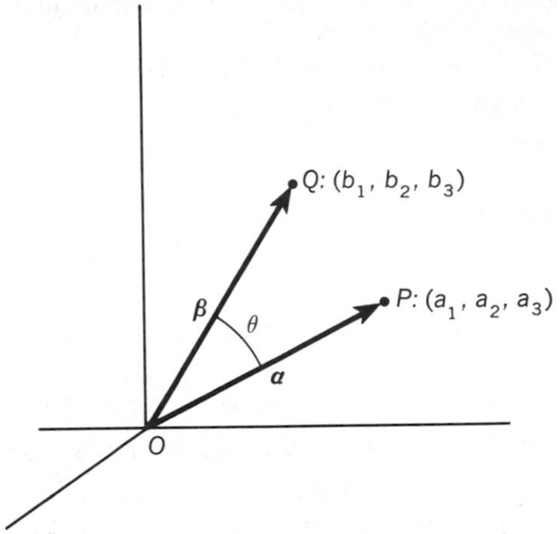

Figure 1.12

pleasant surprise to learn that there *is* a notion of length for solutions of (2.1), which permits a *geometric* analysis of this differential equation [see example (2.13c)]. We will see next how to introduce length and angle in a great variety of vector spaces. These geometric notions are introduced by means of the *inner product*.

Let us begin with $\mathcal{R}^3$. Since we have mentioned before the close relationship between $\mathcal{R}^3$ and the vector space $\mathcal{A}$ of arrows we have a ready made geometry for $\mathcal{R}^3$. If the arrows determined by $\overrightarrow{OP}$ and $\overrightarrow{OQ}$ correspond to vectors $\boldsymbol{\alpha} = (a_1, a_2, a_3)$ and $\boldsymbol{\beta} = (b_1, b_2, b_3)$ in $\mathcal{R}^3$, it is quite natural to define the *lengths* of $\boldsymbol{\alpha}$ and $\boldsymbol{\beta}$ to be the lengths of the displacements $\overrightarrow{OP}$ and $\overrightarrow{OQ}$, respectively, and to define the *angle* between $\boldsymbol{\alpha}$ and $\boldsymbol{\beta}$ to be the angle between $\overrightarrow{OP}$ and $\overrightarrow{OQ}$ (Figure 1.12). (Recall that θ is measured so that $0 \leq \theta \leq \pi$.)

Now analytic geometry provides formulas for the lengths of $\overrightarrow{OP}$ and $\overrightarrow{OQ}$ in terms of the coordinates of the points P and Q, and thereby permits us to specify the lengths of $\boldsymbol{\alpha}$ and $\boldsymbol{\beta}$, respectively. We are going to use the symbol $\|\boldsymbol{\alpha}\|$ to denote the length of any vector $\boldsymbol{\alpha}$. We have

$$
\begin{aligned}
\|\boldsymbol{\alpha}\| &= \|\overrightarrow{OP}\| = [a_1^2 + a_2^2 + a_3^2]^{1/2} \\
\|\boldsymbol{\beta}\| &= \|\overrightarrow{OQ}\| = [b_1^2 + b_2^2 + b_3^2]^{1/2} \qquad (2.2)\\
\|\boldsymbol{\alpha} - \boldsymbol{\beta}\| &= \|\overrightarrow{PQ}\| = [(a_1 - b_1)^2 + (a_2 - b_2)^2 + (a_3 - b_3)^2]^{1/2}.
\end{aligned}
$$

For the angle θ between $\overrightarrow{OP}$ and $\overrightarrow{OQ}$ we have, by the law of cosines,

$$\|\overrightarrow{PQ}\|^2 = \|\overrightarrow{OP}\|^2 + \|\overrightarrow{OQ}\|^2 - 2\|\overrightarrow{OP}\|\,\|\overrightarrow{OQ}\| \cos\theta.$$

On substituting the above expressions for $\|\overrightarrow{PQ}\|$, $\|\overrightarrow{OP}\|$, $\|\overrightarrow{OQ}\|$ into this formula one obtains, after suitable simplification,

$$\|\boldsymbol{\alpha}\|\ \|\boldsymbol{\beta}\| \cos\theta = a_1b_1 + a_2b_2 + a_3b_3.$$

The right side of this relation is called the *inner product*, *dot product*, or *scalar product* of $\boldsymbol{\alpha}$ and $\boldsymbol{\beta}$. It depends on the two vectors $\boldsymbol{\alpha},\boldsymbol{\beta} \in \mathcal{R}^3$ and is denoted by $\boldsymbol{\alpha}\cdot\boldsymbol{\beta}$ or $(\boldsymbol{\alpha}, \boldsymbol{\beta})$; thus

$$\boldsymbol{\alpha}\cdot\boldsymbol{\beta} = a_1b_1 + a_2b_2 + a_3b_3. \tag{2.3}$$

We recapitulate what we have done above. For displacements issuing from O there is a geometric notion of length and of angle between displacements. We have made an identification of each arrow with a triple of numbers. Then for such triples $\boldsymbol{\alpha} = (a_1, a_2, a_3)$, $\boldsymbol{\beta} = (b_1, b_2, b_3), \ldots$, we have *defined* something called *length* $\|\boldsymbol{\alpha}\|$ and something called inner product $\boldsymbol{\alpha}\cdot\boldsymbol{\beta}$. We first defined them geometrically in terms of the corresponding arrows and showed that this leads to formulas (2.2) and (2.3). We could just as well take formulas (2.2) and (2.3) as the *definition* of $\|\boldsymbol{\alpha}\|$ and $\boldsymbol{\alpha}\cdot\boldsymbol{\beta}$ when $\boldsymbol{\alpha}$ and $\boldsymbol{\beta}$ are triples. Note that the geometric fact that $|\cos\theta| \leq 1$ gives an algebraic theorem from (2.2) and (2.3); that is, for any (a_1, a_2, a_3), (b_1, b_2, b_3),

$$|a_1b_1 + a_2b_2 + a_3b_3| \leq \sqrt{a_1^2 + a_2^2 + a_3^2}\,\sqrt{b_1^2 + b_2^2 + b_3^2}. \tag{2.4}$$

If we take (2.2) and (2.3) as definitions, then we can also define the *angle between* $\boldsymbol{\alpha}$ and $\boldsymbol{\beta}$ when $\boldsymbol{\alpha}$ and $\boldsymbol{\beta}$ are triples, neither of which is $\mathbf{0}$. This is the unique angle θ in $0 \leq \theta \leq \pi$ such that

$$\cos\theta = \frac{\boldsymbol{\alpha}\cdot\boldsymbol{\beta}}{\|\boldsymbol{\alpha}\|\ \|\boldsymbol{\beta}\|} = \frac{a_1b_1 + a_2b_2 + a_3b_3}{\sqrt{a_1^2 + a_2^2 + a_3^2}\,\sqrt{b_1^2 + b_2^2 + b_3^2}}.$$

Observe that it is necessary to know that (2.4) is true in order to be able to find θ, since necessarily $\cos\theta$ lies between -1 and 1.

We proceed by analogy to define inner products, lengths, and angles for other vector spaces. We begin with the space $\mathcal{R}^n$.

(2.5) Definition. The **standard inner product** $\boldsymbol{\alpha}\cdot\boldsymbol{\beta}$ for two vectors $\boldsymbol{\alpha} = (a_1, \ldots, a_n)$, $\boldsymbol{\beta} = (b_1, \ldots, b_n) \in \mathcal{R}^n$ is defined by the relation

(a) $\boldsymbol{\alpha}\cdot\boldsymbol{\beta} = a_1b_1 + \cdots + a_nb_n.$

The **length** (or **norm**) of $\boldsymbol{\alpha}$ is denoted by $\|\boldsymbol{\alpha}\|$ and defined by

$$\text{(b)} \qquad \|\boldsymbol{\alpha}\| = [a_1^2 + \cdots + a_n^2]^{1/2} = (\boldsymbol{\alpha} \cdot \boldsymbol{\alpha})^{1/2}.$$

For every $\boldsymbol{\alpha} \in \mathcal{R}^n$ the length of $\boldsymbol{\alpha}$ is a real number, positive or zero. In fact, $\|\boldsymbol{\alpha}\| > 0$ for all $\boldsymbol{\alpha} \neq \mathbf{0}$, and $\|\mathbf{0}\| = 0$.

We shall proceed to show that, just as in $\mathcal{R}^3$, a notion of angle can be obtained for $\mathcal{R}^n$ in terms of its inner product. The formula for angle in $\mathcal{R}^3$ suggests that we try the following. Let $\boldsymbol{\alpha}$, $\boldsymbol{\beta}$ be two nonzero vectors in $\mathcal{R}^n$. We seek an angle θ (in radians) between 0 and π which is to be called the *angle* between $\boldsymbol{\alpha}$ and $\boldsymbol{\beta}$. We would like to define θ by the formula

$$\cos \theta = \frac{\boldsymbol{\alpha} \cdot \boldsymbol{\beta}}{\|\boldsymbol{\alpha}\| \, \|\boldsymbol{\beta}\|}.$$

However, to do this we must be sure that the right member lies between -1 and 1. Hence we want to show that

$$\frac{|\boldsymbol{\alpha} \cdot \boldsymbol{\beta}|}{\|\boldsymbol{\alpha}\| \, \|\boldsymbol{\beta}\|} \leq 1.$$

(2.6) Theorem

(i) *The standard inner product* $\boldsymbol{\alpha} \cdot \boldsymbol{\beta}$ *is bilinear; that is,*

$$(c_1\boldsymbol{\alpha}_1 + c_2\boldsymbol{\alpha}_2) \cdot \boldsymbol{\beta} = c_1(\boldsymbol{\alpha}_1 \cdot \boldsymbol{\beta}) + c_2(\boldsymbol{\alpha}_2 \cdot \boldsymbol{\beta})$$
$$\boldsymbol{\alpha} \cdot (c_1\boldsymbol{\beta}_1 + c_2\boldsymbol{\beta}_2) = c_1(\boldsymbol{\alpha} \cdot \boldsymbol{\beta}_1) + c_2(\boldsymbol{\alpha} \cdot \boldsymbol{\beta}_2)$$

for all $\boldsymbol{\alpha},\boldsymbol{\alpha}_1,\boldsymbol{\alpha}_2,\boldsymbol{\beta},\boldsymbol{\beta}_1,\boldsymbol{\beta}_2 \in \mathcal{R}^n$ *and all scalars* c_1, c_2.

(ii) *The standard inner product is symmetric; that is,*

$$\boldsymbol{\alpha} \cdot \boldsymbol{\beta} = \boldsymbol{\beta} \cdot \boldsymbol{\alpha} \qquad \textit{for all } \boldsymbol{\alpha},\boldsymbol{\beta} \in \mathcal{R}^n.$$

(iii) *The standard inner product is positive definite; that is,*

$$\|\boldsymbol{\alpha}\| \geq 0, \quad \textit{and} \quad \|\boldsymbol{\alpha}\| = 0 \quad \textit{if and only if } \boldsymbol{\alpha} = \mathbf{0}.$$

(iv) *The standard inner product satisfies Schwarz's inequality*

$$|\boldsymbol{\alpha} \cdot \boldsymbol{\beta}| \leq \|\boldsymbol{\alpha}\| \, \|\boldsymbol{\beta}\| \qquad \textit{for all } \boldsymbol{\alpha},\boldsymbol{\beta} \in \mathcal{R}^n.$$

Proof. Properties (i)–(iii) are simple consequences of the definition. We leave the proofs of these facts to the reader. Schwarz's inequality is more subtle and we supply a proof. First observe that (iv) holds if either $\boldsymbol{\alpha}$ or $\boldsymbol{\beta}$ is the zero vector; in this case both sides are zero. Thus (iv) is mysterious only when both $\boldsymbol{\alpha}$ and $\boldsymbol{\beta}$ are nonzero. Now we can form unit vectors (that is, vectors of unit length) $\boldsymbol{\alpha}/\|\boldsymbol{\alpha}\|$ and $\boldsymbol{\beta}/\|\boldsymbol{\beta}\|$. Then by (iii) we have

$$\text{(v)} \qquad \left(\frac{\boldsymbol{\alpha}}{\|\boldsymbol{\alpha}\|} + \frac{\boldsymbol{\beta}}{\|\boldsymbol{\beta}\|}\right) \cdot \left(\frac{\boldsymbol{\alpha}}{\|\boldsymbol{\alpha}\|} + \frac{\boldsymbol{\beta}}{\|\boldsymbol{\beta}\|}\right) \geq 0.$$

By (i) and (ii) we have

$$\begin{aligned}\left(\frac{\boldsymbol{\alpha}}{\|\boldsymbol{\alpha}\|} + \frac{\boldsymbol{\beta}}{\|\boldsymbol{\beta}\|}\right) \cdot \left(\frac{\boldsymbol{\alpha}}{\|\boldsymbol{\alpha}\|} + \frac{\boldsymbol{\beta}}{\|\boldsymbol{\beta}\|}\right) &= \frac{\boldsymbol{\alpha} \cdot \boldsymbol{\alpha}}{\|\boldsymbol{\alpha}\|^2} + \frac{2\boldsymbol{\alpha} \cdot \boldsymbol{\beta}}{\|\boldsymbol{\alpha}\| \, \|\boldsymbol{\beta}\|} + \frac{\boldsymbol{\beta} \cdot \boldsymbol{\beta}}{\|\boldsymbol{\beta}\|^2} \\ &= 1 + 2\frac{\boldsymbol{\alpha} \cdot \boldsymbol{\beta}}{\|\boldsymbol{\alpha}\| \, \|\boldsymbol{\beta}\|} + 1 \\ &= 2\left(1 + \frac{\boldsymbol{\alpha} \cdot \boldsymbol{\beta}}{\|\boldsymbol{\alpha}\| \, \|\boldsymbol{\beta}\|}\right).\end{aligned}$$

This formula, together with (v), yields

$$\text{(vi)} \qquad -1 \leq \frac{\boldsymbol{\alpha} \cdot \boldsymbol{\beta}}{\|\boldsymbol{\alpha}\| \, \|\boldsymbol{\beta}\|}.$$

A computation similar to (v) with

$$\left(\frac{\boldsymbol{\alpha}}{\|\boldsymbol{\alpha}\|} - \frac{\boldsymbol{\beta}}{\|\boldsymbol{\beta}\|}\right) \cdot \left(\frac{\boldsymbol{\alpha}}{\|\boldsymbol{\alpha}\|} - \frac{\boldsymbol{\beta}}{\|\boldsymbol{\beta}\|}\right)$$

yields the inequality

$$\text{(vii)} \qquad \frac{\boldsymbol{\alpha} \cdot \boldsymbol{\beta}}{\|\boldsymbol{\alpha}\| \, \|\boldsymbol{\beta}\|} \leq 1.$$

Multiplying both (vi) and (vii) by the positive quantity $\|\boldsymbol{\alpha}\| \, \|\boldsymbol{\beta}\|$ we deduce

$$-\|\boldsymbol{\alpha}\| \, \|\boldsymbol{\beta}\| \leq \boldsymbol{\alpha} \cdot \boldsymbol{\beta} \leq \|\boldsymbol{\alpha}\| \, \|\boldsymbol{\beta}\|. \qquad \blacksquare$$

(2.7) Definition. If $\boldsymbol{\alpha}$ and $\boldsymbol{\beta}$ are both nonzero vectors in $\mathbb{R}^n$, the **angle** between them is defined to be the unique number θ between 0 and π such that

$$\cos \theta = \frac{\boldsymbol{\alpha} \cdot \boldsymbol{\beta}}{\|\boldsymbol{\alpha}\| \, \|\boldsymbol{\beta}\|}.$$

If either $\boldsymbol{\alpha}$ or $\boldsymbol{\beta}$ is zero, the angle between them is not defined.

If $\boldsymbol{\alpha} \neq 0$, $\boldsymbol{\beta} \neq 0$ but $\boldsymbol{\alpha} \cdot \boldsymbol{\beta} = 0$, then $\theta = \pi/2$; we then say that $\boldsymbol{\alpha}$ and $\boldsymbol{\beta}$ are **orthogonal** to each other.

The success of our preceding introduction of geometry via the dot product into $\mathcal{R}^n$ suggests that we may advantageously do the same with other vector spaces.

(2.8) Definition. A Euclidean vector space is a vector space $\mathcal{V}$ together with a function I which assigns to every pair of vectors $\boldsymbol{\alpha},\boldsymbol{\beta} \in \mathcal{V}$ a real number $I(\boldsymbol{\alpha}, \boldsymbol{\beta})$ in such a way that

(i) I is *bilinear:*

$$I(c_1\boldsymbol{\alpha}_1 + c_2\boldsymbol{\alpha}_2, \boldsymbol{\beta}) = c_1I(\boldsymbol{\alpha}_1, \boldsymbol{\beta}) + c_2I(\boldsymbol{\alpha}_2, \boldsymbol{\beta})$$
$$I(\boldsymbol{\alpha}, c_1\boldsymbol{\beta}_1 + c_2\boldsymbol{\beta}_2) = c_1I(\boldsymbol{\alpha}, \boldsymbol{\beta}_1) + c_2I(\boldsymbol{\alpha}, \boldsymbol{\beta}_2)$$

for all vectors $\boldsymbol{\alpha},\boldsymbol{\alpha}_1,\boldsymbol{\alpha}_2,\boldsymbol{\beta},\boldsymbol{\beta}_1,\boldsymbol{\beta}_2 \in \mathcal{V}$ and all scalars c_1, c_2.

(ii) I is *symmetric:*

$$I(\boldsymbol{\alpha}, \boldsymbol{\beta}) = I(\boldsymbol{\beta}, \boldsymbol{\alpha}) \qquad \text{for all } \boldsymbol{\alpha},\boldsymbol{\beta} \in \mathcal{V}.$$

(iii) I is *positive definite:*

$$I(\boldsymbol{\alpha}, \boldsymbol{\alpha}) \geq 0, \qquad \text{and} \quad I(\boldsymbol{\alpha}, \boldsymbol{\alpha}) = 0 \qquad \text{if and only if } \boldsymbol{\alpha} = \mathbf{0}.$$

The function I is called an *inner product* on $\mathcal{V}$. It is not unique and any function satisfying (i)–(iii) can take the name. [Compare example (2.9c) with the standard inner product.] It is customary to write the inner product simply in the form $\boldsymbol{\alpha} \cdot \boldsymbol{\beta}$ or $(\boldsymbol{\alpha}, \boldsymbol{\beta})$ and we shall usually do so.

(2.9) Examples. Euclidean Vector Spaces

(a) $\mathcal{R}^n$. Letting $\boldsymbol{\alpha} = (a_1, \ldots, a_n)$, $\boldsymbol{\beta} = (b_1, \ldots, b_n)$ be a typical pair of vectors in $\mathcal{R}^n$, we define

$$I(\boldsymbol{\alpha}, \boldsymbol{\beta}) = a_1b_1 + \cdots + a_nb_n.$$

Then by theorem (2.6), I is an inner product on $\mathcal{R}^n$, its *standard inner product.*

(b) $\mathcal{C}[a, b]$. Let $\mathcal{V} = \mathcal{C}[a, b]$, the vector space of continuous functions $f, g, \ldots$ defined on $a \leq t \leq b$. Define I by the formula

$$I(f, g) = \int_a^b f(t)g(t)\, dt.$$

We shall prove that I is an inner product on $\mathcal{C}[a, b]$.

(i) I is bilinear (we give half the argument):

$$\begin{aligned} I(c_1f_1 + c_2f_2, g) &= \int_a^b (c_1f_1(t) + c_2f_2(t))g(t)\,dt \\ &= c_1\int_a^b f_1(t)g(t)\,dt + c_2\int_a^b f_2(t)g(t)\,dt \\ &= c_1I(f_1, g) + c_2I(f_2, g). \end{aligned}$$

(ii) I is symmetric:

$$I(f, g) = \int_a^b f(t)g(t)\,dt = \int_a^b g(t)f(t)\,dt = I(g, f).$$

(iii) I is positive definite: Clearly,

$$I(f, f) = \int_a^b (f(t))^2\,dt \geq 0.$$

It is somewhat deeper that $I(f, f) > 0$ when $f \neq 0$. To show this we prove that $I(f, f) = 0$ implies f is the zero function. Suppose that $I(f, f) = 0$:

$$\int_a^b f^2(t)\,dt = 0.$$

Then for any number x between a and b,

$$0 \leq \int_a^x f^2(t)\,dt \leq \int_a^b f^2(t)\,dt = 0.$$

Thus $\int_a^x f^2(t)\,dt$ is identically zero for all values of x between a and b and thus its derivative is also zero for x between a and b. Since f is a continuous function, so is f^2. Thus by the fundamental theorem of calculus,

$$0 = \frac{d}{dx}\int_a^x f^2(t)\,dt = f^2(x), \qquad a < x < b.$$

This shows that the continuous function f^2 and therefore f is identically zero, $a \leq t \leq b$. Thus $f = \mathbf{0}$, where $\mathbf{0}$ is the null vector of $\mathcal{C}[a, b]$.

(c) $\mathcal{R}^n$. Let $\lambda_1, \ldots, \lambda_n$ be n positive real numbers. For $\boldsymbol{\alpha} = (a_1, \ldots, a_n)$, $\boldsymbol{\beta} = (b_1, \ldots, b_n) \in \mathcal{R}^n$ define

$$I(\boldsymbol{\alpha}, \boldsymbol{\beta}) = \lambda_1a_1b_1 + \cdots + \lambda_na_nb_n.$$

I is an inner product on $\mathcal{R}^n$; the reader should verify this fact.

We now exploit the inner product to obtain a geometry for any Euclidean vector space $\mathcal{V}$.

(2.10) Definition. For any vector $\boldsymbol{\alpha} \in \mathcal{V}$ the I-length or **norm** of $\boldsymbol{\alpha}$ is defined to be the number $[I(\boldsymbol{\alpha}, \boldsymbol{\alpha})]^{1/2}$:

$$\|\boldsymbol{\alpha}\| = [I(\boldsymbol{\alpha}, \boldsymbol{\alpha})]^{1/2}.$$

The I-distance between $\boldsymbol{\alpha}$ and $\boldsymbol{\beta} \in \mathcal{V}$ is defined to be the number

$$\|\boldsymbol{\alpha} - \boldsymbol{\beta}\| = \|\boldsymbol{\beta} - \boldsymbol{\alpha}\|.$$

(2.11) Theorem. *The following inequalities are valid for any pair $\boldsymbol{\alpha}$, $\boldsymbol{\beta}$ of vectors in a Euclidean vector space:*

(i) Schwarz's inequality:

$$|I(\boldsymbol{\alpha}, \boldsymbol{\beta})| \leq \|\boldsymbol{\alpha}\| \, \|\boldsymbol{\beta}\|.$$

(ii) Triangle inequalities:

$$\|\boldsymbol{\alpha} + \boldsymbol{\beta}\| \leq \|\boldsymbol{\alpha}\| + \|\boldsymbol{\beta}\|$$
$$\|\boldsymbol{\alpha} - \boldsymbol{\beta}\| \geq \big|\|\boldsymbol{\alpha}\| - \|\boldsymbol{\beta}\|\big|.$$

Proof. The proof of (i) is exactly the same as the proof of part (iv) of theorem (2.7). To prove (ii) we observe the following fact. By the bilinearity and symmetry of I and the definition of $\| \;\, \|$ we have

$$\begin{aligned}\|\boldsymbol{\alpha} + \boldsymbol{\beta}\|^2 &= I(\boldsymbol{\alpha} + \boldsymbol{\beta}, \boldsymbol{\alpha} + \boldsymbol{\beta}) = I(\boldsymbol{\alpha}, \boldsymbol{\alpha} + \boldsymbol{\beta}) + I(\boldsymbol{\beta}, \boldsymbol{\alpha} + \boldsymbol{\beta}) \\ &= I(\boldsymbol{\alpha}, \boldsymbol{\alpha}) + I(\boldsymbol{\alpha}, \boldsymbol{\beta}) + I(\boldsymbol{\beta}, \boldsymbol{\alpha}) + I(\boldsymbol{\beta}, \boldsymbol{\beta}) \\ &= I(\boldsymbol{\alpha}, \boldsymbol{\alpha}) + 2I(\boldsymbol{\alpha}, \boldsymbol{\beta}) + I(\boldsymbol{\beta}, \boldsymbol{\beta}) \\ &= \|\boldsymbol{\alpha}\|^2 + 2I(\boldsymbol{\alpha}, \boldsymbol{\beta}) + \|\boldsymbol{\beta}\|^2.\end{aligned}$$

By Schwarz's inequality we obtain

$$\text{(iii)} \qquad \|\boldsymbol{\alpha} + \boldsymbol{\beta}\|^2 \leq \|\boldsymbol{\alpha}\|^2 + 2\|\boldsymbol{\alpha}\| \, \|\boldsymbol{\beta}\| + \|\boldsymbol{\beta}\|^2 = (\|\boldsymbol{\alpha}\| + \|\boldsymbol{\beta}\|)^2,$$

and the first part of (ii) follows. To prove the second part of (ii) note that $\boldsymbol{\gamma} = (\boldsymbol{\gamma} - \boldsymbol{\beta}) + \boldsymbol{\beta}$. Hence by the first part,

$$\text{(iv)} \qquad \|\boldsymbol{\gamma}\| \leq \|\boldsymbol{\gamma} - \boldsymbol{\beta}\| + \|\boldsymbol{\beta}\| \qquad \text{or} \qquad \|\boldsymbol{\gamma} - \boldsymbol{\beta}\| \geq \|\boldsymbol{\gamma}\| - \|\boldsymbol{\beta}\|.$$

Note that for any vector $\boldsymbol{\delta}$, $\|\boldsymbol{\delta}\| = \|-\boldsymbol{\delta}\|$. Hence if we interchange $\boldsymbol{\gamma}$ and $\boldsymbol{\beta}$ in (iv) we get

$$\text{(v)} \qquad \|\boldsymbol{\beta} - \boldsymbol{\gamma}\| = \|\boldsymbol{\gamma} - \boldsymbol{\beta}\| \geq \|\boldsymbol{\beta}\| - \|\boldsymbol{\gamma}\|.$$

(iv) and (v) together yield (ii). The reader may draw a picture with arrows to see why these are called triangle inequalities. ▮

(2.12) Definition. For any two nonzero vectors $\boldsymbol{\alpha}$, $\boldsymbol{\beta}$ in a Euclidean vector space, the **angle** between $\boldsymbol{\alpha}$ and $\boldsymbol{\beta}$ is the unique real number θ between 0 and π such that

$$\cos\theta = \frac{I(\boldsymbol{\alpha}, \boldsymbol{\beta})}{\|\boldsymbol{\alpha}\|\,\|\boldsymbol{\beta}\|}.$$

If $\boldsymbol{\alpha}$ or $\boldsymbol{\beta}$ is $\mathbf{0}$, then the angle between them is not defined. As in $\mathbb{R}^n$, two vectors are said to be **orthogonal** if their inner product is zero. We write this as $\boldsymbol{\alpha} \perp \boldsymbol{\beta}$.

(2.13) Examples. Inner Products

(a) Using the standard inner product, compute the angle between the vectors $\boldsymbol{\alpha} = (1, 1, 0, -1)$ and $\boldsymbol{\beta} = (1, 1, 2, 2)$ in $\mathbb{R}^4$. By definition

$$\|\boldsymbol{\alpha}\| = \sqrt{\boldsymbol{\alpha} \cdot \boldsymbol{\alpha}} = \sqrt{1^2 + 1^2 + 0^2 + 1^2} = \sqrt{3}$$
$$\|\boldsymbol{\beta}\| = \sqrt{\boldsymbol{\beta} \cdot \boldsymbol{\beta}} = \sqrt{1^2 + 1^2 + 2^2 + 2^2} = \sqrt{10}$$
$$\boldsymbol{\alpha} \cdot \boldsymbol{\beta} = 1 \cdot 1 + 1 \cdot 1 + 0 \cdot 2 + (-1) \cdot 2 = 0.$$

Hence

$$\cos\theta = \frac{0}{\sqrt{3}\,\sqrt{10}} = 0$$

and $\theta = \pi/2$. That is, $\boldsymbol{\alpha} \perp \boldsymbol{\beta}$.

(b) Find all polynomials of degree 1 having distance $R = 1$ from f, where $f(t) = t$. Use $I(p, q) = \int_0^1 p(t)q(t)\,dt$ as the inner product (see Figure 1.13).

We desire to find all polynomials p of degree 1 for which $\|p - f\| = 1$. Set

$$p(t) = x_0 t + x_1.$$

Then $p - f$ has the form

$$(p - f)(t) = p(t) - f(t) = (x_0 - 1)t + x_1.$$

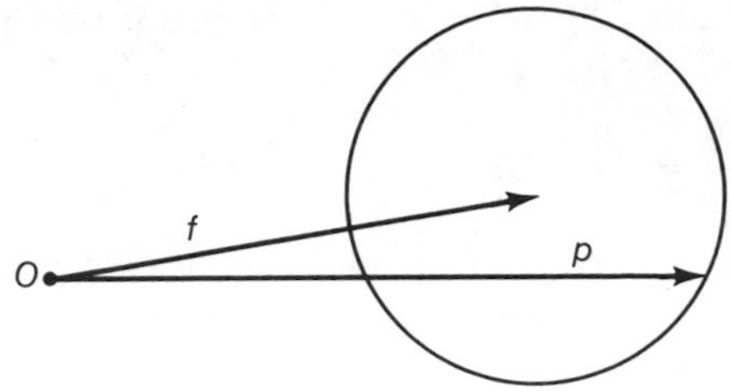

Figure 1.13

Hence the condition to be met is that

$$\begin{aligned}\|p - f\|^2 &= I(p - f, p - f)\\ &= \int_0^1 ((x_0 - 1)t + x_1)^2\, dt = 1^2.\end{aligned}$$

Simplifying, this reduces to

$$\tfrac{1}{3}(x_0 - 1)^2 + x_1(x_0 - 1) + x_1^2 = 1.$$

Thus the class of functions with the stated property consists of all linear polynomials p,

$$p(t) = x_0 t + x_1,$$

for which x_0, x_1 satisfy

$$x_1^2 + x_1 x_0 + \tfrac{1}{3}x_0^2 - (x_1 + \tfrac{2}{3}x_0) = \tfrac{2}{3}.$$

Here are two somewhat more complicated examples.

(c) Consider again the differential equation (0.2). Suppose x is a solution. Then x, dx/dt, and d^2x/dt^2 are continuous functions for all t. Observe from (0.3) that if x is a solution, then

$$\text{(i)}\qquad \begin{aligned}x(t + 2\pi/k) &= A \sin [k(t + 2\pi/k) + B]\\ &= A \sin (kt + B + 2\pi)\\ &= A \sin (kt + B) = x(t).\end{aligned}$$

Equation (i) means that x is *periodic* with period $2\pi/k$. Essentially the same calculation shows that

$$\text{(ii)}\qquad \frac{dx}{dt}(t + 2\pi/k) = \frac{dx}{dt}(t);$$

that is, dx/dt is also periodic with period $2\pi/k$. Now consider any interval of time $a \leq t \leq a + 2\pi/k$. Then x, dx/dt, and d^2x/dt^2 can all be considered as elements of $\mathcal{C}[a, a + 2\pi/k]$. On this space we have an inner product defined; that is, for any two functions f and g we have

$$f \cdot g = \int_a^{a+2\pi/k} f(t)g(t)\,dt.$$

We assert that x and dx/dt are orthogonal with respect to this inner product. Indeed, we have

$$\begin{aligned} x \cdot \frac{dx}{dt} &= \int_a^{a+2\pi/k} x(t)\frac{dx}{dt}(t)\,dt = \tfrac{1}{2}\int_a^{a+2\pi/k} \frac{d}{dt}(x(t)^2)\,dt \\ &= \tfrac{1}{2}[x^2(a + 2\pi/k) - x^2(a)] \end{aligned}$$

and hence $x \cdot (dx/dt)$ is zero by (i). In a similar way, one can show by equation (ii) that dx/dt and d^2x/dt^2 are orthogonal.

(d) Consider the pair of linear algebraic equations

$$\text{(i)} \qquad \begin{aligned} Ax_1 + Bx_2 &= 0 \\ Cx_1 + Dx_2 &= 0. \end{aligned}$$

The reader can verify that equations (i) can have solutions other than $x_1 = 0$, $x_2 = 0$, if and only if $AD - BC = 0$. We consider the related system

$$\text{(ii)} \qquad \begin{aligned} Ay_1 + Cy_2 &= 0 \\ By_1 + Dy_2 &= 0; \end{aligned}$$

that is, B and C are simply interchanged. Again this system can have solutions other than $y_1 = 0$, $y_2 = 0$ only if $AD - BC = 0$. Finally, we consider the nonhomogeneous system,

$$\text{(iii)} \qquad \begin{aligned} Ax_1 + Bx_2 &= m_1 \\ Cx_1 + Dx_2 &= m_2. \end{aligned}$$

We assert that equations (iii) can have a solution only if the vector $\mathbf{m} = (m_1, m_2)$ is orthogonal to every vector $\mathbf{y}$ of the form $\mathbf{y} = (y_1, y_2)$, where y_1 and y_2 form a solution of equations (ii). Here the vector space in question is $\mathcal{R}^2$ with the standard inner product. Indeed, suppose $\mathbf{x} = (x_1, x_2)$ is a solution of (iii) and that $\mathbf{y} = (y_1, y_2)$ is a solution of (ii). Then multiply the first of equations (iii) by y_1 and the second by y_2 and add the results.

We get

$$\begin{aligned} y_1m_1 + y_2m_2 &= y_1(Ax_1 + Bx_2) + y_2(Cx_1 + Dx_2) \\ &= x_1(Ay_1 + Cy_2) + x_2(By_1 + Dy_2) \\ &= x_1 \cdot 0 + x_2 \cdot 0 = 0. \end{aligned}$$

The left side is just $\mathbf{y} \cdot \mathbf{m}$; hence our assertion is proved.

In this chapter we have emphasized the fact that inner products offer one the opportunity to create a *geometry* for vector spaces. In addition, certain other notions can be readily extended to real vector spaces by means of the norm and inner product. One of these is the idea of convergence, which was discussed for sequences of real numbers in the Review of Calculus. We shall encounter this idea in later chapters. Another concept which can be extended is that of continuity and differentiation of functions which have values in vector spaces. This is an extremely important idea in physics and we shall develop it in Chapters 2 and 3. We concern ourselves almost *solely* with Euclidean vector spaces, and consequently we want to make the following special agreement so as not to have to restate it each time.

Convention. *Whenever we speak of a vector space* $\mathcal{V}$ *it will be understood that there is available some inner product defined on this space (although ordinarily the term "vector space" does not imply this).*† *In the case of* $\mathcal{R}^n$ *or* $\mathcal{C}[a, b]$ *this inner product will be the standard inner product or the inner product of* (2.9b), *respectively, unless we explicitly state otherwise.*

PROBLEMS

1. Find the angle between the following pairs of vectors.

$\mathcal{R}^2$

(a) $(1, 1), (1, 0)$

(b) $(1, -1), (1, 0)$

(c) $(1, 2), (-2, 1)$

(d) $(-3, -3), (2, 2)$

(e) $(0, 0), (3, 1)$

(f) $(2, 0), (2, 2\sqrt{3})$

(g) $(0, -1), (3, 1)$

(h) $\left(\frac{1+\sqrt{3}}{2}, \frac{1-\sqrt{3}}{2}\right), (1, 1)$

$\mathcal{R}^3$

(a) $(1, 2, 1), (-1, 1, -1)$

(b) $\left(\frac{1+\sqrt{3}}{2}, 0, \frac{1-\sqrt{3}}{2}\right), (1, 0, 1)$

(c) $\left(\frac{2+3\sqrt{2}}{2}, 1, \frac{2-3\sqrt{2}}{2}\right), (1, 1, 1)$

(d) $(1, 2, 0), \left(1, 2, \frac{-\sqrt{15}}{3}\right)$

(e) $(1, -2, 3)$, $(1-\sqrt{14}, -2+\sqrt{14}, 3+\sqrt{14})$

(f) $(1, -3, 4), (1, 0, 2)$

†The only exceptions to this will be certain spaces of continuous functions defined for all t. On those spaces we shall not use any inner product.

$\mathcal{R}^4$

(a) $(1, -1, 2, 1), (-1, 1, -1, 2)$

(b) $(1, 2, -2, 3), \left(\frac{3 - \sqrt{6}}{3}, \frac{6 + \sqrt{6}}{3}, \frac{-6 + \sqrt{6}}{3}, \frac{9 + \sqrt{6}}{3}\right)$

(c) $\left(\frac{2 + 3\sqrt{2}}{2}, 0, 1, \frac{2 - 3\sqrt{2}}{2}\right), (1, 0, 1, 1)$

(d) $(-1, -1, 1, 1), (0, 0, 1, 1)$

$\mathcal{C}[-1, 1]$

(a) $t^2 - t + 1, t$

(b) $t^2 - 1, t$

2. Find out which of the following systems are orthogonal, which consist of unit vectors, and which are neither. (A system $\alpha_1, \alpha_2, \ldots, \alpha_n$ of unit vectors which are mutually orthogonal is said to be *orthonormal*.)

$\mathcal{R}^2$

(a) $(1, 1), (1, -1)$

(b) $\left(\frac{1 + \sqrt{3}}{2}, \frac{1 - \sqrt{3}}{2}\right), (1, -1)$

(c) $(0.6, 0.8), (0.8, -0.6)$

(d) $(\cos\theta, \sin\theta), (\sin\theta, -\cos\theta)$

(e) $(2, -2)$

$\mathcal{R}^3$

(a) $(\frac{2}{3}, \frac{2}{3}, \frac{1}{3})$

(b) $(\cos\theta, \sin\theta, 0), (\sin\theta, -\cos\theta, 0)$

(c) $(1, 1, 1), (1, 1, -2)$

$\mathcal{R}^4$

(a) $(1, 1, 1, 1), (1, -1, 1, -1)$

$\mathcal{C}[0, 1]$

(a) $\sqrt{5}t^2, t^2 - \frac{3}{5}$

3. Show that if $\boldsymbol{\alpha} \in \mathcal{V}$ has the property that for every $\boldsymbol{\beta} \in \mathcal{V}$, $\boldsymbol{\alpha} \cdot \boldsymbol{\beta} = \mathbf{0}$, then necessarily $\boldsymbol{\alpha} = \mathbf{0}$.

4. PYTHAGOREAN THEOREM. If $\boldsymbol{\alpha}$ and $\boldsymbol{\beta}$ are perpendicular, then

$$\|\boldsymbol{\alpha} + \boldsymbol{\beta}\|^2 = \|\boldsymbol{\alpha}\|^2 + \|\boldsymbol{\beta}\|^2.$$

[*Hint:* $\|\boldsymbol{\alpha} + \boldsymbol{\beta}\|^2 = (\boldsymbol{\alpha} + \boldsymbol{\beta}) \cdot (\boldsymbol{\alpha} + \boldsymbol{\beta})$.]

5. PARALLELOGRAM LAW. For any $\boldsymbol{\alpha}, \boldsymbol{\beta} \in \mathcal{V}$,

$$\|\boldsymbol{\alpha} + \boldsymbol{\beta}\|^2 + \|\boldsymbol{\alpha} - \boldsymbol{\beta}\|^2 = 2\|\boldsymbol{\alpha}\|^2 + 2\|\boldsymbol{\beta}\|^2.$$

6. SCHWARZ'S INEQUALITY: STRONG FORM. For $\boldsymbol{\alpha}, \boldsymbol{\beta} \in \mathcal{V}$,

$$|\boldsymbol{\alpha} \cdot \boldsymbol{\beta}| < \|\boldsymbol{\alpha}\| \, \|\boldsymbol{\beta}\|$$

unless $\boldsymbol{\alpha}$ is a scalar multiple of $\boldsymbol{\beta}$ or $\boldsymbol{\beta}$ is a scalar multiple of $\boldsymbol{\alpha}$.

$$\left[\textit{Hint: } \left(\frac{\boldsymbol{\alpha}}{\|\boldsymbol{\alpha}\|} \pm \frac{\boldsymbol{\beta}}{\|\boldsymbol{\beta}\|}\right) \cdot \left(\frac{\boldsymbol{\alpha}}{\|\boldsymbol{\alpha}\|} \pm \frac{\boldsymbol{\beta}}{\|\boldsymbol{\beta}\|}\right) > 0 \text{ unless } \frac{\boldsymbol{\alpha}}{\|\boldsymbol{\alpha}\|} \pm \frac{\boldsymbol{\beta}}{\|\boldsymbol{\beta}\|} = \mathbf{0}.\right]$$

7. SCHWARZ'S INEQUALITY: ALTERNATIVE PROOF.

(a) For nonzero $\boldsymbol{\alpha}, \boldsymbol{\beta} \in \mathcal{V}$, form the expression

$$\|\boldsymbol{\alpha} + t\boldsymbol{\beta}\|^2 = (\boldsymbol{\alpha} + t\boldsymbol{\beta}) \cdot (\boldsymbol{\alpha} + t\boldsymbol{\beta}).$$

By expanding the right side obtain a quadratic polynomial $p(t)$. Note that the left side is never negative, so that $p(t)$ cannot have distinct real roots. Using the quadratic formula, deduce Schwarz's inequality.

(b) Can the strong form of the inequality be obtained by this means?

8. Let S denote the sequence of functions, on $[-\pi, \pi]$: $\sin x$, $\cos x$, $\sin 2x$, $\cos 2x$, $\ldots$, $\sin nx$, $\cos nx$, $\ldots$. Show that the infinite system S is orthogonal with respect to the inner product I:

$$I(f, g) = \int_{-\pi}^{\pi} f(x)g(x)\,dx$$

9. (a) Let $\mathcal{C}^{(1)}[0, 1]$ consist of all those functions of $\mathcal{C}[0, 1]$ which are continuously differentiable on the interval $0 \leq t \leq 1$. Define addition and scalar multiplication as in example (1.2d). Show that $\mathcal{C}^{(1)}[0, 1]$ is a vector space.

(b) Show that the expression

$$L(y_1, y_2) = \int_0^1 \dot{y}_1(t)\dot{y}_2(t)\,dt$$

is *not* a scalar product on $\mathcal{C}^{(1)}[0, 1]$.

(c) Show that the expression

$$I(y_1, y_2) = \int_0^1 [\dot{y}_1(t)\dot{y}_2(t) + y_1(t)y_2(t)]\,dt$$

is a scalar product on $\mathcal{C}^{(1)}[0, 1]$.

10. Let y_1 and y_2 be solutions of the differential equations

$$\text{(i)} \qquad \ddot{y}_1(t) + k_1 y_1(t) = 0$$

$$\text{(ii)} \qquad \ddot{y}_2(t) + k_2 y_2(t) = 0,$$

where k_1 and k_2 are constants with $k_1 \neq k_2$. Assume, moreover, that

$$\text{(iii)} \qquad y_1(0) = y_2(0) = y_1(1) = y_2(1) = 0.$$

Show that y_1 and y_2 considered as elements of $\mathcal{C}[0, 1]$ are orthogonal. [*Hint:* Proceed as follows. Multiply (i) by $y_2(t)$ and (ii) by $y_1(t)$. Integrate the results from 0 to 1 and subtract. Integrate by parts and use (iii).] Note that $\ddot{y}_1(t)$ and $\ddot{y}_2(t)$ denote the second derivatives of y_1 and y_2 evaluated at t.

2

Calculus for Vector Functions of *t*

0. Introduction

One application of vectors is to the description of the motion of a particle or a system of particles in mechanics. A particle in this context is an idealization of a body in which one neglects all dimensions and visualizes the object under consideration as merely occupying a point of space. In general the same particle will be at different points at different times t. Let us denote by $P(t)$ the point in space occupied by one such particle at time t. P is then a function whose values are points in space and whose arguments are real numbers t. As t varies over some interval of time, the set of points $P(t)$ is called the *path* of the particle. If there are several particles we will write $P_1(t), \ldots, P_n(t)$ to denote the points they occupy at time t.

In mechanics one usually is not so much concerned with the actual path of the particle as with its position relative to something else. For example, a typical problem is, given the paths of two particles P_1 and P_2, to make sure that $P_1(t)$ is never equal to $P_2(t)$ (no collisions) (see Figure 2.1). On the other hand, one may want to make sure that the distance from $P_1(t)$ to $P_2(t)$ is always less than some fixed amount (no getting lost). These examples refer to restrictions on the distance from P_1 to P_2. One might also want P_1 and P_2 to move along the same straight line regardless of their distance apart (a race). Finally, an observer at some point in space P_0 may want to keep track of n particles. Then he simply wants to describe their positions relative to himself.

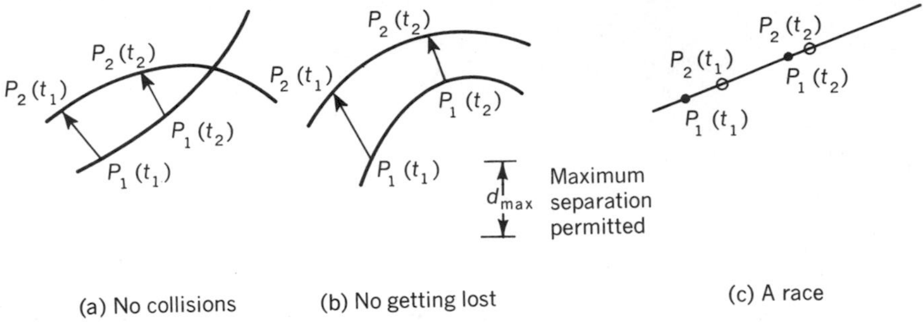

Figure 2.1

All the preceding situations are easily described by means of vectors. If P_1 and P_2 are moving, then $\gamma = \overrightarrow{P_1P_2}$ is a function of time, one whose values are *arrows*. In terms of this function we can describe the three situations of Figure 2.1 as follows:

(a) No collision: $\|\gamma(t)\| = \|\overrightarrow{P_1(t)P_2(t)}\| > 0$, all t.

(b) No getting lost: $\|\gamma(t)\| = \|\overrightarrow{P_1(t)P_2(t)}\| \leq d_{\max}$, all t.

(c) A race: $\gamma(t) = \overrightarrow{P_1(t)P_2(t)} = f(t)\boldsymbol{\alpha}$, $\boldsymbol{\alpha}$ a fixed arrow.

Actually the position of a particle at P relative to a point P_0 is described by the arrow $\overrightarrow{P_0P}$ whether or not there is a particle occupying P_0. The usual situation is that P_0 is a fixed point (see Figure 2.2). Since P is a function of time, we still find that $\overrightarrow{P_0P}$ is a vector function of t. It is customary in such cases to write $\overrightarrow{P_0P(t)} = \mathbf{r}(t)$ and to call $\mathbf{r}(t)$ the **position vector** of $P(t)$ (relative to P_0).

All the above situations introduce a new concept, that of functions of a real variable t with vectors as values. An even simpler illustration occurs as follows. Let $a_1, \ldots, a_n$ denote n (ordinary) functions of the scalar t. We can use these functions to construct at each time t an n-tuple of scalars $\boldsymbol{\alpha}(t)$ by setting

(0.1) $$\boldsymbol{\alpha}(t) = \big(a_1(t), a_2(t), \ldots, a_n(t)\big).$$

Then $\boldsymbol{\alpha}$ is a vector function of time, this time with values in $\mathcal{R}^n$.

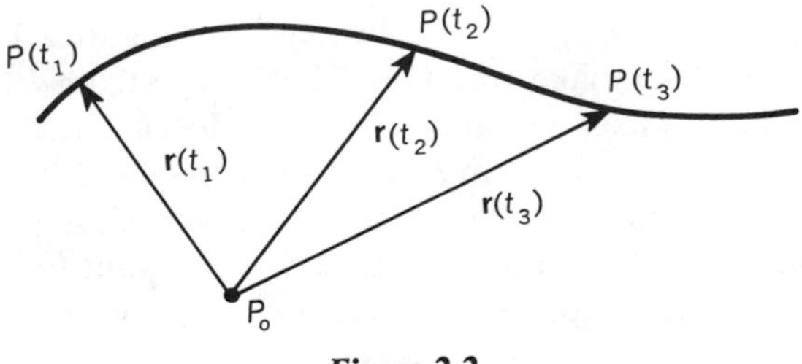

Figure 2.2

We will see further examples of vector-valued functions of t presently. For functions of this kind there are notions of continuity and differentiability which play just as important a role as the notions of continuity and differentiability do for real-valued functions. For convenience of reference, let us restate these notions for real-valued functions.

(0.2) Definition. A function f is **continuous** in the interval $a < t < b$ if for each value t_0 in the given interval it satisfies

$$|f(t_0 + \Delta t) - f(t_0)| \text{ is small} \qquad \text{when } \Delta t \text{ is small.}$$

That is, given any $\varepsilon > 0$ there must be a $\delta > 0$ such that

$$|f(t_0 + \Delta t) - f(t_0)| < \varepsilon \qquad \text{whenever } |\Delta t| < \delta.$$

We shall have occasion to use the phrase "is small" very frequently, and therefore we shall henceforth adopt as a standard abbreviation for it the symbol ~ 0.

(0.3) Definition. A function f is **differentiable** in the interval $a < t < b$ if for each value t_0 in the given interval there is a scalar $b(t_0)$ which is approached by the difference quotients of f at t_0:

$$\left|\frac{f(t_0 + \Delta t) - f(t_0)}{\Delta t} - b(t_0)\right| \sim 0 \qquad \text{when } \Delta t \sim 0.$$

That is, given $\varepsilon > 0$ there must be a $\delta > 0$ such that

$$\left|\frac{f(t_0 + \Delta t) - f(t_0)}{\Delta t} - b(t_0)\right| < \varepsilon \qquad \text{whenever } |\Delta t| < \delta.$$

The scalar $b(t_0)$ is called the *derivative* of f at t_0, and it is designated by any of the following:

$$b(t_0) = \dot{f}(t_0) = \frac{d}{dt} f(t)\bigg|_{t=t_0} = \frac{d}{dt} f(t_0).$$

1. Continuity and Differentiability for Vector Functions

We shall pattern our definition of continuity for vector-valued functions on that for real-valued functions. The only modification is that we must now use a norm in place of an absolute value to state that the difference of two terms is small.†

(1.1) Definition. Let γ denote a function of t whose values are in a vector space $\mathcal{V}$. γ is said to be **continuous** in the interval $a < t < b$ if for each value t_0 in the given interval

$$\|\gamma(t_0 + \Delta t) - \gamma(t_0)\| \sim 0 \qquad \text{when } \Delta t \sim 0. \tag{1.2}$$

That is, given any $\varepsilon > 0$ there must be a $\delta > 0$ such that

$$\|\gamma(t_0 + \Delta t) - \gamma(t_0)\| < \varepsilon \qquad \text{whenever } |\Delta t| < \delta.$$

To understand this definition better, let us see what it means when applied to the $\mathcal{R}^n$-valued function $\boldsymbol{\alpha}$ defined in (0.1):

$$\boldsymbol{\alpha}(t) = \big(a_1(t), a_2(t), \ldots, a_n(t)\big).$$

Using the addition and scalar multiplication defined for $\mathcal{R}^n$ we find that

$$\boldsymbol{\alpha}(t_0 + \Delta t) - \boldsymbol{\alpha}(t_0)$$
$$= \big(a_1(t_0 + \Delta t) - a_1(t_0), a_2(t_0 + \Delta t) - a_2(t_0), \ldots, a_n(t_0 + \Delta t) - a_n(t_0)\big),$$

and therefore

$$\|\boldsymbol{\alpha}(t_0 + \Delta t) - \boldsymbol{\alpha}(t_0)\| \tag{1.3}$$
$$= \sqrt{(a_1(t_0+\Delta t) - a_1(t_0))^2 + (a_2(t_0+\Delta t) - a_2(t_0))^2 + \cdots + (a_n(t_0+\Delta t) - a_n(t_0))^2}.$$

In order for the above square root to be small, it is clearly necessary that *each* of the parenthesized terms be small. Hence (1.2) requires that all the following relations hold:

$$\begin{aligned} |a_1(t_0 + \Delta t) - a_1(t_0)| &\sim 0 \\ |a_2(t_0 + \Delta t) - a_2(t_0)| &\sim 0 \\ &\vdots \\ |a_n(t_0 + \Delta t) - a_n(t_0)| &\sim 0 \qquad \text{when } \Delta t \sim 0. \end{aligned} \tag{1.4}$$

Now by definition (0.2), the first relation in (1.4) states that a_1 is a continuous real-valued function, the second relation in (1.4) states that a_2 is a continuous

†Notice that the norm in the vector space consisting of real numbers is simply the absolute value, so replacing absolute value by norm is a natural thing to do.

real-valued function, and so on. That is, continuity for $\boldsymbol{\alpha}$ implies that each of the scalar functions $a_1, a_2, \ldots, a_n$ is continuous. By reversing the arguments we see also that whenever $a_1, a_2, \ldots, a_n$ are continuous, then all the relations in (1.4) hold, and consequently by (1.3)

$$\|\boldsymbol{\alpha}(t_0 + \Delta t) - \boldsymbol{\alpha}(t_0)\| \sim 0 \qquad \text{when } \Delta t \sim 0.$$

To summarize, we have the following result.

(1.5) Proposition. *An $\mathcal{R}^n$-valued function $\boldsymbol{\alpha}$ is continuous on the interval $a < t < b$ if and only if each of the real-valued functions $a_1, a_2, \ldots, a_n$ is continuous on this interval.*

Next let us turn to the arrow-valued function of t which is furnished by the position vector $\mathbf{r}$ of a moving particle. Here continuity of $\mathbf{r}$ is by definition (1.1) equivalent to the statement

$$\|\mathbf{r}(t_0 + \Delta t) - \mathbf{r}(t_0)\| \sim 0 \qquad \text{when } \Delta t \sim 0.$$

Since $\|\mathbf{r}(t_0 + \Delta t) - \mathbf{r}(t_0)\|$ denotes the *distance* between $P(t_0 + \Delta t)$ and $P(t_0)$ (Figure 2.3), continuity of $\mathbf{r}$ states only that the location of the particle cannot change abruptly.

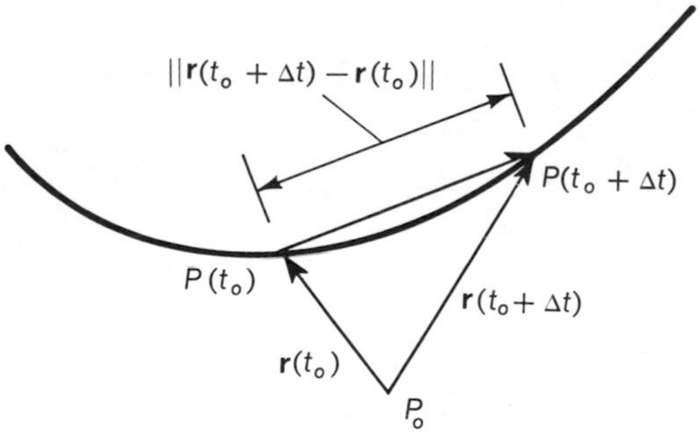

Figure 2.3

As a third illustration we consider a function γ whose values $\gamma(t)$ are in the vector space $\mathcal{C}[0, \pi]$. Let γ be as follows†:

$$[\gamma(t)](x) = t \sin x + (1 - t) \cos x, \qquad 0 \leq x \leq \pi.$$

†To avoid confusion, we are using x as the independent variable in elements of $\mathcal{C}[0, \pi]$.

In order to examine the continuity of γ, we must compute

$$\|\gamma(t_0 + \Delta t) - \gamma(t_0)\|,$$

where the norm is that which was introduced on the vector space $\mathcal{C}[0, \pi]$. We have

$$\begin{aligned}[\gamma(t_0 + \Delta t) - \gamma(t_0)](x) &= [(t_0 + \Delta t)\sin x + \big(1 - (t_0 + \Delta t)\big)\cos x] \\ &\quad - [t_0 \sin x + (1 - t_0)\cos x] \\ &= \Delta t \sin x - \Delta t \cos x.\end{aligned}$$

Consequently,

$$\begin{aligned}\|\gamma(t_0 + \Delta t) - \gamma(t_0)\| &= \sqrt{\int_0^\pi (\Delta t \sin x - \Delta t \cos x)^2\,dx} \\ &= \sqrt{(\Delta t)^2 \int_0^\pi (\sin x - \cos x)^2\,dx} \\ &= |\Delta t| \sqrt{\int_0^\pi (\sin x - \cos x)^2\,dx}.\end{aligned}$$

By evaluating the definite integral we obtain

$$\|\gamma(t_0 + \Delta t) - \gamma(t_0)\| = |\Delta t|\sqrt{\pi}.$$

It is clear from this formula that

$$\|\gamma(t_0 + \Delta t) - \gamma(t_0)\| \sim 0 \qquad \text{when } \Delta t \sim 0.$$

Thus the vector-valued function γ is continuous.

We proceed next to give the definition of differentiability for vector-valued functions. As mentioned earlier, it is patterned on definition (0.3).

(1.6) Definition. Let γ denote a function of t whose values are in a vector space $\mathcal{V}$. γ is said to be **differentiable** on the interval $a < t < b$ if for each value t_0 in the given time interval there is a vector $\boldsymbol{\beta}(t_0) \in \mathcal{V}$ which is approached by the difference quotients of γ:

$$\left\|\frac{1}{\Delta t}\big(\gamma(t_0 + \Delta t) - \gamma(t_0)\big) - \boldsymbol{\beta}(t_0)\right\| \sim 0 \qquad \text{when } \Delta t \sim 0. \tag{1.7}$$

That is, given any $\varepsilon > 0$ there must be a $\delta > 0$ such that

$$\left\| \frac{1}{\Delta t} \big(\boldsymbol{\gamma}(t_0 + \Delta t) - \boldsymbol{\gamma}(t_0)\big) - \boldsymbol{\beta}(t_0) \right\| < \varepsilon \qquad \text{whenever } |\Delta t| < \delta.$$

The vector $\boldsymbol{\beta}(t_0)$ is called the *derivative* of $\boldsymbol{\gamma}$ at time t_0 and is denoted by any one of the following:

$$(1.8)\quad \boldsymbol{\beta}(t_0) = \dot{\boldsymbol{\gamma}}(t_0), \qquad \boldsymbol{\beta}(t_0) = \frac{d}{dt}\boldsymbol{\gamma}(t)\bigg|_{t=t_0}, \qquad \boldsymbol{\beta}(t_0) = \frac{d}{dt}\boldsymbol{\gamma}(t_0).$$

In trying to understand this definition it is helpful to observe that (1.7) necessitates the relationship

$$\|\boldsymbol{\gamma}(t_0 + \Delta t) - \boldsymbol{\gamma}(t_0)\| \sim 0 \qquad \text{when } \Delta t \sim 0;$$

otherwise the length of the first vector in (1.7) would become arbitrarily large for Δt small. Thus, just as with real-valued functions, *differentiability of a vector function of t automatically ensures the continuity of that function.* Of course, continuity does *not* ensure differentiability.

To gain further insight into the definition, let us apply it to the $\mathcal{R}^n$-valued function $\boldsymbol{\alpha}$ defined in (0.1). Here the definitions of addition and scalar multiplication in $\mathcal{R}^n$ imply that

$$\begin{aligned}
&\frac{1}{\Delta t}\big(\boldsymbol{\alpha}(t_0 + \Delta t) - \boldsymbol{\alpha}(t_0)\big) \\
&\qquad = \frac{1}{\Delta t}\big(a_1(t_0 + \Delta t) - a_1(t_0), \ldots, a_n(t_0 + \Delta t) - a_n(t_0)\big) \\
&\qquad = \left(\frac{a_1(t_0 + \Delta t) - a_1(t_0)}{\Delta t}, \ldots, \frac{a_n(t_0 + \Delta t) - a_n(t_0)}{\Delta t}\right).
\end{aligned}$$

If $\boldsymbol{\alpha}$ is differentiable and its derivative is denoted by

$$\dot{\boldsymbol{\alpha}}(t_0) = \boldsymbol{\beta}(t_0) = \big(b_1(t_0), \ldots, b_n(t_0)\big),$$

then $\|(1/\Delta t)\big(\boldsymbol{\alpha}(t_0 + \Delta t) - \boldsymbol{\alpha}(t_0)\big) - \boldsymbol{\beta}(t_0)\|$ has the form

$$\begin{aligned}
(1.9\text{a})\quad &\left\| \frac{1}{\Delta t}\big(\boldsymbol{\alpha}(t_0 + \Delta t) - \boldsymbol{\alpha}(t_0)\big) - \boldsymbol{\beta}(t_0) \right\| \\
&= \left\| \left(\frac{a_1(t_0 + \Delta t) - a_1(t_0)}{\Delta t} - b_1(t_0), \ldots, \frac{a_n(t_0 + \Delta t) - a_n(t_0)}{\Delta t} - b_n(t_0)\right) \right\| \\
&= \sqrt{\left(\frac{a_1(t_0 + \Delta t) - a_1(t_0)}{\Delta t} - b_1(t_0)\right)^2 + \cdots + \left(\frac{a_n(t_0 + \Delta t) - a_n(t_0)}{\Delta t} - b_n(t_0)\right)^2}.
\end{aligned}$$

In order for the above square root to be small, it is clearly necessary that *each* of the terms in parentheses be small. Hence (1.7) requires that all the following relations hold:

$$\tag{1.9b}\begin{aligned}&\left|\frac{a_1(t_0+\Delta t)-a_1(t_0)}{\Delta t}-b_1(t_0)\right|\sim 0\\&\left|\frac{a_2(t_0+\Delta t)-a_2(t_0)}{\Delta t}-b_2(t_0)\right|\sim 0\\&\qquad\vdots\\&\left|\frac{a_n(t_0+\Delta t)-a_n(t_0)}{\Delta t}-b_n(t_0)\right|\sim 0,\qquad\text{when } \Delta t\sim 0.\end{aligned}$$

Now the first relation in (1.9b) states [see definition (0.3)] that a_1 is a differentiable real-valued function with derivative $\dot{a}_1(t_0) = b_1(t_0)$, the second relation states that a_2 is a differentiable real-valued function with derivative $\dot{a}_2(t_0) = b_2(t_0)$, and so on. That is, differentiability for $\boldsymbol{\alpha}$ implies that each of the scalar functions $a_1, a_2, \ldots, a_n$ is differentiable. By reversing the arguments we also see that differentiability of each of the functions $a_1, a_2, \ldots, a_n$ ensures that the square root in (1.9a) is small when Δt is small; note that this requires that $\boldsymbol{\beta}(t_0) = (b_1(t_0), \ldots, b_n(t_0))$ has been chosen as

$$b_1(t_0) = \dot{a}_1(t_0), \ldots, b_n(t_0) = \dot{a}_n(t_0).$$

We summarize as follows.

(1.10) Proposition. *An $\mathbb{R}^n$-valued function $\boldsymbol{\alpha}$ is differentiable if and only if each of the scalar functions $a_1, a_2, \ldots, a_n$ is differentiable; in addition we have the formula*

$$\dot{\boldsymbol{\alpha}}(t_0) = (\dot{a}_1(t_0), \dot{a}_2(t_0), \ldots, \dot{a}_n(t_0)).$$

Next we discuss differentiability for the function of t which is furnished by the position vector $\mathbf{r}$ of a moving particle. By definition (1.6), differentiability of $\mathbf{r}$ is equivalent to the existence for each t_0 in a given time interval of an arrow $\mathbf{v}(t_0)$ such that

$$\tag{1.11}\left\|\frac{1}{\Delta t}(\mathbf{r}(t_0+\Delta t)-\mathbf{r}(t_0))-\mathbf{v}(t_0)\right\|\sim 0\qquad\text{when } \Delta t\sim 0.$$

Now the vector quantity

$$\tag{1.12}\mathbf{v}_{t_0,t_0+\Delta t}=\frac{1}{\Delta t}(\mathbf{r}(t_0+\Delta t)-\mathbf{r}(t_0))=\frac{1}{\Delta t}\overrightarrow{P(t_0)P(t_0+\Delta t)}$$

is a measure of how rapidly on the average the particle is moving along its path. It also gives the direction of the displacement of the particle from time t_0 to $t_0 + \Delta t$ (Figure 2.4a). Equation (1.11) therefore requires that (Figure 2.4b):

(1) The direction of $\mathbf{v}(t_0)$ is the limiting direction for the chords $\overrightarrow{P(t_0)P(t_0 + \Delta t)}$ to the path; that is, $\mathbf{v}(t_0)$ has the direction of the tangent to the path at $P(t_0)$.

(2) The length $\|\mathbf{v}(t_0)\|$ of $\mathbf{v}(t_0)$ is the limit of the average speed $\|\mathbf{v}_{t_0,t_0+\Delta t}\| = \|\overrightarrow{P(t_0)P(t_0 + \Delta t)}\|/|\Delta t|$; that is, $\|\mathbf{v}(t_0)\|$ is the instantaneous speed of the particle at time t_0.

If $\mathbf{r}(t)$ is the position vector of a particle, then the quantity

$$\mathbf{v}(t_0) = \dot{\mathbf{r}}(t_0)$$

defined above is called the *velocity of the particle at time* t_0 (see problem 12), while $\|\mathbf{v}(t_0)\| = \|\dot{\mathbf{r}}(t_0)\|$ is called the *speed of the particle at time* t_0.

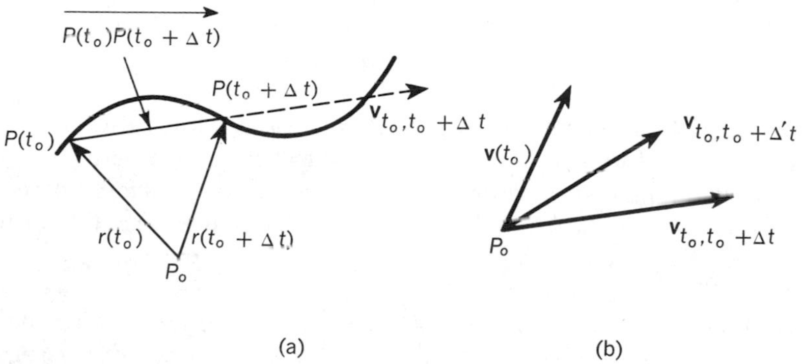

Figure 2.4

Finally, we apply definition (1.6) to investigate whether the vector function γ defined by

(1.13) $[\gamma(t)](x) = t \sin x + (1 - t) \cos x, \qquad -1 < t < 1, 0 \leq x \leq \pi$

is differentiable. For this purpose we must form

$\frac{1}{\Delta t}(\gamma(t_0 + \Delta t) - \gamma(t_0))$ which is the following function of x:

$$\frac{1}{\Delta t}[((t_0 + \Delta t) \sin x + (1 - (t_0 + \Delta t)) \cos x) - (t_0 \sin x + (1 - t_0) \cos x)]$$

$$= \sin x - \cos x.$$

In this case it is quite simple to determine an element $\boldsymbol{\beta}(t_0) \in \mathcal{C}[0, \pi]$ to which these difference quotients converge. If we select $\boldsymbol{\beta}(t_0)$ to be the function $[\boldsymbol{\beta}(t_0)](x) = \sin x - \cos x$, then

$$\left\| \frac{1}{\Delta t} \left(\boldsymbol{\gamma}(t_0 + \Delta t) - \boldsymbol{\gamma}(t_0)\right) - \boldsymbol{\beta}(t_0) \right\| \equiv 0,$$

which certainly suffices in order that equation (1.7) hold. Thus $\boldsymbol{\gamma}$ is differentiable and its derivative is the same for all t_0:

$$[\dot{\boldsymbol{\gamma}}(t_0)](x) = \sin x - \cos x.$$

It is interesting to note that if one drops the interpretation of the expression on the right side of (1.13) as a vector function of t and instead regards it as a function $c(x, t)$ of the variables x, t, then $c(x, t)$ possesses a partial derivative with respect to t. Indeed,

$$\begin{aligned} \frac{\partial}{\partial t} c(x, t)\Big|_{t=t_0} &= \frac{\partial}{\partial t} \left(t \sin x + (1 - t) \cos x\right)\Big|_{t=t_0} \\ &= \sin x - \cos x = [\dot{\boldsymbol{\gamma}}(t_0)](x). \end{aligned}$$

It is desirable with vector-valued functions just as with real-valued functions to develop formulas which permit one to express the derivative of a complicated expression in terms of the derivatives of its simple parts. In particular, we want to know how to differentiate sums and the various products of vector functions.

(1.14) Theorem. *Let $\boldsymbol{\alpha}$ and $\boldsymbol{\beta}$ be differentiable vector functions of t with values in a vector space $\mathcal{V}$ and let f be a differentiable scalar function of t. Then:*

(1) *$\boldsymbol{\alpha} + \boldsymbol{\beta}$ is a differentiable vector function and*

$$\frac{d}{dt} \left(\boldsymbol{\alpha}(t) + \boldsymbol{\beta}(t)\right)\Big|_{t=t_0} = \dot{\boldsymbol{\alpha}}(t_0) + \dot{\boldsymbol{\beta}}(t_0).$$

(2) *If the function $\boldsymbol{\alpha}$ is constant $[\boldsymbol{\alpha}(t) \equiv \boldsymbol{\alpha}_0]$, then $\boldsymbol{\alpha}$ is differentiable and*

$$\dot{\boldsymbol{\alpha}} \equiv \mathbf{0}.$$

(3) *$\boldsymbol{\alpha} \cdot \boldsymbol{\beta}$ is a differentiable scalar function and*

$$\frac{d}{dt} \left(\boldsymbol{\alpha}(t) \cdot \boldsymbol{\beta}(t)\right)\Big|_{t=t_0} = \dot{\boldsymbol{\alpha}}(t_0) \cdot \boldsymbol{\beta}(t_0) + \boldsymbol{\alpha}(t_0) \cdot \dot{\boldsymbol{\beta}}(t_0).$$

(4) *$f\alpha$ is a differentiable vector function and*

$$\frac{d}{dt}\left(f(t)\alpha(t)\right)\Big|_{t=t_0} = \dot{f}(t_0)\alpha(t_0) + f(t_0)\dot{\alpha}(t_0).$$

Proof. The proof of parts (1) and (2) is discussed in the problems. Here we will simply verify parts (3) and (4) for functions having values in $\mathbb{R}^n$. This will shorten the discussion. Thus let $\boldsymbol{\alpha}$, $\boldsymbol{\beta}$ be the following functions:

$$\alpha(t) = \left(a_1(t), a_2(t), \ldots, a_n(t)\right)$$
$$\beta(t) = \left(b_1(t), b_2(t), \ldots, b_n(t)\right).$$

To check (3) note that $\boldsymbol{\alpha} \cdot \boldsymbol{\beta}$ is given by

$$(5) \quad \alpha(t)\cdot\beta(t) = a_1(t)b_1(t) + a_2(t)b_2(t) + \cdots + a_n(t)b_n(t).$$

Since the assumed differentiability of $\boldsymbol{\alpha}$ and $\boldsymbol{\beta}$ means that

$$a_1(t), \ldots, a_n(t), b_1(t), \ldots, b_n(t)$$

are differentiable functions [proposition (1.10)], the real-valued function in (5) is differentiable and

$$\frac{d}{dt}\left(\alpha(t)\cdot\beta(t)\right)\Big|_{t=t_0} = \dot{a}_1(t_0)b_1(t_0) + a_1(t_0)\dot{b}_1(t_0) + \dot{a}_2(t_0)b_2(t_0) + a_2(t_0)\dot{b}_2(t_0) + \cdots + \dot{a}_n(t_0)b_n(t_0) + a_n(t_0)\dot{b}_n(t_0).$$

Rearranging and referring to (1.10) we may write this as

$$\begin{aligned}\frac{d}{dt}\left(\alpha(t)\cdot\beta(t)\right)\Big|_{t=t_0} &= \left(\dot{a}_1(t_0), \dot{a}_2(t_0), \ldots, \dot{a}_n(t_0)\right)\cdot\left(b_1(t_0), b_2(t_0), \ldots, b_n(t_0)\right)\\ &\quad + \left(a_1(t_0), a_2(t_0), \ldots, a_n(t_0)\right)\cdot\left(\dot{b}_1(t_0), \dot{b}_2(t_0), \ldots, \dot{b}_n(t_0)\right)\\ &= \dot{\alpha}(t_0)\cdot\beta(t_0) + \alpha(t_0)\cdot\dot{\beta}(t_0).\end{aligned}$$

To check (4) note that $f\boldsymbol{\alpha}$ is given by

$$(f\alpha)(t) = f(t)\alpha(t) = \left(f(t)a_1(t), f(t)a_2(t), \ldots, f(t)a_n(t)\right) \in \mathbb{R}^n.$$

Since the assumed differentiability of $\boldsymbol{\alpha}$ means that $a_1, \ldots, a_n$ are differentiable functions and since f is a differentiable function, all entries in the above

$\mathcal{R}^n$-valued function are differentiable. Consequently $f\alpha$ is indeed differentiable [proposition (1.10)] and

$$\frac{d}{dt}(f(t)\alpha(t))\Big|_{t=t_0} = \big(\dot{f}(t_0)a_1(t_0) + f(t_0)\dot{a}_1(t_0),\ \dot{f}(t_0)a_2(t_0) + f(t_0)\dot{a}_2(t_0), \ldots, \dot{f}(t_0)a_n(t_0) + f(t_0)\dot{a}_n(t_0)\big).$$

Rearranging and using (1.10) we may write this as

$$\begin{aligned}\frac{d}{dt}(f(t)\alpha(t))\Big|_{t=t_0} &= \dot{f}(t_0)\big(a_1(t_0), a_2(t_0), \ldots, a_n(t_0)\big) \\ &\quad + f(t_0)\big(\dot{a}_1(t_0), \dot{a}_2(t_0), \ldots, \dot{a}_n(t_0)\big) \\ &= \dot{f}(t_0)\alpha(t_0) + f(t_0)\dot{\alpha}(t_0). \qquad \blacksquare\end{aligned}$$

We emphasize that theorem (1.14) is a general result about differentiable vector functions of t in any vector space. Here is another result of the same type. We shall use a special case of this theorem a little later.

(1.15) Theorem. *Let γ be a continuous vector function of t for $a \leq t \leq b$. Suppose that γ is differentiable on $a < t < b$ and that the derivative $\dot{\gamma}$ is identically zero. Then γ is a constant vector; that is, $\gamma(t) \equiv \alpha_0$.*

Proof. For real-valued functions ϕ this should be a familiar theorem. Let us recall the proof. One uses the mean-value theorem. This states that $\phi(t_2) - \phi(t_1) = \dot{\phi}(\tau)(t_2 - t_1)$ for some τ between t_1 and t_2. But if $\dot{\phi}$ is identically zero it follows that $\phi(t_2) - \phi(t_1) = 0$. Since this holds for arbitrary values of t_1 and t_2, it follows that $\phi(t)$ is a constant. We cannot use exactly this proof here, since we do not have the mean-value theorem for vector functions γ. Instead we use a trick. Let β be an arbitrary but fixed vector and consider the real-valued function $\phi(t) = \gamma(t)\cdot\beta$. By theorem (1.14) we have

$$\dot{\phi}(t) = \dot{\gamma}(t)\cdot\beta + \gamma(t)\cdot\dot{\beta} \equiv 0$$

since $\dot{\gamma}(t) = \dot{\beta} \equiv 0$. Hence by the remarks we just made, $\phi(t)$ is a constant. Thus for *any* vector β we have

$$\big(\gamma(t_2) - \gamma(t_1)\big)\cdot\beta = \gamma(t_2)\cdot\beta - \gamma(t_1)\cdot\beta = 0.$$

However, this identity implies $\gamma(t_2) - \gamma(t_1) = \mathbf{0}$, for with t_1 and t_2 fixed we can choose $\beta = \gamma(t_2) - \gamma(t_1)$. Then the above formula gives

$$\|\gamma(t_2) - \gamma(t_1)\|^2 = \big(\gamma(t_2) - \gamma(t_1)\big)\cdot\big(\gamma(t_2) - \gamma(t_1)\big) = 0.$$

Hence $\gamma(t_2) = \gamma(t_1)$ for any t_1 and t_2 and thus γ is constant. $\blacksquare$

PROBLEMS

1. Calculate the derivatives of each of the following vector functions at the value of t indicated.

(a) In $\mathcal{R}^2$: $\boldsymbol{\alpha}(t) = (t^2, 2t^3)$, $t = -1$
(b) In $\mathcal{R}^3$: $\boldsymbol{\alpha}(t) = (\sin t, \cos t, 1)$, $t = \pi$
(c) In $\mathcal{R}^3$: $\boldsymbol{\alpha}(t) = e^t(1, -1, 1)$, $t = 0$

2. The vector function $\boldsymbol{\alpha}(t) = (t, -2t)$ in $\mathcal{R}^2$ is continuous for all t. In particular, at $t = 1$ it must be so that given any $\varepsilon > 0$ there is a $\delta > 0$ such that $\|\boldsymbol{\alpha}(t) - \boldsymbol{\alpha}(1)\| < \varepsilon$ whenever $|t - 1| < \delta$. Find a suitable δ if

(a) $\varepsilon = 1$ (b) $\varepsilon = \frac{1}{10}$

3. The vector function Υ with values in $\mathcal{C}[0, 1]$ which satisfies $[\Upsilon(t)](x) = tx$ is continuous for all t. As in problem 2, given $\varepsilon = 1$ and $t = 1$ find δ.

4. Show directly from the definition that the vector function $\boldsymbol{\alpha}(t) = (1, |t|)$ in $\mathcal{R}^2$ is differentiable in any interval of the form $a < t < b$ with $a > 0$, but is *not* differentiable in the interval $-1 < t < 1$.

5. In any vector space $\mathcal{V}$ consider the vector function $\boldsymbol{\alpha}(t) = f(t)\boldsymbol{\alpha}_0$, where $f(t)$ is a differentiable scalar function and $\boldsymbol{\alpha}_0$ is a fixed vector. Give a formula for the derivative of $\boldsymbol{\alpha}$.

6. Use the result of problem 5 to calculate the derivative at $t = 0$ of the vector function $\boldsymbol{\alpha}$ such that $[\boldsymbol{\alpha}(t)](x) = e^{t+x} \in \mathcal{C}[0, \pi]$. Could the same result be used to calculate the derivative at $t = 0$ of the function $\boldsymbol{\alpha}$ such that $[\boldsymbol{\alpha}(t)](x) = e^{tx}$? Why?

7. Let $\boldsymbol{\alpha}$ be a differentiable vector function in any vector space. Show that $a(t) = \|\boldsymbol{\alpha}(t)\|^2$ is a differentiable *scalar* function with $\dot{a}(t) = 2\boldsymbol{\alpha}(t) \cdot \dot{\boldsymbol{\alpha}}(t)$.

8. Use problem 7 to find a formula for the derivatives of the following scalar functions when $\boldsymbol{\alpha}$ is a differentiable vector function

(a) $a(t) = \|\boldsymbol{\alpha}(t)\|$ (b) $a(t) = \sin \|\boldsymbol{\alpha}(t)\|$

[*Hint:* $\|\boldsymbol{\alpha}(t)\| = \sqrt{\|\boldsymbol{\alpha}(t)\|^2}$.]

9. Find vector functions $\boldsymbol{\alpha}$ in the spaces indicated which satisfy the given identity in t.

(a) In $\mathcal{R}^2$: $\dot{\boldsymbol{\alpha}}(t) = (0, 0)$
(b) In $\mathcal{R}^2$: $\dot{\boldsymbol{\alpha}}(t) = (t, e^t)$
(c) In $\mathcal{C}[0, 1]$: $[\dot{\boldsymbol{\alpha}}(t)](x) = t^2 \sin x + e^t x$

10. Give examples of vector functions in $\mathcal{R}^2$ and in $\mathcal{C}[0, \pi]$ which are continuous but *not* differentiable.

11. Let $P_1(t)$ and $P_2(t)$ denote the locations at time t of two particles. Let $Q(t)$ denote the point midway between them. Let $\mathbf{r}(t)$ denote the position vector of Q from a fixed origin P_0. Find a formula for $\dot{\mathbf{r}}(t)$ in terms of the velocities $\mathbf{v}_1(t)$ and $\mathbf{v}_2(t)$ of the two particles.

12. Let $P(t)$ be the position at time t of a moving particle. Suppose that the particle moves with velocity $\mathbf{v} = \dot{\mathbf{r}}$, where $\mathbf{r}$ denotes the position vector relative to a fixed point P_0. Show that differentiation of the position vector $\mathbf{r}^*$ relative to any different origin P_0^* yields the same vector function $\mathbf{v}$:

$$\dot{\mathbf{r}}^* = \mathbf{v} = \dot{\mathbf{r}}.$$

This result justifies the assumption that the velocity vector of a particle is determined solely by the path of the particle and does not depend on the choice of origin for its position vector. [*Hint:* Draw a diagram in which both $\mathbf{r}(t)$ and $\mathbf{r}^*(t)$ appear and give the algebraic relation between these arrows.]

13. Theorem (1.14) has as one of its consequences the following result for $\mathbb{R}^n$-valued functions [proposition (1.10)]: $\boldsymbol{\alpha}$ is differentiable if and only if $a_1, \ldots, a_n$ are differentiable, and $\dot{\boldsymbol{\alpha}}(t_0) = (\dot{a}_1(t_0), \ldots, \dot{a}_n(t_0))$. Prove this. [*Hint:* Use the decomposition

$$\boldsymbol{\alpha}(t) = a_1(t)(1, 0, \ldots, 0) + a_2(t)(0, 1, \ldots, 0) + \cdots + a_n(t)(0, \ldots, 0, 1)$$

in one half of the proof. Use the formulas

$$a_1(t) = \boldsymbol{\alpha}(t) \cdot (1, 0, \ldots, 0), \ldots, a_n(t) = \boldsymbol{\alpha}(t) \cdot (0, \ldots, 1)$$

in the remainder.]

14. (a) Prove that the solution $\mathbf{x} = (x_1, x_2)$ of a system of equations

$$\begin{aligned} a(t)x_1 + b(t)x_2 &= f(t) \\ c(t)x_1 + d(t)x_2 &= g(t) \end{aligned}$$

is a differentiable vector function on any interval such that

(1) a, b, c, d, f, g are differentiable on the given interval, and

(2) $a(t_0)d(t_0) - b(t_0)c(t_0) \neq 0$ for any value t_0 in the given interval.

(b) Show that condition (2) cannot be omitted in part (a). [*Hint:* Take $a(t) = b(t) = c(t) = t$, $d(t) = 1 + t$, $f(t) = \cos t$, $g(t) = 0$.]

2. Applications of Differentiability; Kinematics

Here we shall apply the techniques of §1 to analyze a number of situations in which vector functions of t appear. Several of the applications will be to particle motions. For this reason we wish to introduce the notion of acceleration. Suppose a particle has a velocity $\mathbf{v}(t) = \dot{\mathbf{r}}(t)$ for all t_0 in a given time interval. If the vector function $\mathbf{v}$ is itself differentiable, then we say that the particle has an *acceleration* throughout the given time interval and we define $\mathbf{a}$ by

$$\mathbf{a}(t_0) = \dot{\mathbf{v}}(t_0) = \ddot{\mathbf{r}}(t_0). \tag{2.1}$$

That is, the acceleration is the *second* derivative of the position vector.

(2.2) Examples. Continuous and Differentiable Vector Functions

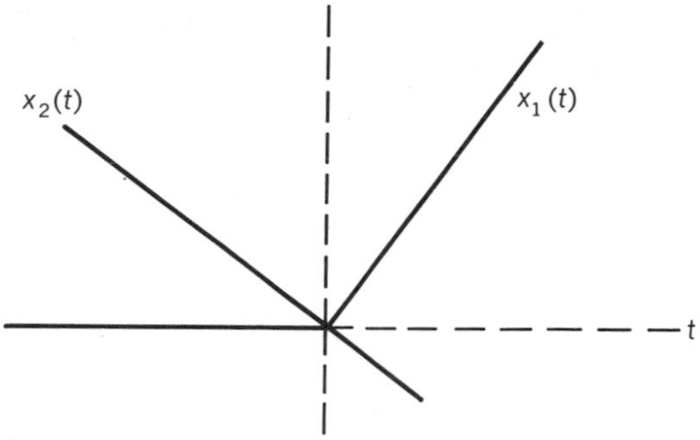

Figure 2.5

(a) AN $\mathcal{R}^2$-VALUED FUNCTION. Consider the system of equations

$$2x_1 - 3x_2 = 5t + 2|t| \qquad (2.3)$$
$$x_1 + x_2 = |t|.$$

Since the right sides of (2.3) are functions of time, so is the solution. By a straightforward computation we obtain

$$x_1 = t + |t|, \qquad x_2 = -t.$$

This gives us the following $\mathcal{R}^2$-valued function of t (see Figure 2.5):

$$\mathbf{x}(t) = (t + |t|, -t).$$

Since the scalar functions $t + |t|$ and $-t$ are both continuous for all t, it follows by (1.5) that $\mathbf{x}$ is a continuous $\mathcal{R}^2$-valued function on any interval. However, since $t + |t|$ fails to be differentiable at $t_0 = 0$, it follows by (1.10) that $\mathbf{x}$ is *not* differentiable on any interval $a < t < b$ which includes $t_0 = 0$.

(b) CIRCULAR MOTION (CONSTANT SPEED). Let $\mathbf{r}$ be the position vector relative to P_0 of a particle which moves in a circular path around P_0 (see Figure 2.6). Suppose that the path has radius 2 ft and that the particle moves at a constant speed of 5 ft/sec. To determine whether $\mathbf{r}$ is continuous we utilize definition (1.1). Let us examine $\|\mathbf{r}(t_0 + \Delta t) - \mathbf{r}(t_0)\| = \|\overrightarrow{P(t_0)P(t_0 + \Delta t)}\|$. This quantity represents the length of the chord joining $P(t_0)$ to $P(t_0 + \Delta t)$. Since the speed of the particle is 5 ft/sec, it follows that the length of the

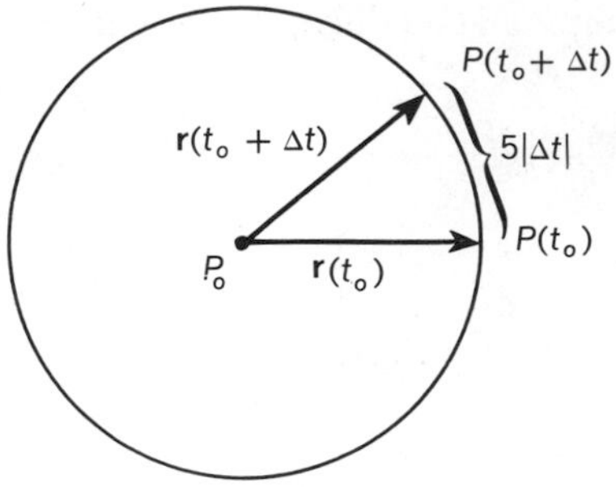

Figure 2.6

circular arc joining $P(t_0)$ to $P(t_0 + \Delta t)$ is $5|\Delta t|$. However, the chord joining any two points is shorter than the arc joining them, so we obtain the inequality

$$\|\mathbf{r}(t_0 + \Delta t) - \mathbf{r}(t_0)\| \leq 5|\Delta t|. \tag{2.4}$$

Since (2.4) implies

$$\|\mathbf{r}(t_0 + \Delta t) - \mathbf{r}(t_0)\| \sim 0 \qquad \text{when } \Delta t \sim 0,$$

we conclude that $\mathbf{r}$ is continuous. It is possible to show that $\mathbf{r}$ is differentiable as well, but we postpone this analysis until later.

(c) RECTILINEAR MOTION. Let a particle perform rectilinear motion. This means that with Q denoting a fixed point on the line of motion the arrows $\overrightarrow{QP(t)}$ are multiples of any arrow $\boldsymbol{\beta}$ parallel to that line (Figure 2.7):

$$\overrightarrow{QP(t)} = f(t)\boldsymbol{\beta}. \tag{2.5}$$

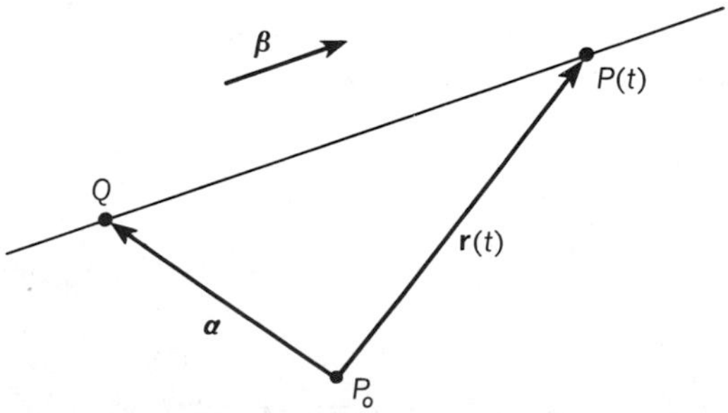

Figure 2.7

If the position vector to Q from an origin P_0 is denoted by $\boldsymbol{\alpha}$, then the position vector to the particle is given by the formula (Figure 2.7)

$$\mathbf{r}(t) = \boldsymbol{\alpha} + f(t)\boldsymbol{\beta}. \tag{2.5'}$$

Let us consider first a particular case. Suppose that $f(t) = 2 + \sin t$ so that

$$\mathbf{r}(t) = \boldsymbol{\alpha} + (2 + \sin t)\boldsymbol{\beta}, \qquad -\infty < t < \infty.$$

The direct way to see whether or not $\mathbf{r}$ is continuous involves examining

$$\mathbf{r}(t_0 + \Delta t) - \mathbf{r}(t_0) = [\boldsymbol{\alpha} + (2 + \sin (t_0 + \Delta t))\boldsymbol{\beta}] - [\boldsymbol{\alpha} + (2 + \sin t_0)\boldsymbol{\beta}]$$

and utilizing definition (1.1). However, theorem (1.14) permits a simpler analysis. By using this theorem together with the knowledge that $2 + \sin t$ is a differentiable scalar function, we see that the above function $\mathbf{r}$ is differentiable and hence automatically continuous. In addition, we can utilize theorem (1.14) to compute the velocity vector of the particle in question:

$$\begin{aligned}\mathbf{v}(t_0) = \dot{\mathbf{r}}(t_0) &= \dot{\boldsymbol{\alpha}} + (\cos t_0)\boldsymbol{\beta} + (2 + \sin t_0)\dot{\boldsymbol{\beta}} \\ &= (\cos t_0)\boldsymbol{\beta}.\end{aligned}$$

Next, using the fact that $\cos t$ is a differentiable function we are able to conclude from the above formula that $\mathbf{v}$ is differentiable, so that the particle has an acceleration

$$\begin{aligned}\mathbf{a}(t_0) = \dot{\mathbf{v}}(t_0) &= -(\sin t_0)\boldsymbol{\beta} + (\cos t_0)\dot{\boldsymbol{\beta}} \\ &= -(\sin t_0)\boldsymbol{\beta}.\end{aligned}$$

The same kind of argument applies to the general situation (2.5′). The particle has a velocity provided that the scalar function f is differentiable on the given time interval:

$$\mathbf{v}(t_0) = \dot{\mathbf{r}}(t_0) = \dot{f}(t_0)\boldsymbol{\beta}.$$

If f has a second derivative, then the particle has an acceleration as well and the acceleration is given by

$$\mathbf{a}(t) = \dot{\mathbf{v}}(t) = \ddot{f}(t)\boldsymbol{\beta}.$$

In particular, if $f(t) = ct + d$ with c, d constants, then the velocity is constant and the acceleration is 0.

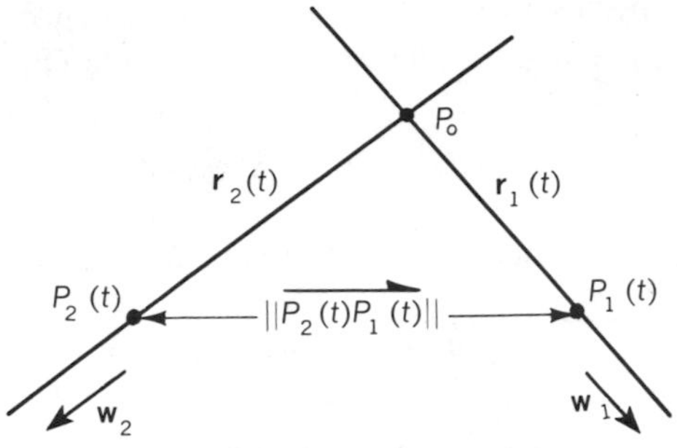

Figure 2.8

(d) RECTILINEAR MOTION OF TWO PARTICLES. Next let us consider two particles performing rectilinear motion along intersecting lines (Figure 2.8). Using position vectors relative to the point of intersection of the lines we may write the equations of the particle paths as follows:

$$\text{(2.6)}\qquad \begin{aligned} &\textit{Particle 1:}\quad \mathbf{r}_1(t) = \overrightarrow{P_0P_1(t)} = f_1(t)\mathbf{w}_1.\\ &\textit{Particle 2:}\quad \mathbf{r}_2(t) = \overrightarrow{P_0P_2(t)} = f_2(t)\mathbf{w}_2.\end{aligned}$$

Let us find the rate at which the particles approach one another. Since the distance between the particles is given by the formula

$$\|\overrightarrow{P_1(t)P_2(t)}\| = \|\mathbf{r}_2(t) - \mathbf{r}_1(t)\| = \sqrt{(\mathbf{r}_2(t) - \mathbf{r}_1(t))\cdot(\mathbf{r}_2(t) - \mathbf{r}_1(t))},$$

we find that

$$\text{(2.7)}\qquad \begin{aligned} \frac{d}{dt}\|\overrightarrow{P_1(t)P_2(t)}\| &= \frac{1}{2\sqrt{(\mathbf{r}_2(t) - \mathbf{r}_1(t))\cdot(\mathbf{r}_2(t) - \mathbf{r}_1(t))}}\\ &\qquad \times \frac{d}{dt}\left[(\mathbf{r}_2(t) - \mathbf{r}_1(t))\cdot(\mathbf{r}_2(t) - \mathbf{r}_1(t))\right]\\ &= \frac{(\dot{\mathbf{r}}_2(t) - \dot{\mathbf{r}}_1(t))\cdot(\mathbf{r}_2(t) - \mathbf{r}_1(t))}{\sqrt{(\mathbf{r}_2(t) - \mathbf{r}_1(t))\cdot(\mathbf{r}_2(t) - \mathbf{r}_1(t))}}.\end{aligned}$$

Substituting from equation (2.6) we obtain the formula

$$\frac{d}{dt}\|\overrightarrow{P_1(t)P_2(t)}\| = \frac{(\dot{f}_2(t)\mathbf{w}_2 - \dot{f}_1(t)\mathbf{w}_1)\cdot(f_2(t)\mathbf{w}_2 - f_1(t)\mathbf{w}_1)}{\sqrt{(f_2(t)\mathbf{w}_2 - f_1(t)\mathbf{w}_1)\cdot(f_2(t)\mathbf{w}_2 - f_1(t)\mathbf{w}_1)}}.$$

Observe that the particles are coming closer when

$$(\dot{f}_2(t)\mathbf{w}_2 - \dot{f}_1(t)\mathbf{w}_1) \cdot (f_2(t)\mathbf{w}_2 - f_1(t)\mathbf{w}_1) < 0$$

and are separating when

$$(\dot{f}_2(t)\mathbf{w}_2 - \dot{f}_1(t)\mathbf{w}_1) \cdot (f_2(t)\mathbf{w}_2 - f_1(t)\mathbf{w}_1) > 0.$$

(e) A $\mathcal{C}[0, \pi]$-VALUED FUNCTION. Let γ be the following vector function of t with values in the vector space $\mathcal{C}[0, \pi]$:

(2.8) $$[\gamma(t)](x) = \sin(x + t) + e^{x+t}, \qquad 0 \leq x \leq \pi.$$

In order to apply theorem (1.14) we write for γ the equivalent formula

(2.8′) $$[\gamma(t)](x) = \cos t \sin x + \sin t \cos x + e^t e^x, \qquad 0 \leq x \leq \pi.$$

Now (2.8′) is obviously a sum of elements in $\mathcal{C}[0, \pi]$ multiplied by certain differentiable scalar functions of t. Hence by theorem (1.14) γ is differentiable, therefore automatically continuous, for all t. For $\dot{\gamma}$ we obtain

$$[\dot{\gamma}(t_0)](x) = -\sin t_0 \sin x + \cos t_0 \cos x + e^{t_0}e^x.$$

Observe once again that the expression for $\gamma(t)$, when regarded merely as a function of two variables

$$c(x, t) = \sin(x + t) + e^{x+t} = \cos t \sin x + \sin t \cos x + e^t e^x,$$

possesses a partial derivative with respect to t, and that

$$\frac{\partial}{\partial t} c(x, t_0) = -\sin t_0 \sin x + \cos t_0 \cos x + e^{t_0}e^x = [\dot{\gamma}(t_0)](x).$$

In order to analyze some examples to follow it will be convenient to express certain facts in terms of another kind of product for vectors. This type of product, called the *vector* (or *cross*) *product*, is restricted to the vector space of arrows (or $\mathcal{R}^3$) and does not extend to general vector spaces. Nevertheless, we wish to introduce it because it is quite useful in particle mechanics.

(2.9) Definition. The **vector product** of two nonparallel arrows **a** and **b** is by definition the arrow $\mathbf{c} = \mathbf{a} \times \mathbf{b}$ which satisfies:

(a) $\|\mathbf{c}\| = \|\mathbf{a}\|\,\|\mathbf{b}\| \sin \theta$ where θ is the angle ($0 < \theta < \pi$) between **a** and **b**,

(b) **c** is perpendicular to the plane of **a** and **b**:

$$\mathbf{c} \cdot \mathbf{a} = \mathbf{c} \cdot \mathbf{b} = 0$$

(c) **c** has the sense prescribed by the "right-hand rule": If **a** and **b** were drawn on the head of a right-hand screw, then the direction of advance of the screw as it was turned so as to make **a** turn toward **b** through the angle θ would be the direction of **c**.

The case in which **a** and **b** are parallel (that is, $\theta = 0$ or $\theta = \pi$) is consistent with formula (a) only if we define

$$\mathbf{c} = \mathbf{a} \times \mathbf{b} = \mathbf{0} \qquad \text{when } \mathbf{a} \text{ and } \mathbf{b} \text{ are parallel.}$$

One interesting feature of the vector product is that it is noncommutative. From the definition of $\mathbf{a} \times \mathbf{b}$ and $\mathbf{b} \times \mathbf{a}$ it follows that these arrows have the same direction and magnitude but opposite sense:

$$\mathbf{b} \times \mathbf{a} = -(\mathbf{a} \times \mathbf{b}).$$

On the other hand, the vector product does obey the useful laws

(2.10a) $$(\mathbf{a} + \mathbf{c}) \times \mathbf{b} = \mathbf{a} \times \mathbf{b} + \mathbf{c} \times \mathbf{b}$$

(2.10b) $$(k\mathbf{a}) \times \mathbf{b} = k(\mathbf{a} \times \mathbf{b}) = \mathbf{a} \times (k\mathbf{b}), \qquad k \text{ a scalar.}$$

There is also a formula for the derivative of the cross product of two arrow-valued functions.

(2.11) Proposition. *Let $\boldsymbol{\alpha}$ and $\boldsymbol{\beta}$ be differentiable arrow-valued functions. Then $\boldsymbol{\alpha} \times \boldsymbol{\beta}$ is a differentiable arrow-valued function and*

$$\frac{d}{dt}\left(\boldsymbol{\alpha}(t) \times \boldsymbol{\beta}(t)\right)\Big|_{t=t_0} = \dot{\boldsymbol{\alpha}}(t_0) \times \boldsymbol{\beta}(t_0) + \boldsymbol{\alpha}(t_0) \times \dot{\boldsymbol{\beta}}(t_0).$$

The proof will not be given.

(2.12) Examples. Differentiable Vector Functions (Continued)

(a) PLANAR MOTION. Suppose that the motion of a particle takes place in a fixed plane (Figure 2.9). Let **N** denote a unit normal vector to that plane and let Q denote a fixed point lying in the plane. If the position vector to Q

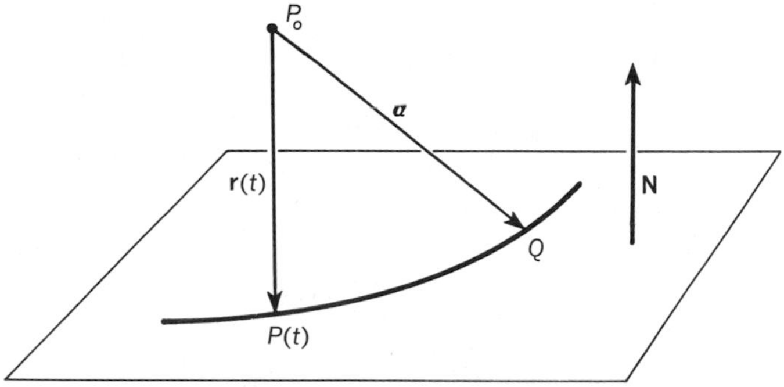

Figure 2.9

from an origin P_0 is denoted by $\boldsymbol{\alpha}$, then the arrow

$$\overrightarrow{QP}(t) = \mathbf{r}(t) - \boldsymbol{\alpha}$$

is always parallel to the plane. Hence

$$(\mathbf{r}(t) - \boldsymbol{\alpha}) \cdot \mathbf{N} = 0. \tag{2.13}$$

Assuming that $\mathbf{r}$ is differentiable, we find by differentiating (2.13) that

$$\dot{\mathbf{r}}(t) \cdot \mathbf{N} = 0. \tag{2.14}$$

In other words, when a particle moves in a plane, its velocity is at all times parallel to that plane. By differentiating (2.14) we likewise deduce that the acceleration of the particle is parallel to the plane at all times.

We can also reverse these arguments. Let a motion be such that its velocity $\mathbf{v}$ satisfies

$$\mathbf{v}(t) \cdot \mathbf{N} = 0 \qquad \text{for all } t.$$

for some fixed unit arrow $\mathbf{N}$. If $\mathbf{r}$ is the position vector of the particle, then

$$\frac{d}{dt}(\mathbf{r}(t) \cdot \mathbf{N}) = \dot{\mathbf{r}}(t) \cdot \mathbf{N} = \mathbf{v}(t) \cdot \mathbf{N} = 0.$$

Hence $\mathbf{r} \cdot \mathbf{N}$ is a constant c. But then (see Figure 2.9)

$$(\mathbf{r}(t_1) - \mathbf{r}(t_0)) \cdot \mathbf{N} = \mathbf{r}(t_1) \cdot \mathbf{N} - \mathbf{r}(t_0) \cdot \mathbf{N} = c - c = 0,$$

so that the particle moves in a plane perpendicular to N.

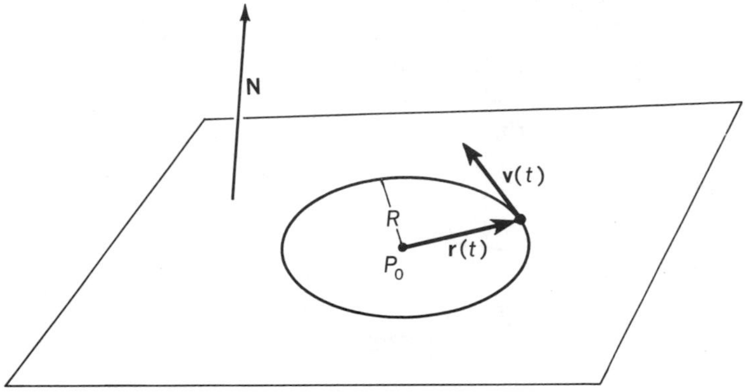

Figure 2.10

On the other hand, the condition

$$\mathbf{a}(t) \cdot \mathbf{N} = 0 \qquad \text{for all } t$$

does *not* ensure that the motion is performed in a fixed plane. The analysis of this condition will be carried out in the problems.

(b) CIRCULAR MOTION. Suppose that a particle moves in a circular path around a point P_0, not necessarily at constant speed. The path of the particle is then certainly planar, so that if $\mathbf{r}$ is the position vector relative to P_0 and $\mathbf{N}$ is the normal to the plane of the circle, then

(2.15a) $$\mathbf{r}(t) \cdot \mathbf{N} = 0.$$

In addition, the arrow $\mathbf{r}$ has a constant magnitude

(2.15b) $$\mathbf{r}(t) \cdot \mathbf{r}(t) = R^2,$$

where R is the radius of the circle (Figure 2.10). To analyze the velocity and acceleration of the particle we proceed as follows. Differentiation of (2.15a) and (2.15b) yields

(2.16a) $$\dot{\mathbf{r}}(t) \cdot \mathbf{N} = \mathbf{v}(t) \cdot \mathbf{N} = 0$$

(2.16b) $$\dot{\mathbf{r}}(t) \cdot \mathbf{r}(t) + \mathbf{r}(t) \cdot \dot{\mathbf{r}}(t) = 2\mathbf{v}(t) \cdot \mathbf{r}(t) = 0.$$

The first equation states that at all times $\mathbf{v}$ is perpendicular to $\mathbf{N}$. The second equation states that the velocity at time t is perpendicular to the position vector (relative to P_0) at time t. Since an arrow which is perpendicular to both **N** and **r** is parallel to $\mathbf{r} \times \mathbf{N}$, we can write

$$\dot{\mathbf{r}}(t) = \mathbf{v}(t) = \omega(t)(\mathbf{N} \times \mathbf{r}(t)), \tag{2.17}$$

where $\omega(t)$ is a scalar function. Using property (2.11b) of the vector product we can also write this in the alternative form

$$\dot{\mathbf{r}}(t) = \mathbf{v}(t) = (\omega(t)\mathbf{N}) \times \mathbf{r}(t) = \boldsymbol{\omega}(t) \times \mathbf{r}(t), \tag{2.17$'$}$$

where the vector function $\boldsymbol{\omega}$ is defined by $\boldsymbol{\omega}(t) = \omega(t)\mathbf{N}$.

In order to compute the speed of the particle we refer to equation (2.17), keeping in mind that **r** and **N** are perpendicular:

$$\begin{aligned} \|\mathbf{v}(t)\| &= |\omega(t)|\ \|\mathbf{N} \times \mathbf{r}(t)\| \\ &= |\omega(t)|\ \|\mathbf{r}(t)\| \cdot 1 \cdot \sin \pi/2 = |\omega(t)|R. \end{aligned} \tag{2.18}$$

Finally, to calculate the acceleration we differentiate equation (2.17) with the help of proposition (2.12):

$$\begin{aligned} \ddot{\mathbf{r}}(t) &= \dot{\omega}(t)(\mathbf{N} \times \mathbf{r}(t)) + \omega(t)\frac{d}{dt}(\mathbf{N} \times \mathbf{r}(t)) \\ &= \dot{\omega}(t)(\mathbf{N} \times \mathbf{r}(t)) + \omega(t)(\mathbf{N} \times \dot{\mathbf{r}}(t) + \dot{\mathbf{N}} \times \mathbf{r}(t)) \\ &= \dot{\omega}(t)(\mathbf{N} \times \mathbf{r}(t)) + \omega(t)(\mathbf{N} \times \dot{\mathbf{r}}(t)). \end{aligned} \tag{2.19}$$

Substituting for $\dot{\mathbf{r}}$ from (2.17) we may write this as

$$\mathbf{a}(t) = \dot{\omega}(t)(\mathbf{N} \times \mathbf{r}(t)) + \omega^2(t)\mathbf{N} \times (\mathbf{N} \times \mathbf{r}(t)). \tag{2.19$'$}$$

The reader should convince himself that the first term is perpendicular to $\mathbf{r}(t)$ while the second is parallel to $\mathbf{r}(t)$. For this reason the terms in (2.19′) are called the *tangential* and the *normal acceleration*, respectively.

PROBLEMS

1. Two particles move along the horizontal straight lines indicated in Figure 2.11. At time t the particles are at points P and P' at distances t and t^2, respectively,

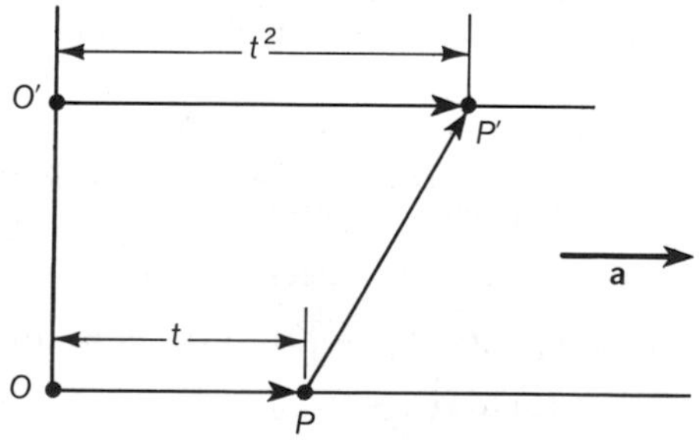

Figure 2.11

from the points O and O'. Let $\mathbf{a}$ be a horizontal vector of unit length. Show that the vector function $\overrightarrow{PP'}$ is differentiable with respect to t for all t and find its derivative in terms of $\mathbf{a}$.

2. Particles move along the straight lines OL and OL' as indicated in Figure 2.12. $\mathbf{a}$ and $\mathbf{b}$ are vectors of unit length.

(a) Express $\overrightarrow{PP'}$ in terms of $\mathbf{a}$ and $\mathbf{b}$.

(b) Show that $\overrightarrow{PP'}$ is a differentiable function of t for each t.

3. Let $\mathbf{r}$ be the vector function equal at time t to the arrow $\overrightarrow{OP(t)} = |t|\mathbf{a}$ (Figure 2.13). Here $\mathbf{a}$ is a unit vector. Show that $\mathbf{r}$ is not differentiable on any interval $c \leq t \leq d$ which includes $t_0 = 0$.

4. Two particles are moving along paths $P_0(t)$ and $P(t)$ as shown in Figure 2.14. The vector $\mathbf{r}(t)$ is called the position vector of P relative to P_0. Find an expression for $\dot{\mathbf{r}}(t)$ (the *relative velocity* of P) in terms of the velocities $\mathbf{v}_P(t)$ and $\mathbf{v}_{P_0}(t)$ of P and P_0 at time t.

5. $\boldsymbol{\alpha}$ and $\boldsymbol{\beta}$ are vectors of unit length in the plane of the paper (Figure 2.15). Describe the vectors $(\boldsymbol{\alpha} \times \boldsymbol{\beta})$, $(\boldsymbol{\alpha} \times -\boldsymbol{\beta})$, and $(-\boldsymbol{\alpha} \times 2\boldsymbol{\beta})$.

6. If $\boldsymbol{\alpha} \times \boldsymbol{\beta}$ equals the vector $\boldsymbol{\gamma}$, what are the vectors $2\boldsymbol{\alpha} \times \boldsymbol{\beta}$, $\boldsymbol{\alpha} \times 2\boldsymbol{\beta}$, and $-\boldsymbol{\alpha} \times \boldsymbol{\beta}$ in terms of $\boldsymbol{\gamma}$? What is the vector $c_1\boldsymbol{\alpha} \times c_2\boldsymbol{\beta}$ in terms of $\boldsymbol{\gamma}$ if c_1 and c_2 are any real numbers?

7. Let the arrow functions $\mathbf{a}$ and $\mathbf{b}$ be defined by $\mathbf{a}(t) = (2t + 1)\boldsymbol{\alpha}$, $\mathbf{b}(t) = t^2\boldsymbol{\beta}$, where $\boldsymbol{\alpha}$ and $\boldsymbol{\beta}$ are the vectors in problem 5.

(a) Verify proposition (2.12) for these two vector functions.

(b) Let $A(t)$ denote the area of the parallelogram determined by $\mathbf{a}(t)$ and $\mathbf{b}(t)$. Calculate $A(1)$.

8. If $\boldsymbol{\alpha}$ is a vector such that $\boldsymbol{\alpha} \times \boldsymbol{\beta} = \mathbf{0}$ for every vector $\boldsymbol{\beta}$, show that $\boldsymbol{\alpha}$ must be the zero vector.

9. Consider the system of equations

$$\begin{aligned} tx_1 + 3x_2 &= t \\ 3x_1 + tx_2 &= |t + 1|. \end{aligned}$$

Denote the solution (x_1, x_2) at each value t by $(x_1(t), x_2(t)) = \boldsymbol{\alpha}(t)$. This is a vector in $\mathbb{R}^2$. For what intervals of t is $\boldsymbol{\alpha}$ continuous? For what intervals is it differentiable?

10. Let $\boldsymbol{\alpha}$ be a differentiable vector function in any vector space. Show that at any value of t at which $\|\boldsymbol{\alpha}(t)\|$ has a maximum or minimum one must have $\dot{\boldsymbol{\alpha}}(t)$ orthogonal to $\boldsymbol{\alpha}(t)$.

11. Show that a particle moves so that its distance from a fixed point P_0 is constant if and only if its velocity is always perpendicular to the position vector from P_0. (Note that there are two things to prove.)

12. Show that if a particle has constant velocity it must be moving along a straight line. [*Hint:* Let $\mathbf{r}$ be the position vector then $\dot{\mathbf{r}}(t) \equiv \mathbf{v}_0$. But also $\frac{d}{dt}(t\mathbf{v}_0) = \mathbf{v}_0$. Now apply theorem (1.15) to $\mathbf{r}(t) - t\mathbf{v}_0$.]

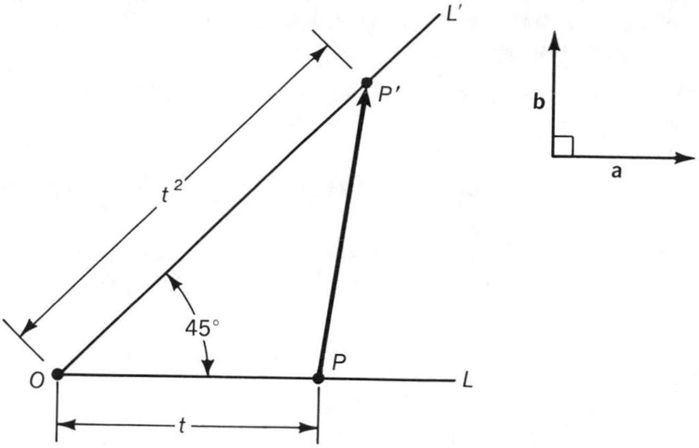

Figure 2.12

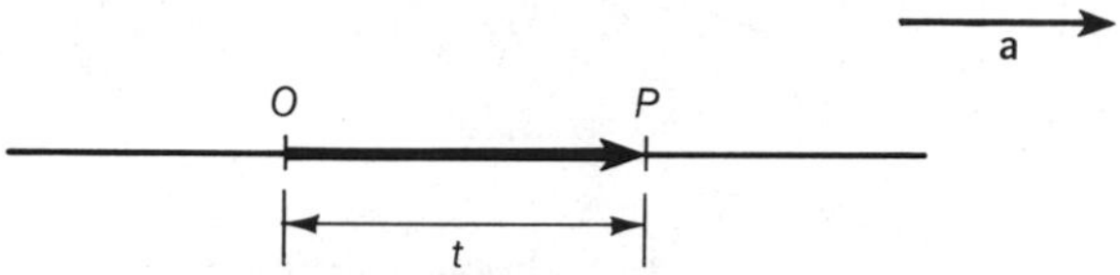

Figure 2.13

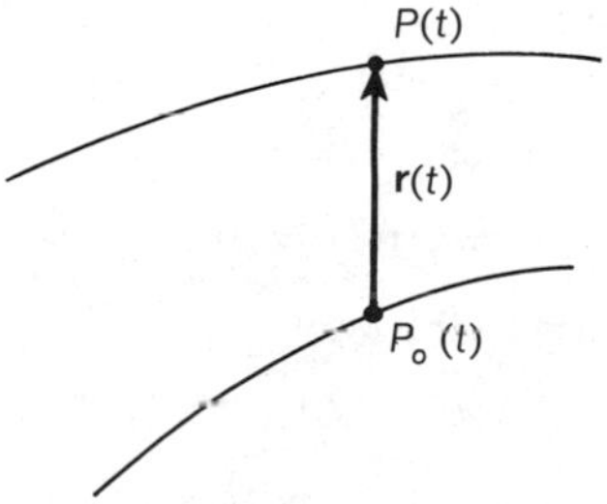

Figure 2.14

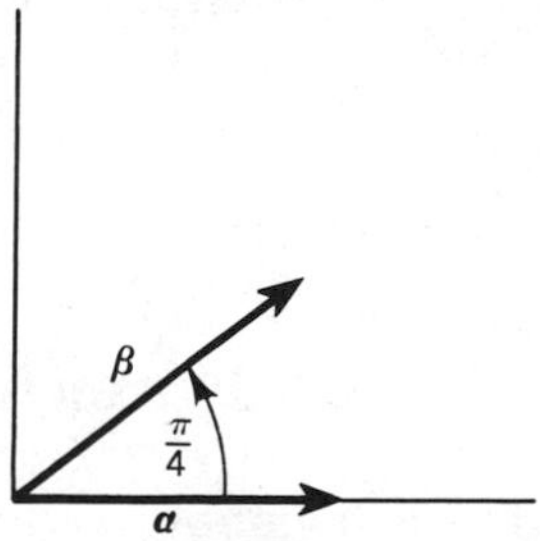

Figure 2.15

13. (a) A particle moves in a plane at constant distance from a fixed point P_0 in the plane. If it has constant speed, show that its acceleration is directed along the position vector from P_0.

(b) A particle moves so that its velocity satisfies

$$\mathbf{v}(t) \times \boldsymbol{\alpha} = \mathbf{0}, \qquad -\infty < t < \infty$$

where $\boldsymbol{\alpha}$ is a fixed vector. Show that the particle moves along a straight line (or stands still).

14. A particle moves so that its velocity is always parallel to its position vector relative to a fixed point P_0. Show that its acceleration is parallel to the same vector.

15. A rigid rod is pivoted at a fixed point P_0. Let $\mathbf{r}_1$ denote the position vector of one end relative to P_0 (Figure 2.16).

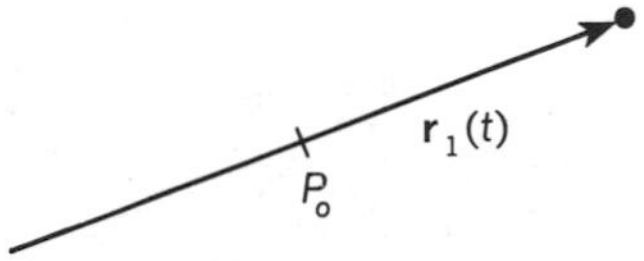

Figure 2.16

(a) Show that there exists a vector function $\boldsymbol{\omega}$ such that

$$\dot{\mathbf{r}}_1(t) = \boldsymbol{\omega}(t) \times \mathbf{r}_1(t).$$

(b) For any such choice of $\boldsymbol{\omega}$, show that the velocity of *any* point in the rod is given by $\boldsymbol{\omega}(t) \times \mathbf{r}(t)$, where $\mathbf{r}(t)$ is *its* position vector relative to P_0.

(c) Show that $\boldsymbol{\omega}$ will be uniquely determined if we require it to have the form

$$\boldsymbol{\omega}(t) = \omega(t)(\mathbf{r}_1 \times \dot{\mathbf{r}}_1)$$

and that if $\boldsymbol{\omega}$ is chosen in this way, then

$$\dot{\boldsymbol{\omega}} \cdot \mathbf{r}_1 \equiv 0.$$

16. A particle moves in such a way that its acceleration is always perpendicular to a fixed vector $\mathbf{N}$.

(a) If at some time t_0 its *velocity* is perpendicular to $\mathbf{N}$, show that it moves in a plane.

(b) Draw a picture to illustrate the most general motion possible.

3. Integration of Vector Functions

In developing a notion of differentiation for vector functions, we observed that this notion is patterned directly on differentiation for real-valued functions. Now for real-valued functions there is an inverse operation to differentiation: integration. Hence it should come as no surprise to learn that there is also an inverse operation to differentiation of vector functions. The present section will be devoted to the development of this latter operation, which by the way is still called integration.

The basic idea underlying the applications of integration to real-valued functions is the notion of definite integral. For convenience of reference we restate the definition of this quantity. Lengthy sums play an important role in this definition, so it will be helpful to utilize the abbreviation for such sums provided by "sigma notation." For instance, we denote

$$k_1 + k_2 + \cdots + k_n = \sum_{i=1}^{n} k_i.$$

(3.1) Definition. A function f defined over a time interval $c \leq t \leq d$ is said to be **integrable** if there is a number B which is approached by the sums

$$\text{(a)} \qquad \sum_{i=1}^{n} f(\tau_i)\,\Delta_i t,$$

when $\Delta_1 t, \ldots, \Delta_n t$ tend to zero. Here $t_1, \ldots, t_n$ subdivide the given interval and the values $\tau_1, \ldots, \tau_n$ are selected within the corresponding time subintervals

$$\text{(b)} \qquad c \leq \tau_1 \leq t_1, \quad t_1 \leq \tau_2 \leq t_2, \ldots, \quad t_{n-1} \leq \tau_n \leq t_n = d,$$

while the quantities

$$\Delta_1 t = t_1 - c, \quad \Delta_2 t = t_2 - t_1, \ldots, \quad \Delta_n t = t_n - t_{n-1}$$

denote the lengths of these subintervals.

What this means is that given any $\varepsilon > 0$ there must be a $\delta > 0$ such that

$$\left| \sum_{i=1}^{n} f(\tau_i)\,\Delta_i t - B \right| < \varepsilon \qquad \text{whenever } |\Delta_1 t|, |\Delta_2 t|, \ldots, |\Delta_n t| < \delta,$$

for any choice of $\tau_1, \ldots, \tau_n$ satisfying (b). The number B is called the **definite integral** of f over $c \leq t \leq d$ and it is designated by

$$B = \int_c^d f(t)\,dt.$$

If $d < c$, then we *define*

$$\int_c^d f(t)\,dt = -\int_d^c f(t)\,dt.$$

If $d = c$, then we set the integral equal to zero.

Our definition of integration for vector-valued functions is patterned on that for real-valued functions. Once again the only modification is that we must use a norm in place of an absolute value to state that the difference of two terms is small.

(3.2) Definition. Let $\boldsymbol{\gamma}$ denote a function of t whose values are in a vector space $\mathcal{V}$. $\boldsymbol{\gamma}$ is said to be **integrable** over a given time interval $c \leq t \leq d$ if there is a vector $\boldsymbol{\beta} \in \mathcal{V}$ which is approached by the sums of $\boldsymbol{\gamma}$ on this interval:

$$\left\| \sum_{i=1}^{n} \boldsymbol{\gamma}(\tau_i)\,\Delta_i t - \boldsymbol{\beta} \right\| \sim 0 \qquad \text{when } \Delta_1 t, \ldots, \Delta_n t \sim 0. \tag{3.3}$$

That is, given any $\varepsilon > 0$ there must be a $\delta > 0$ such that

$$\left\| \sum_{i=1}^{n} \boldsymbol{\gamma}(\tau_i)\,\Delta_i t - \boldsymbol{\beta} \right\| < \varepsilon \qquad \text{whenever } |\Delta_1 t|, |\Delta_2 t|, \ldots, |\Delta_n t| < \delta, \tag{3.3$'$}$$

for any choice of $\tau_1, \ldots, \tau_n$ satisfying (3.1b). The vector $\boldsymbol{\beta}$ is called the **definite integral** of $\boldsymbol{\gamma}$ over $c \leq t \leq d$ and it is designated by

$$\boldsymbol{\beta} = \int_c^d \boldsymbol{\gamma}(t)\,dt. \tag{3.4}$$

If d is less than c, we proceed just as in the case of real-valued functions by defining

$$\int_c^d \boldsymbol{\gamma}(t)\,dt = -\int_d^c \boldsymbol{\gamma}(t)\,dt.$$

Likewise, if $d = c$, we set the result equal to $\mathbf{0}$.

To gain insight into the above definition, let us apply it to an $\mathcal{R}^n$-valued function $\boldsymbol{\alpha}$. Here the definitions of addition and scalar multiplication in $\mathcal{R}^n$ imply that

$$\begin{aligned}
\sum_{i=1}^{n} \boldsymbol{\alpha}(\tau_i)\,\Delta_i t
&= \Delta_1 t\big(a_1(\tau_1), \ldots, a_n(\tau_1)\big) + \Delta_2 t\big(a_1(\tau_2), \ldots, a_n(\tau_2)\big) + \cdots \\
&\quad + \Delta_n t\big(a_1(\tau_n), \ldots, a_n(\tau_n)\big) \\
&= \big(a_1(\tau_1)\,\Delta_1 t + \cdots + a_1(\tau_n)\,\Delta_n t,\ \ldots,\ a_n(\tau_1)\,\Delta_1 t + \cdots + a_n(\tau_n)\,\Delta_n t\big) \\
&= \left(\sum_{i=1}^{n} a_1(\tau_i)\,\Delta_i t, \ldots, \sum_{i=1}^{n} a_n(\tau_i)\,\Delta_i t\right).
\end{aligned}$$

If $\boldsymbol{\alpha}$ is integrable and its integral is denoted by

$$\int_c^d \boldsymbol{\alpha}(t)\,dt = \boldsymbol{\beta} = (b_1, \ldots, b_n),$$

then

$$\left\| \sum_{i=1}^{n} \boldsymbol{\alpha}(\tau_i)\,\Delta_i t - \boldsymbol{\beta} \right\|$$

has the form

$$\begin{aligned}
\text{(3.5a)}\qquad \left\| \sum_{i=1}^{n} \boldsymbol{\alpha}(\tau_i)\,\Delta_i t - \boldsymbol{\beta} \right\|
&= \left\| \left(\sum_{i=1}^{n} a_1(\tau_i)\,\Delta_i t - b_1, \ldots, \sum_{i=1}^{n} a_n(\tau_i)\,\Delta_i t - b_n \right) \right\| \\
&= \sqrt{\left(\sum_{i=1}^{n} a_1(\tau_i)\,\Delta_i t - b_1 \right)^2 + \cdots + \left(\sum_{i=1}^{n} a_n(\tau_i)\,\Delta_i t - b_n \right)^2}.
\end{aligned}$$

For the above square root to be small it is necessary that *each* of the terms in parentheses be small. Hence (3.3) requires that all the following relations hold:

$$\text{(3.5b)}\qquad \begin{aligned}
\left| \sum_{i=1}^{n} a_1(\tau_i)\,\Delta_i t - b_1 \right| &\sim 0 \\
\left| \sum_{i=1}^{n} a_2(\tau_i)\,\Delta_i t - b_2 \right| &\sim 0 \\
&\ \vdots \\
\left| \sum_{i=1}^{n} a_n(\tau_i)\,\Delta_i t - b_n \right| &\sim 0 \qquad \text{when } \Delta_1 t, \ldots, \Delta_n t \sim 0.
\end{aligned}$$

Now, the first relation in (3.5b) states that a_1 is an integrable real-valued function over $c \leq t \leq d$ with integral $\int_c^d a_1(t)\,dt = b_1$, the second relation states that a_2 is an integrable real-valued function over $c \leq t \leq d$ with integral $\int_c^d a_2(t)\,dt = b_2$, and so on. That is, integrability for $\boldsymbol{\alpha}$ implies that each of the scalar functions $a_1, a_2, \ldots, a_n$ is integrable. By reversing the arguments we also see that integrability of each of the functions $a_1, a_2, \ldots, a_n$ ensures that the square root in (3.5a) is small when $\Delta_1 t, \ldots, \Delta_n t$ are small; of course, this requires that $\boldsymbol{\beta} = (b_1, \ldots, b_n)$ is chosen as

$$b_1 = \int_c^d a_1(t)\,dt, \ldots, b_n = \int_c^d a_n(t)\,dt.$$

We summarize as follows.

(3.6) Proposition. *An $\mathcal{R}^n$-valued function $\boldsymbol{\alpha}$ is integrable over an interval $c \leq t \leq d$ if and only if each of the scalar functions $a_1, a_2, \ldots, a_n$ is integrable over that interval; in addition the following formula holds:*

$$\int_c^d \boldsymbol{\alpha}(t)\,dt = \left(\int_c^d a_1(t)\,dt, \ldots, \int_c^d a_n(t)\,dt\right) \cdot$$

Let us now recall that the importance for real-valued functions of the (rather technical) definition of definite integral is mainly theoretical. One does not often proceed to evaluate areas, volumes, distances, and so on, by directly applying the *definition*. Instead, one utilizes a body of theorems about integration to obtain the desired results. To illustrate, the problem of finding a function f such that $\dot{f}(t) = 3t^2$ is a simple exercise in inverting a differentiation formula: $f(t) = t^3$ is a solution; yet the problem of finding a function f such that $\dot{f}(t) = e^{t^2}$ cannot be solved by this means.† Nevertheless, the theorems of calculus guarantee that there *is* a solution to the latter problem as well. The essential result which shows that such problems have solutions even when one cannot simply invert differentiation formulas (and which permits easy evaluation of definite integrals when one *can* invert) is the so-called *fundamental theorem* (of calculus). We state it here for convenience.

(3.7) Fundamental Theorem. *If a function g is continuous on a given time interval $c \leq t \leq d$, then it is integrable over that time interval as well as over any subinterval of that time interval. In addition, the problem of finding an f*

†Although correct, the statement that no expression involving the standard functions can yield e^{t^2} upon differentiation is very difficult to prove.

such that

$$\text{(a)} \qquad \dot{f}(t) = g(t), \qquad c < t < d,$$

always has a solution. One solution of (a) *is the function defined over* $c \leq t \leq d$ *by*

$$\text{(b)} \qquad f(t) = \int_c^t g(s)\, ds;$$

that is,

$$\text{(c)} \qquad \frac{d}{dt}\left(\int_c^t g(s)\, ds\right) = g(t).$$

All other solutions of (a) *differ from the solution* (b) *by a constant.*

To see why similar results are important for vector functions let us consider the following situation in mechanics. Suppose an observer is riding on a particle. He measures his velocity $\mathbf{v}$ at all times (that is, he has a compass to measure the direction in which he is heading and a device to measure his speed). The problem is, can he tell where he is at any time? This problem has two aspects which we shall encounter often and which we call *uniqueness* and *existence*. What is it that the observer is trying to find? He seeks to determine a particle path such that the function $\mathbf{v}$ he has is its velocity. Another way of saying the same thing is that he picks some fixed point P_0 and tries to find his position vector $\mathbf{r}$ relative to P_0, given $\dot{\mathbf{r}}$.

Before the observer worries about whether he can *calculate* $\mathbf{r}$, he needs to ask two questions. Is there any such $\mathbf{r}$? Could there be more than one? Consider the second question first. Could it happen that there might be two vector functions $\mathbf{r}_1$ and $\mathbf{r}_2$ having the same derivative; that is, such that $\dot{\mathbf{r}}_1(t) = \dot{\mathbf{r}}_2(t) = \mathbf{v}(t)$? Suppose so. Then consider the new vector function $\bar{\mathbf{r}} = \mathbf{r}_1 - \mathbf{r}_2$. We would have

$$\text{(3.8)} \qquad \dot{\bar{\mathbf{r}}}(t) = \dot{\mathbf{r}}_1(t) - \dot{\mathbf{r}}_2(t) = \mathbf{v}(t) - \mathbf{v}(t) \equiv \mathbf{0}.$$

We would like to conclude from (3.8) that $\bar{\mathbf{r}}$ itself is identically zero, for this would mean that $\mathbf{r}_1(t) \equiv \mathbf{r}_2(t)$ and the particle path would be fully determined. A little reflection will show that this is not quite right. Clearly a particle can move along two different paths with the same velocity if it starts at two different positions (Figure 2.17). Observe that if the difference $\mathbf{r}_2 - \mathbf{r}_1$ is constant, then the velocities $\dot{\mathbf{r}}_1$ and $\dot{\mathbf{r}}_2$ will be identical even though the paths are not the same. What this means is that the observer must have another piece of information besides his velocity: he must know where he is at some time t_0. In terms of position vectors this means that he has to know $\mathbf{r}(t_0)$ as a vector $\mathbf{r}^0$. For then the two candidates $\mathbf{r}_1(t)$ and $\mathbf{r}_2(t)$ for his position

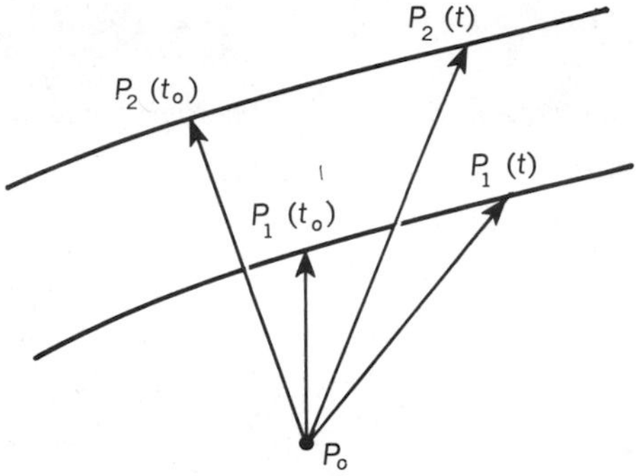

Figure 2.17

vector must both equal $\mathbf{r}^0$ at time t_0. Hence

$$\bar{\mathbf{r}}(t_0) = \mathbf{r}_1(t_0) - \mathbf{r}_2(t_0) = \mathbf{r}^0 - \mathbf{r}^0 = \mathbf{0}. \tag{3.9}$$

Thus the difference $\bar{\mathbf{r}} = \mathbf{r}_1 - \mathbf{r}_2$ must satisfy both (3.8) and (3.9). Now (3.8) together with theorem 1.15 implies that $\mathbf{r}$ is identically constant. On the other hand, (3.9) shows that this constant must be zero; that is, $\mathbf{r}_1(t) \equiv \mathbf{r}_2(t)$. This shows that if the observer can find some $\mathbf{r}$ such that $\dot{\mathbf{r}}(t) \equiv \mathbf{v}(t)$ and $\mathbf{r}(t_0) = \mathbf{r}^0$, then it will be the only one.

The reader should study the above reasoning very carefully. Note that it does not in any way imply that there need *be* any arrow function $\mathbf{r}$ such that $\dot{\mathbf{r}} = \mathbf{v}$. That is the existence part of the problem, which is much more complicated. It is to discuss existence that we will need a vector-function analog of the Fundamental Theorem.

Unfortunately an exact analog of theorem (3.7) does not hold for all vector spaces. In this respect we come for the first time to a situation in which the various vector spaces we have considered have different properties. What is true is that a direct analog of theorem (3.7) holds for many vector spaces, including the spaces $\mathcal{R}^n$ and $\mathcal{A}$ of n-tuples and arrows, respectively, but *does not* hold for the spaces $\mathcal{C}[a, b]$ of continuous functions on an interval.

More comprehensive theories of integration have made it possible to extend theorem (3.7) to more general vector spaces including the spaces $\mathcal{C}[a, b]$, but these theories are much beyond this course. For the application to mechanics that we discussed above, however, we do in fact have a *Fundamental Theorem* at our disposal. For the sake of precision we are going to state this theorem under the hypothesis that the vector space is *finite-dimensional*. The definition of this term will be given in Chapter 5. For the present it suffices simply to say that both $\mathcal{R}^n$ and the space $\mathcal{A}$ of arrows are finite-dimensional.

(3.10) Fundamental Theorem (Vector Version). *If a vector function γ defined in a finite-dimensional vector space is continuous on a given time interval $c \leq t \leq d$, then it is integrable over that time interval as well as over any subinterval. In addition, the problem of finding a function φ such that*

$$\text{(a)} \qquad \dot{\varphi}(t) = \gamma(t), \qquad c < t < d$$

always has a solution. The vector function defined over $c \leq t \leq d$ by

$$\varphi(t) = \int_c^t \gamma(s)\, ds \tag{3.11}$$

is one solution; that is,

$$\frac{d}{dt}\left(\int_c^t \gamma(s)\, ds\right) = \gamma(t), \qquad c < t < d. \tag{3.11$'$}$$

All other solutions differ from that in (3.11) *by a constant vector.*

We shall not attempt to prove the above theorem. Note, however, that it really does answer the existence question discussed earlier. If the observer knows that the $\mathbf{v}$ he has observed is continuous for some interval $t_0 \leq t \leq d$, then it is possible to define a function $\mathbf{r}$ through the formula

$$\mathbf{r}(t) = \int_{t_0}^t \mathbf{v}(s)\, ds + \mathbf{r}^0, \qquad t_0 \leq t \leq d. \tag{3.12}$$

The theorem shows that $\mathbf{r}$ is differentiable and

$$\dot{\mathbf{r}}(t) = \mathbf{v}(t) + \dot{\mathbf{r}}^0 = \mathbf{v}(t), \qquad t_0 < t < d. \tag{3.13a}$$

Moreover, we have

$$\mathbf{r}(t_0) = \int_{t_0}^{t_0} \mathbf{v}(s)\, ds + \mathbf{r}^0 = \mathbf{r}^0. \tag{3.13b}$$

This last statement follows from the definition of integral. Hence the observer has found one function $\mathbf{r}$ such that $\dot{\mathbf{r}} = \mathbf{v}$ and $\mathbf{r}(t_0) = \mathbf{r}^0$. Rather he can establish that one such $\mathbf{r}$ exists. This is the importance of existence theorems. The observer at least knows that there is a well-determined function $\mathbf{r}$ to look for.

Just as with differentiation, it is helpful to develop formulas which permit one to express the integral of a complicated expression in terms of simpler quantities. We collect a few such formulas below.

(3.14) Theorem. *Let $\boldsymbol{\alpha}$ and $\boldsymbol{\beta}$ be integrable vector functions over $c \le t \le d$ with values in a finite-dimensional vector space $\mathcal{V}$. Then*

$$(1)\quad \int_c^d (a\boldsymbol{\alpha}(t) + b\boldsymbol{\beta}(t))\,dt = a\int_c^d \boldsymbol{\alpha}(t)\,dt + b\int_c^d \boldsymbol{\beta}(t)\,dt, \quad a, b \text{ constants},$$

$$(2)\quad \int_c^d \boldsymbol{\alpha}(t)\,dt = \int_c^e \boldsymbol{\alpha}(t)\,dt + \int_e^d \boldsymbol{\alpha}(t)\,dt \qquad \text{if } c < e < d,$$

$$(3)\quad \int_c^d \dot{\boldsymbol{\alpha}}(t)\,dt = \boldsymbol{\alpha}(d) - \boldsymbol{\alpha}(c).$$

The proofs will be omitted.

Although the fundamental theorem guarantees the existence of the $\mathbf{r}$ desired above, it is not too helpful in actually calculating it. The question of finding $\mathbf{r}$, given $\mathbf{v}$, in some simple analytic form usually has to be answered by introducing components, which we shall do later.

As our final topic let us undertake to find all $\mathcal{C}[0, \pi]$-valued functions $\boldsymbol{\varphi}$ (if any exist) which on differentiation give the function $\boldsymbol{\gamma}$ studied in §2 [formula (2.8)]. We emphasize that the existence of such $\boldsymbol{\varphi}$'s is *not* guaranteed by theorem (3.10). Here we shall actually construct such $\boldsymbol{\varphi}$'s directly. Recall that $\boldsymbol{\gamma}$ had the form

$$[\boldsymbol{\gamma}(t)](x) = \sin(x + t) + e^{x+t}, \qquad 0 \le x \le \pi,\ -\infty < t < \infty.$$

If we write $\boldsymbol{\gamma}$ in the form (2.8′)

$$\boldsymbol{\gamma}(t) = \cos t \sin x + \sin t \cos x + e^t e^x,$$

then it is easy to spot a function $\boldsymbol{\varphi}$ whose derivative is $\boldsymbol{\gamma}$. We merely invert differentiation formulas for the scalar functions $\sin t$, $\cos t$, and e^t. For instance, if we define $\boldsymbol{\varphi}$ by

$$(3.15) \qquad [\boldsymbol{\varphi}(t)](x) = \sin t \sin x - \cos t \cos x + e^t e^x, \qquad 0 \le x \le \pi,$$

then an application of theorem (1.14)-(3) gives

$$[\dot{\boldsymbol{\varphi}}(t)](x) = \cos t \sin x - (-\sin t)\cos x + e^t e^x = [\boldsymbol{\gamma}(t)](x),$$
$$0 \le x \le \pi,\ -\infty < t < \infty,$$

so $\dot{\boldsymbol{\varphi}} = \boldsymbol{\gamma}$. To get the most general $\boldsymbol{\varphi}$ which satisfies $\dot{\boldsymbol{\varphi}} = \boldsymbol{\gamma}$ we observe that the difference of two such $\boldsymbol{\varphi}$'s has derivative 0 and is therefore a constant, that is, a fixed element in $\mathcal{C}[0, \pi]$ for all t [theorem (1.15)]. Thus the general φ has the form

$$(3.16)\qquad [\varphi(t)](x) = \sin t \sin x - \cos t \cos x + e^t e^x + a(x), \qquad -\infty < t < \infty,$$

where $\mathbf{a} \in \mathcal{C}[0, \pi]$ is any fixed element of that space.

PROBLEMS

1. Let $\mathcal{V}$ be any vector space and let $\boldsymbol{\alpha}$ be the function defined by $\boldsymbol{\alpha}(t) = \boldsymbol{\alpha}_0$ for all t, where $\boldsymbol{\alpha}_0$ is a constant vector. Show that

$$\int_c^d \boldsymbol{\alpha}(t)\, dt = \boldsymbol{\alpha}_0(d - c)$$

for any c and d with $c < d$. Use the defining equation (3.3).

2. Calculate the following integrals:

(a) In $\mathcal{R}^2$: $\boldsymbol{\alpha}(t) = (\sin t, \cos t)$, $\int_0^\pi \boldsymbol{\alpha}(t)\, dt$

(b) In $\mathcal{R}^3$: $\boldsymbol{\alpha}(t) = (2t - 1, t^2, 0)$, $\int_0^1 \boldsymbol{\alpha}(t)\, dt$

3. In each of the following, find φ from the information given:

(a) In $\mathcal{R}^2$: $\dot{\varphi}(t) = (1, t)$, $\varphi(0) = \mathbf{0}$

(b) In $\mathcal{R}^3$: $\dot{\varphi}(t) = (t - 1, 0, t - 1)$, $\varphi(1) = (-2, 0, 1)$

(c) In $\mathcal{C}[0, \pi]$: $[\dot{\varphi}(t)](x) = t \sin x - t^2 \cos x$, $[\varphi(1)](x) = -2 \sin x$

(d) In $\mathcal{C}[0, \pi]$: $[\dot{\varphi}(t)](x) = e^{x+t}$, $[\varphi(0)](x) \equiv 0$

(e) In $\mathcal{R}^2$: $\dot{\varphi}(t) = (e^{t^2}, e^{-t^2})$, $\varphi(0) = 0$

4. (a) Let $\mathcal{V}$ be a finite-dimensional vector space and let $\boldsymbol{\alpha}$ be a function of the form

$$\boldsymbol{\alpha}(t) = f(t)\boldsymbol{\alpha}_0,$$

where $f(t)$ is a continuous scalar function and $\boldsymbol{\alpha}_0$ is a fixed vector. If F is a differentiable function of t such that $\dot{F}(t) = f(t)$, show that

$$\int_c^d \boldsymbol{\alpha}(t)\, dt = \big(F(d) - F(c)\big)\boldsymbol{\alpha}_0.$$

[*Hint:* Use formula (3) of theorem (3.14.]

*(b) Show by use of definition (3.2) that the above formula is valid for *any* vector space $\mathcal{V}$.

5. Use the result of problem 4(b) to evaluate the following integrals:

(a) In $\mathcal{C}[0, \pi]$: $[\boldsymbol{\alpha}(t)](x) = te^x + (t - 1)x$, $\int_0^1 \boldsymbol{\alpha}(t)\, dt$

(b) In $\mathcal{C}[0, \pi]$: $[\boldsymbol{\alpha}(t)](x) = \sin(x + 2t)$, $\int_0^\pi \boldsymbol{\alpha}(t)\, dt$

6. Use the result of problem 4 to show that if a particle has a velocity $\mathbf{v}$ of the form $\mathbf{v}(t) = (t^2 + 1)\mathbf{v}_0$, where $\mathbf{v}_0$ is a fixed vector, then the particle moves along a straight line.

7. An arrow-valued function $\boldsymbol{\alpha}$ is determined as follows. The arrows $\mathbf{e}_1$, $\mathbf{e}_2$ are orthogonal unit vectors, and $\boldsymbol{\alpha}(t)$ lies in the plane of $\mathbf{e}_1$ and $\mathbf{e}_2$ and makes an angle $\theta(t) = t^2$ with $\mathbf{e}_1$ (Figure 2.18). Determine $\int_0^1 \boldsymbol{\alpha}(t)\,dt$ in each of the following cases:

(a) $\|\boldsymbol{\alpha}(t)\| = 2$ for all t

(b) $\|\boldsymbol{\alpha}(t)\| = t$ for all t

[*Hint:* Express $\boldsymbol{\alpha}(t)$ in terms of $\mathbf{e}_1$ and $\mathbf{e}_2$ and use theorem (3.14)–(1) and problem 4.]

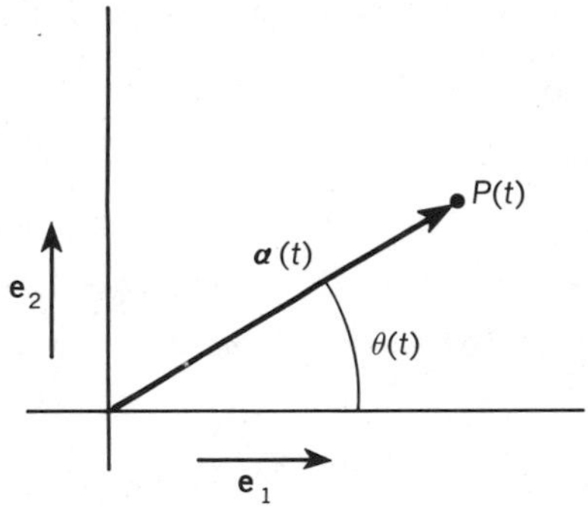

Figure 2.18

8. (a) A particle starts from a point O at time $t = 0$. Its velocity is $\mathbf{v}(t) = t^2\mathbf{v}_0$, $\mathbf{v}_0$ a constant vector. If its position at time $t = 1$ is denoted by P_1 find $\overrightarrow{OP_1}$.

(b) Suppose that instead of the velocity one is given the acceleration $\mathbf{a}$ as $\mathbf{a}(t) = t^2\mathbf{a}_0$. Again the particle starts at O at time $t = 0$. Can its position at $t = 1$ be determined? Why?

3

Particle Dynamics

1. Newton's Law

In this chapter we wish to indicate how some of the ideas we have developed can be used to formulate the laws of motion of a system of particles. This will lead to the notion of differential equations, which is an important subject in many branches of physics. Chapter 4 is devoted to a detailed discussion of differential equations. In Chapter 3 our goal will be to indicate how such equations arise.

We are concerned with the motion of a system of n particles. We recall from previous chapters that we can describe the motion of these particles by choosing a fixed point O and specifying the position vectors $\mathbf{r}_1, \ldots, \mathbf{r}_n$ relative to O (Figure 3.1). Each of the position vectors is an (arrow) vector function of time. The velocities $\mathbf{v}_1, \ldots, \mathbf{v}_n$ and the accelerations $\mathbf{a}_1, \ldots, \mathbf{a}_n$, we recall, are simply the first and second derivatives, respectively, of the position vectors.

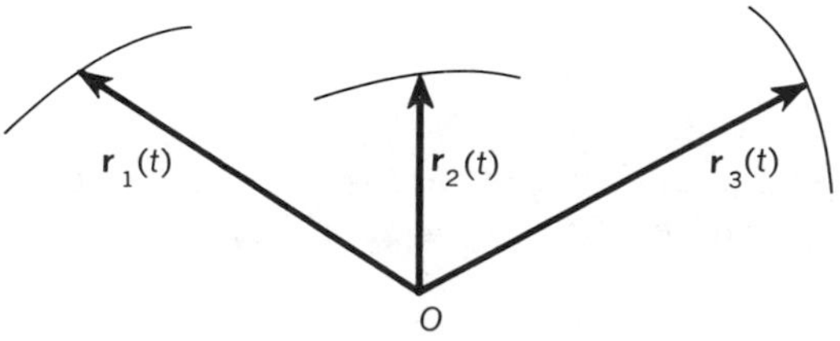

Figure 3.1

We suppose that we are given the forces acting on the particles. These are simply another set of arrow functions $\mathbf{F}_1, \ldots, \mathbf{F}_n$, where $\mathbf{F}_k(t)$ measures the magnitude and direction of the "push" on the kth particle at time t. The basis for particle mechanics is the following law.

(1.1) Newton's Law. *There exist constants $m_1, \ldots, m_n$, where m_k is called the mass of the kth particle, such that*

$$
\begin{aligned}
m_1\mathbf{a}_1(t) &= \mathbf{F}_1(t) \\
m_2\mathbf{a}_2(t) &= \mathbf{F}_2(t) \\
&\vdots \\
m_n\mathbf{a}_n(t) &= \mathbf{F}_n(t).
\end{aligned}
\tag{1.2}
$$

This result is an empirical law. More precisely, it is an idealization of the empirical laws of motion, first to rigid bodies and then to particles.

We showed in Chapter 2 that if we specify the velocity of a particle as a function of time, then we can, in principle, determine the position vector, that is, the path, if we know the position at one particular time. Something similar is true for accelerations, as we show presently. First, however, we consider a very simple example.

(1.3) Example. Let $\boldsymbol{\alpha}$ be a fixed vector of unit length. A particle of mass m is acted on by a force $\mathbf{F}$ such that $\mathbf{F}(t) = -\boldsymbol{\alpha}$ for all t. At time $t = 0$ the particle is at position $\mathbf{r}_0 = 2\boldsymbol{\alpha}$ and has velocity $\mathbf{v}_0 = \boldsymbol{\alpha}$.

(a) Find an expression for its position vector function $\mathbf{r}$.

(b) Determine how far the particle moves before it comes to a stop.

Solution. Equation (1.2) becomes in this case

(c) $m\ddot{\mathbf{r}}(t) = -\boldsymbol{\alpha}$.

We assert that there is a solution $\mathbf{r}$ of this equation having the form $\mathbf{r}(t) = \rho(t)\boldsymbol{\alpha}$. We insert this formula into the equation of motion and obtain

$$m\ddot{\rho}(t)\boldsymbol{\alpha} = -\boldsymbol{\alpha} \qquad \text{or} \qquad \ddot{\rho}(t) = -\frac{1}{m}\cdot$$

The second equation implies that $\dot{\rho}(t) = -(1/m)t + C$, where C is a constant. But we must have $\dot{\mathbf{r}}(0) = \mathbf{v}_0 = \boldsymbol{\alpha}$; hence

$$\boldsymbol{\alpha} = \dot{\mathbf{r}}(0) = \dot{\rho}(0)\boldsymbol{\alpha} = \left(-\frac{1}{m}\cdot 0 + C\right)\boldsymbol{\alpha}.$$

Thus $C = 1$ and $\dot{\rho}(t) = -(1/m)t + 1$. We integrate once again and find

$$\rho(t) = -\frac{1}{2m}t^2 + t + D,$$

where D is another constant. But $\mathbf{r}(0) = \mathbf{r}_0 = 2\boldsymbol{\alpha}$; hence

$$2\boldsymbol{\alpha} = \mathbf{r}(0) = \rho(0)\boldsymbol{\alpha} = \left(-\frac{1}{2m}\cdot 0^2 + 0 + D\right)\boldsymbol{\alpha}.$$

Thus $D = 2$ and we have

$$\rho(t) = -\frac{1}{2m}t^2 + t + 2 \qquad \text{or} \qquad \mathbf{r}(t) = \left(-\frac{1}{2m}t^2 + t + 2\right)\boldsymbol{\alpha}.$$

Note that this solution of (c) indicates that the particle is moving along a straight line (see Figure 3.2).

We have found the expression for $\mathbf{r}$ requested in part (a). To answer part (b), we calculate the time t_s at which $\mathbf{v}(t) = \dot{\mathbf{r}}(t) = \dot{\rho}(t)\boldsymbol{\alpha} = \mathbf{0}$. This means that $\dot{\rho}(t_s) = 0$; that is,

$$-\frac{1}{m}t_s + 1 = 0 \qquad \text{or} \qquad t_s = m.$$

When $t_s = m$ we have

$$\mathbf{r}(t_s) = \left(-\frac{1}{2m}\cdot m^2 + m + 2\right)\boldsymbol{\alpha} = \left(2 + \frac{m}{2}\right)\boldsymbol{\alpha}.$$

Initially, the particle was at position $\mathbf{r} = \mathbf{r}_0 = 2\boldsymbol{\alpha}$. Its displacement from time $t = 0$ to time t_s is given by the difference

$$\mathbf{r}(t_s) - \mathbf{r}(0) = \left(2 + \frac{m}{2}\right)\boldsymbol{\alpha} - 2\boldsymbol{\alpha} = \frac{m}{2}\boldsymbol{\alpha}.$$

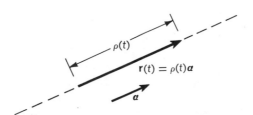

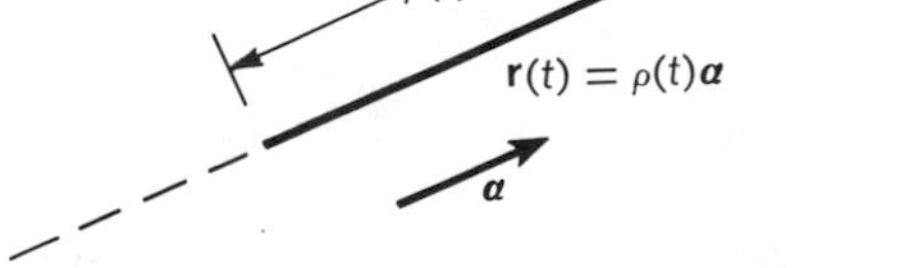

Figure 3.2

Since the motion is along a straight line the distance traveled is simply the length of this vector; that is,

$$\|\mathbf{r}(t_s) - \mathbf{r}(0)\| = \left\|\frac{m}{2}\boldsymbol{\alpha}\right\| = \frac{m}{2}\|\boldsymbol{\alpha}\| = \frac{m}{2},$$

since $\boldsymbol{\alpha}$ is a vector of unit length.

The above calculation is quite straightforward, but we remark that there is a subtle point involved. We produced one possible arrow function $\mathbf{r}$ but we did not show that there could not be other possible $\mathbf{r}$'s satisfying the same conditions. Thus there is again a question of uniqueness [see formula (3.9) of Chapter 2]. Physical considerations indicate that there should be only one possible motion, that is, that the $\mathbf{r}$ we have found should be the only one. That this is indeed true will be seen by the theorem to be given next. This theorem is really a general theorem about vector functions and hence we state it that way. Later we will show how it applies to particle motions.

(1.4) Theorem. *Let* $\mathbf{a}$ *be a function of* t *with values in a finite-dimensional vector space* $\mathcal{V}$ *and let* $\mathbf{a}$ *be continuous for all* t. *Let* $\mathbf{r}^0$ *and* $\mathbf{v}^0$ *be two vectors in* $\mathcal{V}$. *Then there exists one and only one function* $\mathbf{r}$ *with values in* $\mathcal{V}$ *which is twice differentiable and satisfies*

(a) $\ddot{\mathbf{r}} = \mathbf{a}$.

(b) $\mathbf{r}(t_0) = \mathbf{r}^0$, $\dot{\mathbf{r}}(t_0) = \mathbf{v}^0$.

Proof. The proof of this theorem is just like that of theorem (3.10) of Chapter 2 except that we must give the argument twice. First we show that there is one $\mathbf{r}$ satisfying (a) and (b). The procedure for this is to integrate twice, which is just what we did in the special example above. Define the function $\mathbf{v}$ by the formula

(c) $\mathbf{v}(t) = \int_{t_0}^{t} \mathbf{a}(s)\, ds + \mathbf{v}^0.$

By theorem (3.10) of Chapter 2 we see that

(d) $\dot{\mathbf{v}}(t) = \mathbf{a}(t)$
$\mathbf{v}(t_0) = \mathbf{v}^0.$

Now set

(e) $\mathbf{r}(t) = \int_{t_0}^{t} \mathbf{v}(s)\, ds + \mathbf{r}^0.$

Then

(f) $\dot{\mathbf{r}}(t) = \mathbf{v}(t)$ and $\mathbf{r}(t_0) = \mathbf{r}^0.$

If we differentiate again and use the first of equations (d), we find in addition that

(g) $\ddot{\mathbf{r}}(t) = \dot{\mathbf{v}}(t) = \mathbf{a}(t).$

Moreover, the second of equations (d) shows that

$$\dot{\mathbf{r}}(t_0) = \mathbf{v}(t_0) = \mathbf{v}^0.$$

We have thus shown that there is at least one function satisfying (a) and (b). Now we show that there is only one. Suppose $\mathbf{r}_1$ and $\mathbf{r}_2$ both satisfy (a) and (b). Set $\bar{\mathbf{r}} = \mathbf{r}_1 - \mathbf{r}_2$. Then we have

$$\ddot{\bar{\mathbf{r}}}(t) \equiv \mathbf{0}, \qquad \bar{\mathbf{r}}(t_0) = \mathbf{0}, \qquad \dot{\bar{\mathbf{r}}}(t_0) = \mathbf{0}.$$

Now by theorem (1.15) of Chapter 2, $\ddot{\bar{\mathbf{r}}}(t) \equiv 0$ implies that $\dot{\bar{\mathbf{r}}}$ is a constant. This constant must be zero since $\dot{\bar{\mathbf{r}}}(t_0) = 0$; hence $\dot{\bar{\mathbf{r}}}(t) \equiv 0$. Then once again, theorem (1.15) of Chapter 2 implies that $\bar{\mathbf{r}}$ is a constant. Since $\bar{\mathbf{r}}(t_0) = \mathbf{0}$ we have $\bar{\mathbf{r}}(t) \equiv \mathbf{0}$; that is, $\mathbf{r}_1(t) \equiv \mathbf{r}_2(t)$. ▌

We can apply the above theorem to the motion of several particles as discussed in Newton's law (1.1). According to the theorem, if we are given any continuous arrow function $\mathbf{a}_k$ and any arrows $\mathbf{r}_k^0$ and $\mathbf{v}_k^0$, then there exists a unique arrow function $\mathbf{r}_k$ such that

$$\ddot{\mathbf{r}}_k = \mathbf{a}_k, \qquad \mathbf{r}_k(t_0) = \mathbf{r}_k^0, \qquad \mathbf{r}_k(t_0) = \mathbf{v}_k^0.$$

Thus, if we are given the accelerations of the particles, together with their *positions and velocities* at some particular time, then we can uniquely determine their position vectors. According to (1.2), however, giving the forces is the same as giving the accelerations.

The above discussion makes mechanics sound deceptively simple. If we know the forces $\mathbf{F}_k$ explicitly as functions of t, we can recover the $\mathbf{r}_k$'s by integration. The difficulty is that in most situations the forces themselves depend not only on t but also on the *positions or velocities* of the n particles. Thus we are not given the forces, at the outset, as functions of time. Instead, we have to solve equations (1.2) both for the forces *and* for the $\mathbf{r}_k$'s. This will lead us to the study of differential equations.

We illustrate the above paragraph with a very simple example.

(1.5) Example. Suppose a single particle, of mass m, moves along a straight line. The particle is subject to a force which is proportional to the velocity but oppositely directed. (This is a common assumption in the case of a force due to air resistance.) Find its position and velocity as a function of time.

We have already discussed rectilinear motion. Recall that we can describe it by choosing our reference point O on the line of motion. Then the position vector $\mathbf{r}$ can be written

$$\mathbf{r}(t) = \rho(t)\boldsymbol{\alpha},$$

where $\boldsymbol{\alpha}$ is a fixed vector determining the direction of the line. We have then for the velocity $\mathbf{v}$ and acceleration $\mathbf{a}$,

$$\mathbf{v}(t) = \dot{\mathbf{r}}(t) = \dot{\rho}(t)\boldsymbol{\alpha}, \qquad \mathbf{a}(t) = \ddot{\mathbf{r}}(t) = \ddot{\rho}(t)\boldsymbol{\alpha}.$$

The force $\mathbf{F}$ is to be proportional to the velocity; hence it has the form $\mathbf{F}(t) = -k\mathbf{v}(t) = -k\dot{\rho}(t)\boldsymbol{\alpha}$, where $-k < 0$ is a negative constant. Thus (1.2) becomes in this case

(a) $m\mathbf{a}(t) = m\ddot{\rho}(t)\boldsymbol{\alpha} = -k\dot{\rho}(t)\boldsymbol{\alpha}$,

or, equivalently,

(b) $m\ddot{\rho}(t) = -k\dot{\rho}(t)$.

Equation (b) is an example of a differential equation. It relates derivatives of the scalar function ρ. Observe that the right side is not known in advance but rather we must first find ρ. We can, in fact, determine ρ here by a special trick. We shall show in §2 of Chapter 4 that this trick can be applied in many situations. We write (b) in the form

$$\ddot{\rho}(t) + \frac{k}{m}\dot{\rho}(t) = 0,$$

and then we multiply the equation by $e^{(k/m)t}$. The result is

(c) $e^{(k/m)t}\ddot{\rho}(t) + \dfrac{k}{m}e^{(k/m)t}\dot{\rho}(t) = 0.$

Now we note that the left side of this equation is just the derivative with respect to t of the product $e^{(k/m)t}\,\dot{\rho}(t)$. Hence we have

$$\frac{d}{dt}\left(e^{(k/m)t}\dot{\rho}(t)\right) = 0 \qquad \text{or} \qquad e^{(k/m)t}\dot{\rho}(t) = c,$$

where c is a constant. It follows that

(d) $\dot{\rho}(t) = ce^{-(k/m)t}$.

Now suppose we specify the velocity $\mathbf{v}^0 = \dot{\mathbf{r}}(t_0)$ of the particle at time t_0. Since the particle is moving along the line, $\mathbf{v}^0$ must have the form $\mathbf{v}^0 = v^0\boldsymbol{\alpha}$; hence $\dot{\rho}(t_0) = v^0$. We substitute this into (d) and determine the constant c. That is, we have

(e) $\dot{\rho}(t_0) = v^0 = ce^{-(k/m)t_0} \qquad \text{or} \qquad c = v^0e^{(k/m)t_0}.$

Hence

$$\dot{\rho}(t) = v^0e^{-(k/m)(t-t_0)}.$$

We have thus determined the velocity of the particle as

(f) $\mathbf{v}(t) = \dot{\mathbf{r}}(t) = v^0 e^{-(k/m)(t-t_0)}\boldsymbol{\alpha}.$

Now we are in the same position as in the discussion in Chapter 2. That is, we have the velocity and therefore can determine the position vector by integration if we give as additional information the position at time t_0. This means that we can determine $\mathbf{r}$ if $\mathbf{r}(t_0)$ is specified as $\mathbf{r}^0 = r^0\boldsymbol{\alpha}$. In fact, we then have

$$\mathbf{r}(t) = \int_{t_0}^{t} \mathbf{v}(\tau)\, d\tau + \mathbf{r}^0.$$

Now problem 4 in §3 of Chapter 2 shows that this yields

(g) $\mathbf{r}(t) = \left(\frac{m}{k} v^0(1 - e^{-(k/m)(t-t_0)}) + r^0\right)\boldsymbol{\alpha}.$

It is to be noted that the condition $-k < 0$ corresponded to the fact that the friction force opposes the motion. Equation (f) shows then that the particle slows down very quickly but never quite comes to a stop. Equation (g) shows that the total distance traveled approaches mv^0/k.

PROBLEMS

1. Let $\boldsymbol{\alpha}$ be a fixed vector of unit length. In each of the following a particle of mass $m = 1$ is acted on by the given force $\mathbf{F}$ and has the given initial position and velocity. Calculate its position vector $\mathbf{r}$.

   (a) $\mathbf{F}(t) = -t\boldsymbol{\alpha}$, $\mathbf{r}(1) = \boldsymbol{\alpha}$, $\mathbf{v}(1) = \boldsymbol{\alpha}$

   (b) $\mathbf{F}(t) = -e^{-t}\boldsymbol{\alpha}$, $\mathbf{r}(0) = \mathbf{0}$, $\mathbf{v}(0) = \boldsymbol{\alpha}$

   (*Hint:* Remember that $0\boldsymbol{\alpha} = \mathbf{0}$.)

   (c) $\mathbf{F}(t) = (\cos 2t)\boldsymbol{\alpha}$, $\mathbf{r}(0) = \boldsymbol{\alpha}$, $\mathbf{v}(0) = \mathbf{0}$

2. In problem 1(a) determine how far the particle moves before coming to a stop.
3. In problem 1(c) let $P(t)$ denote the position of the particle at time t. Determine the largest distance between any two points on its path.
4. Two particles of masses $m_1 = 1$ and $m_2 = 2$ move along a straight line. Each is acted on by the same constant force $\mathbf{F}$, with $\|\mathbf{F}\| = 1$ and $\mathbf{F}$ in the direction indicated. Both particles are initially at rest and are four units apart (see Figure 3.3). How long will it take particle 1 to catch up to particle 2?

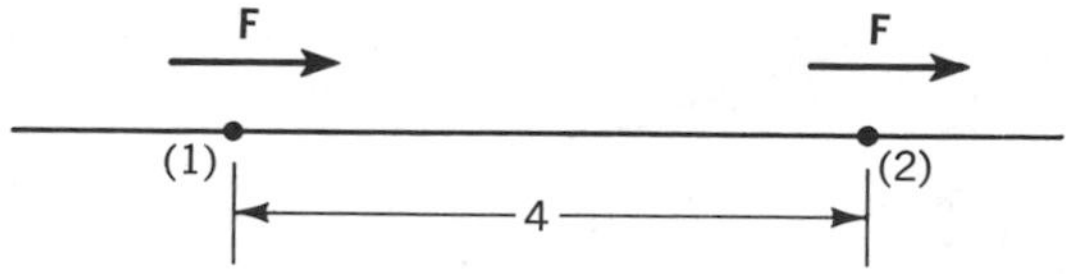

Figure 3.3

5. A particle moves in a plane at a fixed distance from a point P_0. If it moves with constant speed, show that the force acting on it must always be directed along the line joining the particle and the point P_0. (*Hint:* Use the formulas of Chapter 3.)

6. Let $\boldsymbol{\alpha}$ be a fixed vector. In each of the following problems, state whether there will be one, none, or many vector functions $\mathbf{r}$ satisfying the given conditions.

   (a) $\ddot{\mathbf{r}} = \boldsymbol{\alpha}$, $\mathbf{r}(0) = \mathbf{0}$, $\dot{\mathbf{r}}(1) = \mathbf{0}$

   (b) $\ddot{\mathbf{r}} = \boldsymbol{\alpha}$, $\mathbf{r}(0) = \mathbf{0}$, $\mathbf{r}(1) = \boldsymbol{\alpha}$, $\mathbf{r}(2) = \mathbf{0}$

   (c) $\dddot{\mathbf{r}} = \boldsymbol{\alpha}$, $\mathbf{r}(0) = \boldsymbol{\alpha}$, $\dot{\mathbf{r}}(0) = \mathbf{0}$

   (d) $\dddot{\mathbf{r}} = \boldsymbol{\alpha}$, $\mathbf{r}(0) = \boldsymbol{\alpha}$, $\dot{\mathbf{r}}(0) = -\boldsymbol{\alpha}$, $\ddot{\mathbf{r}}(0) = \mathbf{0}$

7. A particle is acted on by a force of the form $\mathbf{F}(t) = f(t)\boldsymbol{\alpha}$, where $\boldsymbol{\alpha}$ is a fixed vector. Let $\boldsymbol{\beta}$ be a vector orthogonal to $\boldsymbol{\alpha}$.

   (a) Show that $\dot{\mathbf{r}} \cdot \boldsymbol{\beta}$ is a constant.

   (b) If the velocity $\dot{\mathbf{r}}(t_0)$ is in the direction of $\boldsymbol{\alpha}$ at some particular time t_0, show that the velocity will always be orthogonal to $\boldsymbol{\beta}$.

2. Components

In §1 we formulated Newton's law in terms of the geometric notion of arrows in space. It is useful to formulate physical laws in terms of such geometric ideas, since it makes them more intuitive. Also, there are various general principles which are most easily stated and proved in the language of vectors. (Some of these principles will be discussed in §4). On the other hand, when one makes a detailed study of a particular problem it is often easiest to do computations using a description of arrows which is tailored to that problem. Let us give two simple examples.

(2.1) Examples

(a) A PARTICLE SLIDING ALONG A STRAIGHT WIRE (FIGURE 3.4). Here it is clear from the outset that the motion is going to be along a straight line. We saw in examples (1.3) and (1.5) of §1 that in such situations the forces

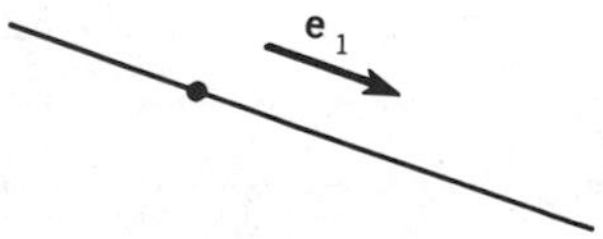

Figure 3.4

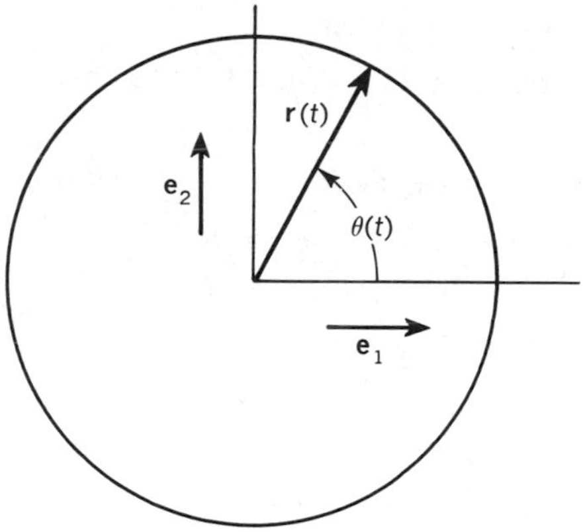

Figure 3.5

and position vectors can always be described by scalar multiples of a fixed vector parallel to the line ($\mathbf{e}_1$ in Figure 3.4). Thus we will have

$$\mathbf{F}(t) = f(t)\mathbf{e}_1 \quad \text{and} \quad \mathbf{r}(t) = \rho(t)\mathbf{e}_1.$$

Newton's law will then yield

$$m\ddot{\mathbf{r}}(t) = m\ddot{\rho}(t)\mathbf{e}_1 = f(t)\mathbf{e}_1 \quad \text{or} \quad \ddot{\rho}(t) = \frac{f(t)}{m}.$$

Thus in all problems of this type, the *vector* equation (1.2) will reduce to an equation relating two scalar functions.

(b) A PARTICLE MOVING IN A CIRCLE IN A PLANE (FIGURE 3.5). Let the radius of the circle be R and let $\mathbf{r}$ be the position vector relative to the center. Thus $\|\mathbf{r}(t)\| = R$ for all t. From the figure it can be seen that if $\mathbf{e}_1$ and $\mathbf{e}_2$ are perpendicular vectors of unit length and θ is as indicated, then

(2.2) $$\mathbf{r}(t) = R\cos\theta(t)\mathbf{e}_1 + R\sin\theta(t)\mathbf{e}_2.$$

It follows from theorem (1.14) of Chapter 2 that the velocity $\mathbf{v}$ and acceleration $\mathbf{a}$ are given by

(2.3) $$\mathbf{v}(t) = \dot{\mathbf{r}}(t) = R\dot{\theta}(t)[-\sin\theta(t)\mathbf{e}_1 + \cos\theta(t)\mathbf{e}_2]$$

(2.4) $$\mathbf{a}(t) = \ddot{\mathbf{r}}(t) = R\ddot{\theta}(t)[-\sin\theta(t)\mathbf{e}_1 + \cos\theta(t)\mathbf{e}_2] + R\dot{\theta}(t)^2[-\cos\theta(t)\mathbf{e}_1 - \sin\theta(t)\mathbf{e}_2].$$

We see here that with the introduction of $\mathbf{e}_1$ and $\mathbf{e}_2$ we are able to describe the motion completely by means of the single scalar function $\theta(t)$.

Observe that $\mathbf{e}_1$ and $\mathbf{e}_2$ are such that $\mathbf{e}_1 \cdot \mathbf{e}_1 = \mathbf{e}_2 \cdot \mathbf{e}_2 = 1$ while $\mathbf{e}_1 \cdot \mathbf{e}_2 = \mathbf{e}_2 \cdot \mathbf{e}_1 = 0$. It follows that if a, b, c, d are any numbers, then

$$(2.5) \qquad (a\mathbf{e}_1 + b\mathbf{e}_2) \cdot (c\mathbf{e}_1 + d\mathbf{e}_2) = ac\mathbf{e}_1 \cdot \mathbf{e}_1 + ad\mathbf{e}_1 \cdot \mathbf{e}_2 + bc\mathbf{e}_2 \cdot \mathbf{e}_1 + bd\mathbf{e}_2 \cdot \mathbf{e}_2 = ac + bd.$$

Using this formula and (2.2) and (2.3) we have

$$\mathbf{v}(t) \cdot \mathbf{r}(t) = -R\dot{\theta}(t) \sin \theta(t) R \cos \theta(t) + R\dot{\theta}(t) \cos \theta(t) R \sin \theta(t) = 0.$$

This gives another proof [see example (2.2g) of Chapter 2 for the first] of the fact that $\mathbf{v}$ and $\mathbf{r}$ are orthogonal. Further illustrations of the use of formulas (2.3), (2.4), and (2.5) are found in problem 6.

It turns out to be useful to describe most motions by means of a special set of vectors like those in example (2.1b). Consider an arrow $\boldsymbol{\alpha}$. Let $\mathbf{e}_1$, $\mathbf{e}_2$, $\mathbf{e}_3$ be any set of mutually orthogonal arrows of unit length as shown in Figure 3.6. Since it is immaterial where we draw the arrows, we let them all start at O. Now draw axes Ox^1, Ox^2, and Ox^3 as shown. Figure 3.6 is then simply a reproduction of Figure 1.7. We saw in Chapter 1 that the arrow $\boldsymbol{\alpha}$ could be described by means of the coordinates (x^1, x^2, x^3) of the end point P. It is clear, moreover, from Figure 3.6 and our definition of addition of arrows that $\boldsymbol{\alpha}$ can also be written as the following sum of multiples of the special arrows $\mathbf{e}_1$, $\mathbf{e}_2$, and $\mathbf{e}_3$:

$$(2.6) \qquad \boldsymbol{\alpha} = x^1\mathbf{e}_1 + x^2\mathbf{e}_2 + x^3\mathbf{e}_3.$$

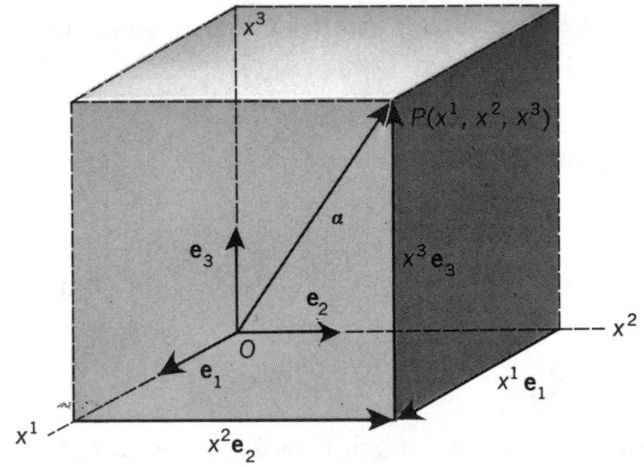

Figure 3.6

(2.7) Definition. The scalars x^1, x^2, x^3 in (2.6) are called the **components of $\boldsymbol{\alpha}$** (relative to the arrows $\mathbf{e}_1$, $\mathbf{e}_2$, $\mathbf{e}_3$).

Note that the qualifier "relative to $\mathbf{e}_1$, $\mathbf{e}_2$, and $\mathbf{e}_3$" is necessary. If we change the vectors $\mathbf{e}_1$, $\mathbf{e}_2$, $\mathbf{e}_3$ we will change the components as illustrated in Figure 3.7. The $\boldsymbol{\alpha}$'s in this figure are arrows of length 2, *always the same arrow.*

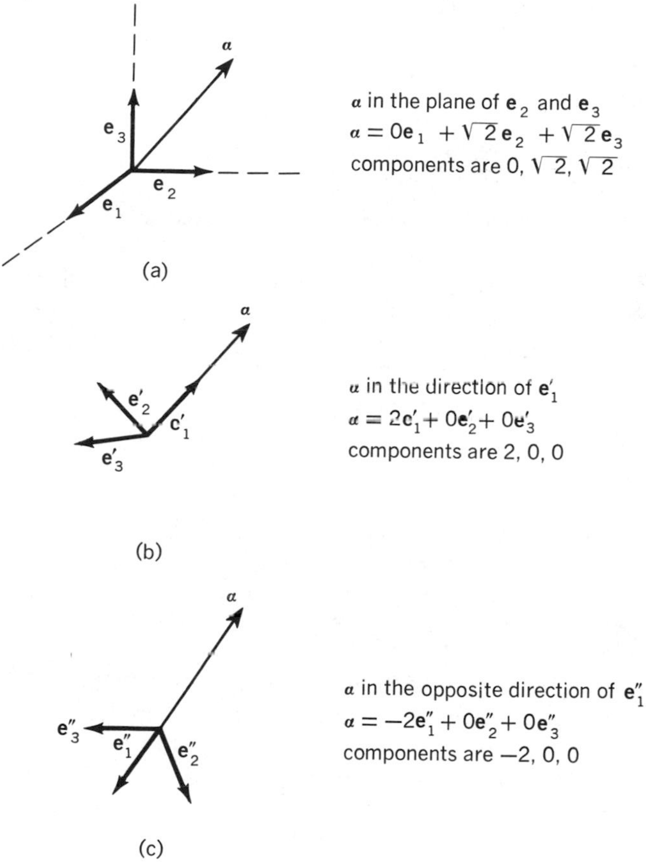

Figure 3.7

It is also possible to talk about components relative to sets of vectors which are not mutually orthogonal (see problem 5). Sometimes this latter approach is useful, but in the present chapter we shall always assume that we are talking about a fixed set of mutually orthogonal vectors $\mathbf{e}_1$, $\mathbf{e}_2$, $\mathbf{e}_3$ of unit length.

(2.8) Proposition. *If* $\boldsymbol{\alpha} = x^1\mathbf{e}_1 + x^2\mathbf{e}_2 + x^3\mathbf{e}_3$ *and* $\boldsymbol{\beta} = y^1\mathbf{e}_1 + y^2\mathbf{e}_2 + y^3\mathbf{e}_3$, *where* $\mathbf{e}_1, \mathbf{e}_2, \mathbf{e}_3$ *are mutually orthogonal unit vectors, then*

(i) $c\boldsymbol{\alpha} = (cx^1)\mathbf{e}_1 + (cx^2)e_2 + (cx^3)\mathbf{e}_3$.

(ii) $\boldsymbol{\alpha} + \boldsymbol{\beta} = (x^1 + y^1)\mathbf{e}_1 + (x^2 + y^2)\mathbf{e}_2 + (x^3 + y^3)\mathbf{e}_3$.

(iii) $\boldsymbol{\alpha} \cdot \boldsymbol{\beta} = x^1y^1 + x^2y^2 + x^3y^3$.

(iv) $\boldsymbol{\alpha} = \boldsymbol{\beta}$ if and only if $x^1 = y^1$, $x^2 = y^2$, $x^3 = y^3$.

The first two of these results follow immediately from the axioms (A_1), (A_2), (M_2), (M_3) for a vector space as applied to the space of arrows. These axioms say that we can move terms around and group them as we please in sums. (iii) follows from the bilinearity of the inner product and the relations

$$\mathbf{e}_1 \cdot \mathbf{e}_1 = \mathbf{e}_2 \cdot \mathbf{e}_2 = \mathbf{e}_3 \cdot \mathbf{e}_3 = 1, \qquad \mathbf{e}_1 \cdot \mathbf{e}_2 = \mathbf{e}_1 \cdot \mathbf{e}_3 = \mathbf{e}_2 \cdot \mathbf{e}_3 = 0.$$

We leave it to the reader to carry out this computation.

The proof of (iv) is quite important and will occur again in more complicated situations, so we want to give it carefully. First of all, equality of $\boldsymbol{\alpha}$ and $\boldsymbol{\beta}$ is clear when the x's and y's are respectively equal. Hence we may turn to the converse. We have $\boldsymbol{\alpha} = \boldsymbol{\beta}$; hence $\boldsymbol{\alpha} \cdot \mathbf{e}_1 = \boldsymbol{\beta} \cdot \mathbf{e}_1$. However,

$$\begin{aligned}\boldsymbol{\alpha} \cdot \mathbf{e}_1 &= (x^1\mathbf{e}_1 + x^2\mathbf{e}_2 + x^3\mathbf{e}_3) \cdot \mathbf{e}_1 \\ &= x^1(\mathbf{e}_1 \cdot \mathbf{e}_2) + x^2(\mathbf{e}_2 \cdot \mathbf{e}_1) + x^3(\mathbf{e}_3 \cdot \mathbf{e}_1) = x^1 \\ \boldsymbol{\beta} \cdot \mathbf{e}_1 &= (y^1\mathbf{e}_1 + y^2\mathbf{e}_2 + y^3\mathbf{e}_3) \cdot \mathbf{e}_1 \\ &= y^1\mathbf{e}_1 \cdot \mathbf{e}_1 + y^2\mathbf{e}_2 \cdot \mathbf{e}_1 + y^3\mathbf{e}_3 \cdot \mathbf{e}_1 = y^1;\end{aligned}$$

hence $x^1 = y^1$. Similarly, $\boldsymbol{\alpha} \cdot \mathbf{e}_2 = \boldsymbol{\beta} \cdot \mathbf{e}_2$ implies $x^2 = y^2$ and $\boldsymbol{\alpha} \cdot \mathbf{e}_3 = \boldsymbol{\beta} \cdot \mathbf{e}_3$ implies $x^3 = y^3$. ▌

The computation used in the above proof also demonstrates the following useful fact: The components of a vector $\boldsymbol{\alpha}$ are determined by the formulas

$$x^1 = \boldsymbol{\alpha} \cdot \mathbf{e}_1, \qquad x^2 = \boldsymbol{\alpha} \cdot \mathbf{e}_2, \qquad x^3 = \boldsymbol{\alpha} \cdot \mathbf{e}_3. \tag{2.9}$$

Observe that statement (2.9) will be true *only* if the vectors $\mathbf{e}_1$, $\mathbf{e}_2$, $\mathbf{e}_3$ are mutually orthogonal and each of unit length.

We return now to the motion of a system of n particles. Let $\mathbf{r}_1, \ldots, \mathbf{r}_n$ be their position vectors relative to a point O and let $\mathbf{e}_1$, $\mathbf{e}_2$, $\mathbf{e}_3$ be a fixed set of orthogonal vectors of unit length (Figure 3.8). Each of the vectors $\mathbf{r}_k$ will have a set of components relative to $\mathbf{e}_1$, $\mathbf{e}_2$, $\mathbf{e}_3$. Since the $\mathbf{r}_k$'s change with time, their components will, of course, also change with time; that is, they will be functions of t. We denote the components of $\mathbf{r}_k$ by x_k^1, x_k^2, x_k^3, so that, according to (2.6),

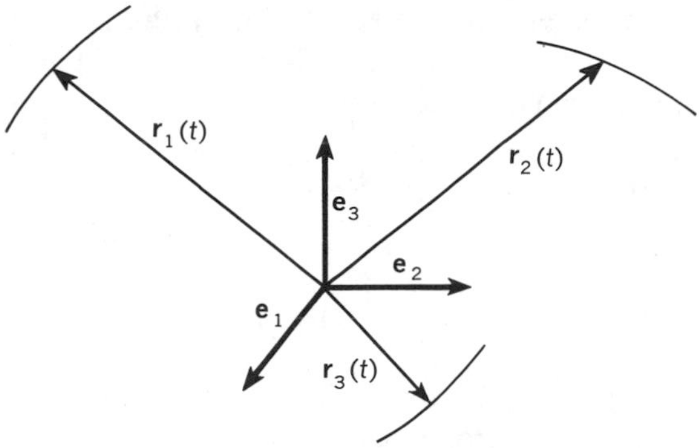

Figure 3.8

$$\text{(2.10)}\quad \begin{aligned} \mathbf{r}_1(t) &= x_1^1(t)\mathbf{e}_1 + x_1^2(t)\mathbf{e}_2 + x_1^3(t)\mathbf{e}_3 \\ &\vdots \\ \mathbf{r}_n(t) &= x_n^1(t)\mathbf{e}_1 + x_n^2(t)\mathbf{e}_2 + x_n^3(t)\mathbf{e}_3. \end{aligned}$$

We can calculate the velocities and accelerations of the particles by simply differentiating equations (2.10). Remember that $\mathbf{e}_1$, $\mathbf{e}_2$, $\mathbf{e}_3$ are constant vectors, so that their derivatives are zero. Hence one obtains from theorem (1.14) of Chapter 2 the formulas

$$\text{(2.11)}\quad \begin{aligned} \dot{\mathbf{r}}_1(t) &= \dot{x}_1^1(t)\mathbf{e}_1 + \dot{x}_1^2(t)\mathbf{e}_2 + \dot{x}_1^3(t)\mathbf{e}_3 \\ &\vdots \\ \dot{\mathbf{r}}_n(t) &= \dot{x}_n^1(t)\mathbf{e}_1 + \dot{x}_n^2(t)\mathbf{e}_2 + \dot{x}_n^3(t)\mathbf{e}_3 \end{aligned}$$

and

$$\text{(2.12)}\quad \begin{aligned} \ddot{\mathbf{r}}_1(t) &= \ddot{x}_1^1(t)\mathbf{e}_1 + \ddot{x}_1^2(t)\mathbf{e}_2 + \ddot{x}_1^3(t)\mathbf{e}_3 \\ &\vdots \\ \ddot{\mathbf{r}}_n(t) &= \ddot{x}_n^1(t)\mathbf{e}_1 + \ddot{x}_n^2(t)\mathbf{e}_2 + \ddot{x}_n^3(t)\mathbf{e}_3. \end{aligned}$$

We can now formulate Newton's law in component form. Each of the forces $\mathbf{F}_k$ is an arrow and so has a set of components relative to $\mathbf{e}_1$, $\mathbf{e}_2$, $\mathbf{e}_3$. These components are again scalar functions of time; we call them F_k^1, F_k^2, F_k^3. Thus we have

$$\text{(2.13)}\quad \begin{aligned} \mathbf{F}_1(t) &= F_1^1(t)\mathbf{e}_1 + F_1^2(t)\mathbf{e}_2 + F_1^3(t)\mathbf{e}_3 \\ &\vdots \\ \mathbf{F}_n(t) &= F_n^1(t)\mathbf{e}_1 + F_n^2(t)\mathbf{e}_2 + F_n^3(t)\mathbf{e}_3. \end{aligned}$$

Now Newton's law requires that $m_k\ddot{\mathbf{r}}_k(t) = \mathbf{F}_k(t)$. But according to proposition (2.8)–(iv), this will be so if and only if the respective components of these vectors are equal. This means that

$$
\text{(2.14)}\quad
\begin{array}{lll}
m_1\ddot{x}_1^1(t) = F_1^1(t), & m_1\ddot{x}_1^2(t) = F_1^2(t), & m_1\ddot{x}_1^3(t) = F_1^3(t) \\
\vdots \qquad \vdots & \vdots \qquad \vdots & \vdots \qquad \vdots \\
m_n\ddot{x}_n^1(t) = F_n^1(t), & m_n\ddot{x}_n^2(t) = F_n^2(t), & m_n\ddot{x}_n^3(t) = F_n^3(t).
\end{array}
$$

These equations constitute Newton's law as it is expressed relative to $\mathbf{e}_1$, $\mathbf{e}_2$, $\mathbf{e}_3$. Note that instead of n vector equations, there are now $3n$ scalar equations. We illustrate their use by an example.

(2.15) Example. Constant Force. Suppose a particle of mass m is acted on by a constant force $\mathbf{F}_0$ (for example, the force of gravity). We choose our set of three orthogonal unit vectors $\mathbf{e}_1$, $\mathbf{e}_2$, $\mathbf{e}_3$ with $\mathbf{e}_3$ in the direction of $\mathbf{F}_0$, that is, $\mathbf{F}_0 = \|\mathbf{F}_0\|\mathbf{e}_3$ (Figure 3.9). We have now for the components of $\mathbf{F}(t)$, $F^1(t) = 0$, $F^2(t) = 0$, $F^3(t) = \|\mathbf{F}_0\|$. Hence equations (2.14) become

(a) $m\ddot{x}^1(t) = 0, \qquad m\ddot{x}^2(t) = 0, \qquad m\ddot{x}^3(t) = \|\mathbf{F}_0\|,$

where $x^1(t)$, $x^2(t)$, $x^3(t)$ are the components of $\mathbf{r}(t)$. From the first of these equations we obtain, by integrating,

(b) $\dot{x}^1(t) = c_1, \qquad c_1$ a constant.

Integrating again we obtain

(c) $x^1(t) = c_1 t + d_1,$

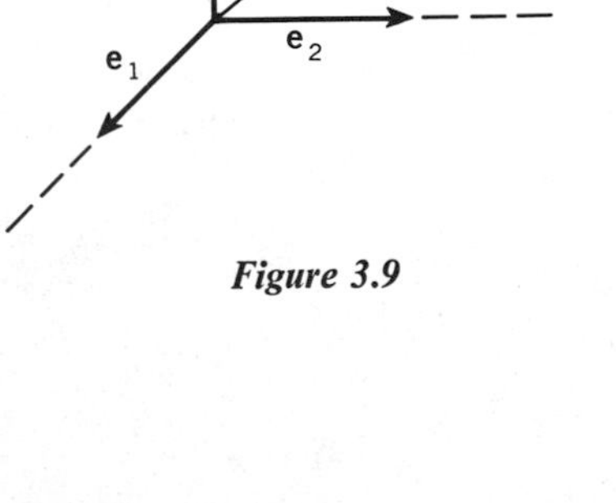

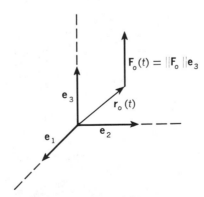

Figure 3.9

where d_1 is another constant. Similarly, if we integrate the second equation twice we obtain

$$\text{(d)}\quad \dot{x}^2(t) = c_2, \qquad x^2(t) = c_2 t + d_2.$$

The third equation, on the other hand, gives, after two integrations,

$$\text{(e)}\quad \dot{x}^3(t) = \frac{1}{m}\|\mathbf{F}_0\|t + c_3, \qquad x^3(t) = \frac{1}{2m}\|\mathbf{F}_0\|t^2 + c_3 t + d_3.$$

Now suppose the velocity and position at time t_0 are $\mathbf{v}_0$ and $\mathbf{r}_0$, respectively. Once again we write these in terms of their components. For the velocity this gives

$$\dot{\mathbf{r}}(t_0) = \dot{x}^1(t_0)\mathbf{e}_1 + \dot{x}^2(t_0)\mathbf{e}_2 + \dot{x}^3(t_0)\mathbf{e}_3 = \mathbf{v}_0 = v_0^1\mathbf{e}_1 + v_0^2\mathbf{e}_2 + v_0^3\mathbf{e}_3,$$

or, by (2.8)–(iv),

$$\text{(f)}\quad \dot{x}^1(t_0) = v_0^1, \qquad \dot{x}^2(t_0) = v_0^2, \qquad \dot{x}^3(t_0) = v_0^3.$$

Similarly, the condition $\mathbf{r}(t_0) = \mathbf{r}_0 = r_0^1\mathbf{e}_1 + r_0^2\mathbf{e}_2 + r_0^3\mathbf{e}_3$ yields

$$\text{(g)}\quad x^1(t_0) = r_0^1, \qquad x^2(t_0) = r_0^2, \qquad x^3(t_0) = r_0^3.$$

These formulas enable us to determine the constants $c_1, \ldots, d_3$. For example, (e) and the third equation of (f) yield

$$\frac{1}{m}\|\mathbf{F}_0\|t_0 + c_3 = v_0^3 \qquad \text{or} \qquad c_3 = v_0^3 - \frac{1}{m}\|\mathbf{F}_0\|t_0.$$

Then (e) and the third equation of (g) yields

$$\frac{1}{2m}\|\mathbf{F}_0\|t_0^2 + c_3 t_0 + d_3 = \frac{1}{2m}\|\mathbf{F}_0\|t_0^2 + \left(v_0^3 - \frac{1}{m}\|\mathbf{F}_0\|t_0\right)t_0 + d_3 = r_0^3$$

or

$$d_3 = r_0^3 - v_0^3 t_0 + \frac{1}{2m}\|\mathbf{F}_0\|t_0^2.$$

Hence

$$x^3(t) = \frac{1}{2m}\|\mathbf{F}_0\|t^2 + \left(v_0^3 - \frac{1}{m}\|\mathbf{F}_0\|t_0\right)t + r_0^3 - v_0^3 t_0 + \frac{1}{2m}\|\mathbf{F}_0\|t_0^2.$$

Similar calculations from the first and second equations of (f) and (g) yield

$$x^1(t) = v_0^1 t + r_0^1, \qquad x^2(t) = v_0^2 t + r_0^2.$$

PROBLEMS

1. A particle is moving to the right along the line of $\mathbf{e}_1$ with speed $\|\mathbf{v}_1(t)\| = 3t^2$ (Figure 3.10). Another particle moves up along the 45° line with speed $\|\mathbf{v}_2(t)\| = \sqrt{2}t$. Find the rate at which the distance between them is increasing at $t = 1$.

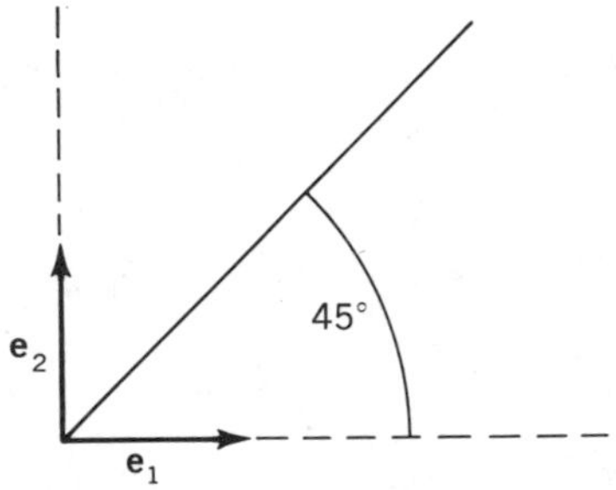

Figure 3.10

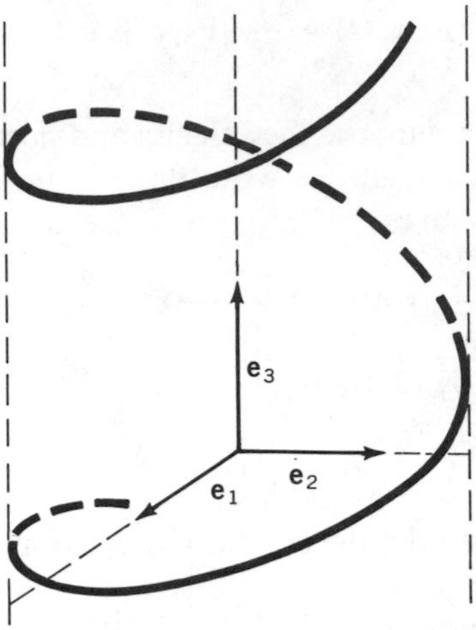

Figure 3.11

2. A particle moves around a circular cylinder of radius 1 ft in a helical path as shown in Figure 3.11. It moves with a constant speed of $\sqrt{2}$ ft/sec. Its height above the plane of $\mathbf{e}_1$ and $\mathbf{e}_2$ is increasing at 1 ft/sec.
   (a) Show that $\dot{x}^3(t) = 1$ ft/sec.
   (b) Show that there is a function $\theta(t)$ such that
   $$x^1(t) = \cos\theta(t), \qquad x^2(t) = \sin\theta(t).$$
   (c) Show that $\dot{\theta}(t) = 1$ rad/sec.
   (d) Determine the acceleration of the particle.
3. Consider example (2.15). Assume $v_0^1 = 0$.
   (a) Show that the particle moves in a plane.
   (b) Show that the particle either moves along a parabola or a straight line. Indicate how $\mathbf{r}_0$ and $\mathbf{v}_0$ should be chosen to make it move along a straight line.
4. Find an expression for $\boldsymbol{\alpha} \times \boldsymbol{\beta}$ in terms of the components of $\boldsymbol{\alpha}$ and $\boldsymbol{\beta}$. (*Hint:* Compute $\mathbf{e}_1 \times \mathbf{e}_2$, $\mathbf{e}_1 \times \mathbf{e}_3$, and $\mathbf{e}_2 \times \mathbf{e}_3$.)
5. Given two arrows $\mathbf{e}_1$ and $\mathbf{e}_2$ which are not necessarily orthogonal, show by means of an illustration that every vector $\boldsymbol{\alpha}$ in the plane of $\mathbf{e}_1$ and $\mathbf{e}_2$ can be written in the form $\boldsymbol{\alpha} = a\mathbf{e}_1 + b\mathbf{e}_2$ for some numbers a and b.

6. The following problems refer to example (2.1b).

(a) Show that for all t the speed $\|\mathbf{v}(t)\|$ of the particle is $R|\dot{\theta}(t)|$.

(b) If the speed of the particle is constant, show that for all t the force on it must be directed along the position vector $\mathbf{r}(t)$ toward the center.

7. A particle of mass m slides down a straight wire at an angle of 30° under the action of gravity, which acts vertically downward with a magnitude equal to mg. The wire is in the plane of $\mathbf{e}_1$, $\mathbf{e}_2$ and this plane is vertical (Figure 3.12).

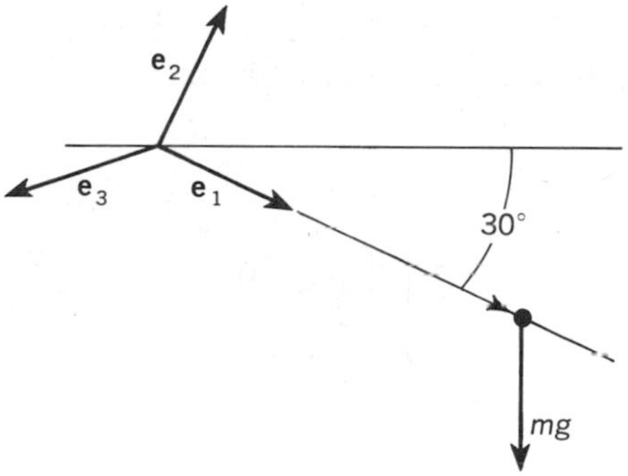

Figure 3.12

(a) Write Newton's law in component form for this problem using $\mathbf{e}_1$, $\mathbf{e}_2$, $\mathbf{e}_3$ as shown.

(b) Find an expression for $\mathbf{r}(t)$ if the particle starts from rest at O at time t.

3. Differential Equations of Motion

In §1 we alluded to the fact that in many mechanics problems the forces depend on the positions and velocities of the particles and that this gives rise to differential equations. Here we want to give some illustrations of this idea. We do so by deriving some differential equations which arise in this way.

(3.1) Example. Equations of a Particle Subject to Resistance Force. Suppose a particle is moving and is subject to a resistance force which acts in a direction opposite to that of the velocity $\mathbf{v}$ and has a magnitude proportional that of $\mathbf{v}$. Thus the force has the form $\mathbf{F} = -k\mathbf{v}$, where k is a positive constant. Then Newton's law, equation (1.2), becomes

(a) $m\ddot{\mathbf{r}} = -k\mathbf{v}(t) = -k\dot{\mathbf{r}}(t)$.

If we introduce components relative to $\mathbf{e}_1$, $\mathbf{e}_2$, $\mathbf{e}_3$ equation (a) yields the three scalar equations

$$\text{(b)}\quad m\ddot{x}^1(t) = -k\dot{x}^1(t), \qquad m\ddot{x}^2(t) = -k\dot{x}^2(t), \qquad m\ddot{x}^3(t) = -k\dot{x}^3(t).$$

Observe that each of these equations could be solved exactly as in example (1.5).

(3.2) Example. Equations of Particle Subject to Spring Force. Suppose a particle of mass m is attached to a spring which is fastened at the point O (see Figure 3.13). The force exerted by the spring on the particle will be directed along the spring. Its magnitude will be proportional to the length L of the spring minus a fixed constant L_0 (the unstretched length of the spring).

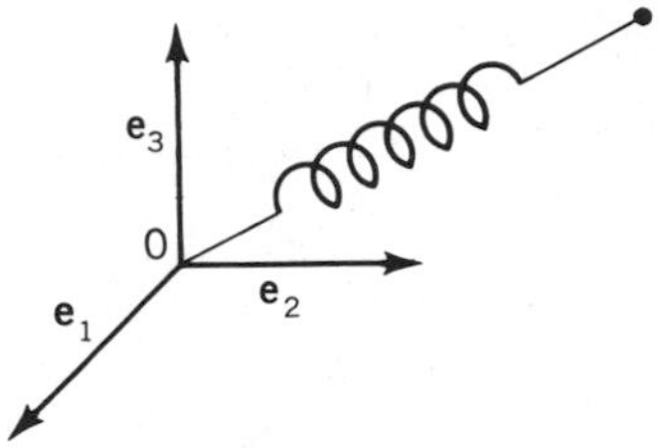

Figure 3.13

This force will be toward O if $L > L_0$ and away from O if $L < L_0$. Let $\mathbf{r}$ denote the position of the particle relative to O. Then $L = \|\mathbf{r}\|$ and we can write the force in the form

$$\text{(a)}\quad \mathbf{F} = -k(\|\mathbf{r}\| - L_0)\frac{\mathbf{r}}{\|\mathbf{r}\|}, \qquad k > 0.$$

(The reader should convince himself that this formula is an accurate restatement of all the assumptions made above about the force.) Thus Newton's law becomes

$$\text{(b)}\quad m\ddot{\mathbf{r}}(t) = -k\big(\|\mathbf{r}(t)\| - L_0\big)\frac{\mathbf{r}(t)}{\|\mathbf{r}(t)\|} = -k\mathbf{r}(t) + kL_0\frac{\mathbf{r}(t)}{\|\mathbf{r}(t)\|}.$$

If we write $\mathbf{r}(t) = x^1(t)\mathbf{e}_1 + x^2(t)\mathbf{e}_2 + x^3(t)\mathbf{e}_3$, then equation (b) yields

$$m\ddot{x}^1(t) = -kx^1(t) + kL_0\frac{x^1(t)}{\sqrt{x^1(t)^2 + x^2(t)^2 + x^3(t)^2}}$$

$$\text{(c)}\quad m\ddot{x}^2(t) = -kx^2(t) + kL_0\frac{x^2(t)}{\sqrt{x^1(t)^2 + x^2(t)^2 + x^3(t)^2}}$$

$$m\ddot{x}^3(t) = -kx^3(t) + kL_0\frac{x^3(t)}{\sqrt{x^1(t)^2 + x^2(t)^2 + x^3(t)^2}}.$$

(3.3) Example. Equations of Two Particles under Electrical Attraction. Suppose two particles of masses m_1 and m_2 carry electric charges q_1 and q_2 (Figure 3.14). Then the two charges will exert a force on each other. We assume that the particles move under the action of this force alone. Let $\mathbf{r}_1$ and $\mathbf{r}_2$ denote their position vectors relative to O. Coulomb's law states that the force between the particles is directed along the line joining them and its magnitude is proportional to q_1q_2 and inversely proportional to the square of the distance between them. Note that the vector $\mathbf{r}_2 - \mathbf{r}_1$ is along the line joining the particles and that the distance between them is equal to $\|\mathbf{r}_2 - \mathbf{r}_1\|$. Note too, that the vector $(\mathbf{r}_2 - \mathbf{r}_1)/\|\mathbf{r}_2 - \mathbf{r}_1\|$ is in the direction of the line but has unit magnitude. Coulomb's law further states that the charges repel each other if q_1 and q_2 have the same sign and attract each other if they have different signs. Let us fix attention on particle 2. The force on this particle has the form

$$\text{(a)}\quad \mathbf{F} = k\left(\frac{q_1q_2}{\|\mathbf{r}_2 - \mathbf{r}_1\|^2}\right)\frac{\mathbf{r}_2 - \mathbf{r}_1}{\|\mathbf{r}_2 - \mathbf{r}_1\|} = \frac{kq_1q_2(\mathbf{r}_2 - \mathbf{r}_1)}{\|\mathbf{r}_2 - \mathbf{r}_1\|^3},$$

where k is a constant. We assert that k must be positive. For if q_1 and q_2 have the same sign, then the particles repel each other and hence the force on particle 2 must be in the direction of $\mathbf{r}_2 - \mathbf{r}_1$. Thus kq_1q_2 must be positive and hence k is positive.

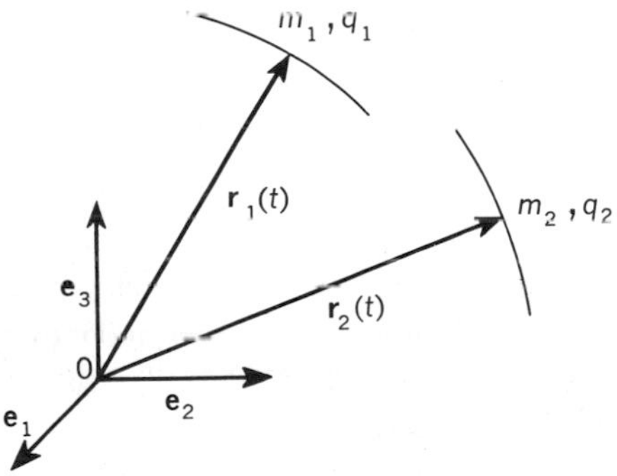

Figure 3.14

The force on particle 1 is equal in magnitude and direction to the force in (a) but opposite in sense, hence is its negative. Thus the force on particle 1 (exerted by particle 2) is $-\mathbf{F}$. These are the forces which go into Newton's law. Thus equations (1.2) become

$$\text{(b)}\quad \begin{aligned} m_1\ddot{\mathbf{r}}_1(t) &= -\frac{kq_1q_2(\mathbf{r}_2(t) - \mathbf{r}_1(t))}{\|\mathbf{r}_2(t) - \mathbf{r}_1(t)\|^3}, \\ m_2\ddot{\mathbf{r}}_2(t) &= \frac{kq_1q_2(\mathbf{r}_2(t) - \mathbf{r}_1(t))}{\|\mathbf{r}_2(t) - \mathbf{r}_1(t)\|^3}. \end{aligned}$$

Let us rewrite equations (b) using components relative to $\mathbf{e}_1$, $\mathbf{e}_2$, $\mathbf{e}_3$. We have

$$\mathbf{r}_1 = x_1^1\mathbf{e}_1 + x_1^2\mathbf{e}_2 + x_1^3\mathbf{e}_3, \qquad \mathbf{r}_2 = x_2^1\mathbf{e}_1 + x_2^2\mathbf{e}_2 + x_2^3\mathbf{e}_3.$$

Then

$$\mathbf{r}_2 - \mathbf{r}_1 = (x_2^1 - x_1^1)\mathbf{e}_1 + (x_2^2 - x_1^2)\mathbf{e}_2 + (x_2^3 - x_1^3)\mathbf{e}_3$$

and

$$\|\mathbf{r}_2 - \mathbf{r}_1\| = \sqrt{(x_2^1 - x_1^1)^2 + (x_2^2 - x_1^2)^2 + (x_2^3 - x_1^3)^2}.$$

Thus, if we equate components of $\mathbf{e}_1$, $\mathbf{e}_2$, and $\mathbf{e}_3$ on the two sides of (b), we obtain six scalar equations. The first of these will be

$$\text{(c)} \quad m_1\ddot{x}_1(t) = kq_1q_2\big(x_1^1(t) - x_2^1(t)\big) \times \\ [(x_2^1(t) - x_1^1(t))^2 + (x_2^2(t) - x_2^1(t))^2 + (x_2^3(t) - x_1^3(t))^2]^{-3/2}.$$

The other five are quite similar.

All the examples above illustrate the differential equations of motion. A reasonable physical problem in each case is to give the position and velocity of the particle or particles at some particular time t_0 and then to determine the subsequent motions. Also, observe that in each case the forces are given in the following form. We are told how to calculate the force on each particle *if we know the positions and velocities of all the particles.* It will be extremely helpful in understanding Chapter 4 if the reader keeps this physical model in mind.

PROBLEMS

1. Show that the particle in example (3.1) will never stop unless it is always at rest.
2. A particle of mass m carrying an electric charge and moving in a magnetic field is subject to a force. If q is the charge and $\mathbf{v}$ is the velocity, then the force $\mathbf{F}$ on the particle is given by

$$\mathbf{F}(t) = q\mathbf{v}(t) \times \mathbf{B}(t),$$

where $\mathbf{B}$ is a vector which denotes the magnetic field intensity. Write Newton's law in component form for such a motion.
3. A particle of mass m is acted on by a force of constant magnitude F_0. The force is always directed from the particle toward a fixed point O.

(a) Express the force in terms of the position vector from O.

(b) Write Newton's law in both vector and component form.
4. A particle of mass m is acted on by a frictional force which acts in the direction of $-\mathbf{v}$, where $\mathbf{v}$ is the velocity. The magnitude of the force is proportional to the *square* of the magnitude of $\mathbf{v}$. Write out Newton's law in vector and component form.

5. Two particles of masses m_1 and m_2 are attached by a spring (Figure 3.15). Assume that the force in the spring is as in example (3.2) and that the unstretched length of the spring is zero. Write Newton's law in both vector and component form.

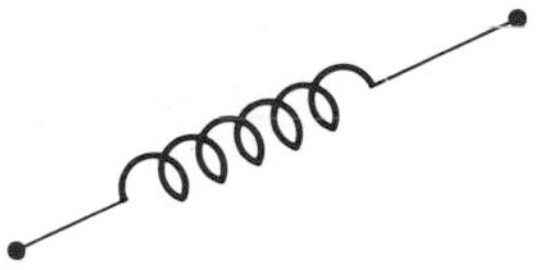

Figure 3.15

6. A particle of mass m slides along a wire at an angle of 45°. It is acted on by the force of gravity which is vertically downward with a magnitude of mg. It is attached to a spring fastened at O. If the unstretched length of the spring is zero, write Newton's law with $\mathbf{e}_1$, $\mathbf{e}_2$, $\mathbf{e}_3$ as shown in Figure 3.16.

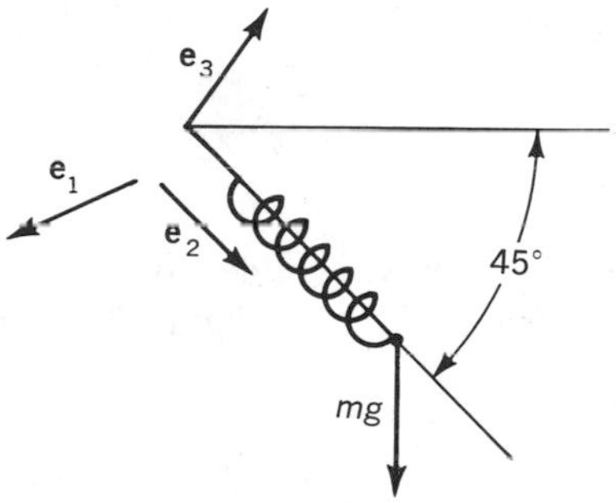

Figure 3.16

7. A particle of mass m moves under the action of a force which is in the direction of the velocity and has a magnitude which is proportional to the *cube* of the speed. Let $Q = \|\mathbf{v}\|^2$, where $\mathbf{v}$ is the velocity.

(a) Show that, for this particle,

$$\dot{Q}(t) = \beta Q(t)^2, \qquad \text{where } \beta \text{ is a constant.}$$

(b) Show that

$$Q(t) = \frac{1}{1 - \beta t}$$

is a solution of the equation in part (a) satisfying $Q(0) = 1$. Discuss the differences in the motion when $\beta > 0$ or $\beta < 0$ and explain the results physically.

4. Principles of Dynamics

In this section we wish to give some examples of the direct use of arrows in a geometric description of mechanics. We shall derive some general principles of mechanics and show how the arrow description can be used in solving specific problems.

(4.1) Center of Mass.

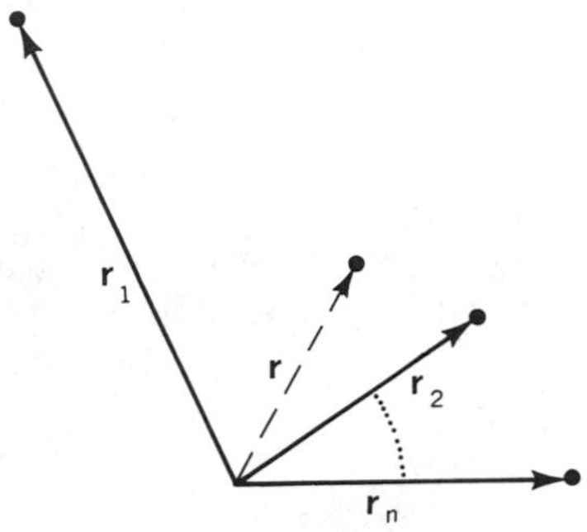

Figure 3.17

Suppose we have n particles moving under the action of forces $\mathbf{F}_1, \ldots, \mathbf{F}_n$. Let $\mathbf{r}_1, \ldots, \mathbf{r}_n$ be their position vectors (Figure 3.17). Then Newton's law is

$$\begin{aligned} m_1\ddot{\mathbf{r}}_1(t) &= \mathbf{F}_1(t) \\ &\vdots \\ m_r\ddot{\mathbf{r}}_n(t) &= \mathbf{F}_n(t). \end{aligned} \tag{4.2}$$

Let

$$M = m_1 + \cdots + m_n, \qquad \mathbf{r} = \frac{1}{M}(m_1\mathbf{r}_1 + \cdots + m_n\mathbf{r}_n),$$

$$\mathbf{F} = \mathbf{F}_1 + \cdots + \mathbf{F}_n.$$

Now we add together equations (4.2) and obtain

$$m_1\ddot{\mathbf{r}}_1(t) + \cdots + m_n\ddot{\mathbf{r}}_n(t) = \mathbf{F}_1(t) + \cdots + \mathbf{F}_n(t).$$

This can be written

$$M\frac{d^2}{dt^2}\left(\frac{m_1\mathbf{r}_1(t) + \cdots + m_n\mathbf{r}_n(t)}{M}\right) = M\ddot{\mathbf{r}}(t) = \mathbf{F}_1(t) + \cdots + \mathbf{F}_n(t) = \mathbf{F}(t),$$

or simply

(a) $M\ddot{\mathbf{r}}(t) = \mathbf{F}(t)$.

The point in space whose position vector is $\mathbf{r}(t)$ is called the *center of mass* of the system of particles. Equation (a) shows that the motion of *this* point is exactly what would occur if the system were a single particle of mass M moving along the path of the center of mass under the action of a force equal to the sum of the forces on all the particles.

(4.3) Principle of Linear Impulse and Momentum.

Once again we sum equations (4.2). We can write the result in the form

(a) $$\frac{d}{dt}\big(m_1\dot{\mathbf{r}}_1(t) + \cdots + m_n\dot{\mathbf{r}}_n(t)\big) = \mathbf{F}_1(t) + \cdots + \mathbf{F}_n(t).$$

Now integrate both sides from $t = t_1$ to $t = t_2$. If we use (3) of theorem (3.14) of Chapter 2 to evaluate the integral on the left, we obtain

(b) $$(m_1\dot{\mathbf{r}}_1(t_2) + \cdots + m_n\dot{\mathbf{r}}_n(t_2)) - (m_1\dot{\mathbf{r}}_1(t_1) + \cdots + m_n\dot{\mathbf{r}}_n(t_1)) = \int_{t_1}^{t_2} \big(\mathbf{F}_1(t) + \cdots + \mathbf{F}_n(t)\big)\, dt.$$

The quantity $m_1\dot{\mathbf{r}}_1 + \cdots + m_n\dot{\mathbf{r}}_n$ is called the *linear momentum* of the system of particles. The integral on the right side of (b) is called the *linear impulse* over the time interval $t_1 \le t \le t_2$. Equation (b) is called the *principle of linear impulse and momentum.* It states that the change in momentum over a time interval is equal to the impulse over that time interval. There is also a principle of angular momentum, which will be developed in a problem.

(4.4) Principle of Work and Energy.

Again we start with (4.2). Take the scalar product of each equation with the corresponding $\dot{\mathbf{r}}_k(t)$. This yields

(a) $$\begin{aligned} m_1\dot{\mathbf{r}}_1(t)\cdot\ddot{\mathbf{r}}_1(t) &= \dot{\mathbf{r}}_1(t)\cdot\mathbf{F}_1(t)\\ &\vdots \\ m_n\dot{\mathbf{r}}_n(t)\cdot\ddot{\mathbf{r}}_n(t) &= \dot{\mathbf{r}}_n(t)\cdot\mathbf{F}_n(t). \end{aligned}$$

Note that the left sides of these equations are equal to

$$\frac{d}{dt}\left(\tfrac{1}{2}m_1\|\dot{\mathbf{r}}_1(t)\|^2\right), \ldots, \frac{d}{dt}\left(\tfrac{1}{2}m_n\|\dot{\mathbf{r}}_n\|^2(t)\right).$$

Hence, if we add together the equations in (a), we obtain

$$\text{(b)}\quad \frac{d}{dt}\left(\tfrac{1}{2}m_1\|\dot{\mathbf{r}}_1(t)\|^2 + \cdots + \tfrac{1}{2}m_n\|\dot{\mathbf{r}}_n(t)\|^2\right) = \dot{\mathbf{r}}_1(t)\cdot\mathbf{F}_1(t) + \cdots + \dot{\mathbf{r}}_n(t)\cdot\mathbf{F}_n(t).$$

Once again we integrate from t_1 to t_2. The result is

$$\text{(c)}\quad \left(\tfrac{1}{2}m_1\|\dot{\mathbf{r}}_1(t_2)\|^2 + \cdots + \tfrac{1}{2}m_n\|\dot{\mathbf{r}}_n(t_2)\|^2\right) - \left(\tfrac{1}{2}m_1\|\dot{\mathbf{r}}_1(t_1)\|^2 + \cdots + \tfrac{1}{2}m_n\|\dot{\mathbf{r}}_n(t_1)\|^2\right) = \int_{t_1}^{t_2}\left(\dot{\mathbf{r}}_1(t)\cdot\mathbf{F}_1(t) + \cdots + \dot{\mathbf{r}}_n(t)\cdot\mathbf{F}_n(t)\right)dt.$$

The quantity

$$\tfrac{1}{2}m_1\|\dot{\mathbf{r}}_1\|^2 + \cdots + \tfrac{1}{2}m_n\|\dot{\mathbf{r}}_n\|^2$$

is called the *kinetic energy* of the system of particles. The quantity on the right side of (c) is called the *work* done by the forces in the time interval t_1 to t_2. Equation (c) expresses the *principle of work and energy*, which states that work done over any time interval is equal to the change in kinetic energy over that time interval.

(4.5) Example. A Particle Subject to Spring Force. As an application of the principle of work and energy, we consider again example (3.2) of §3. We study here the simple (but rather unrealistic) case in which the unstretched length L_0 is zero. The general case is treated in problem 9. When $L_0 = 0$ we found the force to be $-k\mathbf{r}(t)$. Hence the expression on the right side of (4.4c) for the work done becomes

$$-k\int_{t_1}^{t_2}\dot{\mathbf{r}}(t)\cdot\mathbf{r}(t)\,dt.$$

Observe that

$$\dot{\mathbf{r}}(t)\cdot\mathbf{r}(t) = \frac{1}{2}\frac{d}{dt}\|\mathbf{r}(t)\|^2.$$

Hence we can carry out the integration on the right side of (4.4c) and find

$$\int_{t_1}^{t_2}\dot{\mathbf{r}}(t)\cdot\mathbf{F}(t)\,dt = -k\int_{t_1}^{t_2}\dot{\mathbf{r}}(t)\cdot\mathbf{r}(t)\,dt = -\tfrac{1}{2}k\left(\|\mathbf{r}(t_2)\|^2 - \|\mathbf{r}(t_1)\|^2\right).$$

Thus, equation (4.4c) can in this case be written in the form

$$\text{(a)}\quad \tfrac{1}{2}m\|\dot{\mathbf{r}}(t_2)\|^2 + \tfrac{1}{2}k\|\mathbf{r}(t_2)\|^2 = \tfrac{1}{2}m\|\dot{\mathbf{r}}(t_1)\|^2 + \tfrac{1}{2}k\|\mathbf{r}(t_1)\|^2.$$

The quantity $\tfrac{1}{2}k\|\mathbf{r}\|^2$ is called the *potential energy* of the spring. Equation (a) is a statement that the *sum* of the kinetic energy and the potential energy is the same for any two values of t; that is,

(b) $\frac{1}{2}m\|\dot{\mathbf{r}}(t)\|^2 + \frac{1}{2}k\|\mathbf{r}(t)\|^2 = c,$

where c is a constant. It follows from (b) that the particle will have speed zero when it is at its maximum distance from 0.

(4.6) Example. Charged Particle in a Magnetic Field. Consider the situation in problem 2 of §1. There the force was

$$\mathbf{F}(t) = q\mathbf{v}(t) \times \mathbf{B}(t).$$

Observe that the force in this case is orthogonal to the velocity. Hence $\dot{\mathbf{r}}(t) \cdot \mathbf{F}(t) = 0$ for all t. This means that the integrand on the right side of (4.4c) is identically zero; hence the integral is zero. The conclusion is that a charged particle moving in a magnetic field must have constant speed.

PROBLEMS

1. A particle is whirled in a circle at the end of a string. The only force acting is the tension in the string. Show that it must have constant speed.
2. Use the principle of work and energy to show that the particle in example (3.1) must have decreasing speed as time increases.
3. Show that if m_1 and m_2 are equal in example (3.3), then the center of mass of the two particles remains stationary.
4. A particle of mass m slides down a wire at an angle of 45° (Figure 3.18). It is acted on by gravity (mg down) and a fixed frictional force $\mathbf{F}_0$. It it starts from rest at the point O at time $t = 0$, find an expression for its speed at time t in terms of m, $\|\mathbf{F}_0\|$, and the distance $h(t)$ below O. Use the principle of work and energy.

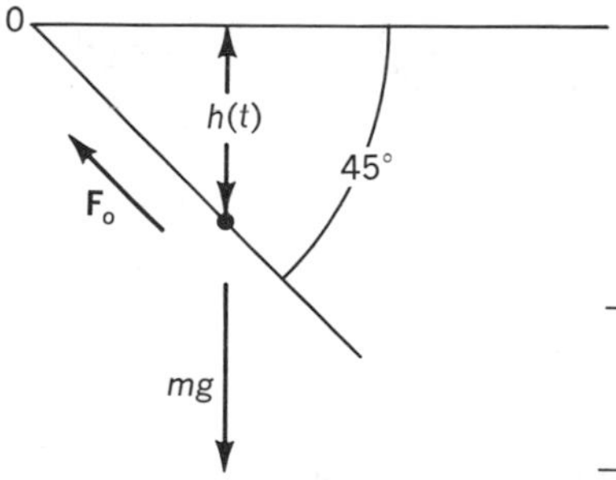

Figure 3.18

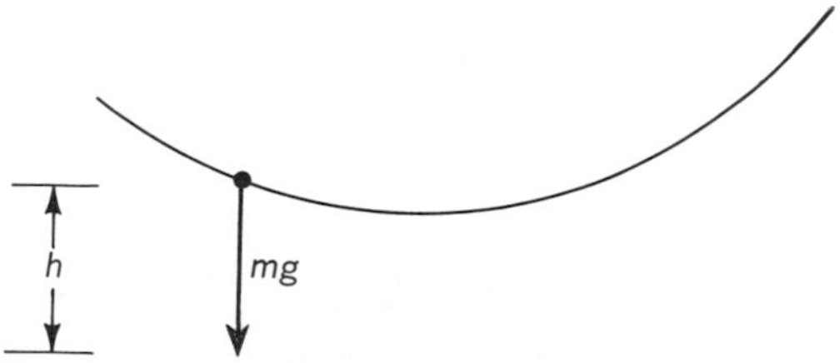

Figure 3.19

5. A particle slides on a wire without friction under the action of gravity (Figure 3.19). h is the distance of the particle above a fixed plane as shown. Show that

$$\tfrac{1}{2}m\|\mathbf{v}(t)\|^2 + mgh = c, \qquad \text{where } c \text{ is a constant,}$$

no matter what the shape of the wire.

6. The quantity

$$\mathbf{A}(t) = m_1\mathbf{r}_1(t) \times \dot{\mathbf{r}}_1(t) + \cdots + m_n\mathbf{r}_n(t) \times \dot{\mathbf{r}}_n(t)$$

is called the *angular momentum* of the system of particles with respect to the origin O. The quantity

$$\mathbf{L}(t) = \mathbf{r}_1(t) \times \mathbf{F}_1(t) + \cdots + \mathbf{r}_n(t) \times \mathbf{F}_n(t)$$

is called the *moment* of the forces $\mathbf{F}_1(t), \ldots, \mathbf{F}_n(t)$ with respect to the origin O (see Figure 3.20). Establish the *principle of angular momentum*, which states that

$$\mathbf{A}(t_2) - \mathbf{A}(t_1) = \int_{t_1}^{t_2} \mathbf{F}(t)\,dt.$$

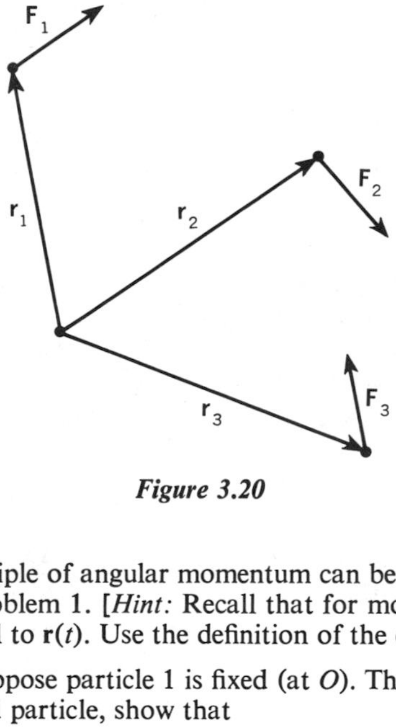

Figure 3.20

7. Show that the principle of angular momentum can be used to obtain the same conclusion as in problem 1. [*Hint:* Recall that for motion in a circle we must have $\dot{\mathbf{r}}(t)$ orthogonal to $\mathbf{r}(t)$. Use the definition of the cross product.]

8. In example (3.3) suppose particle 1 is fixed (at O). Then if $\mathbf{r}_2(t)$ is the position vector of the second particle, show that

$$\tfrac{1}{2}m\|\dot{\mathbf{r}}_2(t)\|^2 - kq_1q_2\,\frac{1}{\|\mathbf{r}_2(t)\|}$$

is a constant.

9. Consider the particle on a spring in example (4.5) when the unstretched length L_0 is not zero.

(a) Show that

$$\frac{1}{\|\mathbf{r}(t)\|}\mathbf{r}(t)\cdot\dot{\mathbf{r}}(t) = \frac{d}{dt}\|\mathbf{r}(t)\|.$$

(b) Show that the quantity on the right side of (4.4c) becomes

$$-\frac{k}{2}\frac{d}{dt}(\|\mathbf{r}(t)\|^2 - 2\|\mathbf{r}\|L_0).$$

(c) Show that the principle of work and energy yields

$$\tfrac{1}{2}m\|\dot{\mathbf{r}}(t)\|^2 + \tfrac{1}{2}k(\|\mathbf{r}(t)\| - L_0)^2 = c,$$

where c is a constant.

10. We return to the situation of the rod in problem 15, §2 of Chapter 2. Suppose that the rod itself has negligible mass but that there are particles of masses m_1 and m_2 at the two ends. Forces $\mathbf{F}_1$ and $\mathbf{F}_2$ act on particles 1 and 2, respectively. Choose $\boldsymbol{\omega}$ as in problem 15(c) and let $\mathbf{r}_1$ and $\mathbf{r}_2$ denote the position vectors of the two ends (relative to P_0). (Then $\boldsymbol{\omega}\cdot\mathbf{r}_1 = \boldsymbol{\omega}\cdot\mathbf{r}_2 = 0$.) Show that

$$(m_1\|\mathbf{r}_1\|^2 + m_2\|\mathbf{r}_2\|^2)\dot{\boldsymbol{\omega}} = \mathbf{L}_1 + \mathbf{L}_2,$$

where $\mathbf{L}_1$ and $\mathbf{L}_2$ are the moments of the forces as defined in problem 6.

4

Ordinary Differential Equations

0. Introduction

This chapter concerns ordinary differential equations. These are equations which relate the derivatives of one or several functions of a single variable. We use the term "ordinary" to distinguish them from equations involving partial derivatives. The latter will be discussed in Chapter 7.

This section is by way of orientation in the subject. A physical origin of differential equations was given in Chapter 3. Here we want to motivate the subject in a more mathematical way. The reader has already encountered the simplest of all differential equation problems in his study of elementary integration. There one is asked to find an "indefinite integral" of a function g. This means that one is to find another function f such that the derivative of f is identically equal to the given function g. That is, we are to find a solution f of the equation

$$\dot{f}(t) = g(t). \tag{0.1}$$

Equation (0.1) is an example of a differential equation. The first thing that one learns in integration theory is how to find solutions of (0.1) for certain simple functions. For example, if $g(t) = t + 1$, e^t, or $\sin t$, then solutions of (0.1) are given by $f(t) = (t^2/2) + t$, e^t, or $-\cos t$, respectively. The next thing that one learns is that there are many solutions of (0.1). Thus, if one has found one solution f_0 of (0.1), then any function f of the form $f = f_0 + c$, where c is a constant, will be a solution. This is the "arbitrary constant of integration." For example, the function $f(t) = e^t + c$ is a solution of $\dot{f}(t) = e^t$ for any c. It is called the "indefinite integral" of e^t.

The reason that $e^t + c$ is called *the* indefinite integral of e^t is that *all* solutions of $\dot{f}(t) = e^t$ have the form $e^t + c$ for some choice of c. This fact comes from the following result [which we have used before in proving theorem (1.15) of Chapter 2].

(0.2) Proposition. *If $\dot{G}(t)$ is identically zero,† then $G(t)$ is identically equal to a constant.*

We use this fact in the following manner. Consider the equation $\dot{f}(t) = e^t$, one solution of which is e^t itself. Suppose f is any solution and consider the function G defined by $G(t) = f(t) - e^t$. We have

$$\dot{G}(t) = \dot{f}(t) - e^t = e^t - e^t = 0;$$

hence by (0.2) $G(t)$ is identically equal to a constant c, that is,

$$f(t) = e^t + c.$$

It is clear that there is really nothing special about the function e^t in this calculation. We state the general principle involved [see theorem (3.7) of Chapter 2].

(0.3) Proposition. *If f_0 is a solution of $\dot{f}(t) = g(t)$, then every solution of that equation has the form $f = f_0 + c$ for some constant c.*

The presence of the constant c makes it clear that it is not a meaningful question to ask for *the* solution of (0.1), since there will be many solutions. To specify which solution we want to talk about we have to give some other conditions. For example, suppose we look for solutions of $\dot{f}(t) = e^t$ such that $f(0) = 1$. Now there *is* only one solution, $f(t) = e^t$. For suppose f is any such solution. Then we know by (0.3) that $f(t) = e^t + c$ for some c. But c in this case must be zero, since $f(0) = 1$:

$$f(0) = 1 = e^0 + c = 1 + c.$$

Once again there is a principle involved which we state now. This is a simpler version of the principle in kinematics that velocity and initial position de-

† From now on we shall tacitly assume that functions are defined and continuous for all values of t, whenever the interval is not explicitly given.

termine the path [formula (3.8) of Chapter 2; see also theorem (1.4) of Chapter 3].

(0.4) Proposition. *There exists at most one function f such that*

$$\dot{f}(t) = g(t) \qquad \textit{and} \qquad f(t_0) = a.$$

Proof. Suppose f_1 and f_2 satisfy the conditions of the proposition. Then if G is defined by $G(t) = f_1(t) - f_2(t)$, we have

$$\dot{G}(t) = \dot{f}_1(t) - \dot{f}_2(t) = g(t) - g(t) = 0.$$

Hence by (0.2) $G(t)$ is identically equal to a constant. This constant must be 0, however, since $G(t_0) = f_1(t_0) - f_2(t_0) = a - a = 0$. Thus any two solutions must be identically equal. ▮

Proposition (0.4) is a simple example of a *uniqueness theorem*. It says there can be no more than one solution of the problem. It *does not*, however, say that there need be any solutions at all. That there are indeed solutions is the content of equation (c) of theorem (3.7) of Chapter 2. In fact, this formula states that if g is continuous and we define the function f by

$$f(t) = \int_c^t g(\tau)\, d\tau \tag{0.5}$$

for some c, then f is differentiable and $\dot{f}(t) = g(t)$.

On the basis of equation (0.5) we can prove the following:

(0.6) Proposition. *Suppose g is a continuous function of t. Then there exists a function f such that*†

$$\dot{f}(t) = g(t) \qquad \textit{and} \qquad f(t_0) = a. \tag{0.7}$$

Proof. Define f_1 by

$$f_1(t) = \int_{t_0}^t g(\tau)\, d\tau.$$

Then by (0.5) $\dot{f}_1(t) = g(t)$. Moreover, $f_1(t_0) = 0$. Now the desired function f is given by $f(t) = f_1(t) + a$. ▮

†If g is continuous only on an interval $\alpha < t < \beta$, then the proposition is still true except that f will be defined and differentiable only on this interval and one must choose the value t_0 so that $\alpha < t_0 < \beta$.

Proposition (0.6) is an example of what is called an *existence theorem*. It guarantees that there is a solution, even though it does not necessarily describe the solution in terms of simple functions. Thus, for example, the function f given by

$$f(t) = \int_0^t e^{\tau^2}\, d\tau$$

is the (unique) solution of the equation $\dot{f}(t) = e^{t^2}$ such that $f(0) = 0$. Moreover, this solution cannot be described in terms of simpler functions.

The first goal in differential equation problems is to establish *both* a uniqueness and an existence theorem. This says that the problem has exactly one solution. We emphasize that the conditions in such theorems are always quite precise. Thus, if we delete the second condition in (0.7), we shall lose uniqueness. On the other hand, if we tried to append the condition $\dot{f}(t_0) = 0$ to (0.7) there would be, in general, no solution at all; that is, we would lose existence. This chapter will emphasize uniqueness and existence of solutions throughout. One of its major purposes is to bring the reader to the point where he can recognize when the auxiliary conditions for a differential equation are such that uniqueness and existence of a solution is to be expected. In this respect the physical origin of initial conditions, as described in Chapter 3, will be helpful.

PROBLEMS

1. Find the solution f of each of the following problems.

(a) $\dot{f}(t) = 0, f(2) = 0$

(b) $\dot{f}(t) = \sin t, f(0) = 1$

(c) $\dot{f}(t) = 1 + t, f(1) = 0$

(d) $\dot{f}(t) = e^t + \cos t, f(0) = 0$

(e) $\dot{f}(t) = 2t - e^t + 3 \sin t, f(-1) = 0$

2. Write out a proof of proposition (0.3). Use statement (0.2).

3. Consider the equation

$$\ddot{f}(t) = e^t.$$

(a) Show that e^t is a solution.

(b) Show that $e^t + At + B$, for any constants A and B, is also a solution.

(c) If f is any solution, use proposition (0.3) to show that $\dot{f}(t) = e^t + A$ for some constant A.

(d) Use proposition (0.3) again to show that any solution f has the form $f(t) = e^t + At + B$ for some A and B.

(e) Show that there is one and only one solution of $\ddot{f}(t) = e^t$ such that $f(0) = 1$, $\dot{f}(0) = 0$.

4. Use problem 3 as a model to state and prove an analog of proposition (0.4) for the equation $\ddot{f}(t) = g(t)$.

5. Try to prove an analog of proposition (0.6) for problem 4. [*Hint:* Use proposition (0.6) twice, first to get $\dot{f}$ and then to get f.]

6. What would be an appropriate problem for the equation $\dddot{f}(t) = g(t)$? For the equation $f^{(n)}(t) = g(t)$?

7. What would be an appropriate problem for the two equations

$$\dot{f}_1(t) - \dot{f}_2(t) = g_1(t) \qquad \text{and} \qquad \dot{f}_1(t) + 2\dot{f}_2(t) = g_2(t)?$$

1. First-Order Linear Equations

An ordinary differential equation is an equation connecting the derivatives of a function. We shall use t for the independent variable in our equations and $y(t)$ for the value of the solution of the equation at t. A differential equation is said to be of *nth order* if the order of the highest derivative which occurs is n. For example, the equations

$$(1.1) \qquad \dot{y}(t) = 0, \qquad \dot{y}(t) = y(t), \qquad \dot{y}(t) = ty(t)^2, \qquad \big(\dot{y}(t)\big)^2 = y(t)$$

are all of first order. The equations

$$(1.1') \qquad \ddot{y}(t) = y(t), \qquad \ddot{y}(t) + \dot{y}(t) = 0, \qquad \ddot{y}(t)\dot{y}(t) + \dot{y}(t)^2 + y(t) = 0$$

are of second order.

This section concerns a special kind of first-order equation. These equations have the form

$$(1.2) \qquad \dot{y}(t) = p(t)y(t) + f(t),$$

where p and f are given functions of t.

Examples of such first-order equations occur in many places. We give two such examples.

(1.3) Examples. Linear Nonhomogeneous Equations

(a) FALLING PARTICLE. Suppose a particle of mass m falls vertically under the action of the force of gravity and an air resistance force (Figure 4.1). The

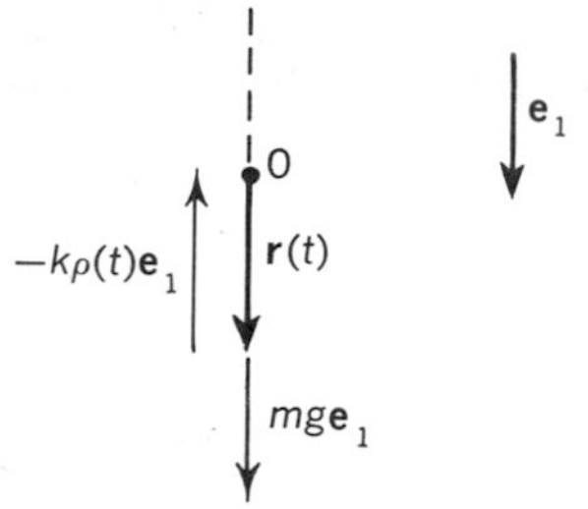

Figure 4.1

latter acts in the direction of $-\mathbf{v}(t)$, where $\mathbf{v}(t)$ is the particle velocity and has a magnitude proportional to $\|\mathbf{v}(t)\|$. We indicated in example (1.5) of Chapter 3 how to reduce the differential equation of motion to a single scalar equation. We take a unit vector $\mathbf{e}_1$ directed vertically downward. Then the position vector $\mathbf{r}(t)$ relative to a point O can be written $\mathbf{r}(t) = \rho(t)\mathbf{e}_1$, and $\mathbf{v}(t) = \dot{\rho}(t)\mathbf{e}_1$. The force of gravity has the form $mg\mathbf{e}_1$ and the resistance force is $-k\dot{\rho}(t)\mathbf{e}_1$; hence Newton's law becomes

$$m\ddot{\rho}(t)\mathbf{e}_1 = -k\dot{\rho}(t)\mathbf{e}_1 + mg\mathbf{e}_1 \qquad \text{or} \qquad m\ddot{\rho}(t) = -k\dot{\rho}(t) + mg.$$

If we set $y(t) = \dot{\rho}(t)$ and divide by m we obtain

$$\dot{y}(t) = -\frac{k}{m}y(t) + g.$$

This is of the form (1.2) with $p(t) = -k/m$ and $f(t) = g$.

(b) *LR* CIRCUIT. Consider an electric circuit which contains an inductance, a resistance, and an electromotive force (Figure 4.2). There will be potential drops across the resistance and inductance which are proportional to the current and its derivative, respectively. If y denotes the current, these two potential drops then have the form Ry and $L\dot{y}$, respectively. The laws of

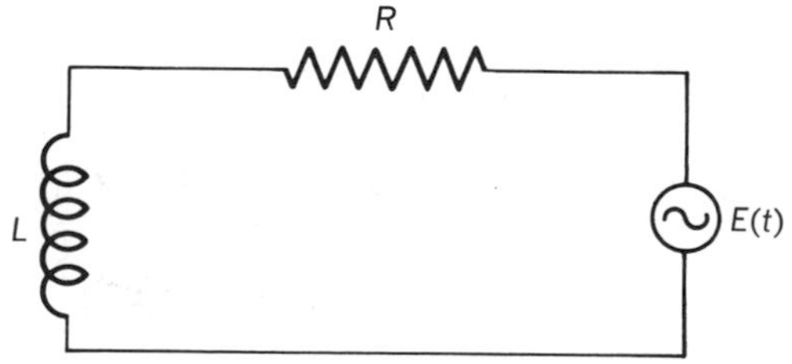

Figure 4.2

circuits state that the sum of these potential drops at time t equals the electromotive force at time t, which we denote by $E(t)$. Hence we have

$$L\dot{y}(t) + Ry(t) = E(t) \qquad \text{or} \qquad \dot{y}(t) = -\frac{R}{L}\,y(t) + \frac{1}{L}\,E(t).$$

Again this is of the form (1.2). The quantities R and L may change with time so that the ratio R/L might not be a constant but rather some other function of time.

We have chosen to begin our discussion with equation (1.2) not only because it occurs often in physics but also because it is sufficiently simple so that we can give a complete discussion along the lines of the Introduction. It turns out to be desirable to consider first a special case, that in which f is identically zero. Thus (1.2) becomes

$$\dot{y}(t) = p(t)y(t). \tag{1.4}$$

Equation (1.4) is called a *first-order linear homogeneous equation.*

We obtain a solution of (1.4) by a special trick. This is an extension of the device we used in example (1.5) of Chapter 3. Let P be a function of t such that $\dot{P}(t) = p(t)$. Then consider the function e^P. We have

$$\frac{d}{dt}\,(e^{P(t)}) = e^{P(t)}\dot{P}(t) = p(t)e^{P(t)}. \tag{1.4$'$}$$

Hence e^P is one solution of (1.4); that is, it is one function such that its derivative is p times the function itself. Observe, moreover, that not only is e^P a solution but so is ce^P, where c is any constant. Indeed we have

$$\frac{d}{dt}\,(ce^{P(t)}) = ce^{P(t)}\dot{P}(t) = p(t)(ce^{P(t)}).$$

We show now that we can always adjust the constant c so that ce^P is a solution of (1.4) which also satisfies

$$y(t_0) = a, \tag{1.5}$$

where t_0 and a are arbitrary. Indeed, if we substitute ce^P into (1.5) we obtain

$$ce^{P(t_0)} = a \qquad \text{or} \qquad c = ae^{-P(t_0)}; \tag{1.6}$$

hence the desired solution is $ae^{P(t)-P(t_0)}$.

(1.7) Examples. Linear Homogeneous Equations

(a) $\dot{y}(t) = y(t)$, $y(0) = 1$. Here $p(t) = 1$, so we can choose $P(t) = t$. Hence (1.6) becomes

$$ce^0 = 1, \qquad \text{so } c = 1 \text{ and } y(t) = e^t.$$

(b) $\dot{y}(t) = e^{-t}y(t)$, $y(1) = 1$. Here $p(t) = e^{-t}$ and we can choose

$$P(t) = -e^{-t}.$$

By (1.6) then,

$$ce^{-e^{-1}} = 1, \qquad \text{so } c = e^{e^{-1}} \text{ and } y(t) = e^{-e^{-t}+e^{-1}}.$$

(c) $\dot{y}(t) = (\sin t)y(t)$, $y(\pi) = -1$. Here $p(t) = \sin t$ and we can choose $P(t) = -\cos t$. By (1.6)

$$ce^{-\cos\pi} = ce = -1, \qquad \text{so } c = -e^{-1} \text{ and } y(t) = -e^{-\cos t-1}.$$

In these three examples we have provided an existence theorem for equation (1.4) with condition (1.5), by explicitly calculating a solution. Equation (1.4′) shows, however, that even in the general case all we need do to ensure the *existence* of a solution of (1.4) is to guarantee the availability of some P such that $\dot{P}(t) = p(t)$. Now the existence of a solution of this last equation was exactly what was discussed in the Introduction. If p is continuous, then proposition (0.6) tells us that any function of the form

$$P(t) = \int_\alpha^t p(\tau)\, d\tau$$

will satisfy $\dot{P}(t) = p(t)$. Thus we have a general existence theorem for the solution of (1.4) and (1.5).

(1.8) Remark. Observe that *any* choice of the function P which satisfies $\dot{P}(t) = p(t)$ will lead to the same final result. For instance, in example (1.7b) we could have chosen $P(t) = -e^{-t} + 2$. Then (1.6) would have been

$$ce^{-e^{-1}+2} = 1 \qquad \text{or} \qquad c = e^{e^{-1}-2}.$$

But then $y(t) = e^{e^{-1}-2}e^{-e^{-t}+2} = e^{-e^{-t}+e^{-1}}$, as before.

We have established above the *existence* of a solution of (1.4) and (1.5). Now we shall prove uniqueness.

(1.9) Proposition. *There exists at most one solution of equations* (1.4) *and* (1.5).

Proof. The proof is a little like that of (0.4). Suppose that y_1 and y_2 are solutions. Define y by $y(t) = y_1(t) - y_2(t)$. Then we have

$$\begin{aligned}\dot{y}(t) = \dot{y}_1(t) - \dot{y}_2(t) &= p(t)y_1(t) - p(t)y_2(t)\\ &= p(t)\big(y_1(t) - y_2(t)\big) = p(t)y(t).\end{aligned}$$

Hence y is a solution of (1.4), also. Equivalently,

$$\dot{y}(t) - p(t)y(t) = 0.$$

Multiply this equation by e^{-P}, where P is such that $\dot{P}(t) = p(t)$. This gives

$$\begin{aligned}e^{-P(t)}\dot{y}(t) - p(t)e^{-P(t)}y(t) &= e^{-P(t)}\dot{y}(t) + \frac{d}{dt}\,(e^{-P(t)})y(t)\\ &= \frac{d}{dt}\,(e^{-P(t)}y(t)) = 0.\end{aligned}$$

Hence by (0.2) we deduce that $e^{-P(t)}y(t)$ is a constant c. But this constant must be zero, since $y_1(t_0) = y_2(t_0) = a$ and hence

$$y(t_0) = y_1(t_0) - y_2(t_0) = a - a = 0.$$

That is, $e^{-P(t)}y(t)$ is identically zero and, since $e^{-P(t)}$ is never zero, y must be zero. Thus y_1 and y_2 are identically equal. ▮

We have now established the existence and uniqueness of the solution of (1.4) and (1.5). The reader should convince himself that the above proof also yields the following result (see problem 13).

(1.10) Proposition. *If a solution of* (1.4) *is zero at one point, then it must be identically zero.*

[Another way of stating this is that if a solution of (1.4) is nonzero at some point, then it *can never be zero*.]

We turn now to the general equation (1.2). If f is not identically zero this equation is called *first-order linear nonhomogeneous*. What we are going to show is that this equation has one and only one solution satisfying the same condition [(1.5)] as in the homogeneous case. The uniqueness this time is very easy. Let y_1 and y_2 be solutions and again set $y = y_1 - y_2$. Then

$$\begin{aligned}\dot{y}(t) = \dot{y}_1(t) - \dot{y}_2(t) &= p(t)y_1(t) + f(t) - p(t)y_2(t) - f(t)\\ &= p(t)\big(y_1(t) - y_2(t)\big) = p(t)y(t).\end{aligned}$$

Hence y is a solution of the homogeneous equation (1.4). Moreover, $y(t_0) = y_1(t_0) - y_2(t_0) = a - a = 0$. Hence, by (1.10), $y(t) \equiv 0$ or $y_1(t) \equiv y_2(t)$.

We shall establish existence in this case by another device. Let us apply it to an example first.

(1.11) Example. We solve $\dot{y}(t) = y(t) + 1$ with $y(0) = 2$. Write the equation as $\dot{y}(t) - y(t) = 1$. Now multiply by e^{-t} and obtain

(a) $e^{-t}\dot{y}(t) - e^{-t}y(t) = e^{-t}$.

But now observe that the left side is simply the derivative of $e^{-t}y(t)$. Hence

(b) $\dfrac{d}{dt}\left(e^{-t}y(t)\right) = e^{-t}$,

and therefore, by (0.3), $e^{-t}y(t) = -e^{-t} + c$. That is, $y(t) = -1 + ce^t$, where c is a constant. We can now adjust the constant c so as to make this function satisfy $y(0) = 2$. Indeed, we have

$$2 = y(0) = -1 + ce^0 = -1 + c \qquad \text{or} \qquad c = 3.$$

This yields $y(t) = -1 + 3e^t$. The reader should check that this is indeed a solution.

The above procedure can be generalized to (1.2). Consider what was done. There are two observations to make. First, the quantity e^{-t} by which we multiplied is the reciprocal of one solution of the linear homogeneous equation $\dot{y}(t) = y(t)$ which is obtained simply by deleting the 1. Second, the term involving the arbitrary constant is simply the most general solution of that linear homogeneous equation. We outline the procedure in general.

(1.12) Solution Procedure for Linear Nonhomogeneous Equations

(i) Write the equation as $\dot{y}(t) - p(t)y(t) = f(t)$.
(ii) Divide by $e^{P(t)}$, where $\dot{P}(t) = p(t)$, thus obtaining

$$e^{-P(t)}\dot{y}(t) - p(t)e^{-P(t)}y(t) = \frac{d}{dt}\left(e^{-P(t)}y(t)\right) = e^{-P(t)}f(t).$$

(iii) Find some function F_0 such that $\dot{F}_0(t) = e^{-P(t)}f(t)$.
(iv) Then

$$y(t) = e^{P(t)}F_0(t) + ce^{P(t)},$$

where c is an arbitrary constant.
(v) Determine c by condition (1.5); that is,

$$a = y(t_0) = e^{P(t_0)}F_0(t_0) + ce^{P(t_0)} \qquad \text{or} \qquad c = ae^{-P(t_0)} - F_0(t_0).$$

Then the solution is

(1.13) $y(t) = e^{P(t)}F_0(t) + (ae^{-P(t_0)} - F_0(t_0))e^{P(t)}.$

Once again the reader should check that this is indeed a solution.

(1.14) Examples. Linear Nonhomogeneous Equations

(a) $\dot{y}(t) = 2y(t) + e^t$, $y(0) = 0$. Here $p(t) = 2$ so we can take $P(t) = 2t$. Thus we obtain

$$e^{-2t}\dot{y}(t) - 2e^{-2t}y(t) = \frac{d}{dt}(e^{-2t}y(t)) = e^{-2t}e^t = e^{-t}.$$

We can take $F_0(t)$ to be $-e^{-t}$, since then $\dot{F}_0(t) = e^{-t}$. Hence we have

$$y(t) = e^{2t}F_0(t) + ce^{2t} = -e^t + ce^{2t}.$$

Then $y(0) = 0$ gives $-e^0 + ce^0 = 0$ or $c = 1$, and the solution is

$$y(t) = -e^t + e^{2t}.$$

(b) $\dot{y}(t) = -(\sin t)y(t) + \sin t$, $y(\pi/2) = 2$. Here $p(t) = -\sin t$ so we take $P(t) = \cos t$. Then we obtain

$$e^{-\cos t}\dot{y}(t) + (\sin t)e^{-\cos t}y(t) = \frac{d}{dt}(e^{-\cos t}y(t)) = e^{-\cos t}\sin t.$$

This time we can take $F_0(t) = e^{-\cos t}$ and hence

$$y(t) = e^{\cos t}e^{-\cos t} + ce^{\cos t} = 1 + ce^{\cos t}.$$

Moreover, $2 = y(\pi/2) = 1 + ce^0$; hence $c = 1$ and the solution is $y(t) = 1 + e^{\cos t}$.

All the examples we have studied so far have had the feature that the functions p and f are continuous for all values of t. With a little care, however, the procedure can also be used in cases where p or f or both can become discontinuous. We illustrate with some examples.

(1.15) Examples. Equations with Discontinuities

(a) $\dot{y}(t) = (1/t)y(t)$, $y(1) = 2$. Here $p(t) = 1/t$ is infinite at $t = 0$. For $t > 0$ we can take $P(t) = \log t$ and hence $e^{P(t)} = e^{\log t} = t$. Thus, by

(1.12)–(iv), $y(t) = ct$. Then $y(1) = 2$ gives $c \cdot 1 = 2$ or $c = 2$, so that the solution is $y(t) = 2t$. Note that this solution is actually defined for all t.

(b) $\dot{y}(t) = (1/t)y(t) + t$, $y(1) = 2$. Again for $t > 0$ we can take $P(t) = e^{\log t} = t$. Hence by (1.12)–(ii), we obtain

$$\frac{1}{t}\dot{y}(t) - \frac{1}{t^2}y(t) = \frac{d}{dt}\left(\frac{1}{t}y(t)\right) = 1.$$

Now we can take $F_0(t) = t$ since $\dot{F}_0(t) = 1$ and we have $(1/t)y(t) = t + c$ or $y(t) = t^2 + ct$. To determine c we write

$$y(1) = 2 = 1^2 + c \cdot 1 \text{ or } c = 1, \qquad \text{so } y(t) = t^2 + t.$$

Again this solution is defined for all t.

(c) $\dot{y}(t) = (1/t)y(t), y(-1) = 2$. Once again we have $p(t) = 1/t$ but now the choice $P(t) = \log t$ is not suitable, since it is not defined for $t < 0$ and we want to evaluate things at $t = -1$. We can choose instead $P(t) = \log(-t)$, since

$$\frac{d}{dt}\log(-t) = \frac{1}{-t}(-1) = \frac{1}{t}\cdot$$

Then $y(t) = ce^{\log(-t)} = -ct$, and $y(-1) = 2$ gives $-c(-1) = 2$ or $c = 2$. Hence $y(t) = -2t$, again defined for all t.

(d) $\dot{y}(t) = (\cos t/\sin t)y(t) + \cos t$, $y(\pi/4) = 0$. Here $p(t) = \cos t/\sin t$. This time some care is required to obtain $P(t)$. Note that the function $\log \sin t$ has $p(t)$ as a derivative. However, $\log \sin t$ is only defined when $\sin t$ is positive, that is, for $0 < t < \pi$, $2\pi < t < 3\pi, \ldots$. Since we want to evaluate at $t = \pi/4$ we can in fact use this function, so we choose

$$P(t) = \log \sin t.$$

Then $e^{P(t)} = \sin t$ and we obtain

$$\frac{1}{\sin t}\dot{y}(t) - \frac{\cos t}{\sin^2 t}y(t) = \frac{d}{dt}\left(\frac{y(t)}{\sin t}\right) = \frac{\cos t}{\sin t}\cdot$$

The function $F_0(t) = \log \sin t$ will have the property that $\dot{F}_0(t) = \cos t/\sin t$ provided that t is in the interval $0 < t < \pi$. Hence we have

$$\frac{y(t)}{\sin t} = \log \sin t + c \qquad \text{or} \qquad y(t) = \sin t \log \sin t + c \sin t.$$

Then $y(\pi/4) = 0$ gives $0 = \sin(\pi/4)\log\sin(\pi/4) + c\sin(\pi/4)$ or $c = -\log(1/\sqrt{2})$. Hence a solution is

$$y(t) = \sin t \log \sin t - \log(1/\sqrt{2}) \sin t.$$

The reader can verify that this function is indeed a solution of the equation provided that $0 < t < \pi$.

These examples indicate that some caution is in order if p or f can become infinite. It is a good idea in such cases to check the final answer to see that it really is a solution.

It is useful to make the following observation concerning the form of the solution at step (iv) of (1.12). The first term $e^{P(t)}F_0(t)$ is itself a solution of (1.2), as can be verified directly. The second term is the most general solution of the corresponding linear homogeneous equation (1.4). This decomposition illustrates the following result.

(1.16) Proposition. *Let y_1 be some particular solution of* (1.2). *Then every solution y can be written in the form $y = y_1 + y_0$, where y_0 is a solution of* (1.4) [*and hence has the form $y_0(t) = ce^{P(t)}$ for some constant c*].

Proof. Let y_1 be a solution of (1.2) and let y be any other solution. Then we have

$$\begin{aligned}\frac{d}{dt}\big(y(t) - y_1(t)\big) &= \dot{y}(t) - \dot{y}_1(t) = p(t)y(t) + f(t) - p(t)y_1(t) - f(t)\\ &= p(t)\big(y(t) - y_1(t)\big).\end{aligned}$$

Hence the difference $y_0 = y - y_1$ must be a solution of (1.4). ▮

This proposition is a special case of a more general result to be discussed in later chapters. Its immediate interest here is that sometimes one can find a particular solution y_1 of (1.2) by some device which is simpler than the one we described in (1.12). Then (1.16) shows that this special solution combined with solutions of the homogeneous equation yields all solutions of (1.2).

(1.17) Examples. Particular Solutions

(a) $\dot{y}(t) = 3y(t) - 2$. By inspection the constant function $y_1(t) = \frac{2}{3}$ is one solution. The linear homogeneous equation, $\dot{y}(t) = 3y(t)$ has ce^{3t} as its general solution. Hence the most general solution of the linear nonhomogeneous equation is $\frac{2}{3} + ce^{3t}$. The constant c must then be determined by another condition.

(b) $\dot{y}(t) = -2y(t) + e^t$. We try to get a solution y_1 which is simply a multiple of e^t, that is, $y_1(t) = \alpha e^t$. Then we must have

$$\dot{y}(t) = \alpha e^t = -2\alpha e^t + e^t, \text{ so } \alpha = \tfrac{1}{3} \text{ and } y_1(t) = \tfrac{1}{3}e^t.$$

(c) $\dot{y}(t) = y(t) + \cos t$. We try to get a solution in the form

$$y(t) = A\cos t + B\sin t.$$

Then we find

$$\dot{y}(t) = -A\sin t + B\cos t = A\cos t + B\sin t + \cos t.$$

We equate coefficients of $\cos t$ and $\sin t$ and obtain

$$-A = B,\ B = A + 1 \qquad \text{or} \qquad A = -\tfrac{1}{2},\ B = \tfrac{1}{2}.$$

There are a great variety of such special solutions, mainly in the case where p is a constant and f is a combination of polynomials and exponential and trigonometric functions (problem 6). This procedure for obtaining a solution of a linear nonhomogeneous equation is called the *method of undetermined coefficients*.

(1.18) Remark. The reader will observe that the auxiliary conditions given for equations (0.1), (1.4), and (1.2) were all the same: the specification of the solution at some particular value of t. The feature that these three equations have in common is that they are all of first order. It turns out that for a first-order equation, the specification of the solution at one point is almost always the appropriate condition. It will also be seen that *in general* the number and type of auxiliary conditions to be given is determined solely by the order of the differential equation.

As a final part of this section, we want to comment on the reason the term "linear" is attached to equations of the form (1.2). The results of this section show that if t_0 is a fixed number and if we specify a continuous function f and a number a, then we are guaranteed that there is one and only one solution y of (1.2) such that $y(t_0) = a$. These uniqueness and existence theorems yield two examples of what are called "linear transformations". This is an extremely important idea and will be discussed in detail in Chapter 8. Take the function p to be fixed once and for all in what follows. Now let us fix the function f and examine the solutions y of (1.2) for different choices of the initial value a. For each a we have a unique y. We call this a *transformation* from the vector space $\mathcal{R}^1$ of real numbers into the vector space of continuous functions. (Observe that a different choice of f would result in a different transformation.) For this transformation the input is the value the solution is to have at $t = t_0$ and the output is the corresponding solution of (1.2). The following describes one reason that the term linear is attached to (1.2).

(1.19) Proposition. *Let y_1 and y_2 be solutions of* (1.4) *such that* $y_1(t_0) = a_1$ *and* $y_2(t_0) = a_2$. *Then the function* $\alpha_1 y_1 + \alpha_2 y_2$ *is the solution of* (1.4) *such that* $y(t_0) = \alpha_1 a_1 + \alpha_2 a_2$.

This states that when f is zero, the transformation above is *linear* [see example (1.3) of Chapter 8]. When f is not identically zero, this transformation is *not* linear (see problem 10).

A second transformation arises if we fix the value of a and let f vary. For each continuous function f we have a unique y. Thus we now have a transformation from the vector space of continuous functions to itself. For this transformation the input is the continuous function f and the output is the solution y of (1.2) for that f satisfying $y(t_0) = a$. (Thus a different choice of a would result in a different transformation.) Again there is a kind of linearity attached to this transformation.

(1.20) Proposition. *Let y_1 and y_2 be solutions of* (1.2) *for* $f = f_1$ *and* $f = f_2$, *respectively, which satisfy* $y_1(t_0) = 0$ *and* $y_2(t_0) = 0$. *Then the function* $y = \alpha_1 y_1 + \alpha_2 y_2$ *is a solution of* (1.2) *with* $f = \alpha_1 f_1 + \alpha_2 f_2$ *and* $y(t_0) = 0$.

This proposition states that the above transformation is linear if $a = 0$. When a is not zero, the transformation is not linear [problem 10(d)]. The reader is asked in problem 10 to prove propositions (1.19) and (1.20).

PROBLEMS

1. Find the solutions of each of the following differential equation problems.

   (a) $\dot{y}(t) = 3ty(t), \quad y(0) = 2$
   (b) $\dot{y}(t) = -\sin ty(t), \quad y(\pi) = 1$
   (c) $\dot{y}(t) = e^{-3t}y(t), \quad y(0) = 1$
   (d) $\dot{y}(t) = te^{t^2}y(t) + t, \quad y(0) = 0$
   (e) $\dot{y}(t) = -2y(t) + e^{-t}, \quad y(-1) = 1$

2. In example (1.3a) show that the speed of the falling particle approaches mg/k as t becomes large.
3. In example (1.3b) show that if $E(t)$ equals $E_0 \cos \omega t$ for some constant ω, then the current approaches $(E_0/R) \cos \omega t$ as t becomes large.
4. In example (1.3a) suppose the particle is initially thrown upward with a velocity $\mathbf{v}_0$. Find an expression for the distance the particle goes upward before coming to a stop in terms of g, m, k, and $\mathbf{v}_0$. Assume the same resistance law.

5. If $E(t)$ is zero identically in example (1.3b), show, without solving the equation, that the current is either identically zero or never zero.

6. Find particular solutions of the following differential equations in the form indicated.

(a) $\dot{y}(t) = 2y(t) + t + 1, \quad y(t) = At + B$

(b) $\dot{y}(t) = 2y(t) + t^2 - t + 2, \quad y(t) = At^2 + Bt + C$

(c) $\dot{y}(t) = y(t) + e^{2t}, \quad y(t) = Ae^{2t}$

(d) $\dot{y}(t) = -y(t) + \cos 3t - \sin t,$
$y(t) = A \cos 3t + B \sin 3t + C \cos t + D \sin t$

(e) $\dot{y}(t) = y(t) + te^{2t}, \quad y(t) = (At + B)e^{2t}$

7. (a) Show that one *cannot* find a solution of the following equations in the form indicated.

$$\begin{aligned} \dot{y}(t) &= y(t) + e^t, & y(t) &= Ae^t \\ \dot{y}(t) &= -2y(t) + e^{-2t}, & y(t) &= Ae^{-2t} \\ \dot{y}(t) &= ky(t) + e^{kt}, & y(t) &= Ae^{kt}. \end{aligned}$$

Observe that in each case the function $f(t)$ is itself a solution of the corresponding homogeneous equation. We shall encounter a generalization of this situation in a later chapter.

(b) Show that in each case one *can* obtain a solution having the form $e^{P(t)}F_0(t)$, where this denotes the first term in (1.13).

8. Find solutions of each of the following problems [see examples (1.15)].

(a) $\dot{y}(t) = \dfrac{1}{t^2} y(t), \; y(\pi) = 1$

(b) $\dot{y}(t) = (\cot t)y(t) + \dfrac{1}{\csc t}, \; y(\pi/4) = 0$

(c) $\dot{y}(t) = \dfrac{\cos t}{\sin t} y(t) + \cos t, \; y(3\pi/4) = 0$

9. Consider the equation $\dot{y}(t) = (1/t)y(t)$. Suppose y is a solution throughout some interval $a < t < b$ with $a < 0$, $b > 0$. Show then that $y(0)$ must be zero. Hence here we cannot specify $y(0) = a$ arbitrarily.

10. (a) Prove propositions (1.19) and (1.20).

(b) Illustrate proposition (1.19) by calculating the solutions of the following three problems

$$\dot{y}_1(t) = ty_1(t), \quad y_1(1) = -1; \qquad \dot{y}_2(t) = ty_2(t), \quad y_2(1) = 2;$$
$$\dot{y}(t) = ty(t), \quad y(1) = 1.$$

(c) Illustrate proposition (1.20) by an example.

(d) Show that if $\dot{y}_1(t) = y_1(t) + 1, y_1(0) = 1$ and $\dot{y}_2(t) = y_2(t) + t, y_2(0) = 0$, then $y_1(t) - 2y_2(t)$ is *not* a solution of $\dot{y}(t) = y(t) + 1 - 2t$ satisfying $y(0) = 1 + 0 = 1$.

11. Show that if $\dot{y}(t) = (3t^2 + e^{1+4t^2} + \sin t)y(t)$ and $y(-1) = 2$, then $y(t)$ can never be zero.

12. If $y_1(t)$ and $y_2(t)$ are both solutions of the equation

$$\dot{y}(t) = e^{t^2}y(t) + \sin t$$

and $y_1(2) > y_2(2)$, show that $y_1(t)$ will always be greater than $y_2(t)$. (*Hint:* Consider the equation satisfied by $y_1 - y_2$.)

13. Give a proof of proposition (1.10).

14. Solve when possible, and discuss uniqueness:

(a) $\dot{y}(t) - \frac{1}{t}y(t) = 0,\ y(0) = 1$

(b) $\dot{y}(t) - \frac{1}{t}y(t) = 0,\ y(0) = 0$

(c) $\dot{y}(t) + \frac{1}{t}y(t) = 0,\ y(0) = 1$

(d) $\dot{y}(t) + \frac{1}{t}y(t) = 0,\ y(0) = 0$

(e) $\dot{y}(t) - \frac{1}{t^{1/3}}y(t) = 0,\ y(0) = a$

2. First-Order Nonlinear Equations

In §1 we referred to the differential equation (1.2) as a linear nonhomogeneous differential equation. However, it is also desirable to apply the term *linear differential equation* in the following way:

(2.1) Definition. A differential equation (of any order) is called a **solution-linear** differential equation if whenever y_1 and y_2 are solutions then any function of the form

$$y = \alpha y_1 + \beta y_2 \qquad \alpha, \beta \text{ constants},$$

is also a solution. Equations not satisfying this condition we will call **nonlinear**. The term **solution-linear** will usually be contracted to **s-linear**.

There are a number of observations to make about this definition.

(i) The definition *concerns the equation only*. It has nothing to do with initial conditions.

(ii) The linear homogeneous equation (1.4) *is* s-linear according to definition (2.1). Indeed since both y_1 and y_2 satisfy (1.4), we have

$$\begin{aligned}\dot{y}(t) &= \frac{d}{dt}\big(\alpha y_1(t) + \beta y_2(t)\big) = \alpha\dot{y}_1(t) + \beta\dot{y}_2(t) = \alpha p(t)y_1(t) + \beta p(t)y_2(t)\\ &= p(t)\big(\alpha y_1(t) + \beta y_2(t)\big) = p(t)y(t).\end{aligned}$$

(iii) The linear nonhomogeneous equation is *not* s-linear according to (2.1) unless $f(t)$ is identically equal to zero. Thus we have the slightly paradoxical situation notationally that a "linear nonhomogeneous" equation is "nonlinear"!

(iv) The kind of linearity in (2.1) is related to the kind of linearity in the first part of proposition (1.19). Again, we leave this as a problem (problem 2).

(2.2) Example. A Nonlinear Equation. Note that $y_1(t) = 1/t$ is a solution of $\dot{y}(t) = -y(t)^2$ and so is $y_2(t) = 0$, but $y(t) = 2y_1(t) + 1y_2(t) = 2/t$ does not satisfy $\dot{y}(t) = -y(t)^2$. Hence $\dot{y}(t) = -y(t)^2$ is nonlinear.

It will be seen presently that nonlinear equations have some very unpleasant properties as compared to s-linear ones. First, though, let us recall that examples with equations of the form (1.2) revealed that one must exercise care whenever the functions p and f have discontinuities. Here is another example illustrating this point.

(2.3) Example. A Discontinuous Linear Equation. Find the solution of the linear homogeneous equation $\dot{y}(t) = -(1/t)y(t)$ such that $y(1) = 1$. One can go through the process of §1 and one will find that the solution is $y(t) = 1/t$. Note that this function becomes infinite at $t = 0$.

The above example illustrates a general principle about linear nonhomogeneous equations which we shall not attempt to prove. In fact, we shall only state it in a very vague way. Namely, trouble with the solutions can arise *only* at points where either p or f or both become discontinuous. Thus one is always forewarned of difficulties with linear nonhomogeneous equations.

Usually the situation with nonlinear equations is very different. Difficulties in the solution can arise without any apparent reason. We illustrate with some further examples. Later in this section we will see how these solutions were obtained.

(2.4) Examples. Discontinuous Solutions (Nonlinear Equations)

(a) $\dot{y}(t) = -y^2(t), \quad y(t_0) = a, \quad a \neq 0$. A solution is

$$y(t) = \big(t - t_0 + (1/a)\big)^{-1}.$$

This solution becomes infinite when $t = t_0 - (1/a)$. Note that if $y(t_0) = 0$, then a solution is $y(t) \equiv 0$.

(b) $\dot{y}(t) = -e^{-y(t)}$, $y(t_0) = a$. A solution is $y(t) = \log(t_0 - t + e^a)$. This becomes infinite at $t = t_0 + e^a$.

Observe that in both of these cases the functions that occur on the right sides are perfectly well behaved for all possible values of $y(t)$. Hence there is no advance warning that discontinuities in the solution should arise.

A second major difficulty with nonlinear equations is that the uniqueness of the solution may be lost. Again we give an example.

(2.5) Example. Nonuniqueness

$$\dot{y}(t) = \sqrt{y(t)}, \qquad y(0) = 0.$$

One solution of this problem is clearly $y(t) \equiv 0$. However, there is also another solution, $y(t) = \frac{1}{4}t^2$, $t \geq 0$. Even worse, there are a whole family of solutions, as we indicate now (Figure 4.3).

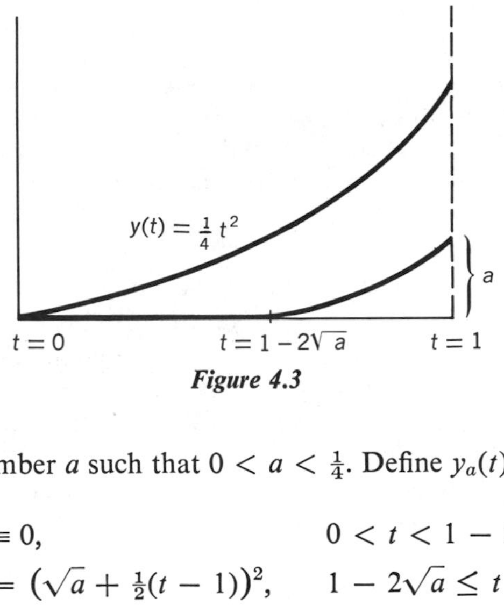

Figure 4.3

Choose any number a such that $0 < a < \frac{1}{4}$. Define $y_a(t)$ by the formula

$$\begin{aligned} y_a(t) &\equiv 0, && 0 < t < 1 - 2\sqrt{a} \\ y_a(t) &= (\sqrt{a} + \tfrac{1}{2}(t-1))^2, && 1 - 2\sqrt{a} \leq t \leq 1. \end{aligned}$$

With a little calculation one can verify that this function satisfies $\dot{y}(t) = \sqrt{y(t)}$, $y(0) = 0$. Hence there is one solution for each a!

In contrast to example (2.5), which involves a breakdown in uniqueness, examples (2.4) represent a breakdown in the *existence* of a solution. Thus, although the solutions we gave there do exist for a certain interval of time before and after t_0, they do not exist for all t. One might ask whether there are any other solutions which satisfy the same equations and the same initial conditions but do not become infinite. That is, one might be willing to give up uniqueness of the solution to obtain existence. In fact, there are no other solutions in these two cases, so existence is definitely lost.

The examples given are rather disturbing from the point of view of mechanics. To illustrate this fact we now give an interpretation of a more general class of first-order equations which resemble that of example (1.3a). Suppose a particle of unit mass moves along a straight line under the action of a force which acts in the direction of $-\mathbf{v}$, where $\mathbf{v}$ is the velocity and has a magnitude which is a function F of $\|\mathbf{v}\|$. As in example (1.3a) we write $\mathbf{r}(t) = \rho(t)\mathbf{e}_1$ and $\mathbf{v}(t) = \dot{\rho}(t)\mathbf{e}_1$. Then $\|\mathbf{v}(t)\| = |\dot{\rho}(t)|$ and the equation of motion assumes the form

$$\ddot{\rho}(t) = F(|\dot{\rho}(t)|)$$

or, if we set $\dot{\rho}(t) = y(t)$,

$$\dot{y}(t) = F(|y(t)|). \tag{2.6}$$

Example (2.4a) corresponds to choosing the function F according to the formula $F(|y(t)|) = -|y(t)|^2 = -y(t)^2$. (An illustration would be an air resistance assumed to be proportional to the square of the speed.) Suppose that we know that at time $t_0 = 0$ the particle has velocity $a > 0$. Then as in example (2.4a) we find that $\dot{\rho}(t) = (t + (1/a))^{-1}$. For $t > 0$ this formula says that the particle simply slows down as time increases and everything is quite reasonable. Observe, however, that the particle cannot possibly have been moving under the same force law for all past time. For if it had then we would also have $\dot{\rho}(t) = (t + (1/a))^{-1}$ for $t < 0$, which means that at the time $t = -1/a$ its speed would have been infinite.

Example (2.5) corresponds to choosing F according to the formula $F(|y(t)|) = \sqrt{y(t)}$, under the assumption that $y(t)$ is nonnegative. Suppose that we know that the particle is at rest at time $t_0 = 0$. Then by example (2.5) we could have $\dot{\rho}(t) \equiv 0$ or $\dot{\rho}(t) = \frac{1}{4}t^2$ or any of the functions of Figure 4.3. There is nothing in our equations which will tell us which motion is actually going to occur.

The above discussion gives some hint as to how existence and uniqueness theorems may be of use in physical problems. If a problem is formulated in terms of a differential equation, then a kind of check on the validity of the formulation is provided by such theorems. If either uniqueness or existence fails one should seriously question the formulation.

The examples we have given are all drawn from a certain class of equations. This is an important class since it provides examples and also covers many equations in physics, including all those of the form (2.6). We want to discuss this class now. The equations to be considered have the form

$$\dot{y}(t) = p(t)Y(y(t)). \tag{2.7}$$

Note that their special feature is that the right sides all have the form of a product of a function p of t and a function Y of y. These equations are called *separable*.

There is a formal procedure for the solution of (2.7). Let us write the equation in the form

$$\frac{1}{Y(y(t))}\,\dot{y}(t) = p(t). \tag{2.8}$$

Now suppose that M is a function *of the variable* y which has the property that for each y in some range $\alpha < y < \beta$ we have

$$\frac{dM(y)}{dy} = \frac{1}{Y(y)}. \tag{2.9}$$

Then we can apply the chain rule for differentiation to deduce that

$$\frac{d}{dt}\,M(y(t)) = \left(\frac{dM(y)}{dy}\right)\bigg|_{y=y(t)}\dot{y}(t) = \frac{1}{Y(y(t))}\,\dot{y}(t).$$

Hence (2.8) can be written

$$\frac{d}{dt}\,M(y(t)) = p(t). \tag{2.10}$$

Suppose next that P is a function *of the variable* t such that its derivative with respect to t is p; that is, $\dot{P}(t) = p(t)$. Then, by (2.10),

$$\frac{d}{dt}\,M(y(t)) = \frac{d}{dt}\,P(t) \qquad \text{or} \qquad M(y(t)) = P(t) + c, \tag{2.11}$$

where c is a constant.

The second equation in (2.11) is what is called an *implicit solution* of (2.7). The idea is the following. Fix the constant c. Then for each t suppose that one can solve equation (2.11) for $y(t)$. This will yield a function y which, hopefully, will be a solution of (2.7). Let us illustrate by showing how we obtained the solutions in examples (2.4) and (2.5).

(2.12) Examples. Separable Equations

(a) $\dot{y}(t) = -y(t)^2$, $y(t_0) = a$. This has the form (2.7) with $Y(y) = y^2$ and $p(t) = -1$. Thus we can choose $M(y) = -1/y$ and $P(t) = -t$. Then (2.11) becomes

$$-\frac{1}{y(t)} = -t + c \qquad \text{or} \qquad y(t) = \frac{1}{t - c}.$$

We evaluate the constant c by the condition $y(t_0) = a$ and obtain

$$-\frac{1}{a} = -t_0 + c \qquad \text{or} \qquad c = t_0 - \frac{1}{a}.$$

Hence

$$y(t) = \frac{1}{t - t_0 + (1/a)},$$

which is the solution we gave.

(b) $\dot{y}(t) = -e^{-y(t)}$, $y(t_0) = a$. Here we have $Y(y) = e^{-y}$ with $p(t) = -1$. Hence we can choose $P(t) = -t$ and $M(y) = e^y$ [since $(d/dy)e^y = e^y = 1/Y(y)$]. Thus (2.11) becomes

$$e^{y(t)} = -t + c.$$

Then $y(t_0) = a$ yields

$$e^a = -t_0 + c \qquad \text{or} \qquad c = e^a + t_0.$$

Hence

$$y(t) = \log(t_0 + a^a - t).$$

(c) $\dot{y} = \sqrt{y(t)}$, $y(0) = 0$. Here $Y(y) = \sqrt{y}$ and $p(t) = 1$. Hence we can choose $M(y) = 2\sqrt{y}$ and $P(t) = t$. Thus (2.11) yields

$$2\sqrt{y(t)} = t + c.$$

Then $y(0) = 0$ yields $c = 0$, so that $y(t) = \frac{1}{4}t^2$. Thus we obtain *one* of the solutions in (2.5) by this process but not the others.

(d) $\dot{y}(t) = p(t)y(t)$, $y(t_0) = a$. This is simply the linear homogeneous equation (1.4) together with the initial condition (1.5). We show here that we can obtain the solution of this equation by the above procedure. Here $Y(y) = y$. Hence we can choose $M(y) = \log y$. Thus if P is such that $\dot{P}(t) = p(t)$, then (2.11) becomes

$$\log y(t) = P(t) + c.$$

The condition $y(t_0) = a$ yields $\log a = P(t_0) + c$ or $c = \log a - P(t_0)$. Thus we have

$$\log y(t) = P(t) + \log a - P(t_0) \qquad \text{or} \qquad y(t) = ae^{P(t)-P(t_0)}.$$

Note that the equation (1.2) is *not* separable unless $f(t) \equiv 0$.

The procedure we have outlined for separable equations has various difficulties associated with it. We have seen in the examples that it can give rise to solutions which exist only over a finite interval of time and eventually become infinite. Also we have seen that it may give rise to only one solution when actually there is more than one. In addition, the problem of solving equation (2.11) may be quite complicated. We illustrate by two further examples.

(2.13) Examples. Separable Equations (Continued)

(a) $\dot{y}(t) = t/y(t), y(0) = 1$. Here $Y(y) = 1/y$, so a suitable $M(y)$ is $\frac{1}{2}y^2$. $p(t)$ is t, so we can take $P(t) = t^2/2$. Thus (2.11) becomes

$$\tfrac{1}{2}y(t)^2 = \tfrac{1}{2}t^2 + c.$$

Then $y(0) = 1$ gives $c = \frac{1}{2}$ and hence we have

$$y(t)^2 = t^2 + 1.$$

Now we have two choices of $y(t)$ for each t,

$$y_1(t) = \sqrt{1 + t^2} \qquad \text{and} \qquad y_2(t) = -\sqrt{1 + t^2}.$$

The reader can verify that each of these satisfies the differential equation but only $y_1(t)$ satisfies the initial condition. This example shows that equation (2.11) may give rise to extraneous solutions of the differential equation which do not satisfy the initial condition. Hence one should always verify that a supposed solution really does satisfy the differential equation and the initial conditions.

(b) $\dot{y}(t) = \left(2y(t)^2 e^{y(t)^2} + e^{y(t)^2}\right)^{-1}, y(t_0) = a$. Here $p(t) = 1$ but $Y(y)$ is the complicated function

$$Y(y) = (2y^2 e^{y^2} + e^{y^2})^{-1}.$$

One can check that a suitable $M(y)$ is $M(y) = ye^{y^2}$. Thus (2.11) becomes

$$y(t)e^{y(t)^2} = t + c, \tag{2.14}$$

and the condition $y(t_0) = a$ yields

$$ae^{a^2} = t_0 + c \qquad \text{or} \qquad c = ae^{a^2} - t_0.$$

Thus (2.14) becomes

$$y(t)e^{y(t)^2} - ae^{a^2} = t - t_0. \tag{2.15}$$

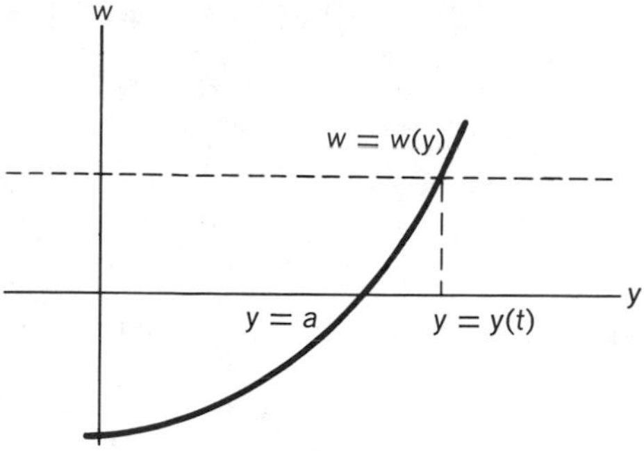

Figure 4.4

It is now a real question as to whether or not it is possible to solve (2.15) for $y(t)$. We show that it is indeed possible but this requires a rather complicated argument. Consider Figure 4.4. Let w be the function of y defined by $w(y) = ye^{y^2} - ae^{a^2}$. The curve $w = w(y)$ is plotted in Figure 4.4. Note that $w'(y) = 2y^2e^{y^2} + e^{y^2} > 0$, so that $w(y)$ is monotone increasing. Moreover, $w(y) \to \infty$ as $y \to \infty$ and $w(y) \to -\infty$ as $y \to -\infty$. Hence the curve $w = w(y)$ will intersect any line $w = t - t_0$ in exactly one point $y = y(t)$. This function will be the solution of (2.15).

PROBLEMS

1. State whether the following equations are s-linear or nonlinear.

(a) $\dot{y}(t) = 2y(t) + ty(t)$
(b) $\dot{y}(t) = 2y(t) + ty(t) + 1$
(c) $\dot{y}(t) = e^{y(t)}$
(d) $\dot{y}(t) = \sin y(t)$
(e) $\ddot{y}(t) + 2t\dot{y}(t) + y(t) = 0$
(f) $\ddot{y}(t) + 2y(t)^2 = 0$

2. If a first-order equation is s-linear and y_1 and y_2 are solutions such that $y_1(t_0) = a_1$ and $y_2(t_0) = a_2$, show that $y = \alpha_1 y_1 + \alpha_2 y_2$ is a solution such that $y(t_0) = \alpha_1 a_1 + \alpha_2 a_2$.

3. Find solutions of the following problems. In each case state for what values of t the solution exists and verify that it is a solution in this range.

(a) $\dot{y}(t) = e^{-y(t)}$, $y(0) = 0$

(b) $\dot{y}(t) = y(t)^2$, $y(0) = 1$

(c) $\dot{y}(t) = y(t)^3$, $y(0) = 1$

(d) $\dot{y}(t) = \dfrac{1}{y(t)e^{y(t)^2}}$, $y(0) = 1$

(e) $\dot{y}(t) = \dfrac{t}{y(t)^2}$, $y(1) = \frac{1}{3}$

(f) $\dot{y}(t) = \dfrac{\sqrt{1 - y(t)^2}}{y(t)}$, $y(0) = \frac{1}{2}$

[What would be the answer in (f) if one required that $y(0) = 2$?]

*4. A particle starts from rest and falls under gravity. It is subject to a frictional force which opposes the motion and has a magnitude proportional to the square of the magnitude of the velocity. Show that as time tends to infinity the velocity tends to a finite value (the terminal velocity).

5. A particle of unit mass moves along a line. Its velocity is $\mathbf{v}(t) = \dot{\rho}(t)\mathbf{e}_1$. It is acted on by a force of the form

$$\mathbf{F}(t) = k(\dot{\rho}(t))^n \mathbf{e}_1,$$

where n is a positive integer greater than 1, and its velocity at time t_0 is $\mathbf{v}_0 = \dot{\rho}_0 \mathbf{e}_1$. Show that the velocity will always become infinite at some sufficiently large time if any of the following sets of conditions hold:

(i) n even, $k > 0$, $\dot{\rho}_0 > 0$.
(ii) n even, $k < 0$, $\dot{\rho}_0 < 0$.
(iii) n odd, $k > 0$, $\dot{\rho}_0 > 0$ or $\dot{\rho}_0 < 0$.

Show that if n is odd and $k < 0$, the velocity always decreases as t increases for $t > t_0$ and, in fact, that the velocity tends to zero as $t \to \infty$ no matter what $\dot{\rho}_0$ is. Explain these results physically.

6. Consider the problem

$$\dot{y}(t) = p(t)(y(t))^{\alpha}, \qquad y(0) = 0.$$

Show that for certain values of α at least two distinct solutions exist.

7. Find two distinct solutions of the following problems.

(a) $\dot{y}(t) = \sqrt{1 - y(t)},\ y(1) = 1$

(b) $\dot{y}(t) = \dfrac{\sqrt{\sin y}}{\cos y},\ y(0) = 0$

(c) $\dot{y}(t) = (y(t) + 2)^{1/4},\ y(-1) = -2$

8. In each of the following examples show by means of a graph those values of t for which equation (2.11) can be solved for $y(t)$.

(a) $\dot{y}(t) = e^t e^{y(t)},\ y(0) = 0$

(b) $\dot{y}(t) = \dfrac{1}{1 + \log y(t)},\ y(0) = 1$

3. The Method of Successive Approximations

The examples of §2 show that not all differential equations have unique solutions existing for all t. In mechanics this means that if one specifies force laws in an arbitrary way one cannot expect that the differential equations of motion will predict a uniquely determined motion existing for all time. There may be several possible motions of a particle, or a given one may have the property that its velocity becomes arbitrarily large after a finite time.

In this section we are going to study the general differential equation

$$\dot{y}(t) = f(t, y(t)) \tag{3.1}$$

subject to the condition

$$y(t_0) = y_0. \tag{3.2}$$

This corresponds to a force law in which the force is a function of $\dot{\mathbf{r}}$ and t; and $y(t)\mathbf{e}_1$ represents the velocity $\dot{\mathbf{r}}(t)$. Once again, though, we emphasize that we are obtaining general facts about differential equations.

What we are going to do is give conditions under which there will be unique solutions of (3.1) and (3.2) for at least some range of t values about t_0. We shall not attempt to rule out the possibility that the solution we construct will become infinite somewhere *outside* this range. In fact, the theorem is often applied in just the other way. For example, we shall see that our theorem applies to the equation $\dot{y} = y^2$ studied in §2. It shows that $(1 - t)^{-1}$ gives *the* solution satisfying $y(0) = 1$. Hence the velocity of a motion produced by this force law *must* become infinite at $t = 1$.

We shall rule out nonuniqueness. The example $\dot{y} = \sqrt{y}$ of §2 will be seen to violate the hypotheses of our theorem, which explains why uniqueness can fail for this differential equation.

The method we use is called *successive approximations*. This method occurs in many other places in mathematics. We shall illustrate another of its applications in the problems (problem 8).

It is a good idea to think of the solution of (3.1) in terms of a picture. To start with we want the equation to make sense at least at t_0, hence we want $f(t, y)$ to be defined at least at $t = t_0$, $y = y_0$. We require more than that. We assume that $f(t, y)$ is defined for points (t, y) in some region R containing (t_0, y_0) (Figure 4.5). A solution $y(t)$ of (3.1) represents a curve $y = y(t)$. Condition (3.2) states that this curve must pass through the point (t_0, y_0). Moreover, it is appropriate to say that $y(t)$ is a solution only for a time interval corresponding to points $(t, y(t))$ which are in the region where f is defined. Thus in Figure 4.5 one can hope to say $y(t)$ is a solution only in the interval $\alpha < t < \beta$.

The idea of successive approximations is as follows. A first crude guess at a solution would be to assume that $y(t) \equiv y_0$. This satisfies (3.2) but of course in general does not satisfy (3.1). Suppose we put this guess, $y \equiv y_0$, into the right side of (3.1). Then we have $f(t, y_0)$, a known function of t, on the interval $\alpha_1 \leq t \leq \beta_1$ in Figure 4.5. We denote by $y_1(t)$ the function we obtain by solving (3.1) with this (incorrect) right side, subject to condition (3.2); that is,

$$\dot{y}_1(t) = f(t, y_0), \qquad y_1(t_0) = y_0. \tag{3.1i}$$

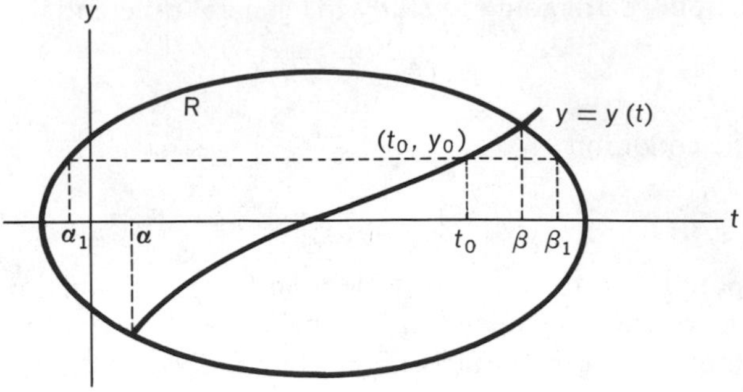

Figure 4.5

The solution is easy. This is the case treated in proposition (0.4). If $f(t, y_0)$ is continuous, then the solution is given by

$$y_1(t) = y_0 + \int_{t_0}^{t} f(\tau, y_0)\, d\tau. \tag{3.3}$$

The next step is to repeat this process. That is we substitute $y_1(t)$ into the right side of (3.1). This gives $f(t, y_1(t))$, a new (known) function of t. Then we determine $y_2(t)$ as the solution of (3.1) with this new right side, still subject to (3.2); that is,

$$\dot{y}_2(t) = f(t, y_1(t)), \qquad y_2(t_0) = y_0. \tag{3.1ii}$$

Now of course there is a new difficulty, as we see in Figure 4.6. That is, $f(t, y_1(t))$ is defined only for t values such that $(t, y_1(t))$ lies in R, namely $\alpha_2 \leq t \leq \beta_2$ in Figure 4.6. Hence we can define y_2 only in this interval. y_2 is easy to find there though. Again it is simply

$$y_2(t) = y_0 + \int_{t_0}^{t} f(\tau, y_1(\tau))\, d\tau. \tag{3.4}$$

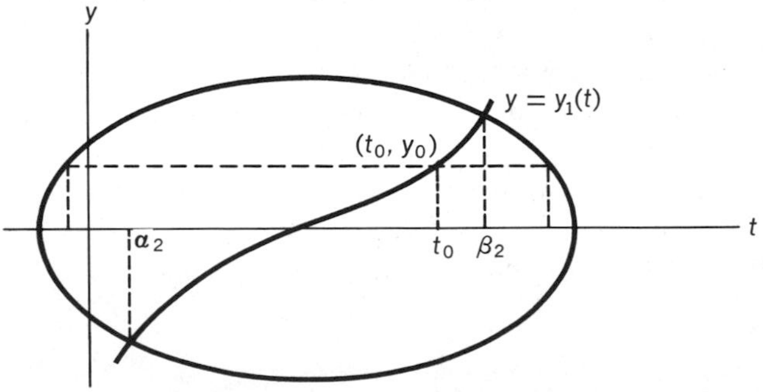

Figure 4.6

We continue the process indefinitely: once we have $y_n(t)$ we solve the equation

$$\dot{y}_{n+1}(t) = f(t, y_n(t))$$

with the condition $y_{n+1}(t_0) = y_0$. The solution is

$$y_{n+1}(t) = y_0 + \int_{t_0}^{t} f(\tau, y_n(\tau))\, d\tau. \tag{3.5}$$

Of course there remains the problem that the functions $f(\tau, y_n(\tau))$ may be defined on different τ intervals.

(3.6) Example. Successive Approximations

$$\dot{y}(t) = y(t), \qquad y(0) = 1.$$

It is easy to find the solution of this problem by the methods of §1. The solution is e^t as the reader can verify. Let us calculate the first few terms by successive approximations. Here we have $t_0 = 0$ and $y_0 = 1$ while the function $f(t, y)$ is simply y. The first guess is $y(t) \equiv 1$. Then the approximation $y_1(t)$ is, by (3.3),

$$y_1(t) = 1 + \int_0^t 1\, d\tau = 1 + t.$$

By (3.4) the second approximation is then

$$y_2(t) = 1 + \int_0^t y_1(\tau)\, d\tau = 1 + \int_0^t (1 + \tau)\, d\tau = 1 + t + \frac{t^2}{2}.$$

By (3.5), with $n = 2$, $y_3(t)$ is given by

$$y_3(t) = 1 + \int_0^t y_2(\tau)\, d\tau = 1 + \int_0^t \left(1 + \tau + \frac{\tau^2}{2}\right) d\tau$$

$$= 1 + t + \frac{t^2}{2} + \frac{t^3}{2 \cdot 3}.$$

It is possible in this case to write down a formula for $y_n(t)$ for all n. The formula is

$$y_n(t) = 1 + t + \frac{t^2}{2} + \frac{t^3}{2 \cdot 3} + \frac{t^4}{2 \cdot 3 \cdot 4} + \cdots + \frac{t^n}{n!}. \tag{3.7}$$

(One can verify this formula by mathematical induction.)

Table 4.1, which gives values of the solution and of the first, second, and third approximations, for four values of t, is quite useful in understanding what to expect of successive approximations. These results are illustrated in Figure 4.7. The underlying idea of successive approximations is illustrated

TABLE 4.1

t	e^t	$y_1(t)$	$y_2(t)$	$y_3(t)$
0	1.00	1.00	1.00	1.00
0.5	1.65	1.50	1.63	1.65
1.0	2.72	2.00	2.50	2.68
2.0	7.39	3.00	5.00	6.13

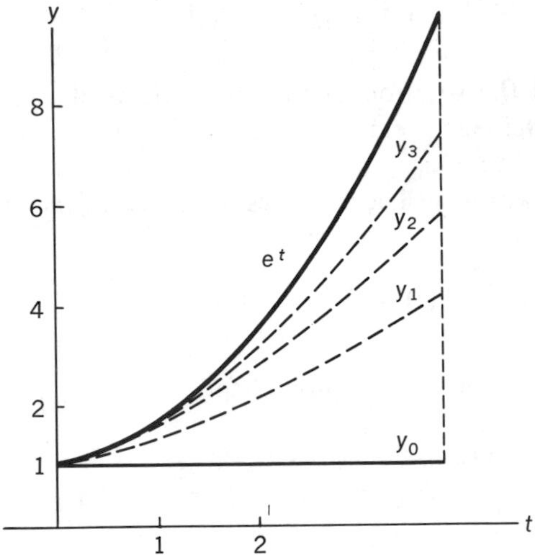

Figure 4.7

by the values in Table 4.1. At each of the values of t at which computations are made, the reader will observe that we get closer and closer to the correct value of the solution by computing y_n for larger values of n. At $t = 0, 0.5$, or 1.0, it is to be observed that $y_3(t)$ gives almost the exact answer. However, at $t = 2.0$, $y_3(t)$, although better than either $y_1(t)$ or $y_2(t)$, is still quite far from the correct result.

We can make this idea of improving the approximation more precise by using the notion of convergence of a sequence to a limit. Note that the sequence $\{y_n(t)\}$ defined by (3.7) is precisely the same sequence encountered in example (3.7b) of the Review of Calculus. We showed there that for any fixed t that sequence converges to something (and we stated that the something is e^t). This means that no matter how small an ε we prescribe we can be sure that if we calculate $y_N(t)$ by (3.7), then for N sufficiently large we shall have a number which differs from e^t by something less than ε. Not only this, but if we calculate *any other* $y_n(t)$, for $n > N$ we shall also be within ε of e^t.

Since we know explicitly the solution of the problem in example (3.6) there is not much reason for using successive approximations there. The point is, however, that we can use this technique on equations for which we do not know the solution. We hope then that the sequence of functions $y_1, y_2, \ldots$ obtained via (3.5) will be close to a solution in the same sense as these functions were close to the solution e^t of the example. The following theorem given an indication of when this program can be expected to succeed.

(3.8) Theorem. *Suppose $f(t, y)$ and $f_y(t, y)$ are continuous functions in a region R containing the point (t_0, y_0) (Figure* 4.6). *Then there exists an interval $\alpha < t < \beta$ with $\alpha < t_0$ and $\beta > t_0$ such that:*

(i) *There exists a unique solution y of equation* (3.1) *in $\alpha < t < \beta$ such that this solution satisfies* (3.2).

(ii) *For each t in $\alpha < t < \beta$ the values $y_n(t)$ of the successive approximations, as computed by* (3.3), (3.4), *and* (3.5) *converge to a number $y(t)$, and the function y defined on the interval $\alpha < t < \beta$ in this way is the solution of* (3.1) *and* (3.2).

Theorem (3.8) applies to example (3.6) since $f(t, y) = y$ and $f_y(t, y) = 1$, so that these are continuous functions in any region R containing $(t_0, y_0) = (0, 1)$.

We shall not attempt at this point to prove theorem (3.8). However, we have included a problem in which the reader is asked to establish, using theorem (3.6) of the Review of Calculus, that in fact the $y_n(t)$'s do converge to some number $y(t)$ (on an appropriate interval). That this function y will be a solution of (3.1) and (3.2) is more difficult to show.

Observe that at $t = t_0$ all the y_n's and the solution y have the same value, y_0. The reader should check his understanding of the definition of convergence [(3.3) of the Review of Calculus] by verifying that indeed the numbers $y_n(t_0)$ do have y_0 as a limit. Here, in fact, the integer N in definition (3.3) of the Review of Calculus can be chosen as $N = 1$ no matter how small ε is to be. One must be careful to observe, however, that for a given ε the number of terms $y_n(t)$ which must be computed in order to get within ε of the true solution will change as t changes. This is illustrated in Table 4.1, where it is seen that as t increases one needs more terms to attain a given accuracy.

The calculation of the interval $\alpha < t < \beta$ which appears in theorem (3.8) is a matter of considerable theoretical difficulty. We shall not attempt to study this question. Rather we simply give some further examples in this section and in the problems. The important thing at this stage is to understand the mechanics of the procedure and to understand what theorem (3.8) says. Note that it is an existence and uniqueness theorem for the problem in question, and that it also gives a constructive method for finding approximations to the solution (which is guaranteed to exist).

(3.9) Further Examples of Successive Approximations

(a) $\dot{y}(t) = -y(t)^2$, $y(0) = 1$. This is example (2.12a) of §2. From that example we know that the solution is $y(t) = 1/(t + 1)$. Let us calculate the first two approximations. Here we have $f(t, y) = -y^2$ and $f_y(t, y) = -2y$, both of which are continuous in any region around $(t_0, y_0) = (0, 1)$. We obtain

$$y_1(t) = 1 - \int_0^t 1^2\, d\tau = 1 - t$$

$$y_2(t) = 1 - \int_0^t (1 - \tau)^2\, d\tau = 1 - t + t^2 - \frac{t^3}{3}.$$

Again we use tabular form to give an indication of the values of $y_1(t)$, $y_2(t)$ and the true solution $y(t) = 1/(t + 1)$ (Table 4.2). Note again that as

TABLE 4.2

t	$y_1(t)$	$y_2(t)$	$1/(1 + t)$
0	1.00	1.00	1.00
−0.25	1.25	1.31	1.33
−0.50	1.50	1.80	2.00
−0.75	1.75	2.44	4.00
−1.00	2.00	3.33	∞

$|t - t_0|$ increases the accuracy decreases and that the first two successive approximations fail altogether to predict the fact that the solution is infinite at $t = -1$.

(b) $\dot{y}(t) = 2t/y^2$, $y(1) = 1$. Here we have $f(t, y) = 2t/y^2$ and $f_y(t, y) = -4t/y^3$. These functions are continuous in any region R about $(t_0, y_0) = (1, 1)$ provided that R lies in $y > 0$. Let us calculate the first approximation. We have

$$y_1(t) = 1 + \int_1^t \left(\frac{2\tau}{1^2}\right) d\tau = 1 + t^2 - 1 = t^2.$$

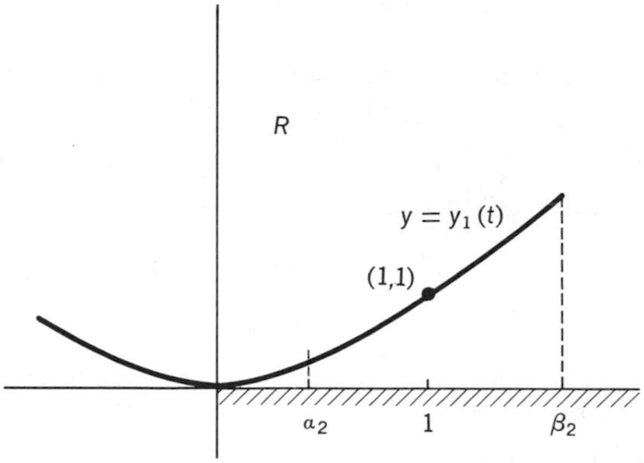

Figure 4.8

We are now confronted with the situation indicated in Figure 4.5. We indicate it again in Figure 4.8. Observe that we cannot define $f(t, y_1(t)) = 2t/y_1(t)^2 = 2t/t^4 = 2/t^3$ when $t = 0$. Hence we can calculate $y_2(t)$ only in some interval of the form $\alpha_2 < t < \beta_2$, as shown, with $\alpha_2 > 0$. For such an interval we have

$$y_2(t) = 1 + \int_1^t \left(\frac{2\tau}{\tau^4}\right) d\tau = 1 - \frac{1}{t^2} + 1 = 2 - \frac{1}{t^2}\cdot$$

Now we observe that $y_2(t)$ is zero when $t = 1/\sqrt{2}$; hence we can calculate $f(t, y_2(t)) = 2t/y_2(t)^2$ only on an interval of the form $\alpha_3 < t < \beta_3$, where $\alpha_3 > 1/\sqrt{2}$, and so on.

(c) $\dot{y}(t) = \sqrt{y(t)}$, $y(0) = 0$. This is the problem studied in example (2.5). Here we can proceed by successive approximations in a formal way. We have $f(t, y) = \sqrt{y}$ and

$$y_1(t) = 0 + \int_0^t (0)\, d\tau = 0$$

$$y_2(t) = 0 + \int_0^t y_1(\tau)\, d\tau = 0 + \int_0^t (0)\, d\tau = 0$$

and in fact all the $y_n(t)$'s are identically zero. Recall that this is one solution of the problem but that there were other solutions. The reason that these other solutions can exist without violating our theorem is that the hypothesis that $f_y(t, y) = 1/(2\sqrt{y})$ is continuous does not hold at $(t_0, y_0) = (0, 0)$.

PROBLEMS

1. Find the first two approximations for each of the following problems.

(a) $\dot{y}(t) = -2y(t), \quad y(0) = 1$

(b) $\dot{y}(t) = ty(t), \quad y(1) = 1$

(c) $\dot{y}(t) = 1 + y(t)^2, \quad y(0) = 0$

(d) $\dot{y}(t) = e^t y(t), \quad y(0) = 1$

2. Consider the problem

$$\dot{y}(t) = \sqrt{1 - t^2 - y(t)^2}, \qquad y(\tfrac{1}{2}) = 0.$$

(a) Calculate the first approximation $y_1(t)$.

(b) Determine the interval over which $y_1(t)$ can be defined and draw a sketch corresponding to Figure 4.6.

3. Consider the problem

$$\dot{y}(t) = \frac{1}{y(t)}, \qquad y(0) = 1.$$

(a) Calculate the first and second approximations y_1 and y_2.

(b) Determine the intervals over which y_1 and y_2 can be defined and draw a sketch corresponding to Figure 4.6.

4. Consider the problem

$$\dot{y}(t) = \frac{1}{t^2} y(t), \qquad y(1) = 1.$$

(a) Calculate the first and second approximations y_1 and y_2.

(b) Determine the intervals over which y_1 and y_2 can be defined and draw a sketch corresponding to Figure 4.6.

5. Consider the problem

$$\dot{y}(t) = f(t, y(t)), \qquad y(t_0) = 0.$$

Suppose that $f(t, 0) = 0$ for all t.

(a) Show that the function y with $y(t) = 0$ for *all* t is a solution.

(b) Show that the successive approximations are all the same—$y_n(t) = 0$ for all t.

6. Consider the equation $\dot{y}(t) = f(t, y(t))$, where, as in problem 5, $f(t, 0) = 0$ for all t.

(a) Assume that there is always a unique solution y of this equation such that $y(t_0) = y_0$, for any t_0 and y_0. Show that a solution y can *never* be zero unless it is identically zero. (*Hint:* If y is zero at $t = t_0$, then use problem 5 and the uniqueness of the solution.)

(b) To which of the following equations does the result of part (a) apply?

$$\dot{y}(t) = e^t \sin y(t), \qquad \dot{y}(t) = e^t \cos y(t), \qquad \dot{y}(t) = p(t)y(t)^3.$$

(c) Give an interpretation of the result in part (a) to the motion of a particle along a line under the action of a force depending only on the velocity.

7. Here is another application of the uniqueness theorem. Let $y_1(t)$ and $y_2(t)$ be solutions of $\dot{y}_1 = \sqrt{y_1^2 - 1}$, $y_1(0) = 1$; $\dot{y}_2 = \sqrt{y_2^2 + 1}$, $y_2(0) = 0$. Assuming that the uniqueness theorem holds, show that $\dot{y}_1 = y_2$. (*Hint:* Show that $\dot{y}_1$ satisfies the same equation and initial condition as y_2. Argue in a similar way that $\dot{y}_2 = y_1$. What are the functions y_1 and y_2?)

8. THE METHOD OF SUCCESSIVE APPROXIMATIONS IN A DIFFERENT SETTING. To find a solution of the equation

$$x = 1 + e^{-x},$$

define

$$x_0 = 1, \qquad x_{n+1} = 1 + e^{-x_n}, \qquad n = 0, 1, 2, \ldots.$$

(i) Calculate x_n for $n \leq 4$ to two decimal places and see how close x_4 is to an answer.

(ii) Do the same for

$$x = -1 + e^{-x} \qquad (x_0 = -1,\ x_{n+1} = -1 + e^{-x_n}).$$

(iii) Draw a picture and explain what is happening in the two cases.

9. (a) Suppose

$$(*) \qquad y_n(t) \geq M \qquad \text{for all } n,$$

and that

$$\lim_{n\to\infty} y_n(t) = y(t).$$

Show that if $y(t) = M - \delta$, where $\delta > 0$, all $y_n(t)$'s for n sufficiently large would have to be less than $M - \delta/2$, which would contradict $(*)$. Hence $y(t)$ must be $\geq M$ also.

(b) Consider the problem

$$\dot{y}(t) = y(t)^2, \qquad y(0) = 1.$$

Show that all the approximations $y_n(t)$ for $n \geq 1$ satisfy $y_n(t) \geq 1 + t$. Assuming that successive approximations works, deduce from this and part (a) that the solution $y(t)$ satisfies $y(t) \geq 1 + t$.

10. Consider Figure 4.9. Let R denote the rectangle $|t - t_0| \leq \alpha$, $|y - y_0| \leq \gamma$. Suppose $f(t, y)$ is defined and continuous in R and that

$$|f(t, y)| \leq \frac{\gamma}{\alpha} \qquad \text{for all } (t, y) \text{ in } R.$$

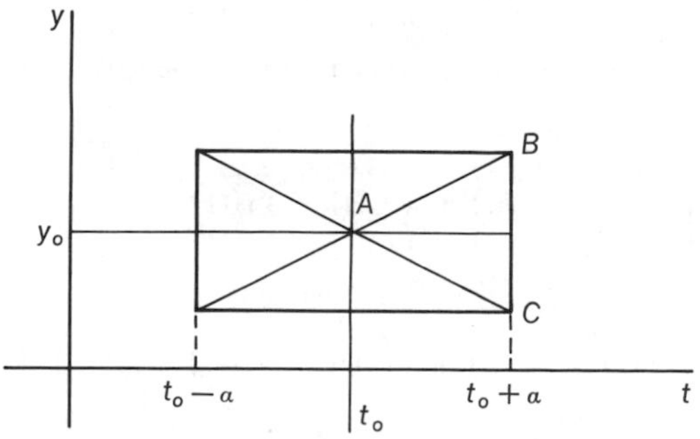

Figure 4.9

(a) Show that the function $y_1(t)$ defined by (3.3) satisfies

$$|y_1(t) - y_0| \leq \frac{\gamma}{\alpha}(t - t_0) \qquad \text{for } t_0 \leq t \leq t_0 + \alpha.$$

This states that the points $(t, y_1(t))$ for $t_0 \leq t \leq t_0 + \alpha$ are inside triangle ABC, hence are in R.

(b) Given that the points $(t, y_n(t))$ are in R for all t in $t_0 \leq t \leq t_0 + \alpha$, show that the function $y_{n+1}(t)$ defined by (3.5) satisfies the same inequality as y_1 in (a). Parts (a) and (b) together show that all the successive approximations y_n are such that the points $(t, y_n(t))$ are in triangle ABC for $t_0 \leq t \leq t_0 + \alpha$.

(c) Suppose that there is a constant k such that $|f_y(t, y)| \leq k$ for all (t, y) in R. Use the law of the mean [0 — (1.5)] to show that if the points (t, y) and (t, y') are in triangle ABC, then

$$|f(t, y') - f(t, y)| \leq k|y' - y|.$$

(d) Subtract (3.3) from (3.4) and obtain

$$y_2(t) - y_1(t) = \int_{t_0}^{t} \left(f(\tau, y_1(\tau)) - f(\tau, y_0(\tau))\right) d\tau, \qquad t_0 \leq t \leq t_0 + \alpha.$$

Now we know that the points $(\tau, y_1(\tau))$ and $(\tau, y_0(\tau))$ all are in triangle ABC for $t_0 \leq \tau \leq t_0 + \alpha$. Use this fact, part (a), and part (b) to deduce that

$$|y_2(t) - y_1(t)| \leq k\frac{\gamma}{\alpha}\int_{t_0}^{t} (\tau - t_0)\, d\tau = \frac{k\gamma}{2\alpha}(t - t_0)^2, \qquad t_0 \leq t \leq t_0 + \alpha.$$

(e) Subtract equations (3.5) for $n = 2$ and $n = 1$ and obtain

$$y_3(t) - y_2(t) = \int_{t_0}^{t} \left(f(\tau, y_2(\tau)) - f(\tau, y_1(\tau))\right) d\tau.$$

Repeat the argument of part (e) to show that

$$|y_3(t) - y_2(t)| \leq \frac{\gamma}{\alpha}\frac{1}{2 \cdot 3}k^2(t - t_0)^3, \qquad t_0 \leq t \leq t_0 + \alpha.$$

(f) By the same arguments show that in general

$$|y_{n+1}(t) - y_n(t)| \leq \frac{\gamma}{\alpha}\frac{1}{2 \cdot 3 \cdots n + 1}k^n(t - t_0)^{n+1}, \qquad t_0 \leq t \leq t_0 + \alpha.$$

(g) Fix t in $t_0 \leq t \leq t_0 + \alpha$. Consider the sequence defined by

$$\begin{aligned}
a_1 &= y_0 \\
a_2 &= y_0(t) + (y_1(t) - y_0) \\
a_3 &= y_0(t) + (y_1(t) - y_0) + (y_2(t) - y_1(t)) \\
a_4 &= y_0(t) + (y_1(t) - y_0) + (y_2(t) - y_1(t)) + (y_3(t) - y_2(t)) \\
&\vdots \\
a_{n+1} &= y_0(t) + (y_1(t) - y_0) + (y_2(t) - y_1(t)) + \cdots + (y_n(t) - y_{n-1}(t)). \\
&\vdots
\end{aligned}$$

This sequence has the form of formula (3.5) of the Review of Calculus, where

$$b_1 = y_0,\ b_2 = y_1(t) - y_0,\ b_3 = y_2(t) - y_1(t), \ldots,\ b_{n+1} = y_n(t) - y_{n-1}(t).$$

From part (f) it follows that if $t_0 \leq t \leq t_0 + \alpha$,

$$|b_n| \leq \frac{\gamma}{\alpha}\frac{1}{2\cdot 3\cdots n}k^{n-1}(t-t_0)^n \leq \frac{\gamma}{\alpha}\frac{1}{2\cdot 3\cdots n}k^{n-1}\alpha^n \equiv \beta_n.$$

Use this result and theorem (3.6) of the Review of Calculus to show that the sequence a_n converges.

(h) Show from (g) that a_{n+1} is actually equal to $y_n(t)$, so that (g) implies that $y_n(t)$ converges.

4. Systems of Equations and Equations of Higher Order

So far in this chapter our efforts have been directed mainly at single first-order differential equations. The idea of successive approximations which we discussed in §3 can be extended, however, to systems of equations and to equations of higher order. In this section we give a brief discussion of how this can be done.

The reason that we group systems of equations and equations of higher order together in this section is that the second can be reduced to the first. We have, in fact, the following statement.

(4.1) Reduction Principle. *Any ordinary differential equation of order n can be written as a system of n first-order equations.*

The proof of this result as well as its content are best illustrated by some examples.

(4.2) Examples. Reduction of Equations to First-Order Systems

(a) $\ddot{y}(t) + 2\dot{y}(t) + y(t) = t^2$. This is a second-order differential equation. We define functions y_1 and y_2 by $y_1(t) = y(t)$ and $y_2(t) = \dot{y}(t)$. Then we have $\ddot{y}(t) = \dot{y}_2(t)$. Hence we can rewrite (a) in the form

(i) $\dot{y}_2(t) + 2y_2(t) + y_1(t) = t^2$.

In addition we have, by definition,

(ii) $\dot{y}_1(t) = y_2(t)$.

Equations (i) and (ii) we call a *system* of two first-order equations. The term "system" simply means that there is more than one equation.

(b) $\dddot{y}(t) + \ddot{y}(t)^2 + 2\dot{y}(t) - y(t) = 0$. This is a third-order equation. We define functions y_1, y_2, y_3 by $y_1(t) = y(t)$, $y_2(t) = \dot{y}(t)$, $y_3(t) = \ddot{y}(t)$. Then we have $\dddot{y}(t) = \dot{y}_3(t)$. Hence we can rewrite (b) in the form

(i) $\dot{y}_3(t) + y_3(t)^2 + 2y_2(t) - y_1(t) = 0.$

In addition we have, by definition,

(ii) $\dot{y}_1(t) = y_2(t)$,

(iii) $\dot{y}_2(t) = y_3(t)$.

Equations (i), (ii), and (iii) are a system of three first-order equations.

These two examples make clear the general method for reduction of an nth-order equation.

(4.3) Reduction Method for an *n*th-Order Equation

(i) Introduce variables $y_1, \ldots, y_n$ by

$$y_1(t) = y(t),\ y_2(t) = \dot{y}(t),\ y_3(t) = \ddot{y}(t), \ldots, y_n(t) = y^{(n-1)}(t).$$

(ii) Obtain $(n - 1)$ first-order equations from these relations:

$$\begin{aligned} \dot{y}_1(t) &= y_2(t) \\ \dot{y}_2(t) &= y_3(t) \\ &\ \vdots \\ \dot{y}_{n-1}(t) &= y_n(t). \end{aligned}$$

Observe that none of these involve $\dot{y}_n(t)$.

(iii) Obtain one more first-order equation by rewriting the original nth-order equation in terms of $y_1, \ldots, y_n$. This equation will involve $\dot{y}_n(t)$, since this is merely $y^{(n)}(t)$.

Not only can we reduce a single nth-order equation to a first-order system but, as we shall see in the problems, we can also reduce systems of equations of arbitrary orders to first-order systems.

The examples we have considered all led to first-order systems of the form

$$\begin{aligned} \dot{y}_1(t) &= f_1\big(t, y_1(t), y_2(t), \ldots, y_n(t)\big) \\ \dot{y}_2(t) &= f_2\big(t, y_1(t), y_2(t), \ldots, y_n(t)\big) \\ &\ \vdots \\ \dot{y}_n(t) &= f_n\big(t, y_1(t), y_2(t), \ldots, y_n(t)\big). \end{aligned} \tag{4.4}$$

The appropriate initial conditions to give for this system turn out to be the following:

$$y_1(t_0) = y_1^0, \quad y_2(t_0) = y_2^0, \ldots, \quad y_n(t_0) = y_n^0. \tag{4.5}$$

We indicate now how to solve the system (4.4) and (4.5) by successive approximations. The first step is to make an initial guess of the form $y_1(t) \equiv y_1^0, \ldots, y_n(t) \equiv y_n^0$. Then we substitute this guess into the right sides of equations (4.4). This gives

$$\begin{aligned} \dot{y}_1(t) &= f_1(t, y_1^0, \ldots, y_n^0), \qquad & y_1(t_0) &= y_1^0 \\ &\vdots & &\vdots \\ \dot{y}_n(t) &= f_n(t, y_1^0, \ldots, y_n^0), \qquad & y_n(t_0) &= y_n^0. \end{aligned} \tag{4.6}$$

Now the right sides in (4.6) are all known functions of t. Hence each of the equations in (4.6) is simply a differential equation of the form (0.1). We can solve these as in proposition (0.6). We shall denote the set of functions we obtain in this way by $y_1^1, y_2^1, \ldots, y_n^1$. Hence we have

$$\begin{aligned} y_1^1(t) &= y_1^0 + \int_{t_0}^t f_1(\tau, y_1^0, \ldots, y_n^0)\, d\tau \\ &\vdots \\ y_n^1(t) &= y_n^0 + \int_{t_0}^t f_n(\tau, y_1^0, \ldots, y_n^0)\, d\tau. \end{aligned} \tag{4.7}$$

To obtain a second approximation we substitute the functions $y_1^1, \ldots, y_n^1$ into the right sides of (4.4) and solve the resulting equations subject to conditions (4.5). This yields a new approximate solution which we shall denote by $y_1^2, y_2^2, \ldots, y_n^2$. Rather than write out general formulas, let us carry the process through for an example.

(4.8) Example. Successive Approximations for a System. Consider the system

$$\begin{aligned} \dot{y}_1(t) &= -y_2(t), \qquad & y_1(0) &= 1 \\ \dot{y}_2(t) &= y_1(t), & y_2(0) &= 0. \end{aligned}$$

Equations (4.6) become

$$\begin{aligned} \dot{y}_1(t) &= 0, \qquad & y_1(0) &= 1 \\ \dot{y}_2(t) &= 1, & y_2(0) &= 0. \end{aligned}$$

Hence, by (4.7),

$$y_1^1(t) = 1 + \int_0^t (0)\, d\tau = 1$$

$$y_2^1(t) = 0 + \int_0^t (1)\, d\tau = t.$$

Now we put these expressions back into the right sides of the equations and obtain

$$\dot{y}_1(t) = -y_2^1(t) = -t, \qquad y_1(0) = 1$$
$$\dot{y}_2(t) = y_1^1(t) = 1, \qquad y_2(0) = 0.$$

Hence

$$y_1^2(t) = 1 + \int_0^t (-\tau)\, d\tau = 1 - \frac{t^2}{2}$$

$$y_2^2(t) = 0 + \int_0^t 1\, d\tau = t.$$

We carry out one more step. Put these expressions into the right sides, obtaining

$$\dot{y}_1(t) = -y_2^2(t) = -t, \qquad y_1(0) = 1$$
$$\dot{y}_2(t) = y_1^2(t) = 1 - \frac{t^2}{2}, \qquad y_2(0) = 0.$$

Then we obtain as solutions y_1^3 and y_2^3 of these equations,

$$y_1^3(t) = 1 + \int_0^t (-\tau)\, d\tau = 1 - \frac{t^2}{2}$$

$$y_2^3(t) = 0 + \int_0^t \left(1 - \frac{\tau^2}{2}\right) d\tau = t - \frac{t^3}{6}.$$

In problem 6 an explicit solution of this problem is given and the reader is asked to compare it with the various approximations.

The goal of successive approximations for systems is the same as for a single equation. That is, one hopes to obtain a sequence of (sets of) functions $y_1^{\mathbf{k}}, y_2^{\mathbf{k}}, \ldots, y_n^{\mathbf{k}}$ such that for each t in some interval, *each* of the sequences $\{y_j^{\mathbf{k}}(t)\} = y_j^1(t), y_j^2(t), \ldots, j = 1, 2, \ldots, n$, has a limit $y_j(t)$. Further one hopes that the functions $y_1, \ldots, y_n$ thus defined will be a solution of equations (4.4) and (4.5). Something like theorem (3.8) is indeed true here, but this time it is required that *each* of the functions $f_1, \ldots, f_n$ have continuous partial derivatives with respect to each of the variables $y_1, y_2, \ldots, y_n$.

Note that the system (4.4) has the same number of equations as unknowns, n of each. In general, if there are *fewer* equations than unknowns, then there will be more than one solution $y_1, y_2, \ldots, y_n$ satisfying (4.5) (see problem 9), while if there are *more* equations than unknowns, then there will be no solutions at all (see problem 10). In these respects, systems of first-order differential equations are just like systems of algebraic equations.

The reduction of nth-order equations or general systems to first-order systems can be used to determine appropriate initial conditions. We can then state the results as general principles.

(4.9) Principles for Initial Conditions

(a) For an nth-order equation, $y, \dot{y}, \ldots, y^{(n-1)}$ should all be prescribed at some point t_0. That is, appropriate conditions are

$$y(t_0) = y_0, \qquad \dot{y}(t_0) = y_0^1, \ldots, \qquad y^{(n-1)}(t_0) = y_0^{n-1}.$$

(b) In a system of equations for functions $y_1, y_2, \ldots, y_n$, let

$$m_1, m_2, \ldots, m_n$$

be the orders of the highest derivatives of $y_1, \ldots, y_n$, respectively. Then appropriate initial conditions will be

$$\begin{array}{lll} y_1(t_0) = y_1^0, & \dot{y}_1(t_0) = y_1^1, \ldots, & y_1^{(m_1-1)}(t_0) = y_1^{m_1-1} \\ \vdots & \vdots & \vdots \\ y_n(t_0) = y_n^0, & \dot{y}_n(t_0) = y_n^1, \ldots, & y_n^{(m_n-1)}(t_0) = y_n^{m_n-1}. \end{array}$$

The reader is asked to verify these principles in the problems.

PROBLEMS

1. Show how to rewrite the following differential equations as first-order systems.

(a) $\ddot{y}(t) + k^2 y(t) = 0$

(b) $y^{(4)}(t) + 2y^{(3)}(t) - y(t)^3 - t$

(c) $\dddot{y}(t) + \ddot{y}(t)\dot{y}(t)y(t) = 0$

(d) $y^{(6)}(t) - y^{(3)}(t) - 0$

2. Rewrite the following systems as first-order systems.

(a) $\ddot{y}_1(t) + y_1(t)\dot{y}_2(t) + (y_1(t))^2 = 0$
$\ddot{y}_2(t) - \dot{y}_1(t) + (y_2(t))^2 = 0$

[*Hint:* Since the system is of second order in both y_1 and y_2, introduce y_1 and y_2 and their first derivatives as new variables. Use the notation $z_1 = y_1$, $z_2 = \dot{y}_1$, $z_3 = y_2$, $z_4 = \dot{y}_2$. Then $\ddot{y}_1 = \dot{z}_2$, $\ddot{y}_2 = \dot{z}_4$. In addition, $\dot{z}_1 = z_2$ and $\dot{z}_3 = z_4$, which provides two more equations.]

(b) $\dddot{y}_1(t) + y_2(t)^2 = 1$
$\ddot{y}_2(t) - y_1(t) = 0$

[*Hint:* Since this system is third order in y_1 and second order in y_2, introduce as new variables

$$z_1 = y_1, \qquad z_2 = \dot{y}_1, \qquad z_3 = \ddot{y}_1, \qquad z_4 = y_2, \qquad z_5 = \dot{y}_2.$$

The final system must then involve five equations.]

3. Show how to rewrite the following systems as first-order systems:

(a) $\ddot{y}_1(t) = y_2(t)$
$\ddot{y}_2(t) = y_3(t)$
$\ddot{y}_3(t) = y_1(t)$

(b) $\ddot{y}_1(t) + \dot{y}_1(t)\dot{y}_2(t) = 0$
$\ddot{y}_2(t) + y_1(t) = 0$

(c) $\dddot{y}_1(t) - \dot{y}_1(t)y_2(t) = 0$
$\ddot{y}_2(t) + \ddot{y}_1(t)y_1(t) = 0$

(d) $\ddot{y}_1(t) + y_2(t)y_3(t) = 0$
$\ddot{y}_2(t) + \dot{y}_1(t)y_2(t) = 0$
$\dot{y}_3(t) + \ddot{y}_1(t) = 0$

4. A particle moves along a line under the action of a force which depends on both the position and the velocity. Its position vector relative to a point on the line can be written $\mathbf{r} = \rho\boldsymbol{\alpha}$, where $\boldsymbol{\alpha}$ is a fixed vector and ρ is a function of time. The force at time t can then be written

$$\mathbf{F}(t) = f(\rho(t), \dot{\rho}(t))\boldsymbol{\alpha}.$$

Show how to write Newton's law for the particle as a system of first-order equations.

5. For each of the equations of problems 1 and 2 state what would be an appropriate set of initial conditions.

6. Show that the functions $y_1(t) = \cos t$, $y_2(t) = \sin t$, give a solution to the problem in example (4.8). Make a table comparing the true solution and the first, second, and third approximations (calculated to two decimal places) at $t = 0, \pi/4, \pi/2$, and π.

7. Calculate the first two approximations (y_1^1, y_2^1), (y_1^2, y_2^2) for each of the following problems.

(a) $\dot{y}_1(t) + 2y_1(t)y_2(t) = 0, \quad y_1(0) = 1$
$\dot{y}_2(t) - y_1(t) = 0, \quad y_2(0) = 0$

(b) $\dot{y}_1(t) = y_2(t)^2, \quad y_1(0) = 0$
$\dot{y}_2(t) = y_1(t)^2, \quad y_2(0) = 1$

(c) $\dot{y}_1(t) + \dfrac{1}{t}y_2(t) = 0, \quad y_1(1) = 1$

$\dot{y}_2(t) + ty_1(t) = 0, \quad y_2(1) = 0$

8. Consider the problem

$$\ddot{y}(t) + 4y(t) = 0, \qquad y(0) = 0, \dot{y}(0) = 1.$$

(a) From formulas (0.2) and (0.3) of Chapter 1 determine an explicit solution of this problem.

(b) Reduce the equation to a first-order system.

(c) Find the first two approximations (y_1^1, y_2^1) and (y_1^2, y_2^2) of the system in part (b).

9. Consider the equation

$$\dot{y}_1(t) + \dot{y}_2(t) = 0, \qquad y_1(0) = 1, y_2(0) = 0.$$

Find two distinct solutions of this equation. (Observe that here one has one equation in two unknowns.)

10. Consider the equations

$$\begin{aligned} \dot{y}_1(t) + y_1(t) &= 0 \\ \dot{y}_1(t) - y_1(t) &= 0 \end{aligned} \qquad y_1(0) = 1$$

Show that there is *no* solution. [*Hint:* The first equation above uniquely determines y_1. (Here we have two equations in one unknown.)]

11. State an analog for the system (4.4) of the result of problem 6 of §3. Give an example of a system to which the result applies.

12. The system (4.4) is called s-*linear* [corresponding to definition (2.1) for a single equation] if whenever $y_1^1, \dots, y_n^1$ and $y_1^2, \dots, y_n^2$ are solutions, then the set of functions

$$\alpha_1 y_1^1 + \alpha_2 y_1^2, \qquad \alpha_1 y_2^1 + \alpha_2 y_2^2, \dots, \qquad \alpha_1 y_n^1 + \alpha_2 y_n^2$$

is also a solution. Show that (4.4) is s-linear if the functions f_j have the form

$$\begin{aligned} f_1(t, y_1, \dots, y_n) &= f_{11}(t)y_1 + f_{12}(t)y_2 + \cdots + f_{1n}(t)y_n \\ f_2(t, y_1, \dots, y_n) &= f_{21}(t)y_1 + f_{22}(t)y_2 + \cdots + f_{2n}(t)y_n \\ &\vdots \\ f_n(t, y_1, \dots, y_n) &= f_{n1}(t)y_1 + f_{n2}(t)y_2 + \cdots + f_{nn}(t)y_n. \end{aligned}$$

13. Show that the system

$$\begin{aligned} \dot{y}_1(t)y_2(t) - \dot{y}_2(t)y_1(t) &= 1 \\ \dot{y}_1(t)y_1(t) + \dot{y}_2(t)y_2(t) &= 0 \end{aligned}$$

can be written in the form (4.4).

5. A Numerical Process

The method of successive approximations which we have developed in the preceding sections is a powerful theoretical tool in the study of differential equations. Moreover, it is useful in other contexts; yet it has serious drawbacks as a practical method of computing the solution. For this reason there have been many numerical techniques developed to compute solutions. In this section we give a very simple example of such methods.

Consider the equation

$$\dot{y}(t) = f(t, y(t)), \qquad y(t_0) = y_0. \tag{5.1}$$

Suppose y is a solution and that this solution happens to have a continuous second derivative. Then a form of the mean-value theorem states that

$$y(t) - y(\bar{t}) = \dot{y}(\bar{t})(t - \bar{t}) + \tfrac{1}{2}\ddot{y}(\xi)(t - \bar{t})^2, \tag{5.2}$$

where ξ is some point between $\bar{t}$ and t. Now we can substitute for $\dot{y}_1(\bar{t})$ from (5.1) and obtain

$$y(t) = y(\bar{t}) + f(\bar{t}, y(\bar{t}))(t - \bar{t}) + \tfrac{1}{2}\ddot{y}(\xi)(t - \bar{t})^2. \tag{5.3}$$

Now let $\bar{t}$ be the point t_0 in (5.1). Then we have

$$y(t) = y_0 + f(t_0, y_0)(t - t_0) + \tfrac{1}{2}\ddot{y}(\xi)(t - t_0)^2. \tag{5.4}$$

Suppose $|\ddot{y}(\xi)| \leq M$ between t_0 and t. Then if $|t - t_0|$ is sufficiently small, the last term in (5.4) will be very small and it will be a reasonably good approximation to say that

$$y(t) = y_0 + f(t_0, y_0)(t - t_0). \tag{5.5}$$

Equation (5.5) suggests a procedure which we could use to find an approximate solution. We know t_0 and y_0 and hence $f(t_0, y_0)$. We can calculate an approximate value of $y(t)$ from (5.5) for $t_0 \leq t \leq t_1$. Equation (5.4) shows that this should be a good approximation if $t_1 - t_0$ is small. Now use this value to calculate $y(t_1) = y_1$ approximately. Then calculate $f(t_1, y_1)$ and calculate $y(t)$ approximately for $t_1 \leq t \leq t_2$ using the formula

$$y(t) = y_1 + f(t_1, y_1)(t - t_1).$$

Then start over at t_2, and so on. The result is an approximation $\tilde{y}(t)$ to the solution $y(t)$. The graph of $\tilde{y}$ consists of a series of straight-line segments with different slopes (Figure 4.10). Hopefully $\tilde{y}(t)$ will stay close to the true solution if the intervals $t_1 - t_0, t_2 - t_1, \ldots$ are kept small.

It is a fact that the above process can be shown to be a valid one in the sense that one can prove that the difference $|y(t) - \tilde{y}(t)|$ can be made arbitrarily small, over any finite interval of time $\alpha \leq t \leq \beta$ where the solution exists, by making all the differences $|t_1 - t_0|, |t_2 - t_1|, \ldots$ sufficiently small. However,

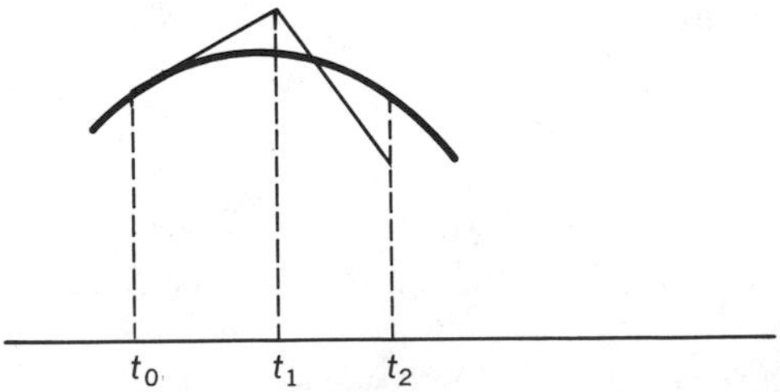

Figure 4.10

this is a hard theorem, much harder than theorem (3.8). Moreover, there is the practical difficulty that it is not always easy to judge in advance how small the intervals should be. One frequently proceeds by a trial and error process.

We hope it is clear that a similar process can be developed for systems of equations.

PROBLEMS

1. Consider the problem

$$\dot{y}(t) = y(t), \qquad y(0) = 1.$$

(a) Find the explicit solution.

(b) Calculate approximate values of the solution at $t = 0$ and 1 by the process described in this section. Take $t_1 = 1$.

(c) Repeat the process using two steps, $t_1 = \frac{1}{2}$ and $t_2 = 1$. Thus recalculate an approximate value of the solution at $t = 1$. How do the results in parts (b) and (c) compare with the true values?

2. Apply the process described in this section to the problem

$$\dot{y}(t) = (y(t))^2, \qquad y(0) = 1$$

on the interval $0 \leq t \leq \frac{1}{2}$. Do it twice, once for a single interval, $t_1 = \frac{1}{2}$, and once for two intervals, $t_1 = \frac{1}{4}$ and $t_2 = \frac{1}{2}$. Compare the results with the exact solution. Also do the process on $0 \leq t \leq 1$ taking two intervals, $t_1 = \frac{1}{2}$ and $t_2 = 1$. What is wrong with this? (This shows one of the pitfalls of this method.)

5

Bases, Coordinates, and Linear Differential Equations

1. Finite-Dimensional Subspaces; Bases

In Chapter 4 we found it very convenient to discuss certain equations involving arrows by forming corresponding scalar equations involving *components* of those arrows. However, the technique of dealing with vector equations by forming equations for components is by no means restricted to the vector space $\mathcal{A}$. One of the things we shall discover in this chapter is the extent to which such component methods generalize to other vector spaces.

One of the axioms for a vector space guarantees the equality of the sums $\boldsymbol{\alpha} + (\boldsymbol{\beta} + \boldsymbol{\gamma})$ and $(\boldsymbol{\alpha} + \boldsymbol{\beta}) + \boldsymbol{\gamma}$. The common value of these sums is denoted by the parenthesis-free expression $\boldsymbol{\alpha} + \boldsymbol{\beta} + \boldsymbol{\gamma}$. Similarly, if $\boldsymbol{\alpha}$, $\boldsymbol{\beta}$, $\boldsymbol{\gamma}$, and $\boldsymbol{\delta}$ are four vectors, then the sums

$$\boldsymbol{\alpha} + (\boldsymbol{\beta} + \boldsymbol{\gamma} + \boldsymbol{\delta}), \qquad (\boldsymbol{\alpha} + \boldsymbol{\beta} + \boldsymbol{\gamma}) + \boldsymbol{\delta}, \qquad \boldsymbol{\alpha} + \boldsymbol{\beta} + (\boldsymbol{\gamma} + \boldsymbol{\delta}),$$
$$\boldsymbol{\alpha} + (\boldsymbol{\beta} + \boldsymbol{\gamma}) + \boldsymbol{\delta}, \qquad (\boldsymbol{\alpha} + \boldsymbol{\beta}) + \boldsymbol{\gamma} + \boldsymbol{\delta}$$

are all equal (problem 11), and their common value is denoted by $\boldsymbol{\alpha} + \boldsymbol{\beta} + \boldsymbol{\gamma} + \boldsymbol{\delta}$. More generally, if $\boldsymbol{\alpha}_1, \ldots, \boldsymbol{\alpha}_m$ is a system of m vectors of $\mathcal{V}$, then the quantity

$$\sum_{i=1}^{m} \boldsymbol{\alpha}_i = \boldsymbol{\alpha}_1 + \boldsymbol{\alpha}_2 + \cdots + \boldsymbol{\alpha}_m$$

is defined in an unambiguous manner. Axiom (A_1), the commutative law for vector addition, guarantees that all such sums are independent of the order in which vectors are added. Now we give an important definition.

(1.1) Definition. Let $\boldsymbol{\alpha}_1, \ldots, \boldsymbol{\alpha}_m$ be a system of vectors in the space $\mathcal{V}$, and let $c_1, \ldots, c_m$ be a system of scalars. Then the vector

$$\sum_{i=1}^{m} c_i\boldsymbol{\alpha}_i = c_1\boldsymbol{\alpha}_1 + c_2\boldsymbol{\alpha}_2 + \cdots + c_m\boldsymbol{\alpha}_m$$

is called a **linear combination** of $\boldsymbol{\alpha}_1, \ldots, \boldsymbol{\alpha}_m$. The set S of all linear combinations of $\boldsymbol{\alpha}_1, \ldots, \boldsymbol{\alpha}_m$ for all possible choices of $c_1, \ldots, c_m$ is called the **span** of $\boldsymbol{\alpha}_1, \ldots, \boldsymbol{\alpha}_m$ and is denoted by $\langle\boldsymbol{\alpha}_1, \ldots, \boldsymbol{\alpha}_m\rangle$. We say that $\boldsymbol{\alpha}_1, \ldots, \boldsymbol{\alpha}_m$ *spans* $\langle\boldsymbol{\alpha}_1, \ldots, \boldsymbol{\alpha}_m\rangle$ or is a *spanner for* $\langle\boldsymbol{\alpha}_1, \ldots, \boldsymbol{\alpha}_m\rangle$. When $\langle\boldsymbol{\alpha}_1, \ldots, \boldsymbol{\alpha}_m\rangle = \mathcal{V}$, then the system $\boldsymbol{\alpha}_1, \ldots, \boldsymbol{\alpha}_m$ is said to *span* $\mathcal{V}$.

As an example, consider the system $\boldsymbol{\alpha}_1 = (1, 0, 0)$, $\boldsymbol{\alpha}_2 = (1, 1, 0)$, $\boldsymbol{\alpha}_3 = (0, 1, 0)$ in $\mathcal{R}^3$. To determine $\langle\boldsymbol{\alpha}_1, \boldsymbol{\alpha}_2, \boldsymbol{\alpha}_3\rangle$ we must describe all vectors obtained as linear combinations:

$$c_1\boldsymbol{\alpha}_1 + c_2\boldsymbol{\alpha}_2 + c_3\boldsymbol{\alpha}_3 = (c_1 + c_2, c_2 + c_3, 0).$$

However, it is easily seen that every vector of the form $(a_1, a_2, 0)$ is given as such a linear combination with an appropriate choice for c_1, c_2, c_3. (The reader should prove this for himself.) Thus $\langle\boldsymbol{\alpha}_1, \boldsymbol{\alpha}_2, \boldsymbol{\alpha}_3\rangle$ is the set of all vectors in $\mathcal{R}^3$ with third term zero.

Now it is useful to observe that a vector space $\mathcal{V}$ has various kinds of subsets, some of which behave better under the operations on $\mathcal{V}$ than others. For instance, consider in $\mathcal{A}$ the set S_1 of all vectors whose end points lie on a line L_1 passing through the origin. Likewise, consider the set S_2 of all vectors whose end points lie on a line L_2 not passing through the origin (Figure 5.1). Although S_1 and S_2 have some analogous features, there is one

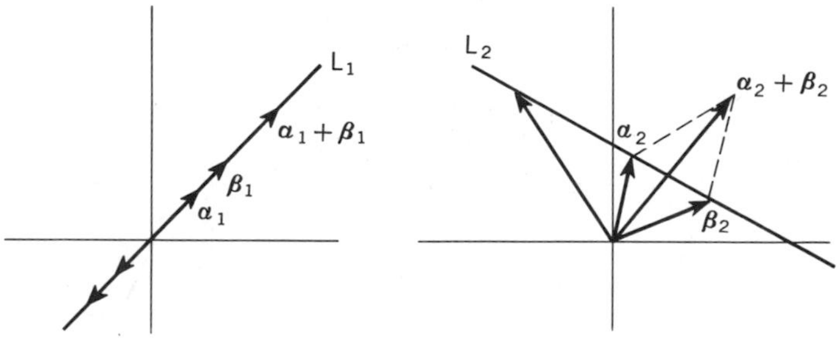

Figure 5.1

very profound difference between them: Given $\boldsymbol{\alpha}_1, \boldsymbol{\beta}_1 \in S_1$ and $\boldsymbol{\alpha}_2, \boldsymbol{\beta}_2 \in S_2$, we always find $\boldsymbol{\alpha}_1 + \boldsymbol{\beta}_1 \in S_1$, while $\boldsymbol{\alpha}_2 + \boldsymbol{\beta}_2 \notin S_2$.

(1.2) Definition. A subset S of $\mathcal{V}$ is said to be **closed under addition** if $\boldsymbol{\alpha} + \boldsymbol{\beta} \in S$ whenever $\boldsymbol{\alpha}$, $\boldsymbol{\beta}$ both belong to S. S is said to be **closed under scalar multiplication** if for every scalar c, $c\boldsymbol{\alpha} \in S$ whenever $\boldsymbol{\alpha} \in S$.

Those subsets of $\mathcal{V}$ which are closed under *both* addition and scalar multiplication are of special importance. For them one can prove the following result.

(1.3) Proposition. *Let S be a nonempty subset of $\mathcal{V}$ which is closed under both addition and scalar multiplication. Then S together with the operation of addition and scalar multiplication inherited from $\mathcal{V}$ is itself a vector space. It is called a* ***subspace*** *of $\mathcal{V}$.*

In the example described above it is easily seen that S_1 is a subspace of $\mathcal{A}$ while S_2 is not. (The reader should be sure he can distinguish clearly between subsets and subspaces; the latter is always one of the former, but not vice versa.)

(1.4) Examples. Subspaces

(a) Let S denote the set of all arrows $\boldsymbol{\alpha}$, $\boldsymbol{\beta}$, ... which are parallel to a fixed plane P in space (Figure 5.2). Then S is easily seen to be a subspace of $\mathcal{A}$.

If we let $\boldsymbol{\alpha}_1$, $\boldsymbol{\alpha}_2$ denote a pair of nonparallel vectors in S it is interesting to observe that S is the span of $\boldsymbol{\alpha}_1$, $\boldsymbol{\alpha}_2$ (see Figure 5.3).

(b) Let S denote the set of all triples whose last entry is zero:

$$S = \{(a_1, a_2, 0)\}.$$

Then S is easily seen to be a subspace of $\mathbb{R}^3$. For if $\boldsymbol{\alpha} = (a_1, a_2, 0)$,

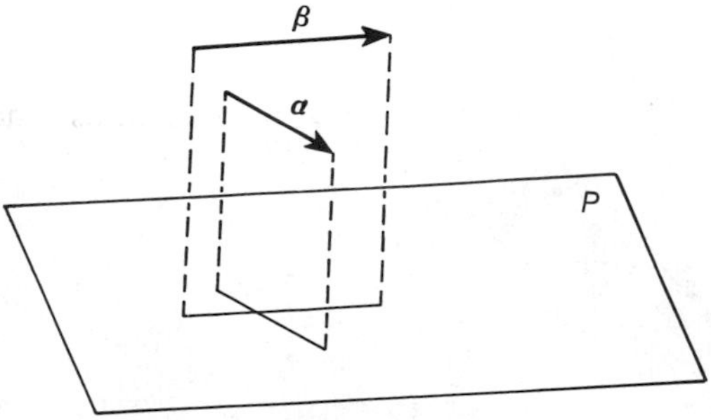

Figure 5.2

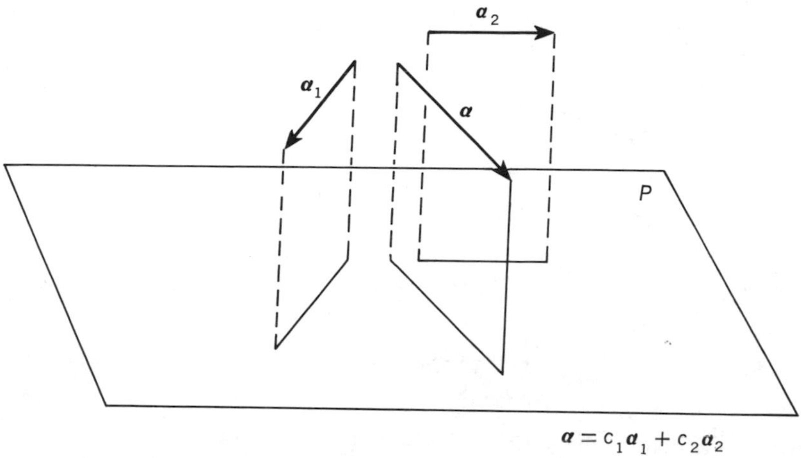

Figure 5.3

$\alpha' = (a_1', a_2', 0)$ belong to S, then the vectors

$$\alpha + \alpha' = (a_1 + a_1', a_2 + a_2', 0) \qquad \text{and} \qquad c\alpha = (ca_1, ca_2, 0)$$

obviously have the requisite form and hence also belong to S.

We have already seen that this subspace is also a span:

$$S = \langle(1, 0, 0), (1, 1, 0), (0, 1, 0)\rangle.$$

(c) Let S denote the subset of $\mathcal{R}^2$ consisting of all vectors $\alpha = (a_1, a_2)$ for which $a_1 > 0$ and $a_2 > 0$ (Figure 5.4). (These correspond to arrows in the plane which point into the first quadrant.) Then S is closed under addition but not under scalar multiplication. For example, if $\alpha \in S$, then $(-1)\alpha = -\alpha$ is not in S. Thus S is *not* a subspace.

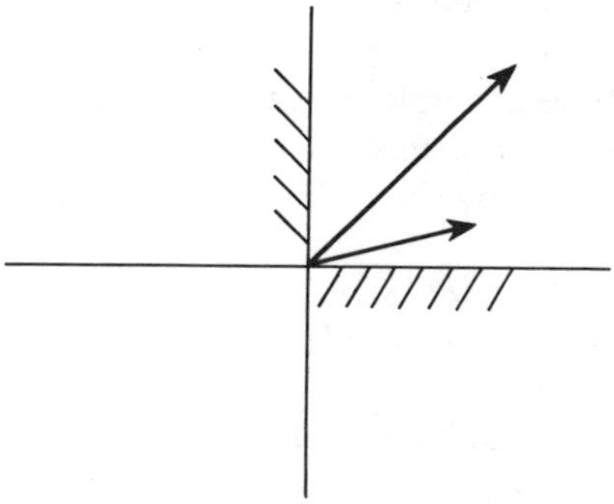

Figure 5.4

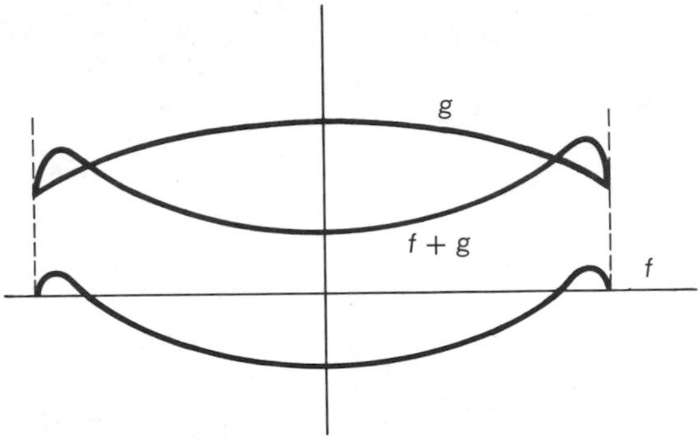

Figure 5.5

(d) Let S denote the subset of $\mathcal{C}[-1, 1]$ consisting of all even functions continuous on $-1 \leq t \leq 1$ (see Figure 5.5). Then S is easily verified to be closed under addition and scalar multiplication and is thereby a subspace of $\mathcal{C}[-1, 1]$.

In this example S is *not* a span. It can be proved that there is no system $f_1, \ldots, f_m \in \mathcal{C}[-1, 1]$ for which $S = \langle f_1, \ldots, f_m \rangle$.

(e) Let S denote the subset of $\mathcal{C}(-\infty, \infty)$ consisting of solutions of the differential equation

$$\ddot{x}(t) + k^2 x(t) = 0.$$

As mentioned in Chapter 1, the solutions are all those functions which can be put in the form

$$x(t) = A \sin (kt + B)$$

for an appropriate amplitude A and phase angle B. It is not hard to show that this collection of functions is closed under addition and scalar multiplication (problem 13). Hence S is a subspace of $\mathcal{C}(-\infty, \infty)$. Here S *is* a span, for it is easily established that $S = \langle \sin kt, \cos kt \rangle$.

In several of the above examples it was observed that the set S was simultaneously a *subspace* and the *span* of a system of vectors. That this is no mere coincidence is shown by the following proposition.

(1.5) Proposition. *Every subset S of $\mathcal{V}$ which is the span of some system $\boldsymbol{\alpha}_1, \ldots, \boldsymbol{\alpha}_m$ of vectors of $\mathcal{V}$ is a subspace of $\mathcal{V}$.*

Proof. According to the definition of subspace it is only necessary to show that the set $S = \langle \boldsymbol{\alpha}, \ldots, \boldsymbol{\alpha}_m \rangle$ is closed under addition and scalar multiplication. Let $\beta,\gamma \in S$. Then for certain scalars $b_1, \ldots, b_m, c_1, \ldots, c_m$ we have

$$\beta = b_1\alpha_1 + \cdots + b_m\alpha_m$$
$$\gamma = c_1\alpha_1 + \cdots + c_m\alpha_m.$$

Consequently, by collecting terms we find

$$\begin{aligned}\beta + \gamma &= (b_1\alpha_1 + \cdots + b_m\alpha_m) + (c_1\alpha_1 + \cdots + c_m\alpha_m)\\ &= (b_1 + c_1)\alpha_1 + \cdots + (b_m + c_m)\alpha_m \in \langle \alpha_1, \ldots, \alpha_m \rangle.\end{aligned}$$

This shows that S is closed under addition. Closure under scalar multiplication is even easier to prove and is left as an exercise. ∎

Since every vector space $\mathcal{V}$ is a subspace of itself, the preceding result leads to the following definition.

(1.6) Definition. A vector space $\mathcal{V}$, or a subspace $S \subset \mathcal{V}$, is said to be **finite-dimensional** if and only if it is a span.

For the remainder of this section we shall confine our attention to subspaces which are finite-dimensional. If S is such a subspace, then by definition there is at least one spanner $\alpha_1, \ldots, \alpha_m$ for S. In general there will be many other spanners for S as well. For instance, we have seen that the set S consisting of all triples whose third entry is zero is a subspace of $\mathcal{R}^3$ spanned by the system $\alpha_1 = (1, 0, 0), \alpha_2 = (1, 1, 0), \alpha_3 = (0, 1, 0)$. On the other hand, when we describe all linear combinations

$$d_1\alpha_1 + d_2\alpha_3 = (d_1, d_2, 0)$$

of the system $\alpha_1 = (1, 0, 0), \alpha_3 = (0, 1, 0)$, it is obvious that every triple with third entry zero can be obtained in this way, too. That is, $S = \langle \alpha_1, \alpha_3 \rangle$. An analogous computation shows that the system

$$\beta_1 = (1, 1, 0), \qquad \beta_2 = (1, -1, 0), \qquad \beta_3 = (2, 1, 0), \qquad \beta_4 = (1, 2, 0)$$

also spans S. (The reader should prove this.) Thus we have found three systems of vectors spanning S, and it is easy to construct others.

Is there any reason for preferring certain spanners of a subspace over other spanners? To answer this question let us study S in the above example. Select a vector γ in S, say $\gamma = (1, 3, 0)$. As is easily checked, γ is given by each of the following sums (where possible, a sketch will help one to visualize the relations):

$$\alpha_1, \alpha_2, \alpha_3$$

$$\gamma = -1 \cdot (1, 0, 0) + 2 \cdot (1, 1, 0) + 1 \cdot (0, 1, 0) = -\alpha_1 + 2\alpha_2 + \alpha_3$$
$$\gamma = 2 \cdot (1, 0, 0) - 1 \cdot (1, 1, 0) + 4 \cdot (0, 1, 0) = 2\alpha_1 - \alpha_2 + 4\alpha_3$$

$$\alpha_1, \alpha_3$$

$$\gamma = 1 \cdot (1, 0, 0) + 3 \cdot (0, 1, 0) = \alpha_1 + 3\alpha_3$$

$$\beta_1, \beta_2, \beta_3, \beta_4$$

$$\begin{aligned}\gamma &= \tfrac{1}{2}(1, 1, 0) - \tfrac{1}{2}(1, -1, 0) + 0 \cdot (2, 1, 0) + 1 \cdot (1, 2, 0)\\ &= \tfrac{1}{2}\beta_1 - \tfrac{1}{2}\beta_2 + 0\beta_3 + \beta_4\\ \gamma &= -1(1, 1, 0) - 1 \cdot (1, -1, 0) + 1 \cdot (2, 1, 0) + 1 \cdot (1, 2, 0)\\ &= -\beta_1 - \beta_2 + \beta_3 + \beta_4.\end{aligned}$$

Moreover, it is not hard to construct additional linear combinations of the systems $\alpha_1, \alpha_2, \alpha_3$ and $\beta_1, \beta_2, \beta_3, \beta_4$ which give γ. On the other hand, the sum $\alpha_1 + 3\alpha_3$ obtained above is obviously the only linear combination of the system α_1, α_3 giving γ. In other words, γ occurs *several* times as one varies the coefficients in constructing all possible sums $c_1\alpha_1 + c_2\alpha_2 + c_3\alpha_3$ or in constructing all possible sums $c_1\beta_1 + c_2\beta_2 + c_3\beta_3 + c_4\beta_4$, but γ occurs only *once* as one varies the coefficients in constructing all possible linear combinations $d_1\alpha_1 + d_2\alpha_3$. This dichotomy leads us to make the following definition.

(1.7) Definition. Any spanner $\alpha_1, \ldots, \alpha_m$ for the subspace S which spans S "nonredundantly" in the sense that for each vector $\gamma \in S$ there is exactly *one* set of coefficients $c_1, \ldots, c_m$ satisfying

$$\gamma = c_1\alpha_1 + \cdots + c_m\alpha_m,$$

is called a **basis** for S. Any spanner which is not a basis for S is called a *linearly dependent spanner* for S.

A system $\alpha_1, \ldots, \alpha_m \in \mathcal{V}$ is said to be **linearly independent** if and only if it is a basis for $\langle\alpha_1, \ldots, \alpha_m\rangle$. Otherwise the system is said to be *linearly dependent*. (The terms *linearly independent* and *linearly dependent* are often contracted to *independent* and *dependent*, respectively.)

In the preceding example neither $\alpha_1, \alpha_2, \alpha_3$, nor $\beta_1, \beta_2, \beta_3, \beta_4$ was a basis for S, so they are both linearly dependent spanners. On the other hand, the system α_1, α_3 gives a unique decomposition for *each* $\gamma \in S$, not merely for $\gamma = (1, 3, 0)$, so it is a basis for S.

(1.8) Examples. Bases and Dependent Spanners

(a) $\mathcal{R}^2$. Consider the system $\boldsymbol{\alpha}_1 = (1, 2)$, $\boldsymbol{\alpha}_2 = (2, 1)$, $\boldsymbol{\alpha}_3 = (2, 2)$. To determine $\langle \boldsymbol{\alpha}_1, \boldsymbol{\alpha}_2, \boldsymbol{\alpha}_3 \rangle$ we must find all vectors (y_1, y_2) which are linear combinations of the $\boldsymbol{\alpha}$'s:

$$\begin{aligned}(y_1, y_2) &= c_1(1, 2) + c_2(2, 1) + c_3(2, 2) \\ &= (c_1 + 2c_2 + 2c_3, 2c_1 + c_2 + 2c_3).\end{aligned} \tag{1}$$

Equivalently, we must find all scalars y_1, y_2 for which the following equations in c_1, c_2, c_3 are solvable.

$$\begin{aligned}c_1 + 2c_2 + 2c_3 &= y_1 \\ 2c_1 + c_2 + 2c_3 &= y_2.\end{aligned} \tag{2}$$

Subtracting twice the first equation from the second yields the system of equations

$$\begin{aligned}c_1 + 2c_2 + 2c_3 &= y_1 \\ 0c_1 - 3c_2 - 2c_3 &= y_2 - 2y_1.\end{aligned}$$

Multiplying the second of these equations by $-\frac{1}{3}$ and then subtracting twice the result from the first equation leads to

$$\begin{aligned}c_1 + 0c_2 + \tfrac{2}{3}c_3 &= -\tfrac{1}{3}y_1 + \tfrac{2}{3}y_2 \\ 0c_1 + c_2 + \tfrac{2}{3}c_3 &= \tfrac{2}{3}y_1 - \tfrac{1}{3}y_2.\end{aligned} \tag{3}$$

Now (3) reveals that *every* vector $(y_1, y_2) \in \mathcal{R}^2$ is a linear combination of the $\boldsymbol{\alpha}$'s. For instance, if we set $c_3 = 0$, (3) gives us as a formula for c_1, c_2, c_3

$$\begin{aligned}c_1 &= -\tfrac{1}{3}y_1 + \tfrac{2}{3}y_2 \\ c_2 &= \tfrac{2}{3}y_1 - \tfrac{1}{3}y_2 \\ c_3 &= 0,\end{aligned} \tag{4}$$

while if we set $c_3 = 1$, (3) gives us the formula

$$\begin{aligned}c_1 &= -\tfrac{2}{3} - \tfrac{1}{3}y_1 + \tfrac{2}{3}y_2 \\ c_2 &= -\tfrac{2}{3} + \tfrac{2}{3}y_1 - \tfrac{1}{3}y_2 \\ c_3 &= 1.\end{aligned} \tag{5}$$

It follows from (1), (4), and (5) that the system $\boldsymbol{\alpha}_1, \boldsymbol{\alpha}_2, \boldsymbol{\alpha}_3$ spans $\mathcal{R}^2$ but is not a basis for $\mathcal{R}^2$.

(b) $\mathcal{R}^n$. Consider the system $\boldsymbol{\beta}_1 = (1, 0, \ldots, 0)$, $\boldsymbol{\beta}_2 = (0, 1, \ldots, 0), \ldots$, $\boldsymbol{\beta}_n = (0, \ldots, 1)$. It is easy to see by inspection that this system spans $\mathcal{R}^n$: for any vector $(y_1, \ldots, y_n) \in \mathcal{R}^n$ we have

$$(y_1, \ldots, y_n) = y_1\boldsymbol{\beta}_1 + \cdots + y_n\boldsymbol{\beta}_n.$$

Moreover, it is equally clear that a different choice of coefficients results in a different vector. That is, the above system spans $\mathcal{R}^n$ nonredundantly; it is a basis for $\mathcal{R}^n$.

(c) $\mathcal{P}^3$. Consider the system $p_1(t) = 1 + t^2, p_2(t) = 2t - 1, p_3(t) = t^2 + t$, $p_4(t) = 2t^2$. To determine $\langle p_1, p_2, p_3, p_4 \rangle$ we must describe all polynomials which are linear combinations of the p's:

$$y_1t^2 + y_2t + y_3 = c_1(1 + t^2) + c_2(2t - 1) + c_3(t^2 + t) + c_4(2t^2).$$

This reduces to the problem of determining all scalars y_1, y_2, y_3 for which the following equations are solvable:

$$\begin{aligned} c_1 + c_3 + 2c_4 &= y_1 \\ 2c_2 + c_3 &= y_2 \\ c_1 - c_2 &= y_3. \end{aligned}$$

With a little work it can be shown that $\langle p_1, p_2, p_3, p_4 \rangle = \mathcal{P}^3$ but that the system p_1, p_2, p_3, p_4 is not a basis.

In the above situations we saw examples both of bases and of linearly dependent spanners for several subspaces. That the above examples are typical is shown by the following nontrivial result, which we do not prove.

(1.9) Theorem. *Every finite-dimensional subspace S has at least one basis. In fact, each* spanner $\boldsymbol{\alpha}_1, \ldots, \boldsymbol{\alpha}_k$ *for S contains one or more subsystems which are bases for S. Moreover, all bases for S, no matter how constructed, contain the same number of vectors. This common number m is called the* ***dimension*** *of S and we write* $m = \dim S$.

According to this result, the fact that the system

$$\boldsymbol{\alpha}_1 = (1, 0, 0), \qquad \boldsymbol{\alpha}_2 = (1, 1, 0), \qquad \boldsymbol{\alpha}_3 = (0, 1, 0)$$

spans—but is not a basis for—that subspace S of $\mathcal{R}^3$ consisting of vectors with third entry zero, guarantees that at least one of its various subsystems

$$\boldsymbol{\alpha}_2, \boldsymbol{\alpha}_3; \quad \boldsymbol{\alpha}_1, \boldsymbol{\alpha}_3; \quad \boldsymbol{\alpha}_1, \boldsymbol{\alpha}_2; \quad \boldsymbol{\alpha}_3; \quad \boldsymbol{\alpha}_2; \quad \boldsymbol{\alpha}_1$$

is a basis for S. We found earlier that the subsystem $\boldsymbol{\alpha}_1, \boldsymbol{\alpha}_3$ is such a basis. In one of the problems the reader will be asked to determine whether any of the other subsystems is a basis for S (see problem 17). Note that since the system $\boldsymbol{\alpha}_1, \boldsymbol{\alpha}_3$ contains two vectors we may write $\dim S = 2$.

Observe, too, that since $\boldsymbol{\alpha}_1 = (1, 0, \ldots, 0)$, $\boldsymbol{\alpha}_2 = (0, 1, 0, \ldots, 0), \ldots, \boldsymbol{\alpha}_n = (0, \ldots, 0, 1)$ is known to be a basis for $\mathcal{R}^n$, we deduce the fact, comforting in view of our notation, that $\mathcal{R}^n$ is n-dimensional.

Theorem (1.9) indicates that if a system A: $\boldsymbol{\alpha}_1, \ldots, \boldsymbol{\alpha}_k$ spans a subspace S, then the following procedure suffices to find a basis for S. First check A itself for nonredundant spanning; if A is not a basis, check the k subsystems of A containing $k - 1$ vectors; if none of these is a basis, check the subsystems of A containing $k - 2$ vectors; and so on. Eventual success is assured. Another method, which is generally much quicker, is described in §2.

TERMS TO BE UNDERSTOOD

linear combination	finite-dimensional	linearly independent
span	basis	dimension
subspace	linearly dependent	

PROBLEMS

1. Check whether the following subsets are subspaces:

(a) $\mathcal{R}^2$: the set of vectors of the form $(a_1, 1)$ for all values of a_1

(b) $\mathcal{R}^3$: the set of vectors of the form $(a_1, 0, a_3)$ for all values of a_1 and a_3

(c) $\mathcal{R}^4$: the set of vectors of the form $(1, 1, 1, a_4)$ for all values of a_4

(d) $\mathcal{R}^4$: the set of vectors of the form $(c + d, c, 0, d)$ for all values of c and d

2. For those subsets in problem 1 which are subspaces, find a basis and determine the dimension.

3. Which one of the following subsets is a subspace of $\mathcal{C}(-\infty, \infty)$? Determine a basis for it.

S_1 = the set of all polynomials of the form $t^2 + at + b$ for all values of a and b

S_2 = the set of all polynomials of the form $at + b$ for all values of a and b.

4. For each of the following differential equations determine whether the set of all solutions forms a subspace of $\mathcal{C}(-\infty, \infty)$.

(a) $\dot{y}(t) = 0$

(b) $\ddot{y}(t) = 0$

(c) $\dot{y}(t) = 1$

(d) $\dot{y}(t) + y(t) = 0$

(e) $\dot{y}(t) + y(t) = 1$

5. For those solution sets in problem 4 which are subspaces, find a basis and determine the dimension.

6. For what values of a and b is the set of all functions y satisfying

$$\ddot{y}(t) = 0, \qquad y(0) = a, \dot{y}(0) = b$$

a subspace of $\mathcal{C}(-\infty, \infty)$? Find a basis for the subspace corresponding to each such pair (a, b).

7. For what values of a and b is the set of all functions satisfying

$$\ddot{y}(t) + ty(t) = 0, \qquad y(0) = a, \ddot{y}(0) = b$$

a subspace of $\mathcal{C}(-\infty, \infty)$?

8. Show that the set of all solutions of the equation

$$\dot{y}(t) = (y(t))^2$$

is *not* a subspace of $\mathcal{C}(-\infty, \infty)$.

9. Prove that the set of all solutions of any s-linear equation [definition (2.1) of Chapter 4] is a subspace of $\mathcal{C}(-\infty, \infty)$.

10. Which of the following subsets of $\mathcal{A}$ are subspaces?

(a) all $\boldsymbol{\alpha}$ such that $\|\boldsymbol{\alpha}\| = 1$

(b) all $\boldsymbol{\alpha}$ such that $\boldsymbol{\alpha} \cdot \boldsymbol{\gamma} > 0$ for some fixed arrow $\boldsymbol{\gamma}$

(c) all $\boldsymbol{\alpha}$ such that $\boldsymbol{\alpha} \cdot \boldsymbol{\gamma} = 0$ for some fixed arrow $\boldsymbol{\gamma}$

(d) all $\boldsymbol{\alpha}$ such that $\boldsymbol{\alpha} = \boldsymbol{\beta} + t\boldsymbol{\gamma}$ for some fixed arrows $\boldsymbol{\beta}$ and $\boldsymbol{\gamma}$ and all values of t

11. Using axiom (A_2) [see definition (1.1) of Chapter 1] prove that for all $\boldsymbol{\alpha},\boldsymbol{\beta},\boldsymbol{\gamma},\boldsymbol{\delta} \in \mathcal{V}$,

$$\boldsymbol{\alpha} + (\boldsymbol{\beta} + \boldsymbol{\gamma} + \boldsymbol{\delta}) = \boldsymbol{\alpha} + (\boldsymbol{\beta} + \boldsymbol{\gamma}) + \boldsymbol{\delta}.$$

12. Let S_L denote the set of all n-tuples $(c_1, c_2, \ldots, c_n)$ which are solutions of the homogeneous system of equations

$$(\mathrm{L}) \qquad \begin{array}{ccc} a_{11}x_1 + a_{12}x_2 + \cdots + a_{1n}x_n & = & 0 \\ \vdots & & \vdots \\ a_{m1}x_1 + a_{m2}x_2 + \cdots + a_{mn}x_n & = & 0. \end{array}$$

Show that S_L is a subspace of $\mathcal{R}^n$.

13. (a) Show explicitly that the set S of functions which can be put in the form

$$x(t) = A \sin (kt + B)$$

for appropriate scalars A and B is a subspace of $\mathcal{C}(-\infty, \infty)$. [*Hint:* By the formula for the sine of a sum we may write

$$\begin{aligned} A \sin (kt + B) + A' \sin (kt + B') &= (A \cos B + A' \cos B') \sin kt \\ &\quad + (A \sin B + A' \sin B') \cos kt \\ &= C \sin kt + D \cos kt \\ &= \sqrt{C^2 + D^2}(c \sin kt + d \cos kt), \end{aligned}$$

where $c^2 + d^2 = 1$. But $c^2 + d^2 = 1$ implies that for some angle B'', $c = \cos B''$ and $d = \sin B''$. The formula for the sine of a sum then permits the expression in parentheses above to be written $\sin (kt + B'')$.]

(b) Give a direct argument [not using the result in part (a)] which shows that if $x_1(t)$ and $x_2(t)$ are solutions of

$$(1) \qquad \ddot{x} + k^2 x = 0,$$

then $x_1(t) + x_2(t)$ and $cx_1(t)$ are also solutions of this equation, so that the solutions of (1) form a subspace of $\mathcal{C}(-\infty, \infty)$.

14. (a) Describe the span of each of the following systems.

$\mathcal{R}^2$: $\boldsymbol{\alpha}_1 = (1, 2)$, $\boldsymbol{\alpha}_2 = (-2, -4)$; $\boldsymbol{\beta}_1 = (1, 2)$, $\boldsymbol{\beta}_2 = (2, 1)$
$\mathcal{R}^3$: $\boldsymbol{\alpha}_1 = (1, -1, 1)$, $\boldsymbol{\alpha}_2 = (1, 1, -1)$, $\boldsymbol{\alpha}_3 = (1, 0, 0)$
$\mathcal{P}^4$: $p_1(t) = t + t^3$, $p_2(t) = t - t^3$, $p_3(t) = t^3$

(b) Find a basis for each of the spans obtained above. Utilize the theorem stated in the text.

15. (a) Show that if the system $\boldsymbol{\alpha}_1, \ldots, \boldsymbol{\alpha}_m$ is linearly dependent, then there are constants $d_1, \ldots, d_m$, *not all zero*, which satisfy

$$(\Delta) \qquad d_1\boldsymbol{\alpha}_1 + \cdots + d_m\boldsymbol{\alpha}_m = \mathbf{0}.$$

(*Hint:* Subtract from each other two different combinations of the $\boldsymbol{\alpha}$'s which give the same vector $\boldsymbol{\gamma}$ in $\langle \boldsymbol{\alpha}_1, \ldots, \boldsymbol{\alpha}_m \rangle$.)

(b) Show that if (Δ) is satisfied for certain scalars $d_1, \ldots, d_m$ not all zero, then the system $\boldsymbol{\alpha}_1, \ldots, \boldsymbol{\alpha}_m$ is linearly dependent. (*Hint:* $\mathbf{0} = 0\boldsymbol{\alpha}_1 + \cdots + 0\boldsymbol{\alpha}_m$.)

The above results give rise to the following frequently used condition:

CRITERION FOR LINEAR INDEPENDENCE. *A system $\boldsymbol{\alpha}_1, \ldots, \boldsymbol{\alpha}_m$ is linearly independent provided that $d_1 = d_2 = \cdots = d_m = 0$ is the* only *solution to* (Δ). *If there are additional solutions to* (Δ), *then the system is linearly dependent.*

16. A *nonhomogeneous* system of (two) linear algebraic equations

$$(\mathrm{L}) \qquad \begin{aligned} a_{11}x_1 + a_{12}x_2 + a_{13}x_3 &= d_1 \\ a_{21}x_1 + a_{22}x_2 + a_{23}x_3 &= d_2 \end{aligned}$$

is one in which at least one of the d's is not zero. Letting S_L denote the set of all triples (c_1, c_2, c_3) which are solutions of (L), determine which choices of the coefficients a_{ij} and right sides d_i give an S_L which is a subspace of R^3.

17. Find each subsystem of $\boldsymbol{\alpha}_1 = (1, 0, 0)$, $\boldsymbol{\alpha}_2 = (1, 1, 0)$, $\boldsymbol{\alpha}_3 = (0, 1, 0)$ which is a basis for $S = \langle \boldsymbol{\alpha}_1, \boldsymbol{\alpha}_2, \boldsymbol{\alpha}_3 \rangle$.

18. Find by inspection a basis for each of the following subspaces:

$S = \{(a, b, a)\}$ for all scalars a and b
$S = \{(a, b, -a, a + b)\}$ for all scalars a and b
$S = \mathcal{P}^3$
$S = \{x(t) = A \sin t + B \sin 2t + C \sin 3t\}$ for all scalars A, B, C

19. (a) Show that a two-vector system $\boldsymbol{\alpha}_1$, $\boldsymbol{\alpha}_2$ in which neither of the $\boldsymbol{\alpha}$'s is a multiple of the other is necessarily a basis. (*Hint:* $\langle\boldsymbol{\alpha}_1\rangle \neq \langle\boldsymbol{\alpha}_1, \boldsymbol{\alpha}_2\rangle$, since it omits $\boldsymbol{\alpha}_2$, for one thing. Similarly, $\langle\boldsymbol{\alpha}_2\rangle \neq \langle\boldsymbol{\alpha}_1, \boldsymbol{\alpha}_2\rangle$.)

(b) Prove without solving linear equations that both of the following are bases for $\mathcal{R}^2$: A: $\boldsymbol{\alpha}_1 = (1, 1)$, $\boldsymbol{\alpha}_2 = (-1, 1)$; B: $\boldsymbol{\beta}_1 = (1, 2)$, $\boldsymbol{\beta}_2 = (1, -2)$. (*Hint:* The dimension of $\mathcal{R}^2$ is already known.)

20. Show that any system A: $\boldsymbol{\alpha}_1, \ldots, \boldsymbol{\alpha}_n$ in which one of the $\boldsymbol{\alpha}$'s is $\mathbf{0}$ is not a basis.

2. *B*-Coordinates; Solution of Algebraic Equations

We are now in a position to use coordinates in other vector spaces besides $\mathcal{A}$. Given a finite-dimensional subspace S of a vector space $\mathcal{V}$, let B: $\boldsymbol{\beta}_1, \ldots, \boldsymbol{\beta}_n$ denote one of the bases of S (this implies dim $S = n$). Then by definition $\langle\boldsymbol{\beta}_1, \ldots, \boldsymbol{\beta}_n\rangle = S$, and for each vector $\boldsymbol{\alpha} \in S$ there is precisely one system of scalars $b_1, \ldots, b_n$ which expresses $\boldsymbol{\alpha}$ as a linear combination of the $\boldsymbol{\beta}$'s:

$$\boldsymbol{\alpha} = b_1\boldsymbol{\beta}_1 + b_2\boldsymbol{\beta}_2 + \cdots + b_n\boldsymbol{\beta}_n. \tag{2.1}$$

(2.2) Definition. The scalars $b_1 = b_1(\boldsymbol{\alpha}), \ldots, b_n = b_n(\boldsymbol{\alpha})$ assigned to the vector $\boldsymbol{\alpha}$ by means of (2.1) are called the ***B*-coordinates** of $\boldsymbol{\alpha}$. We shall indicate this situation by arranging these scalars in a column:

$$[\boldsymbol{\alpha}]_B = \begin{bmatrix} b_1 \\ b_2 \\ \cdot \\ \cdot \\ \cdot \\ b_n \end{bmatrix}. \tag{2.3}$$

This column is called the *B-matrix* of $\boldsymbol{\alpha}$.

Observe that these coordinates are not an attribute of the vector $\boldsymbol{\alpha}$ alone; they signify a *relationship* of $\boldsymbol{\alpha}$ to the basis B and will be different if a different choice is made for B. Nevertheless, as we saw in our discussion of particle motions, it is sometimes very useful to keep track of vectors by keeping track of their coordinates (relative to some *fixed* basis).

(2.4) Examples. *B*-Coordinates

(a) $\mathcal{R}^2$. Consider the system B: $\boldsymbol{\beta}_1 = (1, 2)$, $\boldsymbol{\beta}_2 = (1, -2)$. It is a basis for the space $\mathcal{R}^2$ (see §1, problem 19), and for any $\boldsymbol{\alpha} = (a_1, a_2)$ it is easily checked that

$$\boldsymbol{\alpha} = ((2a_1 + a_2)/4)\boldsymbol{\beta}_1 + ((2a_1 - a_2)/4)\boldsymbol{\beta}_2.$$

Consequently, the B-coordinates of $\boldsymbol{\alpha}$ are given by

$$[\boldsymbol{\alpha}]_B = \begin{bmatrix}(2a_1 + a_2)/4\\(2a_1 - a_2)/4\end{bmatrix}.$$

(b) $\mathcal{R}^n$. Take for B the system

$$\boldsymbol{\beta}_1 = (1, 0, \ldots, 0), \qquad \boldsymbol{\beta}_2 = (0, 1, 0, \ldots, 0), \ldots, \qquad \boldsymbol{\beta}_n = (0, \ldots, 0, 1).$$

We noted in example (1.8b) that this system is a basis for $\mathcal{R}^n$. If $\boldsymbol{\alpha} = (a_1, \ldots, a_n)$ is any vector of $\mathcal{R}^n$, then

$$\boldsymbol{\alpha} = a_1\boldsymbol{\beta}_1 + a_2\boldsymbol{\beta}_2 + \cdots + a_n\boldsymbol{\beta}_n.$$

Hence $a_1, a_2, \ldots, a_n$ are the B-coordinates of $\boldsymbol{\alpha}$:

$$[\boldsymbol{\alpha}]_B = \begin{bmatrix}a_1\\a_2\\\cdot\\\cdot\\\cdot\\a_n\end{bmatrix}.$$

We call this basis the *standard basis* for $\mathcal{R}^n$.

(c) $\mathcal{A}$. As in the preceding chapters, let the system E: $\mathbf{e}_1, \mathbf{e}_2, \mathbf{e}_3$ consist of arrows of unit length along three mutually perpendicular directions. We saw that E is a basis: for every arrow $\mathbf{v}$ there is a unique triple of scalars v^1, v^2, v^3 for which

$$\mathbf{v} = v^1\mathbf{e}_1 + v^2\mathbf{e}_2 + v^3\mathbf{e}_3,$$

namely, $v^1 = \mathbf{v} \cdot \mathbf{e}_1$, $v^2 = \mathbf{v} \cdot \mathbf{e}_2$, $v^3 = \mathbf{v} \cdot \mathbf{e}_3$. In our new notation this is the statement

$$[\mathbf{v}]_E = \begin{bmatrix}\mathbf{v} \cdot \mathbf{e}_1\\\mathbf{v} \cdot \mathbf{e}_2\\\mathbf{v} \cdot \mathbf{e}_3\end{bmatrix}.$$

(d) Let S denote the subspace of $\mathcal{C}(-\infty, \infty)$ consisting of solutions of the differential equation

$$\ddot{x}(t) + k^2x(t) = 0.$$

As noted earlier, S is spanned by D: d_1, d_2, where $d_1(t) = \sin kt$, $d_2(t) = \cos kt$. Moreover, it is not difficult to see that D is a basis for S.

Let us now find the D-coordinates of a solution x having the form

$$x(t) = A \sin (kt + B).$$

Expanding the right side we have

$$\begin{aligned} x(t) &= A \sin kt \cos B + A \cos kt \sin B \\ &= A \cos B\, d_1(t) + A \sin B\, d_2(t). \end{aligned}$$

Thus

$$[x]_D = \begin{bmatrix} A \cos B \\ A \sin B \end{bmatrix}.$$

In order to make effective use of B-coordinates, it is important to know how B-coordinates are affected by the addition and scalar multiplication operations on $\mathcal{V}$. It turns out that the situation is precisely parallel to that for $\mathcal{R}$.

(2.5) Proposition. *Let B: $\beta_1, \ldots, \beta_n$ denote a basis for the subspace S of $\mathcal{V}$. Given vectors $\alpha, \alpha' \in S$, let $b_1, \ldots, b_n$ denote the B-coordinates of α and $b_1', \ldots, b_n'$ denote the B-coordinates of α'. Then for all α, α' and all scalars c:*

$$(1) \qquad [\alpha + \alpha']_B = \begin{bmatrix} b_1 + b_1' \\ b_2 + b_2' \\ \cdot \\ \cdot \\ \cdot \\ b_n + b_n' \end{bmatrix}$$

$$(2) \qquad [c\alpha]_B = \begin{bmatrix} cb_1 \\ cb_2 \\ \cdot \\ \cdot \\ \cdot \\ cb_n \end{bmatrix}.$$

[We can summarize (1) and (2) by stating that the B-coordinates $b_1(\alpha), \ldots, b_n(\alpha)$ of a vector α depend "linearly" on α.]

Proof. By hypothesis we are given

$$\alpha = b_1\beta_1 + \cdots + b_n\beta_n, \qquad \alpha' = b_1'\beta_1 + \cdots + b_n'\beta_n.$$

Adding and collecting terms we obtain

$$\begin{aligned}\boldsymbol{\alpha} + \boldsymbol{\alpha}' &= (b_1\boldsymbol{\beta}_1 + \cdots + b_n\boldsymbol{\beta}_n) + (b_1'\boldsymbol{\beta}_1 + \cdots + b_n'\boldsymbol{\beta}_n)\\ &= (b_1 + b_1')\boldsymbol{\beta}_1 + \cdots + (b_n + b_n')\boldsymbol{\beta}_n.\end{aligned}$$

But this is just the statement that $b_1 + b_1', b_2 + b_2', \ldots, b_n + b_n'$ are the B-coordinates of $\boldsymbol{\alpha} + \boldsymbol{\alpha}'$, as claimed in (1). The proof of (2) is even shorter and will be left as an exercise. ▮

An important feature of the use of coordinates is that the system B must be a basis—otherwise for some vectors $\boldsymbol{\alpha}$ there would be more than one set of scalars satisfying

$$\boldsymbol{\alpha} = b_1\boldsymbol{\beta}_1 + \cdots + b_n\boldsymbol{\beta}_n.$$

Now, in general, the conclusion that a given system is a basis can only be made after solving a system of linear equations. The examples and problems of §1 illustrate this fact. Hence it is essential that anyone using vector spaces know how to solve systems of linear equations. Sometimes the solution of such systems is effortless. Consider the following examples:

$$(\mathrm{L}_1)\qquad \begin{aligned} x_1 - x_2 &= 1\\ x_1 - x_2 &= 0,\end{aligned}$$

$$(\mathrm{L}_2)\qquad \begin{aligned} x_1 - x_2 &= 1\\ 2x_1 - 2x_2 &= 2,\end{aligned}$$

$$(\mathrm{L}_3)\qquad \begin{aligned} 2x_1 - 2x_2 &= 2\\ x_1 + x_2 &= 0.\end{aligned}$$

Clearly (L_1) has *no* solutions, (L_2) has *infinitely many* solutions, and (L_3) has *exactly one* solution: $(x_1, x_2) = (\frac{1}{2}, -\frac{1}{2})$. On the other hand, the situation is far less obvious in the case of

$$(\mathrm{L}_4)\qquad \begin{aligned} 2x_1 - x_2 + 3x_3 + 2x_4 + x_5 &= -1\\ x_1 + 2x_2 + x_3 - x_4 + x_5 &= 2\\ 3x_1 - 4x_2 + 5x_3 + 5x_4 + x_5 &= -4.\end{aligned}$$

We shall now present a technique developed by Gauss and Jordan for solving all systems of linear equations (SLE's). In particular, it is *not* required that there be the same number of equations as unknowns. This technique, which is often called (*Gaussian*) *elimination*, will reveal that the examples (L_1)–(L_3) cover all the possible outcomes of solving an SLE. That is, we shall find that every SLE either has *no* solutions or *infinitely many* solutions or *exactly one* solution. Moreover, there will be produced for each system (L) a recipe which displays all the solutions of (L). The main feature of the method is its reliance on a finite sequence of simple manipulations, not one of which requires a creative decision. Such a procedure is called an *algorithm*.

A preliminary application of the algorithm to the very simple system

$$\begin{aligned} 2x + 4y &= -1 \\ x - y &= 1 \end{aligned} \tag{2.6}$$

will clarify the idea as well as specify the notation we shall use. We systematically modify (2.6) to arrive at a new SLE:

$$\begin{array}{l} 2x + 4y = -1 \\ x - y = 1 \end{array} \xrightarrow{\frac{1}{2}[1]} \begin{array}{l} x + 2y = -\frac{1}{2} \\ x - y = 1 \end{array} \xrightarrow{[2] - 1[1]}$$

$$\begin{array}{l} x + 2y = -\frac{1}{2} \\ 0x - 3y = \frac{3}{2} \end{array} \xrightarrow{-\frac{1}{3}[2]} \begin{array}{l} x + 2y = -\frac{1}{2} \\ 0x + y = -\frac{1}{2} \end{array} \xrightarrow{[1] - 2[2]}$$

$$\begin{aligned} x + 0y &= \tfrac{1}{2} \\ 0x + y &= -\tfrac{1}{2}. \end{aligned} \tag{2.6'}$$

In these manipulations symbols of the type $\xrightarrow{c[i]}$ and $\xrightarrow{[i] + c[j]}$ represent operations used in modifying an SLE: $c[i]$ denotes replacement of equation $[i]$ by its c-multiple while $\xrightarrow{[i] + c[j]}$ denotes replacement of equation $[i]$ by its sum with the c-multiple of equation $[j]$. It is here understood that the system to which an operation is to be applied is always the one most recently constructed. Also, equations which are not operated on are simply copied over.

Let us call operations of the type $\xrightarrow{c[i]}$ or $\xrightarrow{[i] + c[j]}$ *Gauss operations.* It can be easily shown that each of these operations leads from one SLE to another having exactly the same solutions. This explains why the solution $(x, y) = (\frac{1}{2}, -\frac{1}{2})$ of (2.6′) is also the solution of (2.6): the transition from (2.6) to (2.6′) utilized only Gauss operations, which do not alter the solutions of an SLE. This holds in general.

(2.7) Proposition. *Any application of a sequence of Gauss operations to a system of equations leaves the set of solutions unchanged.*

Now let us apply Gauss operations to solve a somewhat more interesting system than (2.6).

(2.8) Example. Gauss-Jordan Algorithm

$$
\text{(L)} \qquad
\begin{aligned}
2x_1 + 2x_2 + 2x_3 + x_4 &= -2\\
x_1 + x_2 + 2x_3 - x_4 &= 1\\
x_1 + 3x_2 - 2x_3 + x_4 &= -1.
\end{aligned}
$$

The following sequence of Gauss operations, which is an immediate extension of the technique used in (2.6), solves this system.

STAGE 1. x_1-REDUCE (L): Scan (L) to find the earliest (highest) equation having a nonzero x_1-coefficient; multiply this equation by a factor making its first coefficient equal to unity; add a multiple of the modified equation to each other equation so as to produce x_1-coefficients equal to zero. In the present example equation [1] has a nonzero x_1-coefficient, so we proceed as follows:

$$
\begin{aligned}
2x_1 + 2x_2 + 2x_3 + x_4 &= -2\\
x_1 + x_2 + 2x_3 - x_4 &= 1\\
x_1 + 3x_2 - 2x_3 + x_4 &= -1
\end{aligned}
\quad \xrightarrow{\frac{1}{2}[1]} \quad
\begin{aligned}
x_1 + x_2 + x_3 + \tfrac{1}{2}x_4 &= -1\\
x_1 + x_2 + 2x_3 - x_4 &= 1\\
x_1 + 3x_2 - 2x_3 + x_4 &= -1
\end{aligned}
$$

$$
\begin{array}{c}
\xrightarrow{[2] - 1[1]}\\
\xrightarrow{[3] - 1[1]}
\end{array}
\quad \text{(L}_1\text{)} \quad
\begin{aligned}
x_1 + x_2 + x_3 + \tfrac{1}{2}x_4 &= -1\\
0x_1 + 0x_2 + x_3 - \tfrac{3}{2}x_4 &= 2\\
0x_1 + 2x_2 - 3x_3 + \tfrac{1}{2}x_4 &= 0.
\end{aligned}
$$

STAGE 2. x_2-REDUCE (L_1): Scan (L_1) for the earliest equation having a zero x_1-coefficient and a nonzero x_2-coefficient; multiply this equation by a factor making its x_2-coefficient equal to unity; add a multiple of the modified equation to each other equation so as to produce x_2-coefficients equal to zero. In the present example equation [3] is the earliest equation satisfying the requirement. Thus we have

$$
\begin{aligned}
x_1 + x_2 + x_3 + \tfrac{1}{2}x_4 &= -1\\
0x_1 + 0x_2 + x_3 - \tfrac{3}{2}x_4 &= 2\\
0x_1 + 2x_2 - 3x_3 + \tfrac{1}{2}x_4 &= 0
\end{aligned}
\quad \xrightarrow{\frac{1}{2}[3]} \quad
\begin{aligned}
x_1 + x_2 + x_3 + \tfrac{1}{2}x_4 &= -1\\
0x_1 + 0x_2 + x_3 - \tfrac{3}{2}x_4 &= 2\\
0x_1 + x_2 - \tfrac{3}{2}x_3 + \tfrac{1}{4}x_4 &= 0
\end{aligned}
$$

$$
\xrightarrow{[1] - 1[3]}
\quad \text{(L}_2\text{)} \quad
\begin{aligned}
x_1 + 0x_2 + \tfrac{5}{2}x_3 + \tfrac{1}{4}x_4 &= -1\\
0x_1 + 0x_2 + x_3 - \tfrac{3}{2}x_4 &= 2\\
0x_1 + x_2 - \tfrac{3}{2}x_3 + \tfrac{1}{4}x_4 &= 0.
\end{aligned}
$$

STAGE 3. x_3-REDUCE (L_2): Scan (L_2) for the earliest equation having zero x_1- and x_2-coefficients but a nonzero x_3-coefficient; multiply this equation by a factor making its x_3-coefficient unity; add a multiple of the modified equation to each other equation so as to produce x_3-coefficients equal to zero. In the present example [2] is the only equation satisfying the requirement and it happens already to have 1 as its x_3-coefficient. Hence we have

$$\begin{aligned} x_1 + 0x_2 + \tfrac{5}{2}x_3 + \tfrac{1}{4}x_4 &= -1 \quad \xrightarrow{[1] - \frac{5}{2}[2]} \\ 0x_1 + 0x_2 + x_3 - \tfrac{3}{2}x_4 &= 2 \\ 0x_1 + x_2 - \tfrac{3}{2}x_3 + \tfrac{1}{4}x_4 &= 0 \quad \xrightarrow{[3] + \frac{3}{2}[2]} \end{aligned}$$

$$(\mathrm{L}_3) \qquad \begin{aligned} x_1 + 0x_2 + 0x_3 + 4x_4 &= -6 \\ 0x_1 + 0x_2 + x_3 - \tfrac{3}{2}x_4 &= 2 \\ 0x_1 + x_2 + 0x_3 - 2x_4 &= 3 \end{aligned}$$

STAGE 4. x_4-REDUCE (L_3): Scan (L_3) to find the earliest equation having zero x_1-, x_2-, and x_3-coefficients but a nonzero x_4-coefficient; multiply this equation by a factor making its x_4-coefficient unity; add a multiple of the modified equation to each other equation so as to produce x_4-coefficients equal to zero.

In the present example there are *no* equations fitting the requirement. Also, since there are no additional unknowns we cannot proceed to a stage 5. Hence our algorithm when applied to (L) terminates with (L_3), which is therefore called the *reduced form* of (L).

By transposing terms in (L_3) we see that (x_1, x_2, x_3, x_4) is a solution if and only if

$$(\mathrm{L}_3') \qquad \begin{aligned} x_1 &= -4x_4 - 6 \\ x_3 &= \tfrac{3}{2}x_4 + 2 \\ x_2 &= 2x_4 + 3. \end{aligned}$$

This formula shows that x_4 may be chosen arbitrarily, and after each such choice there is exactly one value of the quantities x_1, x_2, and x_3 such that (x_1, x_2, x_3, x_4) is a solution of (L_3). According to proposition (2.7) the solutions of (L_3) coincide with solutions of (L), so the algorithm has revealed that (L) has infinitely many solutions, all of them displayed in formula (L_3').

The reader should study the above example carefully. It completely reveals the working of the Gauss–Jordan algorithm for all SLE's. However, we make one additional comment. Occasionally one cannot carry out a given stage of the algorithm because no equation satisfies the given requirements; for instance, it may happen that in stage 2 *every* equation with a zero x_1-coefficient also has its x_2-coefficient zero. Whenever such situations arise one must *bypass* the stage in question and go on to the next stage. This means that counting both actual stages and bypassed stages (possibly including a "bypassed" final stage, as above) there will always be as many stages to the algorithm as there are unknowns in the SLE.

To bring home the ease with which the solutions of an SLE can be read off from its reduced form, we give two additional examples.

(2.9) Examples

(a) Consider the SLE

$$\text{(L)} \qquad \begin{aligned} 3x_1 + 2x_2 + x_3 &= 5 \\ x_1 - x_2 + 2x_3 &= -5 \\ 2x_1 + 2x_2 + x_3 &= 4 \\ 5x_1 + x_2 + 3x_3 &= 1 \\ 3x_1 - 2x_2 + 4x_3 &= -9. \end{aligned}$$

Applying the algorithm we obtain (the reader should check this):

$$(\text{L}_3) \qquad \begin{aligned} x_1 + 0x_2 + 0x_3 &= 1 \\ 0x_1 + x_2 + 0x_3 &= 2 \\ 0x_1 + 0x_2 + x_3 &= -2 \\ 0x_1 + 0x_2 + 0x_3 &= 0 \\ 0x_1 + 0x_2 + 0x_3 &= 0. \end{aligned}$$

The last two equations of (L_3) provide no information since they are identically true. Hence we discard them and by transposing obtain from (L_3) the formula

$$(\text{L}_3') \qquad \begin{aligned} x_1 &= 1 \\ x_2 &= 2 \\ x_3 &= -2. \end{aligned}$$

This demonstrates that (L_3) and thereby (L) has $(x_1, x_2, x_3) = (1, 2, -2)$ as its one solution. Note that this is so despite the fact that (L) involves more equations than the number of unknowns.

(b) Consider the SLE

$$\text{(L)} \qquad \begin{aligned} x_1 + 2x_2 - 3x_3 + x_4 - x_5 &= 1 \\ 2x_1 - 3x_2 + 2x_3 - 2x_4 + x_5 &= 2 \\ -x_1 + 12x_2 - 13x_3 + 7x_4 - 5x_5 &= 0. \end{aligned}$$

The algorithm yields for the reduced form of (L) (the reader should check this):

$$(\mathrm{L}_5)\qquad \begin{aligned} x_1 + 0x_2 - \tfrac{5}{7}x_3 - \tfrac{1}{7}x_4 - \tfrac{1}{7}x_5 &= 1\\ 0x_1 + x_2 - \tfrac{8}{7}x_3 + \tfrac{4}{7}x_4 - \tfrac{3}{7}x_5 &= 0\\ 0x_1 + 0x_2 + 0x_3 + 0x_4 + 0x_5 &= 1. \end{aligned}$$

The last equation of (L_5) cannot be satisfied by *any* x_1, x_2, x_3, x_4, x_5 values. Hence (L_5) and therefore (L) has no solutions. Note that this is so despite the fact that (L) involves fewer equations then the number of unknowns.

We shall end this section with several examples which illustrate the importance of the Gauss–Jordan algorithm for computations in vector spaces.

(2.10) Examples. Vector-Space Computations

(a) Determine whether or not the system A: $\boldsymbol{\alpha}_1, \boldsymbol{\alpha}_2, \boldsymbol{\alpha}_3, \boldsymbol{\alpha}_4$, where

$$\begin{aligned} \boldsymbol{\alpha}_1 &= (1, 2, -1, 3)\\ \boldsymbol{\alpha}_2 &= (1, 2, 2, 1)\\ \boldsymbol{\alpha}_3 &= (2, 0, 1, -1)\\ \boldsymbol{\alpha}_4 &= (-1, 2, -2, 1), \end{aligned}$$

is linearly independent.

Recall that linear independence of A means that A is a basis for $\langle \boldsymbol{\alpha}_1, \boldsymbol{\alpha}_2, \boldsymbol{\alpha}_3, \boldsymbol{\alpha}_4 \rangle$, that is, that every vector $\boldsymbol{\gamma} \in \langle \boldsymbol{\alpha}_1, \boldsymbol{\alpha}_2, \boldsymbol{\alpha}_3, \boldsymbol{\alpha}_4 \rangle$ is expressible as $\boldsymbol{\gamma} = c_1\boldsymbol{\alpha}_1 + c_2\boldsymbol{\alpha}_2 + c_3\boldsymbol{\alpha}_3 + c_4\boldsymbol{\alpha}_4$ in *only one way*. However, according to problem 15 in §1 it suffices to test only the special case $\boldsymbol{\gamma} = \mathbf{0}$. That is, A is independent if and only if there is exactly one choice (c_1, c_2, c_3, c_4) satisfying

$$(1)\qquad c_1\boldsymbol{\alpha}_1 + c_2\boldsymbol{\alpha}_2 + c_3\boldsymbol{\alpha}_3 + c_4\boldsymbol{\alpha}_4 = \mathbf{0}.$$

For the problem at hand this is the equation

$$\begin{aligned} &c_1(1, 2, -1, 3) + c_2(1, 2, 2, 1) + c_3(2, 0, 1, -1) + c_4(-1, 2, -2, 1)\\ &\quad = (c_1 + c_2 + 2c_3 - c_4, 2c_1 + 2c_2 + 0c_3 + 2c_4,\\ &\qquad -c_1 + 2c_2 + c_3 - 2c_4, 3c_1 + c_2 - c_3 + c_4) = (0, 0, 0, 0). \end{aligned}$$

Thus c_1, c_2, c_3, c_4 must satisfy

$$(2)\qquad \begin{aligned} c_1 + c_2 + 2c_3 - c_4 &= 0\\ 2c_1 + 2c_2 + 0c_3 + 2c_4 &= 0\\ -c_1 + 2c_2 + c_3 - 2c_4 &= 0\\ 3c_1 + c_2 - c_3 + c_4 &= 0. \end{aligned}$$

Applying the algorithm, we obtain from (2) the reduced form

$$\begin{aligned} c_1 + 0c_2 + 0c_3 + 0c_4 &= 0 \\ 0c_1 + 0c_2 + c_3 + 0c_4 &= 0 \\ 0c_1 + c_2 + 0c_3 + 0c_4 &= 0 \\ 0c_1 + 0c_2 + 0c_3 + c_4 &= 0. \end{aligned} \tag{3}$$

By inspection (3) requires $c_1 = c_2 = c_3 = c_4 = 0$. Hence (1) has only *one* solution (the obvious one) and A is therefore linearly independent.

(b) Find necessary and sufficient conditions on a_0, a_1, a_2, a_3 in order that the polynomial p defined by $p(t) = a_0t^3 + a_1t^2 + a_2t + a_3$ lie in the subspace of $\mathcal{C}(-\infty, \infty)$ spanned by p_1, p_2, p_3, where

$$\begin{aligned} p_1(t) &= t^3 + t^2 - t + 2 \\ p_2(t) &= t^3 + 2t^2 + 3t - 2 \\ p_3(t) &= t^2 + 4t - 4. \end{aligned}$$

The condition that $p \in \langle p_1, p_2, p_3 \rangle$ is simply that there exist scalars c_1, c_2, c_3 such that

$$c_1p_1 + c_2p_2 + c_3p_3 = p. \tag{1}$$

This is simply the statement

$$(c_1 + c_2)t^3 + (c_1 + 2c_2 + c_3)t^2 + (-c_1 + 3c_2 + 4c_3)t + (2c_1 - 2c_2 - 4c_3) = a_0t^3 + a_1t^2 + a_2t + a_3.$$

Equating coefficients of the various powers of t we have

$$\begin{aligned} c_1 + c_2 + 0c_3 &= a_0 \\ c_1 + 2c_2 + c_3 &= a_1 \\ -c_1 + 3c_2 + 4c_3 &= a_2 \\ 2c_1 - 2c_2 - 4c_3 &= a_3. \end{aligned} \tag{2}$$

The reduced form of (2) is

$$\begin{aligned} c_1 + 0c_2 - c_3 &= 2a_0 - a_1 \\ 0c_1 + c_2 + c_3 &= a_1 - a_0 \\ 0c_1 + 0c_2 + 0c_3 &= 5a_0 - 4a_1 + a_2 \\ 0c_1 + 0c_2 + 0c_3 &= -6a_0 + 4a_1 + a_3. \end{aligned} \tag{3}$$

Obviously (3) has *no* solutions unless the right sides of equations [3] and [4] are zero:

$$(4) \qquad \begin{aligned} 5a_0 - 4a_1 + a_2 &= 0 \\ -6a_0 + 4a_1 + a_3 &= 0. \end{aligned}$$

When (4) holds we can discard equations [3] and [4] in (3). Equations [1] and [2] can be written in the form

$$(3') \qquad \begin{aligned} c_1 &= \quad c_3 + (2a_0 - a_1) \\ c_2 &= -c_3 + (a_1 - a_0). \end{aligned}$$

This reveals that c_3 can be chosen arbitrarily and that a solution (c_1, c_2, c_3) of (3) can then be formed by selecting c_1 and c_2 as prescribed in (3′). We see, therefore, that the relations in (4) among a_0, a_1, a_2 and a_3 are both necessary and sufficient that $p \in \langle p_1, p_2, p_3 \rangle$.

(c) Find a basis for the subspace S of $\mathcal{R}^4$ consisting of all vectors of the form $(a + b + c, a + 2b - c, 3a + b + 7c, a - 2b + 7c)$ for all possible choices of a, b, c.

If we decompose

$$\begin{aligned} &(a + b + c, a + 2b - c, 3a + b + 7c, a - 2b + 7c) \\ &\qquad = (a, a, 3a, a) + (b, 2b, b, -2b) + (c, -c, 7c, 7c) \\ &\qquad = a(1, 1, 3, 1) + b(1, 2, 1, -2) + c(1, -1, 7, 7), \end{aligned}$$

and recall that a, b, c are arbitrary it becomes obvious that the subspace in question is

$$S = \langle (1, 1, 3, 1), (1, 2, 1, -2), (1, -1, 7, 7) \rangle$$

Thus it is natural to wonder whether the vectors

$$\boldsymbol{\alpha}_1 = (1, 1, 3, 1), \qquad \boldsymbol{\alpha}_2 = (1, 2, 1, -2), \qquad \boldsymbol{\alpha}_3 = (1, -1, 7, 7)$$

form a basis for S. We could proceed as in (a) to write

$$c_1\boldsymbol{\alpha}_1 + c_2\boldsymbol{\alpha}_2 + c_3\boldsymbol{\alpha}_3 = \mathbf{0}$$

and determine whether $c_1 = c_2 = c_3 = 0$ is the only solution of this equation.

An alternative procedure which will be helpful in case $\boldsymbol{\alpha}_1, \boldsymbol{\alpha}_2, \boldsymbol{\alpha}_3$ is *not* a basis is to find directly *all* linear combinations of the $\boldsymbol{\alpha}$'s which correspond to any given vector $\boldsymbol{\gamma} \in S$

$$\boldsymbol{\gamma} = (a + b + c,\ a + 2b - c,\ 3a + b + 7c,\ a - 2b + 7c) \in S.$$

Thus we write

$$(1) \qquad c_1\boldsymbol{\alpha}_1 + c_2\boldsymbol{\alpha}_2 + c_3\boldsymbol{\alpha}_3 = \boldsymbol{\gamma} = (a + b + c,\ a + 2b - c,\ 3a + b + 7c,\ a - 2b + 7c),$$

where a, b, c are given constants. This yields the following SLE for c_1, c_2, c_3:

$$(2) \qquad \begin{aligned} c_1 + c_2 + c_3 &= a + b + c \\ c_1 + 2c_2 - c_3 &= a + 2b - c \\ 3c_1 + c_2 + 7c_3 &= 3a + b + 7c \\ c_1 - 2c_2 + 7c_3 &= a - 2b + 7c. \end{aligned}$$

We wish to find all solutions of this system. Now the reduced form of (2) is, as the reader can verify,

$$(3) \qquad \begin{aligned} c_1 + 0c_2 + c_3 &= a + c \\ 0c_1 + c_2 - 2c_3 &= b - 2c \\ 0c_1 + 0c_2 + 0c_3 &= 0 \\ 0c_1 + 0c_2 + 0c_3 &= 0. \end{aligned}$$

Discarding the uninformative last two equations and transposing terms in the remaining equations we may write (3) as

$$(3') \qquad \begin{aligned} c_1 &= -c_3 + (a + c) \\ c_2 &= 2c_3 + (b - 2c). \end{aligned}$$

This formula reveals that there are infinitely many linear combinations of $\boldsymbol{\alpha}_1, \boldsymbol{\alpha}_2, \boldsymbol{\alpha}_3$ producing $\boldsymbol{\gamma}$, one for each arbitrary choice of c_3. Thus $\boldsymbol{\alpha}_1, \boldsymbol{\alpha}_2, \boldsymbol{\alpha}_3$ do *not* form a basis for S. On the other hand, if we set $c_3 = 0$, which corresponds to omitting $\boldsymbol{\alpha}_3$ from the linear combination (1) producing $\boldsymbol{\gamma}$, then (3′) shows that there is still a solution of (1) but *only one*,

$$\begin{aligned} c_1 &= a + c \\ c_2 &= b - 2c. \end{aligned}$$

Thus each $\gamma \in S$ is given by exactly one linear combination (1) involving α_1, α_2 alone. That is,

$$\alpha_1 = (1, 1, 3, 1), \qquad \alpha_2 = (1, 2, 1, -2)$$

is a basis for S.

(d) The system B: f_1, f_2, f_3, where

$$\begin{aligned} f_1(t) &= e^t + e^{-t} - \sin t \\ f_2(t) &= e^t \qquad\quad + 2 \sin t \\ f_3(t) &= e^t + e^{-t} + \sin t, \end{aligned}$$

is a basis for the subspace $S = \langle e^t, e^{-t}, \sin t \rangle$ of $\mathcal{C}(-\infty, \infty)$. Find the B-coordinates of f, where

$$f(t) = a_1 e^t + a_2 e^{-t} + a_3 \sin t.$$

We must solve the equation

$$(1) \qquad c_1 f_1 + c_2 f_2 + c_3 f_3 = f,$$

which is guaranteed to have exactly one solution since it is asserted that B is a basis. Equating coefficients of e^t, of e^{-t}, and of $\sin t$ in (1) we get

$$(2) \qquad \begin{aligned} c_1 + c_2 + c_3 &= a_1 \\ c_1 + 0c_2 + c_3 &= a_2 \\ -c_1 + 2c_2 + c_3 &= a_3. \end{aligned}$$

The algorithm gives

$$(3) \qquad \begin{aligned} c_1 + 0c_2 + 0c_3 &= a_1 - \tfrac{1}{2}a_2 - \tfrac{1}{2}a_3 \\ 0c_1 + c_2 + 0c_3 &= a_1 - \phantom{\tfrac{1}{2}}a_2 \\ 0c_1 + 0c_2 + c_3 &= -a_1 + \tfrac{3}{2}a_2 + \tfrac{1}{2}a_3. \end{aligned}$$

Hence

$$[f]_B = \begin{bmatrix} a_1 - \frac{1}{2}a_2 - \frac{1}{2}a_3 \\ a_1 - \phantom{\frac{1}{2}}a_2 \\ -a_1 + \frac{3}{2}a_2 + \frac{1}{2}a_3 \end{bmatrix}.$$

PROBLEMS

1. Show that the zero vector is never a member of a basis. Is there any other vector with this property? Can the zero vector be a member of a spanning system? Explain.

2. Let S denote the subspace of $\mathcal{C}(-\infty, \infty)$ consisting of solutions of

$$\ddot{x} + k^2x = 0.$$

(a) Find $[\sin(kt + b)]_B$, where B: $\sin kt$, $\cos kt$.

(b) Find $[\sin(kt + b)]_B$, where B: $\sin(kt - \pi/4)$, $\sin(kt + \pi/4)$.

3. Given $\boldsymbol{\beta}_1 = (0, 1, 1)$ and $\boldsymbol{\beta}_2 = (1, 0, 2)$, find a vector $\boldsymbol{\beta}_3$ such that $\boldsymbol{\beta}_1, \boldsymbol{\beta}_2, \boldsymbol{\beta}_3$ is a basis for $\mathcal{R}^3$.

4. Which of the following systems are bases for $\mathcal{R}^3$?

$$B\colon (0, 1, 1),\ (1, 0, 1),\ (1, 1, 0); \qquad B\colon (0, 1, 1),\ (1, 0, 1),\ (2, 1, 3);$$
$$B\colon (1, 0, 0),\ (0, 1, 0),\ (1, 2, 1).$$

Find $[(1, 1, 1)]_B$ for each of the bases.

5. For each of the following systems A determine whether the function f defined by $f(t) = 2e^t + 3\cos t - \sin t$ is a member of the subspace of $\mathcal{C}(-\infty, \infty)$ spanned by A.

(a) A: $-4e^t - 6\cos t + 2\sin t$

(b) A: $e^t + \cos t - \sin t$, $\cos t + \sin t$

(c) A: $e^t + 2\cos t + \sin t$, $3e^t + 5\cos t$

6. Determine which of the following systems span a subspace of $\mathcal{R}^4$ containing the vector $\boldsymbol{\alpha} = (1, 1, -2, 3)$.

(a) A: $(5, 5, 3, 5)$

(b) A: $(1, 2, 0, 4)$, $(3, 5, -2, 3)$

(c) A: $(1, 2, 0, 4)$, $(3, 5, -2, 3)$, $(0, 0, 0, \frac{1}{2})$

7. Determine which of the following systems are linearly independent. In each linearly dependent system indicate which of its vectors can be expressed as linear combinations of the others.

$\mathcal{R}^2$	$\mathcal{R}^3$
A: $(0, 2)$, $(2, 0)$	D: $(1, 1, 1)$, $(1, 0, 1)$, $(0, 1, 0)$
B: $(0, 2)$, $(2, 0)$, $(1, 1)$	E: $(1, 1, 1)$, $(2, 0, 1)$, $(0, 1, 0)$
C: $(1, 1)$, $(0, 0)$	

$\mathcal{C}(-\infty, \infty)$

F: $e^{2t} - 2e^t + e^{-t}$, $e^{2t} + e^t - e^{-t}$, $e^{2t} + e^t + e^{-t}$

G: $2\sin t + \cos 2t$, $\sin t + e^t$, $3\sin t - 2$

8. Prove that if A: $\boldsymbol{\alpha}_1, \boldsymbol{\alpha}_2, \boldsymbol{\alpha}_3$ is an independent system in the vector space $\mathcal{V}$, then so is

$$B\colon \boldsymbol{\beta}_1 = \boldsymbol{\alpha}_1 + \boldsymbol{\alpha}_2 - \boldsymbol{\alpha}_3,\ \boldsymbol{\beta}_2 = \boldsymbol{\alpha}_1 - \boldsymbol{\alpha}_2 + \boldsymbol{\alpha}_3,\ \boldsymbol{\beta}_3 = 2\boldsymbol{\alpha}_1 + \boldsymbol{\alpha}_2 + \boldsymbol{\alpha}_3.$$

9. Find the dimension of the subspace S consisting of all vectors in $\mathcal{R}^5$ of the form

$$(a - b + 2c - 2d,\ 2a + b + 6d,\ 3a + 2b + c + 9d,\ -a + 2c - 4d,\ a + b + c + 3d)$$

for all scalars a, b, c, d.

10. Which of the following systems are bases for $\mathcal{R}^4$?

(a) $(1, 1, 0, 1),\ (2, 0, 3, 1),\ (1, 0, -1, 0)$

(b) $(1, 1, 0, 1),\ (2, 0, 3, 1),\ (1, 0, 1, -1),\ (0, 0, 0, 0)$

(c) $(1, 1, 0, 1),\ (2, 0, 3, 1),\ (1, 0, 1, -1),\ (4, 1, 4, 1)$

11. Find the dimension of each of the subspaces spanned by the systems of problem 10.

3. Second-Order Equations with Constant Coefficients (Homogeneous Case)

In this section we wish to connect some of the ideas of this chapter with existence and uniqueness concepts for differential equations as discussed in Chapter 4. We concentrate on the second-order differential equation

$$\ddot{y}(t) + a\dot{y}(t) + by(t) = 0, \tag{3.1}$$

where a and b are constants.

Equation (3.1) is simple to handle and will illustrate some ideas which are really quite general ones. Also it is an important equation in physics. We give two illustrations of its occurrence.

(3.2) Examples. Equation (3.1)

(a) PARTICLE ON A SPRING. In Chapter 3 we discussed the three-dimensional motion of a particle which was attached to a spring. Here we want to discuss the case in which the particle and spring are constrained to move along a straight line as indicated in Figure 5.6. The motion of the particle can be completely described by specifying its displacement z, measured along the line from a fixed point O. The force on the particle due to the spring is

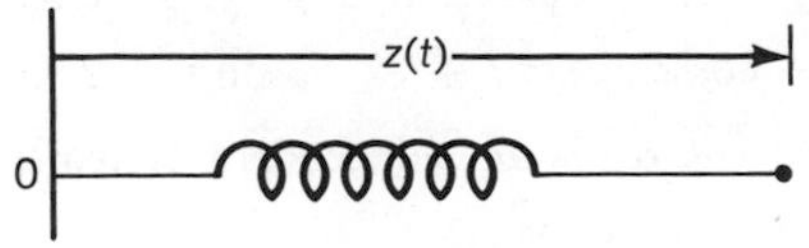

Figure 5.6

directed along the line, opposes the motion, and has a magnitude given by $k(z(t) - z_0)$, where k is a positive constant and z_0 is a constant measuring the unstretched length of the spring. We assume that, in addition, the particle is subject to a frictional force which is directed along the line, opposes the motion, and has magnitude $l\dot{z}(t)$, where l is a positive constant. Then if the mass of the particle is m, the equation of motion is

$$m\ddot{z}(t) = -l\dot{z}(t) - k(z(t) - z_0).$$

If we define y by $y(t) = z(t) - z_0$, this can be rewritten as

$$\ddot{y}(t) + \frac{l}{m}\dot{y}(t) + \frac{k}{m}y(t) = 0.$$

(b) LCR CIRCUIT. We discussed an LR circuit in Chapter 4. If we add to that circuit a capacitor (Figure 5.7) and assume that the impressed potential E is zero, we obtain an equation of the form (3.1). The equation obtained is for the charge y on the capacitor. The derivative $\dot{y}$ of y is the current. As before, there are potential drops of

$$L\frac{d}{dt}\dot{y}(t) = L\ddot{y}(t)$$

and $R\dot{y}(t)$ across the inductance and resistance, respectively. In addition, there is a potential drop across the capacitor given by $y(t)/C$, where C is the capacity. The sum of these drops must equal zero at each t; hence we obtain

$$L\ddot{y}(t) + R\dot{y}(t) + \frac{1}{C}y(t) = 0.$$

If we divide by L we once again obtain an equation of the form (3.1).

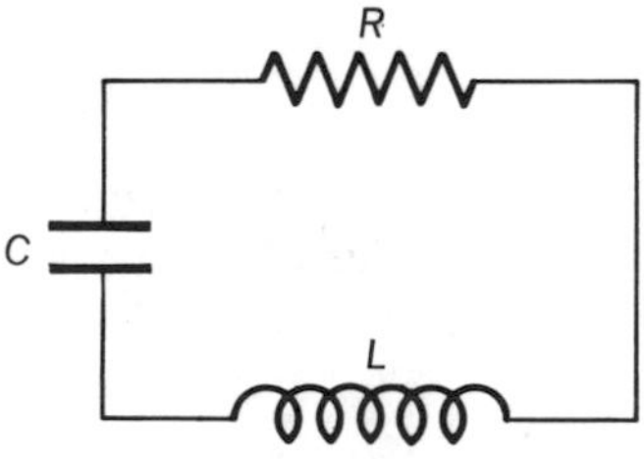

Figure 5.7

It turns out that we can give a procedure which will yield an explicit solution of equation (3.1). The reader will observe as we proceed that there is considerable similarity between the methods we use here and those that were used in §1 of Chapter 4.

We first study the special case of (3.1) in which $a = 0$. This has the form

$$\ddot{y}(t) + by(t) = 0. \tag{3.1'}$$

Equation (3.1′) has different kinds of solutions according to whether b is positive, negative, or zero. The reader can verify for each of the three cases that the two functions y_1 and y_2 given below are solutions of (3.1′):

CASE 1, $b < 0$, $b = -\gamma^2$. $y_1(t) = e^{\gamma t}$, $y_2(t) = e^{-\gamma t}$.

CASE 2, $b > 0$, $b = \gamma^2$. $y_1(t) = \cos \gamma t$, $y_2(t) = \sin \gamma t$.

CASE 3, $b = 0$. $y_1(t) = 1$, $y_2(t) = t$.

What we shall now show is that for all three cases one can use the special solutions y_1 and y_2 to build up all possible solutions of (3.1′). We establish first the following result.

(3.3) Proposition. *Given any numbers, t_0, y_0, and $\dot{y}_0$, there is exactly one set of constants c_1 and c_2 such that the function $y = c_1y_1 + c_2y_2$ is a solution of* (3.1′) *satisfying*

(i) $y(t_0) = y_0$, $\dot{y}(t_0) = \dot{y}_0$.

Proof. Observe that (3.1′) is an s-linear equation in the sense of (2.1) of Chapter 4. That is, any linear combination of solutions is again a solution (the reader should verify this fact). In particular, in any of the three cases the function $y = c_1y_1 + c_2y_2$ will be a solution for any choice of the constants c_1 and c_2. The only question is whether these constants can be determined so that the initial conditions (i) are satisfied. We verify this only for case 1. Here $y(t) = c_1e^{\gamma t} + c_2e^{-\gamma t}$, so the initial conditions require that c_1 and c_2 satisfy the relations

(ii)
$$\begin{aligned} y_0 &= c_1e^{\gamma t_0} + c_2e^{-\gamma t_0} \\ \dot{y}_0 &= \gamma c_1e^{\gamma t_0} - \gamma c_2e^{-\gamma t_0}. \end{aligned}$$

Equations (ii) are a pair of linear algebraic equations for c_1 and c_2. They have a unique solution for any choice of y_0 and $\dot{y}_0$, since their determinant is -2γ, which is not equal to zero†. The reader should verify that the cor-

†Recall that for a system of linear algebraic equations of the form

$$\begin{aligned} a_{11}x_1 + a_{12}x_2 &= w_1 \\ a_{21}x_1 + a_{22}x_2 &= w_2, \end{aligned}$$

the *determinant* of the system is the number $a_{11}a_{22} - a_{12}a_{21}$. It is an easily verified theorem that the system has a unique solution (x_1, x_2) for any (w_1, w_2) if and only if the determinant is not equal to zero.

responding relations in the other two cases can be solved for c_1 and c_2 uniquely. ∎

(3.4) Examples

(a) $\ddot{y}(t) - 4y(t) = 0$; $y(0) = 1$, $\dot{y}(0) = 0$. Here $y_1(t) = e^{2t}$ and $y_2(t) = e^{-2t}$. Equations (ii) are

$$\begin{aligned} 1 &= c_1 e^0 + c_2 e^{-0} = c_1 + c_2 \\ 0 &= 2c_1 e^0 - 2c_2 e^{-0} = 2c_1 - 2c_2. \end{aligned}$$

Hence $c_1 = c_2 = \frac{1}{2}$ and the required solution is

$$y(t) = \tfrac{1}{2}e^{2t} + \tfrac{1}{2}e^{-2t} = \cosh 2t.$$

(b) $\ddot{y}(t) + 9y(t) = 0$; $y(\pi) = 1$, $\dot{y}(\pi) = 1$. Here $y_1(t) = \cos 3t$ and $y_2(t) = \sin 3t$ and the analog of (ii) is

$$\begin{aligned} 1 &= c_1 \cos 3\pi + c_2 \sin 3\pi = -c_1 \\ 1 &= -3c_1 \sin 3\pi + 3c_2 \cos 3\pi = -3c_2. \end{aligned}$$

Hence the required solution is $y(t) = -\cos 3t - \frac{1}{3}\sin 3t$.

We recall that the two initial conditions in proposition (3.3)–(i) are precisely the ones which are appropriate for a single second-order equation such as (3.1′). We have just proved an existence theorem for (3.1′) under conditions (i). That is, we have constructed one solution of (3.1′) satisfying (i). There is also a uniqueness theorem which states that there is at most one solution. A proof (for one of the cases) is outlined in the problems.

Now we want to connect equation (3.1′) with the ideas of this chapter. The connection is provided by the following theorem.

(3.5) Theorem. *The set S of all solutions of* (3.1′) *forms a two-dimensional subspace of the space of all continuous functions. The functions y_1 and y_2 form a basis for S.*

Proof. Let y be any solution of (3.1′). For some t_0 set $y_0 = y(t_0)$ and $\dot{y}_0 = \dot{y}(t_0)$. Then by proposition (3.3) we can uniquely determine constants c_1 and c_2 such that the function $Y = c_1 y_1 + c_2 y_2$ satisfies

$$Y(t_0) = y_0 = y(t_0) \qquad \text{and} \qquad \dot{Y}(t_0) = \dot{y}_0 = \dot{y}(t_0).$$

Thus y and Y are both solutions of (3.2) and both satisfy the same initial conditions. Then the uniqueness theorem referred to above asserts that y and Y are equal for all t; that is,

$$y(t) = Y(t) = c_1 y_1(t) + c_2 y_2(t). \tag{3.6}$$

This shows that y_1 and y_2 span S. Moreover, the constants c_1 and c_2 are uniquely determined so that y_1 and y_2 do indeed form a basis. ∎

The functions y_1 and y_2 which we have presented are not the only possible basis for S. For example, the functions $\tilde{y}_1(t) = \cosh \gamma t$ and $\tilde{y}_2(t) = \sinh \gamma t$ will also serve in case 1. Careful reading of the proofs will reveal that the basic fact that was used in ensuring that y_1 and y_2 formed a basis was that the quantity $D = y_1\dot{y}_2 - y_2\dot{y}_1$ was nonzero for all values of t. This was true for the y_1 and y_2 we gave, but it is also true for $\tilde{y}_1$ and $\tilde{y}_2$. This basic property is further discussed in theorem (3.20).

We turn now to the more general equation (3.1) with $a \neq 0$. We can reduce this equation to equation (3.1′) as follows. Let y be a solution of (3.1) and consider the function z defined by $z(t) = e^{(a/2)t}y(t)$. We have

$$\begin{aligned} y(t) &= e^{-(a/2)t}z(t) \\ \dot{y}(t) &= -(a/2)e^{-(a/2)t}z(t) + e^{-(a/2)t}\dot{z}(t) \\ \ddot{y}(t) &= \frac{a^2}{4}\,e^{-(a/2)t}z(t) - ae^{-(a/2)t}\dot{z}(t) + e^{-(a/2)t}\ddot{z}(t). \end{aligned}$$

We substitute into (3.1) and find

$$\begin{aligned} &e^{-(a/2)t}\left[\ddot{z}(t) - a\dot{z}(t) + a\dot{z}(t) + \left(b - \frac{a^2}{4}\right)z(t)\right] \\ &\qquad = e^{-(a/2)t}\left[\ddot{z}(t) + \left(b - \frac{a^2}{4}\right)z(t)\right] = 0. \end{aligned}$$

Hence z satisfies the differential equation

(3.7) $$\ddot{z}(t) + \left(b - \frac{a^2}{4}\right)z(t) = 0.$$

This is of the form (3.1′) except that b is replaced by $b - (a^2/4)$. According to our discussion of equation (3.1′) we conclude that z must have the form

(3.8) $$z = c_1z_1 + c_2z_2,$$

where c_1 and c_2 are uniquely determined constants and z_1 and z_2 have the following form:

CASE 1, $b - (a^2/4) < 0$. $z_1(t) = e^{\sqrt{a^2/4-b}\,t}$, $z_2(t) = e^{-\sqrt{a^2/4-b}\,t}$.

CASE 2, $b - (a^2/4) > 0$. $z_1(t) = \cos\sqrt{b - \frac{a^2}{4}}\,t$, $z_2(t) = \sin\sqrt{b - \frac{a^2}{4}}\,t$.

CASE 3, $b - (a^2/4) = 0$. $z_1(t) = 1$, $z_2(t) = t$.

We recover the solution y of (3.1) by multiplying $z(t)$ by $e^{-(a/2)t}$. Hence (3.8) shows that all solutions of (3.1) have the form

$$y(t) = e^{-(a/2)t}\big(c_1 z_1(t) + c_2 z_2(t)\big) \tag{3.9}$$

for some uniquely determined constants c_1 and c_2. This shows that the functions y_1 and y_2 defined by†

$$y_1(t) = e^{-(a/2)t} z_1(t), \qquad y_2(t) = e^{-(a/2)t} z_2(t) \tag{3.10}$$

form a basis for the space S of solutions of (3.1). That is, every solution y of (3.1) has the form

$$y = c_1 y_1 + c_2 y_2. \tag{3.11}$$

Hence the set S of all solutions of (3.1) is also a subspace of dimension 2. There is also an analog of proposition (3.3) for equation (3.1).

(3.12) Proposition. *Given any numbers t_0, y_0, and $\dot{y}_0$, there is exactly one set of constants c_1 and c_2 such that the function y defined by* (3.9) *is a solution of* (3.1) *with*

(i) $y(t_0) = y_0, \qquad \dot{y}(t_0) = \dot{y}_0.$

The proof of proposition (3.12) is the same as that of (3.3). One simply substitutes the relation (3.11) into condition (i). This yields the system of linear equations

$$\begin{aligned} c_1 y_1(t_0) + c_2 y_2(t_0) &= y_0 \\ c_1 \dot{y}_1(t_0) + c_2 \dot{y}_2(t_0) &= \dot{y}_0 \end{aligned} \tag{3.13}$$

for the constants c_1 and c_2. It turns out that this system can always be solved uniquely for c_1 and c_2 because of the following important result.

(3.14) Proposition. *Let y_1 and y_2 be defined by* (3.10) *and define the function D by*

$$D(t) = y_1(t)\dot{y}_2(t) - y_2(t)\dot{y}_1(t).$$

Then $D(t)$ is never zero.

Observe that the determinant of the system (3.13) is simply $D(t_0)$ and proposition (3.14) guarantees that this is nonzero; hence we can solve (3.13). We shall not give a general proof of proposition (3.14), although this is a fairly straightforward calculation. Instead we illustrate it with some examples.

†Note that in the special case $a = 0$ these functions reduce to those introduced already as solutions of (3.3).

(3.15) A Mnemonic. There is a convenient way to remember the solutions y_1 and y_2 in the three cases. Suppose we try to find solutions of equation (3.1) having the form $y(t) = e^{\alpha t}$. If we substitute this into (3.1) we obtain

$$\ddot{y}(t) + a\dot{y}(t) + by(t) = (\alpha^2 + a\alpha + b)e^{\alpha t} = 0.$$

In order for $e^{\alpha t}$ to be a solution α would have to satisfy the quadratic equation

$$\alpha^2 + a\alpha + b = 0. \tag{3.16}$$

This equation is called the *auxiliary equation* for (3.1). Its solutions are

$$\text{(3.17)} \quad \alpha_1 = -a/2 + \sqrt{a^2/4 - b}, \qquad \alpha_2 = -a/2 - \sqrt{a^2/4 - b}.$$

If $a^2/4 - b$ is *positive* (case 1), then α_1 and α_2 are two distinct real numbers. In this case the solutions $e^{\alpha_1 t}$ and $e^{\alpha_2 t}$ are precisely y_1 and y_2:

$$\text{(1)} \qquad y_1 = e^{\alpha_1 t}, \qquad y_2 = e^{\alpha_2 t}.$$

If $a^2/4 - b$ is *negative* (case 2), then α_1 and α_2 are conjugate complex numbers.† In this case the solutions $e^{\alpha_1 t}$ and $e^{\alpha_2 t}$ must be interpreted by knowing about complex exponentials (these will be studied in Chapter 10) or else by referring to our previous results. Either way it is found that the real part $-a/2$ of α_1 and α_2 appears in an exponential factor while the imaginary part $\sqrt{b - a^2/4}$ of α_1 appears in a sine and in a cosine term:

$$\text{(2)} \quad y_1(t) = e^{-(a/2)t} \cos \sqrt{b - a^2/4}\, t, \quad y_2(t) = e^{-(a/2)t} \sin \sqrt{b - a^2/4}\, t.$$

If $a^2/4 - b = 0$ (case 3), both α_1 and α_2 are equal to $-a/2$. By comparing with our previous results we see that here in addition to $e^{-\alpha_1 t} = e^{-(a/2)t}$, $te^{-\alpha_1 t}$ is a solution:

$$\text{(3)} \qquad y_1(t) = e^{-\alpha_1 t}, \qquad y_2(t) = te^{-\alpha_1 t}.$$

(3.18) Examples

(a) Find the solution of $\ddot{y}(t) + 10\dot{y}(t) + 16y(t) = 0$ such that $y(1) = 1$, $\dot{y}(1) = 0$. Here $b - a^2/4 = 16 - 25 = -9 = -(3)^2$. Hence (3.8) becomes $\ddot{z}(t) - 9z(t) = 0$. This is case 1; hence the solutions are $z_1(t) = e^{3t}$

---

†See Chapter 10.

and $z_2(t) = e^{-3t}$. We deduce that the solutions of the original equation have the form

$$y(t) = e^{-5t}(c_1e^{3t} + c_2e^{-3t}) = c_1e^{-2t} + c_2e^{-8t}.$$

Then the initial conditions yield [equations (3.14)],

$$1 = c_1e^{-2} + c_2e^{-8}$$
$$0 = -2c_1e^{-2} - 8c_2e^{-8}.$$

Once again this is a system of algebraic equations for c_1 and c_2. The determinant of the system is

$$e^{-2}(-8e^{-8}) + 2e^{-2}(e^{-8}) = -6e^{-10} \neq 0;$$

hence we can solve for c_1 and c_2 uniquely.

(b) Find the solution of $\ddot{y}(t) - 4\dot{y}(t) + 13y(t) = 0$ such that $y(0) = -1$, $\dot{y}(0) - 1$. Here $b \quad a^2/4 = 13 - 4 - 9 = 3^2$. This is case 2; hence $z_1(t) = \cos 3t$ and $z_2(t) = \sin 3t$. Solutions of the original equation have the form

$$y(t) = e^{2t}(c_1 \cos 3t + c_2 \sin 3t).$$

The initial conditions yield [equation (3.14)]

$$-1 = e^0(c_1 \cos 0 + c_2 \sin 0) = c_1$$
$$1 = 2e^0(c_1 \cos 0 + c_2 \sin 0) + e^0(-3c_1 \sin 0 + 3c_2 \cos 0) = 2c_1 + 3c_2.$$

Clearly these equations can be solved, uniquely, for c_1 and c_2.

(c) In example (3.2a) discuss the motion. The equation in question is

$$\ddot{y}(t) + \frac{l}{m}\dot{y}(t) + \frac{k}{m}y(t) = 0.$$

Here we have $b - (a^2/4) = (k/m) - (l^2/4m^2)$. All three cases are possible depending on the relative magnitudes of k, l, m. Let us consider each case separately.

CASE 1, $(k/m) - (l^2/4m^2) < 0$, or $l^2 > 4km$. Solutions now have the form

(i) $y(t) = e^{-(l/2m)t}(c_1e^{\alpha t} + c_2e^{-\alpha t}), \qquad \alpha = \sqrt{\dfrac{l^2}{4m^2} - \dfrac{k}{m}}$.

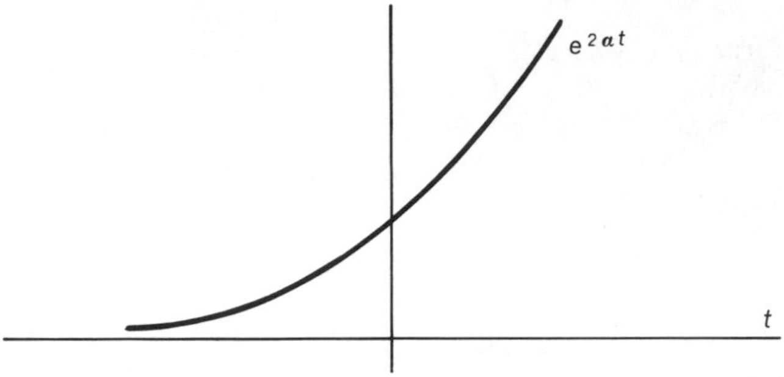

Figure 5.8

The constants c_1 and c_2 have to be determined by specifying the value of y and $\dot{y}$ at some time t_0. We can determine the *nature* of the motion, however, without actually making this computation. Consider what happens to the solution y as t tends to infinity. We write (i) in the form

(ii) $y(t) = c_1 e^{-[(l/2m)-\alpha]t} + c_2 e^{-[(l/2m)+\alpha]t}.$

Since $\alpha < l/2m$, it follows that both exponentials in (ii) have negative exponents and hence $y(t) \to 0$ as $t \to \infty$.

Next we ask how often the solution y can be zero. Since $e^{-lt/2m}$ is never zero, y can vanish at some time $t = t_1$ only if $c_1 e^{\alpha t_1} + c_2 e^{-\alpha t_1} = 0$; that is,

(iii) $e^{2\alpha t_1} = -\dfrac{c_2}{c_1}.$

The function $e^{2\alpha t}$ is plotted in Figure 5.8. We see then that if $c_2/c_1 < 0$, there will be exactly one value t_1 satisfying (iii), while if $c_1/c_2 > 0$ there will be no values. Hence $y(t)$ either changes sign exactly once or else not at all. Thus the motion will have one of the forms indicated in Figure 5.9.

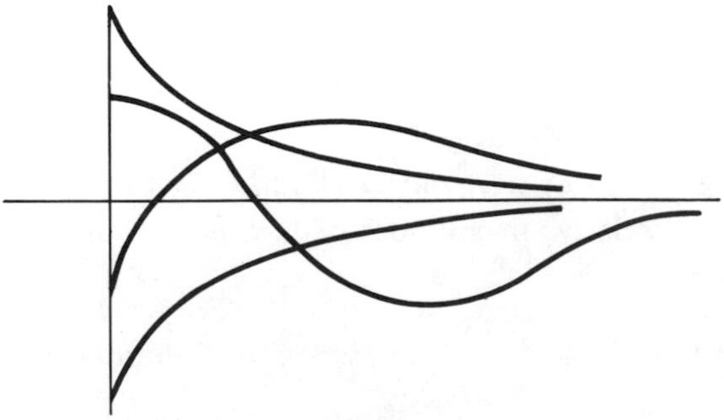

Figure 5.9

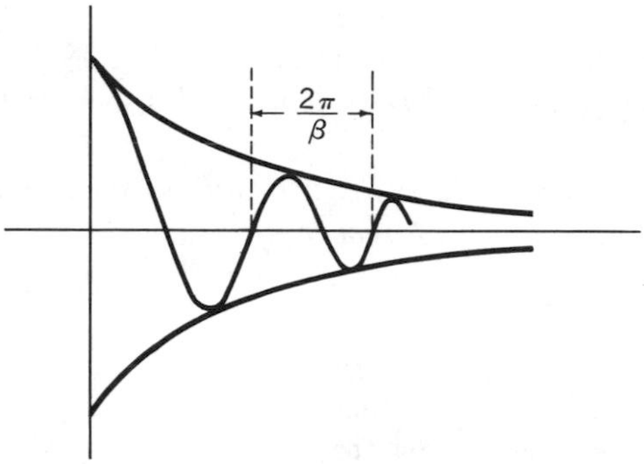

Figure 5.10

CASE 2, $(k/m) - (l^2/4m^2) > 0$, or $l^2 < 4km$. Solutions now have the form

(iv) $y(t) = e^{-lt/2m}(c_1 \cos \beta t + c_2 \sin \beta t), \qquad \beta = \sqrt{\dfrac{k}{m} - \dfrac{l^2}{4m^2}}\,.$

For any choice of c_1 and c_2 [that is, of $y(t_0)$ and $\dot{y}(t_0)$] the function in parentheses in (iv) has the same value for any two times which differ by a multiple of $2\pi/\beta$. Hence the form of the solution is as indicated in Figure 5.10.

CASE 3, $(k/m) - (l^2/4m^2) = 0$, or $l^2 = 4km$. Solutions now have the form

(v) $y(t) = e^{-lt/2m}(c_1 + c_2 t).$

Once again the solution tends to zero as t tends to infinity and it changes sign exactly once, at a time $t = t_1$ determined by $t_1 = -c_1/c_2$ (assuming that $-c_1/c_2 > t_0$).

There is an underlying idea in what we have done in this section and this idea applies to more general problems. We want to outline the concept. It applies to any second-order equation of the form

$$\ddot{y}(t) + a(t)\dot{y}(t) + b(t)y(t) = 0, \tag{3.19}$$

where a and b are continuous functions.† The reader should verify that any equation of this type is s-linear. In the language of this chapter this means that the set of all solutions of (3.19) forms a subspace of the space of continuous functions. We summarize the results in the following theorem.

†The procedure can be extended to nth-order s-linear equations also.

(3.20) Theorem

(a) *Let* y_1 *and* y_2 *be any two solutions of* (3.19) *and define* D *by* $D(t) = y_1(t)\dot{y}_2(t) - y_2(t)\dot{y}_1(t)$. *Then either* $D(t) \equiv 0$ *or else* $D(t)$ *is never zero.*

(b) *The set of solutions of* (3.19) *is a two-dimensional subspace of the set of continuous functions. Moreover, if* y_1 *and* y_2 *are any two solutions of* (3.19) *with* $D = y_1\dot{y}_2 - y_2\dot{y}_1$ *not zero, then* y_1 *and* y_2 *form a basis for* S.

We are not going to prove this theorem but we want to make a few comments on its meaning. We know from Chapter 4 that appropriate initial conditions for (3.19) have the form

$$y(t_0) = y_0, \qquad \dot{y}(t_0) = \dot{y}_0. \tag{3.21}$$

The main content of the theorem is that if y_1 and y_2 are as in (b), then we can choose constants c_1 and c_2, uniquely, in such a way that the function $y = c_1y_1 + c_2y_2$ satisfies (3.21). [Note that y surely is a solution of (3.19) since y_1 and y_2 are solutions and S is a subspace; that is, (3.19) is s-linear.] If we substitute $y = c_1y_1 + c_2y_2$ into (3.19), we obtain

$$\begin{aligned} y_0 &= c_1y_1(t_0) + c_2y_2(t_0) \\ \dot{y}_0 &= c_1\dot{y}_1(t_0) + c_2\dot{y}_2(t_0). \end{aligned} \tag{3.22}$$

This is a set of linear equations for c_1 and c_2 and its determinant is $D(t_0)$, which is nonzero. Thus (3.22) can be solved for c_1 and c_2.

There is one simple way to make sure that a pair of solutions y_1 and y_2 are such that D is nonzero. This is to make these solutions satisfy the conditions

$$y_1(t_0) = 1, \quad \dot{y}_1(t_0) = 0; \qquad y_2(t_0) = 0, \quad \dot{y}_2(t_0) = 1. \tag{3.23}$$

For then we have

$$D(t_0) = y_1(t_0)\dot{y}_2(t_0) - \dot{y}_1(t_0)y_2(t_0) = 1 \cdot 1 - 0 \cdot 0 = 1.$$

The existence and uniqueness of such a pair of solutions is guaranteed by the methods of Chapter 4.

Unfortunately one can obtain *explicit* solutions to (3.19) essentially only in the case we treated, that of constant coefficients. On the other hand, one often wants to obtain solutions of equations of the type (3.19) in physics [for example, the electric circuit of example (3.2b), where L, R, and C can change with time, say through heating]. Then one must have recourse to numerical methods such as those of §5 of Chapter 4. The importance of our theorem in this context is the following. Suppose one wishes to solve the equation many times for various choices of y_0 and $\dot{y}_0$ in (3.22). Then the efficient procedure is to calculate the special solutions y_1 and y_2 described in (3.23). Thereafter we can obtain the solution satisfying (3.22) as simply

$$y = y_0 y_1(t) + \dot{y}_0 y_2(t).$$

The reader should verify that this is indeed the solution satisfying (3.22). A further illustration of the use of a basis y_1, y_2 of the space of solutions of (3.19) occurs in §4.

PROBLEMS

1. Find the most general solution of each of the following differential equations.

(a) $\ddot{y}(t) - 16y(t) = 0$
(b) $\ddot{y}(t) + 4y(t) = 0$
(c) $\ddot{y}(t) + 9y(t) = 0$
(d) $\ddot{y}(t) + 2\dot{y}(t) = 0$
(e) $\ddot{y}(t) = 0$
(f) $\ddot{y}(t) - \dot{y}(t) - 2y(t) = 0$
(g) $\ddot{y}(t) - 4\dot{y}(t) + 5y(t) = 0$
(h) $\ddot{y}(t) - 4\dot{y}(t) + 4y(t) = 0$

2. Find the solution of each of the following initial-value problems.

(a) $\ddot{y}(t) + 9y(t) = 0, \quad y(\pi) = 1, \ \dot{y}(\pi) = -1$

(b) $\ddot{y}(t) - 3\dot{y}(t) = 0, \quad y(0) = 1, \ \dot{y}(0) = 0$

(c) $\ddot{y}(t) - 21\dot{y}(t) + 17y(t) = 0, \quad y(1) = 0, \ \dot{y}(1) = 0$

(d) $\ddot{y}(t) + 2\dot{y}(t) + 6y(t) = 0, \quad y(0) = 0, \ \dot{y}(0) = -1$

(e) $\ddot{y}(t) + 6\dot{y}(t) + 9y(t) = 0, \quad y(0) = 0, \ \dot{y}(0) = 1$

(f) $\ddot{y}(t) + \dot{y}(t) - 6y(t) = 0, \quad y(0) = 1, \ \dot{y}(0) = 1$

3. Show that the charge on the capacitor in example (3.2b) always tends to zero as $t \longrightarrow \infty$ no matter what the initial values (L, R, and C are all positive).

4. Suppose the circuit in example (3.2b) contains a battery which produces a constant potential E_0. Show that the charge on the capacitor tends to a constant value as $t \longrightarrow \infty$ no matter what the initial values. Find this constant value.

5. Consider example (3.18c) for Case 1. The situation in which the solution y_0 never changes sign is called *critical damping*. Let y_0 and $\dot{y}_0$ be the values of y and $\dot{y}$ at $t = 0$. Show that critical damping never occurs if $\dot{y}_0 = 0$.

6. (a) Let y be a solution of (3.1′). Show that the quantity $\dot{y}^2 + by^2$ must be constant for all time.

(b) If the resistance R in example (3.2b) is zero, show that the current is a maximum when the charge is a minimum.

(c) If $b > 0$ and $y(t_0) = \dot{y}(t_0) = 0$ for some t_0, show that y must be identically zero.

(d) Use the result in part (c) to give a uniqueness theorem for the problem in proposition (3.3). [*Hint:* Let u and v be solutions and use part (c) to prove that $y = u - v$ is identically zero.]

7. Consider the equation

$$\text{(i)} \qquad \dddot{y}(t) - \dot{y}(t) = 0.$$

(a) Show that the set S of all solutions of (i) forms a subspace of $\mathcal{C}(-\infty, \infty)$.

(b) Show that $y_1 = e^t$, $y_2 = e^{-t}$, $y_3 = 1$ are all solutions of (i).

(c) Show that given y_0, $\dot{y}_0$, and $\ddot{y}_0$ one can find a unique function of the form $y = c_1y_1 + c_2y_2 + c_3y_3$ which is a solution of (i) and satisfies

$$\text{(ii)} \qquad y(t_0) = y_0, \qquad \dot{y}(t_0) = \dot{y}_0, \qquad \ddot{y}(t_0) = \ddot{y}_0.$$

4. Second-Order Equations with Constant Coefficients (Nonhomogeneous Case)

We can use the results of §3 to discuss a "nonhomogeneous" equation corresponding to (3.1). This is the equation

$$\ddot{y}(t) + a\dot{y}(t) + by(t) = f(t), \tag{4.1}$$

where a and b are constants and f is a continuous function. Prototypes of this equation occur with the examples in (3.2) if in case (a) we subject the particle to an additional external force along the line of motion or in case (b) if we have an impressed potential in the circuit. The corresponding equations are

$$m\ddot{z}(t) = -l\dot{z}(t) - k\big(z(t) - z_0\big) + F(t) \tag{4.2}$$

and

$$Ly(t) + R\dot{y}(t) + \frac{1}{C}y(t) = E(t). \tag{4.3}$$

We note that, in contrast to equation (3.1), the set S of solutions of (4.1) *does not* form a subspace. The reader should verify that if f is not identically zero, then S is *not* closed either under addition or scalar multiplication.

We present now a method called *variation of parameters.* This procedure is designed to obtain one solution of (4.1). Let y_1 and y_2 be the two solutions of the homogeneous equation (3.1) which are given in (3.10). Then we will show that we can find a solution of (4.1) in the form

$$y(t) = \alpha(t)y_1(t) + \beta(t)y_2(t).$$

From this equation it follows that

$$\dot{y}(t) = \dot{\alpha}(t)y_1(t) + \dot{\beta}(t)y_2(t) + \alpha(t)\dot{y}_1(t) + \beta(t)\dot{y}_2(t).$$

We now require that α and β be chosen so that

$$\dot{\alpha}(t)y_1(t) + \dot{\beta}(t)y_2(t) = 0. \tag{4.4}$$

Then we have

$$\begin{aligned}\dot{y}(t) &= \alpha(t)\dot{y}_1(t) + \beta(t)\dot{y}_2(t)\\ \ddot{y}(t) &= \dot{\alpha}(t)\dot{y}_1(t) + \dot{\beta}(t)\dot{y}_2(t) + \alpha(t)\ddot{y}_1(t) + \beta(t)\ddot{y}_2(t).\end{aligned}$$

Now we further require that α and β should satisfy

$$\dot{\alpha}(t)\dot{y}_1(t) + \dot{\beta}(t)\dot{y}_2(t) = f(t). \tag{4.5}$$

Then we have, by (4.5),

$$\begin{aligned}\ddot{y}(t) + a\dot{y}(t) + by(t) &= \big(\dot{\alpha}(t)\dot{y}_1(t) + \dot{\beta}(t)\dot{y}_2(t) + \alpha(t)\ddot{y}_1(t) + \beta(t)\ddot{y}_2(t)\big)\\ &\quad + a\big(\alpha(t)\dot{y}_1(t) + \beta(t)\dot{y}_2(t)\big)\\ &\quad + b\big(\alpha(t)y_1(t) + \beta(t)y_2(t)\big)\\ &= f(t) + \alpha(t)[\ddot{y}_1(t) + a\dot{y}_1(t) + by_1(t)]\\ &\quad + \beta(t)[\ddot{y}_2(t) + a\dot{y}_2(t) + by_2(t)].\end{aligned}$$

Since both y_1 and y_2 are solutions of (3.1), each of the terms in brackets vanishes, hence y is a solution of (4.1).

Equations (4.4) and (4.5) are a pair of linear algebraic equations for $\dot{\alpha}(t)$ and $\dot{\beta}(t)$. Observe that the determinant of this system is once again $D(t)$, which is nonzero by proposition (3.14). Hence we can solve for $\dot{\alpha}$ and $\dot{\beta}$ and then determine α and β by integration. We illustrate with some examples.

(4.6) Examples. Variation of Parameters

(a) $\ddot{y}(t) - 4y(t) = t$. Here $a = 0$, so $y_1(t) = e^{2t}$, $y_2(t) = e^{-2t}$. Equations (4.6) and (4.7) become

$$\begin{aligned}\dot{\alpha}(t)e^{2t} + \dot{\beta}(t)e^{-2t} &= 0\\ 2\dot{\alpha}(t)e^{2t} - 2\dot{\beta}(t)e^{-2t} &= t.\end{aligned}$$

Note that the determinant of this system [that is, $D(t)$] is not zero. The solution of the system is

$$\dot{\alpha}(t) = \tfrac{1}{4}te^{-2t}, \qquad \dot{\beta}(t) = -\tfrac{1}{4}te^{2t}.$$

Thus $\alpha(t)$ and $\beta(t)$ can now be obtained by integration by parts. We have

$$\int \tfrac{1}{4}te^{-2t}\,dt = -\tfrac{1}{8}te^{-2t} - \tfrac{1}{16}e^{-2t} + \text{const.}$$

Hence we have

$$\text{(i)} \qquad \alpha(t) = -\tfrac{1}{8}te^{-2t} - \tfrac{1}{16}e^{-2t} + c_1,$$

where c_1 is a constant. In a similar way we find

$$\text{(ii)} \qquad \beta(t) = -\tfrac{1}{8}te^{2t} + \tfrac{1}{16}e^{2t} + c_2.$$

Thus any function of the form

$$\text{(iii)} \qquad \begin{aligned} y(t) = \alpha(t)e^{2t} + \beta(t)e^{-2t} &= (-\tfrac{1}{8}te^{-2t} - \tfrac{1}{16}e^{-2t} + c_1)e^{2t} \\ &+ (-\tfrac{1}{8}te^{2t} + \tfrac{1}{16}e^{2t} + c_2)e^{-2t} = -\tfrac{1}{4}t + c_1e^{2t} + c_2e^{-2t} \end{aligned}$$

will be a solution of (a).

(b) $\ddot{y}(t) + 2\dot{y}(t) + 2y(t) = e^{-t}$. In this equation $a = 2$, $b = 2$, and $b - (a^2/4) = 1$. Hence we have

$$y_1(t) = e^{-t}\cos t, \qquad y_2(t) = e^{-t}\sin t, \qquad D(t) = e^{-t}.$$

The system (4.5) and (4.6) becomes

$$\text{(i)} \qquad \begin{aligned} 0 &= \dot{\alpha}(t)e^{-t}\cos t + \dot{\beta}(t)e^{-t}\sin t \\ e^{-t} &= \dot{\alpha}(t)(-e^{-t}\cos t - e^{-t}\sin t) + \dot{\beta}(t)(-e^{-t}\sin t + e^{-t}\cos t). \end{aligned}$$

It can be verified that the solutions of (i) are

$$\dot{\alpha}(t) = -\sin t, \qquad \dot{\beta}(t) = \cos t;$$

hence

$$\text{(ii)} \qquad \alpha(t) = \cos t + c_1, \qquad \beta(t) = \sin t + c_2.$$

It follows that the function

$$\text{(iii)} \qquad \begin{aligned} y(t) = e^{-t}\big(\alpha(t)\cos t + \beta(t)\sin t\big) &= e^{-t}\cos t(\cos t + c_1) \\ &+ e^{-t}\sin t(\sin t + c_2) = e^{-t} + [e^{-t}(c_1\cos t + c_2\sin t)] \end{aligned}$$

is a solution of equation (b).

There are a number of things to be learned from these two examples. First we observe that the two constants c_1 and c_2 which appear in formulas (iii) can be used to fit the solutions to the initial conditions appropriate to (4.1). Again we illustrate with an example.

(4.7) Example. Initial Conditions. Find a solution of $\ddot{y}(t) - 4y(t) = t$ such that $y(1) = 1$, $\dot{y}(1) = 0$. We substitute the formula (iii) of example (4.6a) into these conditions and obtain

$$\text{(i)}\qquad \begin{aligned} 1 = y(1) &= -\tfrac{1}{4}\cdot 1 + [c_1e^2 + c_2e^{-2}] \\ 0 = \dot{y}(1) &= -\tfrac{1}{4} + [2c_1e^2 - 2c_2e^{-2}]. \end{aligned}$$

Once again this is a system of algebraic equations for c_1 and c_2 and once again the determinant of the system is $D(1) = y_1(1)\dot{y}_2(1) - y_2(1)\dot{y}_1(1)$ and this is nonzero, as is guaranteed by proposition (3.14). The solution of (i) is

$$c_1 = \tfrac{11}{16}e^{-2}, \qquad c_2 = \tfrac{9}{16}e^2.$$

A second observation about examples (4.6) is that the solution in each case is divided into two parts. The term involving c_1 and c_2, which we have enclosed in brackets, is seen to be simply the most general solution of the corresponding homogeneous equation, that is, (3.1). Thus the bracketed term in each case is simply $c_1y_1 + c_2y_2$. The remaining term in equations (iii) is one particular solution of the nonhomogeneous equation (4.1). This decomposition illustrates a general principle which we formulate now.

(4.8) Proposition. *Let y_0 be a particular solution of* (4.1). *Then every solution of* (4.1) *has the form*

$$y = y_0 + Y,$$

where Y is some solution of the corresponding homogeneous equation (3.1).

Proof. Let y be any solution of (4.1) and let $Y = y - y_0$. Then we have

$$\begin{aligned} \ddot{y}(t) + a\dot{y}(t) + by(t) &= f(t) \\ \ddot{y}_0(t) + a\dot{y}_0(t) + by_0(t) &= f(t). \end{aligned}$$

If we subtract these two equations the functions f cancel and we have

$$\begin{aligned} &\ddot{y}(t) - \ddot{y}_0(t) + a\big(\dot{y}(t) - \dot{y}_0(t)\big) + b\big(y(t) - y_0(t)\big) \\ &\qquad = \ddot{Y}(t) + a\dot{Y}(t) + bY(y) = 0. \end{aligned}$$

Hence Y is a solution of (3.1). ▮

The reader will recall that there was an analogous principle for the first-order linear nonhomogeneous equation in Chapter 4. Both that principle and proposition (4.8) are special cases of a much more general idea which will occur again and to which we shall ultimately attach the term "splitting theorem."

The importance of proposition (4.8) is that it enables one to reduce the problem of determining all solutions of (4.1) to two simpler steps:

(i) Find *some* particular solution of (4.1).

(ii) Find the most general solution of the homogeneous equation (3.1).

The point here is that we may be able to accomplish step (i) by a guess without having to go through the rather complicated procedure of variation of parameters. Thus there is an analog of the method of undetermined coefficients which was introduced for first-order equations. We leave the development of this principle mainly to the problems, but we do want to discuss one special example which is of physical interest.

(4.9) Example. Periodic Forced Vibrations. For the particle in example (3.2a), assume that there is an external force having the form $F(t) = F_0 \cos \omega t$. Assume also that $m = 1$. Discuss the motion. The equation in question is now (4.2) or, if we set $y(t) = z(t) - z_0$,

$$\text{(i)} \quad \ddot{y}(t) + l\dot{y}(t) + ky(t) = F_0 \cos \omega t.$$

We show first of all that in all but a very special case we can find a solution y_0 of (i) having the form

$$\text{(ii)} \quad y_0(t) = A \cos \omega t + B \sin \omega t,$$

where A and B are certain constants. We substitute (ii) into (i) and obtain

$$\text{(iii)} \quad \begin{aligned} F_0 \cos \omega t = {} & -\omega^2 A \cos \omega t - \omega^2 B \sin \omega t \\ & + l(-\omega A \sin \omega t + \omega B \cos \omega t) \\ & + k(A \cos \omega t + B \sin \omega t). \end{aligned}$$

We equate the coefficient of $\cos \omega t$ on the right side of (iii) to F_0 and the coefficient of $\sin \omega t$ to zero. This yields

$$\text{(iv)} \quad \begin{aligned} (k - \omega^2)A + \omega l B &= F_0 \\ -\omega l A + (k - \omega^2)B &= 0. \end{aligned}$$

The system (iv) can be solved for A and B except in the special case

$$\text{(v)} \quad l = 0, \qquad \omega^2 = k.$$

The solution, if (v) is not the case, is

$$\text{(vi)} \quad A = \frac{k - \omega^2}{D} F_0, \qquad B = \frac{\omega l}{D} F_0,$$

where

$$D = (k - \omega^2)^2 + \omega^2 l^2.$$

The solution (ii) can be rewritten in the form (setting $\overline{A} = A/F_0, \overline{B} = B/F_0$)

(vii) $y_0(t) = F_0(\overline{A}\cos\omega t + \overline{B}\sin\omega t)$

$$= F_0\sqrt{\overline{A}^2 + \overline{B}^2}\left(\frac{\overline{A}}{\sqrt{\overline{A}^2 + \overline{B}^2}}\cos\omega t + \frac{\overline{B}}{\sqrt{\overline{A}^2 + \overline{B}^2}}\sin\omega t\right).$$

Now we introduce an angle β by the relations

$$\cos\beta = \frac{\overline{A}}{\sqrt{\overline{A}^2 + \overline{B}^2}}, \qquad \sin\beta = \frac{\overline{B}}{\sqrt{\overline{A}^2 + \overline{B}^2}}.$$

This is possible since the sum of the squares of the right sides is 1. Then we can write (vii) as

(viii) $y_0(t) = \sqrt{\overline{A}^2 + \overline{B}^2}\, F_0 \cos(\omega t - \beta).$

Equation (viii) shows the nature of the solution $y_0(t)$. Like the force F, y_0 repeats itself in time intervals of length $2\pi/\omega$. However, the amplitude, that is, the maximum of $|y_0(t)|$, equals $\sqrt{\overline{A}^2 + \overline{B}^2}$ times the amplitude of F, that is, $|F_0|$. Also the curve for y_0 is shifted to the right by an amount β. We illustrate in Figure 5.11.

The factor $\sqrt{\overline{A}^2 + \overline{B}^2}$ is called the *amplification* and β is called the *phase shift*. From (vi) we have

(ix) $\sqrt{\overline{A}^2 + \overline{B}^2} = \dfrac{1}{\sqrt{D}} = \dfrac{1}{\sqrt{(k - \omega^2)^2 + \omega^2 l^2}}.$

Note that both the amplification and phase depend on the frequency ω.

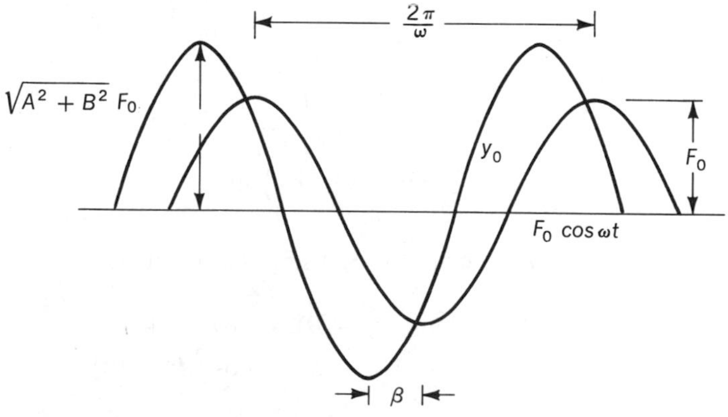

Figure 5.11

A special case of interest is that of $l = 0$, that is, no frictional force. Then we note that $\overline{B} = 0$, which means that $\beta = 0$; that is, the motion and the force are in phase. The amplification becomes simply $1/|k - \omega^2|$. At $\omega^2 = k$ this quantity becomes infinite and our procedure breaks down. This is the phenomenon of *resonance* and $\sqrt{k}$ is called the *natural* frequency of the system. For $\omega^2 = k$ we proceed by the method of variation of parameters. The equation in question is

$$\text{(x)} \quad \ddot{y}(t) + ky(t) = F_0 \cos \sqrt{k}\, t.$$

Set $k = \nu^2$. Then the functions y_1 and y_2 for this equation are $y_1(t) = \cos \nu t$ and $y_2(t) = \sin \nu t$. Equations (4.5) and (4.6) become

$$\begin{aligned} \dot{\alpha}(t) \cos \nu t + \dot{\beta}(t) \sin \nu t &= 0 \\ -\nu\dot{\alpha}(t) \sin \nu t + \nu\dot{\beta}(t) \cos \nu t &= F_0 \cos \nu t. \end{aligned}$$

If we solve these equations we obtain

$$\text{(xi)} \quad \begin{aligned} \dot{\alpha}(t) &= -\frac{F_0}{\nu} \cos \nu t \sin \nu t \\ \dot{\beta}(t) &= \frac{F_0}{\nu} \cos^2 \nu t \end{aligned}$$

We can obtain α and β satisfying (xi) by integration. The reader may verify that α and β must have the form

$$\begin{aligned} \alpha(t) &= \frac{F_0}{4\nu^2} \cos 2\nu t + c_1 \\ \beta(t) &= \frac{F_0}{2\nu} t + \frac{F_0}{4\nu} \sin 2\nu t + c_2. \end{aligned}$$

Hence the solutions of (x) are given by

$$\text{(xii)} \quad y_0(t) = \left(\frac{F_0}{4\nu^2} \cos 2\nu t + c_1\right) \cos \nu t + \left(\frac{F_0}{2\nu} t + \frac{F_0}{4\nu} \sin 2\nu t + c_2\right) \sin \nu t.$$

The expression (xii) may be rewritten by using the formulas

$$\begin{aligned} \cos A \cos B &= \tfrac{1}{2}[\cos (A - B) + \cos (A + B)] \\ \sin A \sin B &= \tfrac{1}{2}[\cos (A - B) - \cos (A + B)]. \end{aligned}$$

If we set $A = 2\nu t$ and $B = \nu t$ in (xii), we obtain

$$y(t) = \left(\frac{F_0}{4\nu^2} + c_1\right)\cos \nu t + \left(\frac{F_0}{2\nu}\, t + c_2\right)\sin \nu t.$$

Thus if we choose $c_2 = 0$ and $c_1 = -F_0/4\nu$ we obtain, as one solution of (x), the function y_0, defined by

$$\text{(xiii)} \quad y_0(t) = \frac{F_0}{2\nu}\, t \sin \nu t.$$

We can now appeal to proposition (4.8) to describe the motion. That proposition states that all solutions of (i) can be written as $y_0 + Y$, where y_0 is given by (viii) if $\omega^2 \neq k$ or (xiii) if $\omega^2 = k$, and Y is a solution of the corresponding homogeneous equation. The latter solutions were discussed in §3 and they are called *transients*. Note that they tend rapidly to zero if $l \neq 0$. The solution y_0, on the other hand, does not tend to zero and, in fact, in the case of resonance, $\omega^2 = k$, actually becomes arbitrarily large.

The method of variation of parameters is capable of generalization to the inhomogeneous version of the more general second-order linear equation (3.19) of §3. The equation is

$$\text{(4.10)} \qquad \ddot{y}(t) + a(t)\dot{y}(t) + b(t)y(t) = f(t).$$

where f is a continuous function. We indicate how to obtain particular solutions of (4.10). Let y_1 and y_2 be two solutions of (3.19) as in theorem (3.20), that is, with D never 0. Then we assert that we can find a solution y of (4.10) in the form

$$\text{(4.11)} \qquad y(t) = \alpha(t)y_1(t) + \beta(t)y_2(t).$$

The calculation proceeds just as in the special case of (4.1). Thus if we determine $\alpha(t)$ and $\beta(t)$ so that

$$\text{(4.12)} \qquad \begin{aligned} \dot{\alpha}(t)y_1(t) + \dot{\beta}(t)y_2(t) &= 0 \\ \dot{\alpha}(t)\dot{y}_1(t) + \dot{\beta}(t)\dot{y}_2(t) &= f(t), \end{aligned}$$

then exactly the same computation as for (4.1) shows that (4.11) yields a solution of (4.10). The reader should also verify that proposition (4.8) remains true if (4.1) and (3.1) are replaced by (4.10) and (3.19), respectively.

PROBLEMS

1. Use the method of variation of parameters to find a solution of each of the following equations:

(a) $\ddot{y}(t) - 4y(t) = te^t$
(b) $\ddot{y}(t) - 3\dot{y}(t) + 2y(t) = t$
(c) $\ddot{y}(t) + 2\dot{y}(t) + y(t) = 2e^{-t}/t^2$
(d) $\ddot{y}(t) + \dot{y}(t) = \cos t$

2. Find the solution of each of the following initial-value problems.

(a) $\ddot{y}(t) + y(t) = \sec t, \quad y(0) = 1, \ \dot{y}(0) = 0$

(b) $\ddot{y}(t) + \dot{y}(t) = \log t, \quad y(1) = 0, \ \dot{y}(1) = 0$

3. THE METHOD OF UNDETERMINED COEFFICIENTS. In each of the following problems show that it is possible to obtain a particular solution of the equation in the form y_0 as indicated.

(a) $\ddot{y}(t) + \dot{y}(t) - y(t) = 2t, \quad y_0(t) = A + Bt$

(b) $\ddot{y}(t) + \dot{y}(t) - y(t) = t^2, \quad y_0(t) = A + Bt + Ct^2$

(c) $\ddot{y}(t) + \dot{y}(t) + 2y(t) = e^{\alpha t}, \quad y_0(t) = Ae^{\alpha t}$

(d) $\ddot{y}(t) - 3\dot{y}(t) + y(t) = 2\cos\omega t - 3\sin\omega t, \quad y_0(t) = A\cos\omega t + B\sin\omega t$

(e) $\ddot{y}(t) + \dot{y}(t) = te^t, \quad y_0(t) = (A + Bt)e^t$

(f) $\ddot{y}(t) - y(t) = t\cos 2t, \quad y_0(t) = (A + Bt)\cos 2t + (C + Dt)\sin 2t$

4. THE METHOD OF UNDETERMINED COEFFICIENTS (Continued). In each of the following problems find a solution by guessing the form.

(a) $\ddot{y}(t) - y(t) = 1 + t^3$

(b) $\ddot{y}(t) + y(t) = t^2e^t$

(c) $\ddot{y}(t) + y(t) = e^t \sin t$

5. Show that in each of the following problems the method of undetermined coefficients fails for the special choices of constants indicated. Use the method of variation of parameters to obtain a solution. (Compare with problem 7 of §1 of Chapter 4.)

(a) $\ddot{y}(t) + y(t) = \cos\alpha t, \ \alpha = 1$

(b) $\ddot{y}(t) - y(t) = e^{\alpha t}, \ \alpha = -1$

(c) $\ddot{y}(t) + 2\dot{y}(t) - 3y(t) = e^{\alpha t}, \ \alpha = -3$

6. Obtain solutions of the following initial-value problems.

(a) $\ddot{y}(t) + 3\dot{y}(t) + 2y(t) = 1 - t, \quad y(0) = 0, \ \dot{y}(0) = 0$

(b) $\ddot{y}(t) - 6\dot{y}(t) + 9y(t) = e^{2t} + 2, \ y(0) = 1, \ \ \dot{y}(0) = 0$

(c) $\ddot{y}(t) - 2\dot{y}(t) + 2y(t) = t + \cos 2t, \ y(0) = 0, \ \ \dot{y}(0) = 1$

7. If the resistance R in the circuit of example (3.2b) is zero and there is an impressed potential $E = E_0 \cos\omega t$, find the frequency ω at which resonance occurs.

8. (a) In the circuit of example (3.2b) suppose there is an impressed potential of the form $E(t) = E_0 e^{-2t}$. Show that the charge always tends to zero as $t \to \infty$ no matter what the initial conditions.

(b) If the potential has the form $E(t) = E_0 + E_1 e^{-2t}$, what happens to the charge as $t \to \infty$?

9. (a) Show that the differential equation

$$e^{-2t}\ddot{y}(t) - e^{-2t}\dot{y}(t) - y(t) = 0$$

has the functions $y_1(t) = e^{e^t}$, $y_2(t) = e^{-e^t}$ as solutions.

(b) Show that these functions satisfy the condition

$$D = y_1\dot{y}_2 - y_2\dot{y}_1 \neq 0.$$

(c) Use the method of variation of parameters to obtain one solution of

$$e^{-2t}\ddot{y}(t) - e^{-2t}\dot{y}(t) - y(t) = e^{2t}.$$

(d) Obtain a solution of the equation in part (c) such that $y(0) = 0$, $\dot{y}(0) = 0$.

10. Show that the solution of $\ddot{y}(t) + k^2 y(t) = f(t)$ such that $y(0) = 0$, $\dot{y}(0) = 0$ can be written

$$\text{(i)} \quad y(t) = \frac{1}{k}\int_0^t \sin k(t - \tau) f(\tau)\, d\tau.$$

11. Problem 10 illustrates the following general proposition. Let y_1 and y_2 be solutions of (4.1) for right sides $f = f_1$ and $f = f_2$, respectively. Assume that

$$\text{(i)} \quad y_1(0) = y_2(0) = 0 \quad \text{and} \quad \dot{y}_1(0) = \dot{y}_2(0) = 0.$$

Then the function $y = c_1 y_1 + c_2 y_2$ is a solution of (4.1) for a right side $f = c_1 f_1 + c_2 f_2$.

(a) Verify that this proposition follows from (i) in problem 10 for the special equation treated there.

(b) Prove the general proposition.

(c) Show that the proposition ceases to be true if any of the initial conditions in (i) is taken to be nonzero.

(d) Show that if the particle in example (3.2a) starts from rest with no velocity, then doubling the force on it doubles its displacement and velocity.

12. Equation (4.1), although not s-linear, is usually called a linear second-order equation. Discuss the reason for this terminology in light of problem 11 and remark (1.18) of Chapter 4.

6

Orthonormal Bases, Least Squares, and Fourier Series

1. Orthonormal Bases

The examples and problems in Chapter 5 show that it is usually necessary to solve an SLE to determine whether a given system of vectors in a vector space $\mathcal{V}$ is a basis. Likewise, one solves an SLE in determining the B-coordinates of a given vector. However, we will see in this section that in certain circumstances one can make use of the inner product to *avoid* such computation. Our first result of this sort concerns a situation in which one wishes to check whether a given system of vectors is a basis.

(1.1) Proposition. *Let $\mathcal{V}$ be a Euclidean vector space. If the system B: $\boldsymbol{\beta}_1, \ldots, \boldsymbol{\beta}_m$ consists of nonzero, mutually orthogonal vectors:*

$$(\pi) \qquad \begin{array}{ll} \boldsymbol{\beta}_i \cdot \boldsymbol{\beta}_j = 0 & i \neq j \\ \boldsymbol{\beta}_i \cdot \boldsymbol{\beta}_i \neq 0 & i = 1, \ldots, m, \end{array}$$

then B is a basis for $S = \langle \boldsymbol{\beta}_1, \ldots, \boldsymbol{\beta}_m \rangle$.

Proof. We must show that for each $\boldsymbol{\alpha} \in S$ there is only one set of scalars $b_1, \ldots, b_m$ such that

$$(1) \qquad \boldsymbol{\alpha} = b_1\boldsymbol{\beta}_1 + \cdots + b_m\boldsymbol{\beta}_m.$$

To do this, take successively the inner product of both sides of (1) with $\beta_1, \beta_2, \ldots, \beta_m$. This gives the equations

$$\begin{aligned}
\alpha \cdot \beta_1 &= (b_1\beta_1 + \cdots + b_m\beta_m) \cdot \beta_1 = b_1(\beta_1 \cdot \beta_1) + \cdots + b_m(\beta_m \cdot \beta_1) \\
\alpha \cdot \beta_2 &= (b_1\beta_1 + \cdots + b_m\beta_m) \cdot \beta_2 = b_1(\beta_1 \cdot \beta_2) + \cdots + b_m(\beta_m \cdot \beta_2) \\
&\vdots \\
\alpha \cdot \beta_m &= (b_1\beta_1 + \cdots + b_m\beta_m) \cdot \beta_m = b_1(\beta_1 \cdot \beta_m) + \cdots + b_m(\beta_m \cdot \beta_m).
\end{aligned}$$

By use of the conditions (π), these equations reduce to

$$(2) \qquad \begin{aligned} &\alpha \cdot \beta_1 = b_1(\beta_1 \cdot \beta_1), \\ &\alpha \cdot \beta_2 = b_2(\beta_2 \cdot \beta_2), \ldots, \alpha \cdot \beta_m = b_m(\beta_m \cdot \beta_m). \end{aligned}$$

These formulas justify the claim that there is only one set of b's for which (1) holds. In fact, by (2) we must have

$$(3) \qquad b_1 = \frac{\alpha \cdot \beta_1}{\beta_1 \cdot \beta_1}, \; b_2 = \frac{\alpha \cdot \beta_2}{\beta_2 \cdot \beta_2}, \ldots, \; b_m = \frac{\alpha \cdot \beta_m}{\beta_m \cdot \beta_m},$$

which specifies the b's in terms of certain inner products. ∎

Note that for the vector space $\mathcal{A}$ the above result reduces to the familiar fact that there is only one way to combine orthogonal arrows to yield a prescribed arrow (see Figure 6.1).

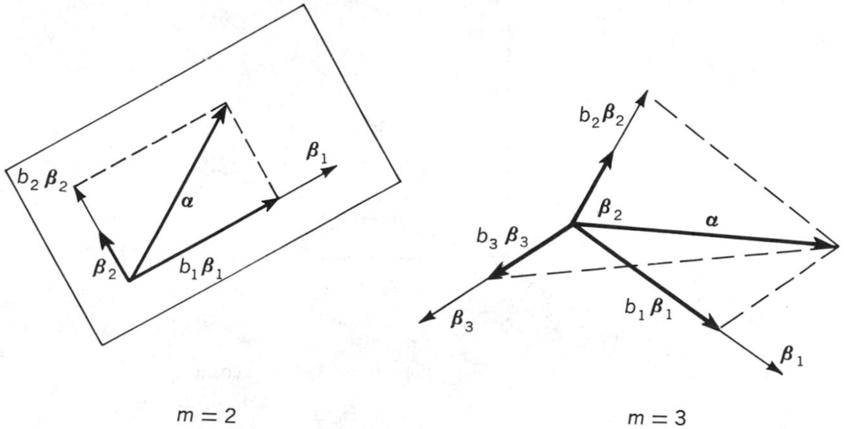

Figure 6.1

For later reference we state an improved form of (1.1) which results when the $\boldsymbol{\beta}$'s are all unit vectors.

(1.2) Definition. If a set of vectors $\boldsymbol{\beta}_1, \ldots, \boldsymbol{\beta}_m$ satisfies (π) and in addition each vector has unit norm, that is,

$$\text{(ON)} \qquad \begin{aligned} \boldsymbol{\beta}_i \cdot \boldsymbol{\beta}_j &= 0, \qquad i \neq j \\ \boldsymbol{\beta}_i \cdot \boldsymbol{\beta}_i &= 1, \qquad i = 1, \ldots, m, \end{aligned}$$

then we call the system **orthonormal**.

(1.3) Proposition. *If B: $\boldsymbol{\beta}_1, \ldots, \boldsymbol{\beta}_m$ is an orthonormal system in $\mathcal{V}$, then the B-coordinates of vectors in $S = \langle \boldsymbol{\beta}_1, \ldots, \boldsymbol{\beta}_m \rangle$ are given by*

$$\text{(a)} \quad [\boldsymbol{\alpha}]_B = \begin{bmatrix} \boldsymbol{\alpha} \cdot \boldsymbol{\beta}_1 \\ \vdots \\ \boldsymbol{\alpha} \cdot \boldsymbol{\beta}_m \end{bmatrix}.$$

Moreover, for vectors $\boldsymbol{\alpha}, \boldsymbol{\alpha}'$ in S with B-coordinates $b_1, \ldots, b_m$ and $b'_1, \ldots, b'_m$, respectively, the inner product $\boldsymbol{\alpha} \cdot \boldsymbol{\alpha}'$ can be expressed as

$$\text{(b)} \quad \boldsymbol{\alpha} \cdot \boldsymbol{\alpha}' = b_1 b'_1 + b_2 b'_2 + \cdots + b_m b'_m.$$

The proof of this important corollary to (1.1) is discussed in the problems (problem 6).

When we analyze proposition (1.3) for the vector space $\mathcal{A}$, it becomes clear why one usually chooses a basis for $\mathcal{A}$ which is orthonormal, not merely orthogonal. It is *only* for that case that the inner product of two vectors is computed by use of (1.3b) (Figure 6.2). The reader should realize

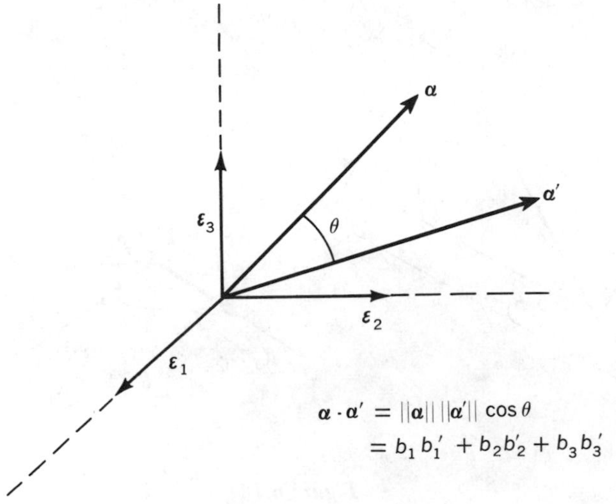

Figure 6.2

that this applies in other vector spaces as well. That is, formula (1.3b) is valid *only* for orthonormal systems, no matter what the space $\mathcal{V}$ is. We now illustrate, by means of an example, what happens when one tries to compute inner products by using B-coordinates relative to a nonorthonormal basis B.

(1.4) Example. Orthonormal Bases and Nonorthonormal Bases. The system B: $\boldsymbol{\beta}_1 = (1, 2)$, $\boldsymbol{\beta}_2 = (1, -2)$ is a basis for $\mathcal{R}^2$. Given a pair of vectors $\boldsymbol{\alpha} = (a_1, a_2)$, $\boldsymbol{\alpha}' = (a_1', a_2')$ in $\mathcal{R}^2$, let us express the standard inner product $\boldsymbol{\alpha} \cdot \boldsymbol{\alpha}' = a_1a_1' + a_2a_2'$ in terms of the B-coordinates of $\boldsymbol{\alpha}$ and $\boldsymbol{\alpha}'$.

By the definition of B-coordinates we have

$$\boldsymbol{\alpha} = b_1\boldsymbol{\beta}_1 + b_2\boldsymbol{\beta}_2, \qquad \boldsymbol{\alpha}' = b_1'\boldsymbol{\beta}_1 + b_2'\boldsymbol{\beta}_2.$$

Thus, using the bilinearity and symmetry of the inner product we get

$$\begin{aligned} \boldsymbol{\alpha} \cdot \boldsymbol{\alpha}' &= (b_1\boldsymbol{\beta}_1 + b_2\boldsymbol{\beta}_2) \cdot (b_1'\boldsymbol{\beta}_1 + b_2'\boldsymbol{\beta}_2) \\ &= b_1b_1'(\boldsymbol{\beta}_1 \cdot \boldsymbol{\beta}_1) + (b_1b_2' + b_2b_1')(\boldsymbol{\beta}_1 \cdot \boldsymbol{\beta}_2) + b_2b_2'(\boldsymbol{\beta}_2 \cdot \boldsymbol{\beta}_2). \end{aligned}$$

By direct calculation, $\boldsymbol{\beta}_1 \cdot \boldsymbol{\beta}_1 = 5$, $\boldsymbol{\beta}_1 \cdot \boldsymbol{\beta}_2 = -3$, $\boldsymbol{\beta}_2 \cdot \boldsymbol{\beta}_2 = 5$ so that the above formula becomes

$$\text{(i)} \qquad \boldsymbol{\alpha} \cdot \boldsymbol{\alpha}' = 5b_1b_1' - 3(b_1b_2' + b_2b_1') + 5b_2b_2'.$$

This formula permits us to compute inner products knowing only B-coordinates. For instance, if we know that

$$[\boldsymbol{\alpha}]_B = \begin{bmatrix} 3 \\ 2 \end{bmatrix}, \qquad [\boldsymbol{\alpha}']_B = \begin{bmatrix} 1 \\ -1 \end{bmatrix},$$

then from (i) we deduce that

$$\boldsymbol{\alpha} \cdot \boldsymbol{\alpha}' = 5 \cdot 3 - 3(-3 + 2) + 5(-2) = 8.$$

However, (i) is far more cumbersome than formula (1.3b), which applies when B is an orthonormal basis. For instance, the system $\overline{B}$: $\overline{\boldsymbol{\beta}}_1 = (0.6, 0.8)$, $\overline{\boldsymbol{\beta}}_2 = (0.8, -0.6)$ is an orthonormal basis for $\mathcal{R}^2$. Hence by (1.3b) we have the formula

$$\text{(ii)} \qquad \boldsymbol{\alpha} \cdot \boldsymbol{\alpha}' = \bar{b}_1\bar{b}_1' + \bar{b}_2\bar{b}_2',$$

where $\bar{b}_1$, $\bar{b}_1'$, $\bar{b}_2$, and $\bar{b}_2'$ denote $\overline{B}$-coordinates.

The above considerations have shown that, when available, orthonormal bases are more convenient than other bases. We will now show that orthonormal bases are *always* available. That is, every finite-dimensional subspace

S' of a Euclidean vector space possesses orthonormal bases. In proving this fact we shall also gain some understanding of a mathematical technique which goes by the name "method of least squares." The latter will be discussed in detail in §2.

Examine first the case of a one-dimensional subspace S' (Figure 6.3). Let B: β_1 be a basis for S'. Then $\beta_1 \neq 0$, so we can form E: $\epsilon_1 = \beta_1/\|\beta_1\|$. E is still a basis for S' and in addition is orthonormal.

Examine next the case of a two-dimensional subspace S'. Assume for the moment that S' is a subspace of $\mathcal{A}$. Let B: β_1, β_2 be a basis for S'. If β_1 and β_2 are perpendicular, then we can construct an orthonormal basis E by simply "normalizing"; in this case the system E: $\epsilon_1 = \beta_1/\|\beta_1\|$, $\epsilon_2 = \beta_2/\|\beta_2\|$ is orthonormal (Figure 6.4a). Otherwise, the above tactic fails. We then begin by setting $\epsilon_1 = \beta_1/\|\beta_1\|$. What we now need to find is a vector β_2' in S' perpendicular to ϵ_1. For this purpose we utilize the perpendicular projection $P\beta_2$ of β_2 on the span $\langle\epsilon_1\rangle$. (Here $P\beta_2$ does *not* mean the product of β with a scalar P.) $P\beta_2$ is given by (Figure 6.4b)

$$P\beta_2 = (\|\beta_2\| \cos \theta)\epsilon_1 = (\beta_2 \cdot \epsilon_1)\epsilon_1. \tag{1.5}$$

It is then clear geometrically that the arrow

$$\beta_2' = \beta_2 - P\beta_2 = \beta_2 - (\beta_2 \cdot \epsilon_1)\epsilon_1 \tag{1.6}$$

is perpendicular to ϵ_1. Thus the system B': $\epsilon_1, \beta_2 - P\beta_2$ consists of perpendicular arrows which span S'. Consequently, by our previous result the normalized system

$$E\colon \epsilon_1 = \frac{\beta_1}{\|\beta_1\|}, \quad \epsilon_2 = \frac{\beta_2 - P\beta_2}{\|\beta_2 - P\beta_2\|} \tag{1.7}$$

is an orthonormal basis for S'.

In the above discussion we assumed that S' is a subspace of $\mathcal{A}$. However this construction for β_2' succeeds in any vector space $\mathcal{V}$. That is, one can verify that the vector β_2' defined in (1.6) is orthogonal to ϵ_1 *without* depending on geometric reasoning; namely,

$$\begin{aligned} \beta_2' \cdot \epsilon_1 &= \big(\beta_2 - (\beta_2 \cdot \epsilon_1)\epsilon_1\big) \cdot \epsilon_1 \\ &= \beta_2 \cdot \epsilon_1 - (\beta_2 \cdot \epsilon_1)(\epsilon_1 \cdot \epsilon_1) = 0. \end{aligned}$$

On further reflection we see that the key idea underlying the procedure developed above is the fact that given a vector $\epsilon_1 \neq \mathbf{0}$ in *any* space $\mathcal{V}$, every vector $\beta \in \mathcal{V}$ has a projection $P\beta$ on $\langle\epsilon_1\rangle$ satisfying $(\beta - P\beta) \cdot \epsilon_1 = 0$. This

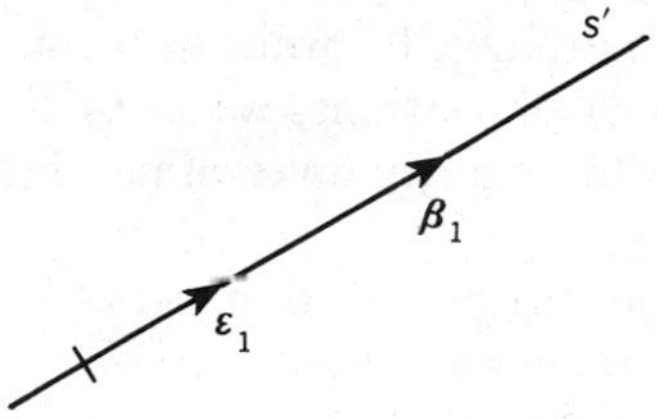

$$\varepsilon_1 \cdot \varepsilon_1 = 1$$

Figure 6.3

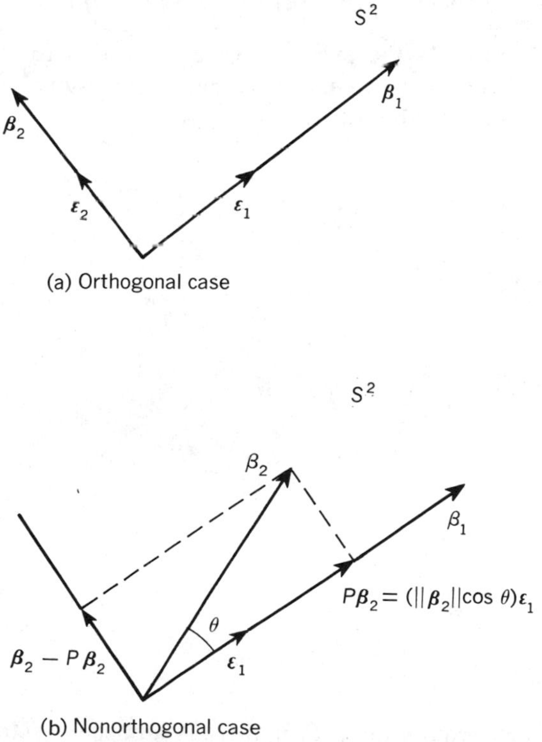

Figure 6.4

is one of the reasons that the geometric notion of scalar product and "angle" between vectors is of importance. In order to prove that a similar procedure can be extended to higher dimensions, we must show that it is possible to orthogonally project vectors on *any* finite-dimensional subspace S in $\mathcal{V}$.

(1.8) Projection Theorem. *Suppose S is a finite-dimensional subspace of the space $\mathcal{V}$, possessing an orthonormal basis E: $\epsilon_1, \ldots, \epsilon_k$. Then for each vector $\beta \in \mathcal{V}$ there is a unique vector $P\beta \in S$ such that $\beta - P\beta$ is perpendicular to S in the sense that*

$$\text{(a)} \qquad (\beta - P\beta) \cdot \gamma = 0 \qquad \text{all } \gamma \in S.$$

The vector $P\beta$ is given by the following linear combination:

$$\text{(b)} \qquad P\beta = (\beta \cdot \epsilon_1)\epsilon_1 + (\beta \cdot \epsilon_2)\epsilon_2 + \cdots + (\beta \cdot \epsilon_k)\epsilon_k.$$

When $\beta \notin S$ the vector $\epsilon_{k+1} = (\beta - P\beta)/\|\beta - P\beta\|$ is a unit vector perpendicular to S and E: $\epsilon_1, \ldots, \epsilon_k, \epsilon_{k+1}$ is an orthonormal system in $\mathcal{V}$.

[Theorem (1.8) asserts the existence of a projection for all $\beta \in V$ only for *finite*-dimensional subspaces. For infinite-dimensional subspaces this property does not always hold.]

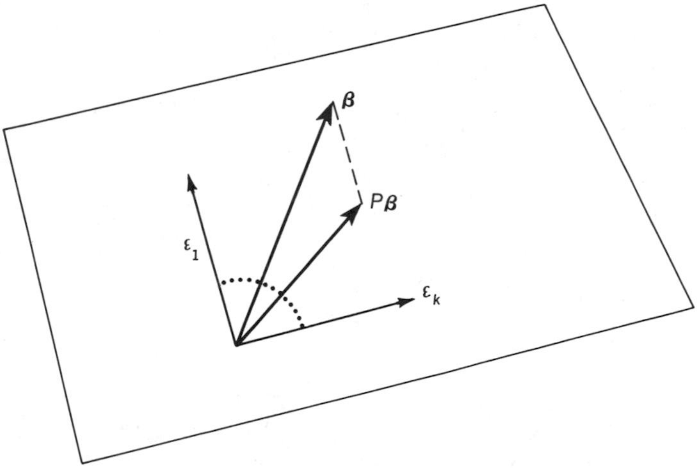

Figure 6.5

Proof. Since we require $P\beta \in S$, if there is any such vector it must be a linear combination of the ϵ's; $P\beta = p_1\epsilon_1 + \cdots + p_k\epsilon_k$. To show that there is at most one vector $P\beta$ satisfying (a) take γ successively equal to ϵ_1, to

$\epsilon_2, \ldots,$ to ϵ_k. This results in the equations

$$\begin{aligned}
0 &= (\beta - (p_1\epsilon_1 + \cdots + p_k\epsilon_k)) \cdot \epsilon_1 = \beta \cdot \epsilon_1 - p_1(\epsilon_1 \cdot \epsilon_1) \\
&\qquad - p_2(\epsilon_2 \cdot \epsilon_1) - \cdots - p_k(\epsilon_k \cdot \epsilon_1) \\
0 &= (\beta - (p_1\epsilon_1 + \cdots + p_k\epsilon_k)) \cdot \epsilon_2 = \beta \cdot \epsilon_2 - p_1(\epsilon_1 \cdot \epsilon_2) \\
&\qquad - p_2(\epsilon_2 \cdot \epsilon_2) - \cdots - p_k(\epsilon_k \cdot \epsilon_2) \\
&\vdots \\
0 &= (\beta - (p_1\epsilon_1 + \cdots + p_k\epsilon_k)) \cdot \epsilon_k = \beta \cdot \epsilon_k - p_1(\epsilon_1 \cdot \epsilon_k) \\
&\qquad - p_2(\epsilon_2 \cdot \epsilon_k) - \cdots - p_k(\epsilon_k \cdot \epsilon_k).
\end{aligned}$$

By the orthonormality of the ϵ's this reduces to the conditions

$$p_1 = \beta \cdot \epsilon_1, \qquad p_2 = \beta \cdot \epsilon_2, \ldots, \qquad p_k = \beta \cdot \epsilon_k,$$

which proves that at most one vector $P\beta$ satisfies (a).

To show that there actually is a vector which satisfies (a) we select $P\beta$ as given by (b) and verify that (a) then holds for all vectors

$$\gamma = c_1\epsilon_1 + \cdots + c_k\epsilon_k$$

in S. This is left as a problem (problem 12).

Finally, when $\beta \not\subset S$, then $\beta - P\beta \neq \mathbf{0}$, whereby $(\beta - P\beta)/\|\beta - P\beta\|$ is a unit vector perpendicular to all $\gamma \in S$ by (a). The orthonormality of E' follows from this fact. ▮

(1.9) Definition. Given both a subspace S and a vector β in the vector space $\mathcal{V}$, the vector $P\beta$ satisfying condition (1.8a) is called the **orthogonal projection** of β on S.

It is instructive to compare β with $P\beta$ when $\beta \in S$. In this case we know that there are scalars $c_1, \ldots, c_k$ such that

$$\beta = c_1\epsilon_1 + \cdots + c_k\epsilon_k,$$

while, on the other hand,

$$P\beta = (\beta \cdot \epsilon_1)\epsilon_1 + \cdots + (\beta \cdot \epsilon_k)\epsilon_k.$$

By equation (1.8a) the vector

$$\beta - P\beta = (c_1 - (\beta \cdot \epsilon_1))\epsilon_1 + \cdots + (c_k - (\beta \cdot \epsilon_k))\epsilon_k$$

is orthogonal to each of the vectors $\epsilon_1, \epsilon_2, \ldots, \epsilon_k$. Expansion of the equations

$$(\beta - P\beta)\cdot\epsilon_1 = 0, \ldots, (\beta - P\beta)\cdot\epsilon_k = 0$$

then permits us to deduce that $\beta - P\beta = \mathbf{0}$. Thus we obtain as a consequence of theorem (1.8) the formula

$$(1.10) \qquad \beta = P\beta = (\beta\cdot\epsilon_1)\epsilon_1 + \cdots + (\beta\cdot\epsilon_k)\epsilon_k \qquad \text{all } \beta \in S.$$

The reader should verify that this formula is equivalent to (1.2a).

Theorem (1.8) permits us among other things to prove the assertion that every finite-dimensional subspace possesses orthonormal bases. (Here the zero subspace $S' = \langle \mathbf{0} \rangle = O$ is to be excluded.)

(1.11) Gram–Schmidt Theorem. *Every nonzero finite-dimensional subspace S' of a space $\mathcal{V}$ possesses an orthonormal basis. In fact, if B: $\beta_1, \ldots, \beta_k$ is a basis for S', then the system E: $\epsilon_1, \ldots, \epsilon_k$ computed by*

$$\text{(G–S)} \qquad \begin{aligned} \epsilon_1 &= \frac{\beta_1}{\|\beta_1\|} \\ \epsilon_2 &= \frac{\beta_2 - (\beta_2\cdot\epsilon_1)\epsilon_1}{\|\beta_2 - (\beta_2\cdot\epsilon_1)\epsilon_1\|} \\ &\;\vdots \\ \epsilon_k &= \frac{\beta_k - (\beta_k\cdot\epsilon_1)\epsilon_1 - \cdots - (\beta_k\cdot\epsilon_{k-1})\epsilon_{k-1}}{\|\beta_k - (\beta_k\cdot\epsilon_1)\epsilon_1 - \cdots - (\beta_k\cdot\epsilon_{k-1})\epsilon_{k-1}\|} \end{aligned}$$

is an orthonormal basis for S'.

Proof. We describe the construction of the basis E. The first two steps have already been discussed. That is, we get the first vector in E by normalizing β_1 (Figure 6.6a):

$$(1) \qquad \epsilon_1 = \frac{\beta_1}{\|\beta_1\|}\cdot$$

For the next vector in E we modify the vector β_2 to obtain a vector β_2' in $\langle \beta_1, \beta_2 \rangle$ orthogonal to ϵ_1. Let us try vectors of the form $\beta_2' = \beta_2 - c_1\epsilon_1$. For this to be orthogonal to ϵ_1 we need to have

$$(2) \qquad 0 = (\beta_2 - c_1\epsilon_1)\cdot\epsilon_1 = \beta_2\cdot\epsilon_1 - c_1.$$

Thus $c_1 = \boldsymbol{\beta}_2 \cdot \boldsymbol{\epsilon}_1$ and $\boldsymbol{\beta}_2 - (\boldsymbol{\beta}_2 \cdot \boldsymbol{\epsilon}_1)\boldsymbol{\epsilon}_1$ is the only vector of this form orthogonal to $\boldsymbol{\epsilon}_1$ (Figure 6.6b). Normalizing this vector we get

$$(3) \qquad \boldsymbol{\epsilon}_2 = \frac{\boldsymbol{\beta}_2 - (\boldsymbol{\beta}_2 \cdot \boldsymbol{\epsilon}_1)\boldsymbol{\epsilon}_1}{\|\boldsymbol{\beta}_2 - (\boldsymbol{\beta}_2 \cdot \boldsymbol{\epsilon}_1)\boldsymbol{\epsilon}_1\|}.$$

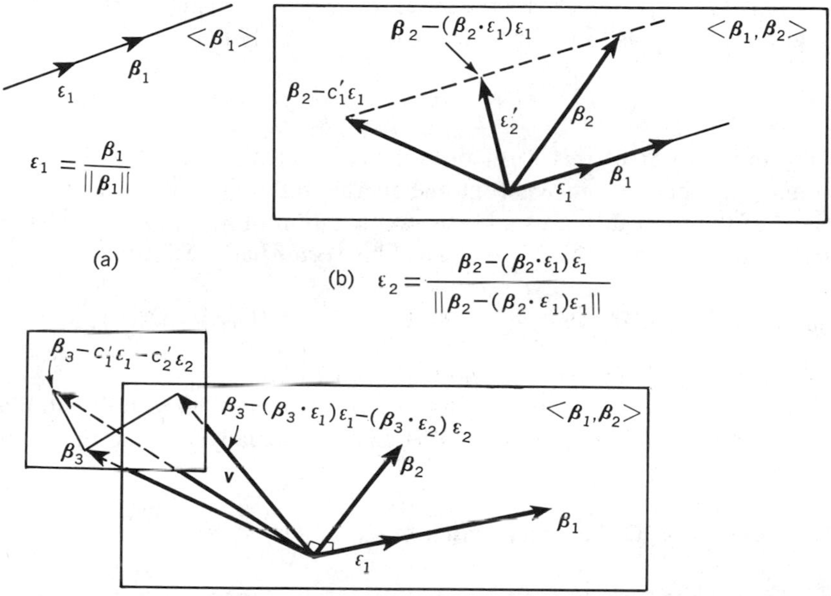

(a)

(b) $\varepsilon_2 = \dfrac{\beta_2-(\beta_2\cdot\varepsilon_1)\varepsilon_1}{\|\beta_2-(\beta_2\cdot\varepsilon_1)\varepsilon_1\|}$

(c) $\varepsilon_3 = \dfrac{\beta_3-(\beta_3\cdot\varepsilon_1)\varepsilon_1-(\beta_3\cdot\varepsilon_2)\varepsilon_2}{\|\beta_3-(\beta_3\cdot\varepsilon_1)\varepsilon_1-(\beta_3\cdot\varepsilon_2)\varepsilon_2\|}$

Figure 6.6

To obtain the third vector in E we modify the vector $\boldsymbol{\beta}_3$ to obtain a vector $\boldsymbol{\beta}_3'$ orthogonal to both $\boldsymbol{\epsilon}_1$ and $\boldsymbol{\epsilon}_2$. Let us try vectors of the form $\boldsymbol{\beta}_3$ minus a linear combination of $\boldsymbol{\epsilon}_1$ and $\boldsymbol{\epsilon}_2$:

$$\boldsymbol{\beta}_3' = \boldsymbol{\beta}_3 - c_1\boldsymbol{\epsilon}_1 - c_2\boldsymbol{\epsilon}_2.$$

In order for this to be orthogonal to $\boldsymbol{\epsilon}_1$ and $\boldsymbol{\epsilon}_2$ we must have

$$(4) \qquad \begin{aligned} 0 &= (\boldsymbol{\beta}_3 - c_1\boldsymbol{\epsilon}_1 - c_2\boldsymbol{\epsilon}_2) \cdot \boldsymbol{\epsilon}_1 = \boldsymbol{\beta}_3 \cdot \boldsymbol{\epsilon}_1 - c_1 - 0 \\ 0 &= (\boldsymbol{\beta}_3 - c_1\boldsymbol{\epsilon}_1 - c_2\boldsymbol{\epsilon}_2) \cdot \boldsymbol{\epsilon}_2 = \boldsymbol{\beta}_3 \cdot \boldsymbol{\epsilon}_2 - 0 - c_2. \end{aligned}$$

This shows that $\beta_3 - (\beta_3 \cdot \epsilon_1)\epsilon_1 - (\beta_3 \cdot \epsilon_2)\epsilon_2$ is the only vector of this form which is orthogonal to ϵ_1 and ϵ_2 (Figure 6.6c). Normalizing this vector we get

$$(5) \qquad \epsilon_3 = \frac{\beta_3 - (\beta_3 \cdot \epsilon_1)\epsilon_1 - (\beta_3 \cdot \epsilon_2)\epsilon_2}{\|\beta_3 - (\beta_3 \cdot \epsilon_1)\epsilon_1 - (\beta_3 \cdot \epsilon_2)\epsilon_2\|}.$$

The next step is to search for a vector of the form β_4 minus a linear combination of $\epsilon_1, \epsilon_2, \epsilon_3$ which is orthogonal to $\epsilon_1, \epsilon_2, \epsilon_3$. Again the orthogonality equations analogous to (2) and (4) show immediately that

$$\beta_4 - (\beta_4 \cdot \epsilon_1)\epsilon_1 - (\beta_4 \cdot \epsilon_2)\epsilon_2 - (\beta_4 \cdot \epsilon_3)\epsilon_3$$

is the only vector of this form orthogonal to all three ϵ's. We get ϵ_4 by normalizing this vector. We continue in this fashion until we arrive at a vector of the form β_k minus a linear combination of $\epsilon_1, \ldots, \epsilon_{k-1}$ which is orthogonal to each of these $k - 1$ ϵ's. This vector has the form

$$\beta_k - (\beta_k \cdot \epsilon_1)\epsilon_1 - (\beta_k \cdot \epsilon_2)\epsilon_2 - \cdots - (\beta_k \cdot \epsilon_{k-1})\epsilon_{k-1}$$

and is the only such vector. We normalize β_k to obtain ϵ_k.

We shall forego the various induction arguments needed to fully establish that the system E constructed in this fashion actually *is* an orthonormal basis for S'. ▌

(1.12) Examples. Orthonormalization

(a) Given the basis B: (1, 0, 1), (1, 1, 0), (0, 1, 1) for $\mathbb{R}^3$ with the standard inner product, "orthonormalize." That is, find the corresponding basis E given by (G–S).

We obtain

$$\epsilon_1 = \frac{(1, 0, 1)}{\|(1, 0, 1)\|} = (\sqrt{\tfrac{1}{2}}, 0, \sqrt{\tfrac{1}{2}}).$$

Then

$$\epsilon_2 = \frac{(1, 1, 0) - (\sqrt{\tfrac{1}{2}})(\sqrt{\tfrac{1}{2}}, 0, \sqrt{\tfrac{1}{2}})}{\|(1, 1, 0) - (\sqrt{\tfrac{1}{2}})(\sqrt{\tfrac{1}{2}}, 0, \sqrt{\tfrac{1}{2}})\|} = \sqrt{\tfrac{2}{3}}\,(\tfrac{1}{2}, 1, -\tfrac{1}{2}).$$

Finally,

$$\begin{aligned}\epsilon_3 &= \frac{(0, 1, 1) - (\sqrt{\tfrac{1}{2}})(\sqrt{\tfrac{1}{2}}, 0, \sqrt{\tfrac{1}{2}}) - \tfrac{1}{2}\sqrt{\tfrac{2}{3}}\,[\sqrt{\tfrac{2}{3}}\,(\tfrac{1}{2}, 1, -\tfrac{1}{2})]}{\|(0, 1, 1) - (\sqrt{\tfrac{1}{2}})(\sqrt{\tfrac{1}{2}}, 0, \sqrt{\tfrac{1}{2}}) - \tfrac{1}{2}\sqrt{\tfrac{2}{3}}\,[\sqrt{\tfrac{2}{3}}\,(\tfrac{1}{2}, 1, -\tfrac{1}{2})]\|}\\ &= \frac{(-\tfrac{2}{3}, \tfrac{2}{3}, \tfrac{2}{3})}{\tfrac{2}{3}\sqrt{3}}\\ &= (-\sqrt{\tfrac{1}{3}}, \sqrt{\tfrac{1}{3}}, \sqrt{\tfrac{1}{3}}).\end{aligned}$$

(b) Consider the space $\mathcal{P}^3$ of all polynomials of degree less than 3 with the inner product, $p \cdot q = \int_{-1}^{+1} p(t)q(t)\,dt$. Let B: p_1, p_2, p_3 be the basis for $\mathcal{P}^3$ in which $p_1(t) = 1$, $p_2(t) = t$, $p_3(t)$. Orthonormalize B.

We obtain $e_1(t) = 1/\|1\| = \sqrt{\frac{1}{2}}$. Thus

$$e_2(t) = \frac{t - [t \cdot (\sqrt{\frac{1}{2}})](\sqrt{\frac{1}{2}})}{\|t - [t \cdot (\sqrt{\frac{1}{2}})](\sqrt{\frac{1}{2}})\|} = \frac{t - 0}{\|t - 0\|} = \sqrt{\tfrac{3}{2}}\, t.$$

Finally,

$$e_3(t) = \frac{t^2 - [t^2 \cdot (\sqrt{\frac{1}{2}})](\sqrt{\frac{1}{2}}) - (t^2 \cdot \sqrt{\frac{3}{2}}\, t)(\sqrt{\frac{3}{2}}\, t)}{\|t^2 - [t^2 \cdot (\sqrt{\frac{1}{2}})](\sqrt{\frac{1}{2}}) - (t^2 \cdot \sqrt{\frac{3}{2}}\, t)(\sqrt{\frac{3}{2}}\, t)\|} = \frac{t^2 - \frac{1}{3}}{\|t^2 - \frac{1}{3}\|} = \tfrac{1}{2}\sqrt{\tfrac{5}{2}}\,(3t^2 - 1).$$

PROBLEMS

1. Verify that the following systems are orthogonal bases for their spaces. Perform an appropriate modification of each basis to make it orthonormal.

$\mathcal{R}^2$

(a) (1, 1), (1, −1)
(b) (1, 0), (0, −1)
(c) (1, 2), (−2, 1)

$\mathcal{R}^3$

(a) (0, 1, 0), (1, 0, 0), (0, 0, 1)
(b) (1, 1, 1), (1, −1, 0), (1, 1, −2)

$\mathcal{C}[-1, 1]$ $\left(f \cdot g = \int_{-1}^{1} f(t)g(t)\,dt\right)$

(a) $1, t, t^2 - \frac{1}{3}$
(b) $1 - t, 1 + 3t, t^2 - \frac{1}{3}$
(c) $\sin \pi t, \cos \pi t, \sin 2\pi t, \cos 2\pi t$

$\mathcal{C}[0, 1]$ $\left(f \cdot g = \int_{0}^{1} f(t)g(t)t\,dt\right)$

(a) $1, t - \frac{2}{3}$
(b) $1, t^2 - \frac{1}{2}$

2. Use the Gram–Schmidt procedure to find an orthonormal basis for the subspace spanned by each of the following independent systems.

$\mathcal{R}^2$

(a) (1, 0), (1, 1)
(b) (1, 1), (1, 0)

[Use diagrams with arrows in the plane to explain the contrasting solutions for (a) and (b).]

(c) (−2, 0), (−3, 1)

$\mathcal{R}^3$

(a) (1, 1, 1), (0, 1, 1)
(b) (0, 1, 1), (1, 1, 1)

[Use diagrams with arrows to explain the contrasting solutions for (a) and (b).]

(c) (−1, 1, 2), (1, 1, 2), (1, 1, 3)

$\mathbb{R}^4$	$\mathcal{C}[-1, 1]$ $\left(f \cdot g = \int_{-1}^{1} f(t)g(t)\,dt\right)$
(a) $(1, -1, 1, 0)$, $(0, 1, 2, 1)$, $(1, 3, 0, 1)$	(a) 1, t, t^2
(b) $(1, 2, 0, 1)$, $(3, -1, 2, 0)$	(b) $1 + t$, $2 - 6t$, $3t^2 - 1$

3. Find an orthonormal basis for the subspace spanned by each of the following:

(a) B: $(1, 2, 0, 4)$, $(1, 1, -2, 1)$, $(-1, 1, 6, 5)$

(b) B: $(1, 1, 3, 5)$, $(1, -1, 2, 1)$, $(1, 5, 5, 13)$, $(1, 1, 0, 1)$

Explain the peculiarities which occur in the Gram–Schmidt procedure.

4. Find a vector orthogonal to the subspace S of $\mathbb{R}^4$ consisting of all vectors of the form

$$(a + b + 2c,\quad 2a - b + c,\quad a - b - 2c,\quad a + b + c)$$

for all values of a, b, c.

5. Find two distinct functions in $\mathcal{C}[-1, 1]$ $\left(f \cdot g = \int_{-1}^{1} f(t)g(t)\,dt\right)$ which are orthogonal to all functions f of the form $f(t) = a + bt + c \sin \pi t$ for all values of a, b, c.

6. Prove the assertion that when B is an orthonormal system, then the relationship of B-coordinates to the inner product is that given in (1.2b):

$$\alpha \cdot \alpha' = b_1 b_1' + b_2 b_2' + \cdots + b_m b_m'.$$

7. If E: ϵ_1, ϵ_2, ϵ_3 is an orthonormal basis for the subspace S of $\mathcal{V}$, then so is

$$E': \epsilon_1' = \frac{1}{\sqrt{3}}(\epsilon_1 + \epsilon_2 + \epsilon_3),\ \epsilon_2' = \frac{1}{\sqrt{2}}(\epsilon_1 - \epsilon_2),\ \epsilon_3' = \frac{1}{\sqrt{6}}(-\epsilon_1 - \epsilon_2 + 2\epsilon_3).$$

Prove this.

8. Prove that orthogonal projection on a subspace S is a *linear transformation* in the sense that it satisfies the identity

$$P(c\alpha + d\beta) = cP\alpha + dP\beta$$

for all $\alpha, \beta \in \mathcal{V}$ and all scalars c, d. (Linear transformations will be discussed in Chapter 8. Compare also with Chapter 4 §1.)

9. Prove that orthogonal projection on a subspace S is an *idempotent* transformation in the sense that it satisfies the identity

$$P(P\beta) = P\beta \qquad \text{all } \beta \in \mathcal{V}.$$

10. If S is any finite-dimensional subspace of $\mathcal{V}$, let $S^{\perp}$ denote the set of vectors in $\mathcal{V}$ orthogonal to S.

(a) Show that $S^{\perp}$ is also a subspace.

(b) Show that every vector $\beta \in \mathcal{V}$ has a unique decomposition

$$(*) \qquad \beta = \beta^0 + \beta', \qquad \beta^0 \in S,\ \beta' \in S^{\perp}.$$

[*Hint:* According to theorem (1.6), $\beta = P\beta + (\beta - P\beta)$ provides one such decomposition. Moreover, if $\beta^0 + \beta' = \beta = \overline{\beta^0} + \overline{\beta'}$, then

$$\beta^0 - \overline{\beta^0} = \overline{\beta'} - \beta',$$

so that $\beta^0 - \overline{\beta^0}$ is in the subspace $S^\perp$ as well as in S (Figure 6.7).]

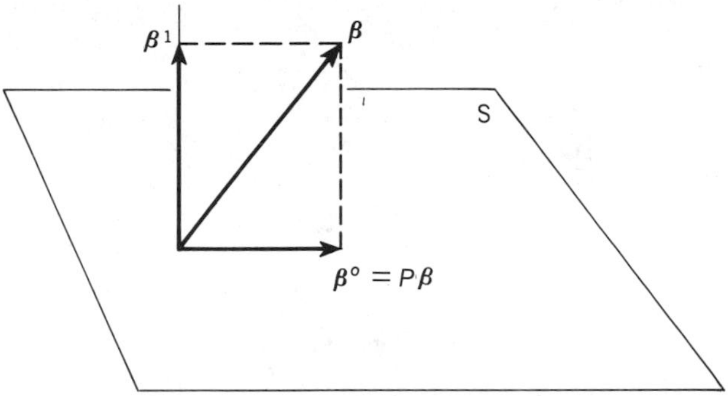

Figure 6.7

11. Find an orthonormal basis for the subspace S of solutions of the SLE

$$\text{(L)}\quad \begin{aligned} 3x_1 + 2x_2 - x_3 + x_4 &= 0 \\ x_1 + x_2 - x_3 + x_4 &= 0. \end{aligned}$$

[*Hint:* (L) requires that (x_1, x_2, x_3, x_4) be orthogonal to $\alpha_1 = (3, 2, -1, 1)$ and to $\alpha_2 = (1, 1, -1, 1)$. Hence $S = \langle\alpha_1, \alpha_2\rangle^\perp$. Find one basis for S by applying the Gauss–Jordan algorithm to (L). Then use Gram–Schmidt.]

12. Show that for any $\beta \in \mathcal{V}$ the vector $\beta - P\beta$ satisfies the relation (1.8a)

$$(\beta - P\beta) \cdot \gamma = 0 \qquad \text{all } \gamma \in S,$$

provided that $P\beta = (\beta \cdot \epsilon_1)\epsilon_1 + (\beta \cdot \epsilon_2)\epsilon_2 + \cdots + (\beta \cdot \epsilon_k)\epsilon_k$, where the ϵ's are an orthonormal basis for S. (*Hint:* Examine first the special cases

$$\gamma = \epsilon_1, \gamma = \epsilon_2, \ldots, \gamma = \epsilon_k.)$$

13. PYTHAGOREAN THEOREM. With S and $S^\perp$ as in problem 10, let us denote $\beta - P\beta = P^\perp\beta$.

(a) Prove that

$$\|\beta\|^2 = \|P\beta\|^2 + \|P^\perp\beta\|^2 \qquad \text{all } \beta \in \mathcal{V}.$$

(b) Explain why the notation $P^\perp\beta$ is a good one (see Figure 6.7).

(c) Prove that

$$\alpha \cdot \beta = P\alpha \cdot P\beta + P^\perp\alpha \cdot P^\perp\beta \qquad \text{all } \alpha, \beta \in \mathcal{V}.$$

2. Method of Least Squares

Consider the following problem. Given a plane R in space and a point P outside R, find the point Q in R which is closest to P (Figure 6.8a). The answer is, of course, well known; Q is the foot of the perpendicular from P to R.

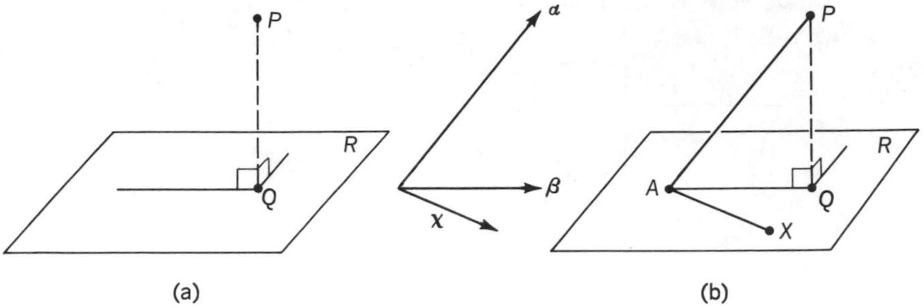

Figure 6.8

There is an equivalent formulation in terms of arrows. Given the set S of all arrows parallel to the fixed plane R and given an arrow $\boldsymbol{\alpha} \notin S$, find the arrow $\boldsymbol{\beta}$ in S which is "closest" to $\boldsymbol{\alpha}$ in the sense that $\|\boldsymbol{\alpha} - \boldsymbol{\beta}\|$ is as small as possible. Letting $\overline{AP}$ be a representative of $\boldsymbol{\alpha}$ with initial point A in R, we see that every arrow in S can be represented by a displacement $\overline{AX}$ with X in R (Figure 6.8b). Hence the arrow $\boldsymbol{\beta}$ such that $\|\boldsymbol{\alpha} - \boldsymbol{\beta}\|$ is a minimum is the one corresponding to $\overline{AQ}$, where Q is the foot of the perpendicular from P to R.

We will see in this chapter that an important class of mathematical techniques is generated when the preceding problem for $\mathcal{A}$ is extended to other vector spaces $\mathcal{V}$. Let us state the generalized problem.

(2.1) Approximation Problem. *Let S denote a finite-dimensional subspace of $\mathcal{V}$ and let a vector $\boldsymbol{\alpha} \notin S$ be given. Find a vector $\boldsymbol{\alpha}_s \in S$ which is closest to $\boldsymbol{\alpha}$ in the sense that*

$$\text{(A)} \qquad \|\boldsymbol{\alpha} - \boldsymbol{\alpha}_s\|^2 \leq \|\boldsymbol{\alpha} - \mathbf{x}\|^2 \qquad \text{for all } \mathbf{x} \in S.$$

Observe that (2.1) requires us to find two things. We are to find the smallest value which the quantity $\|\boldsymbol{\alpha} - \mathbf{x}\|$ achieves for vectors $\mathbf{x} \in S$ and we are to find those vectors $\mathbf{x}$ for which $\|\boldsymbol{\alpha} - \mathbf{x}\|$ achieves this minimum value. For $\mathcal{A}$ we saw that the solution is obtained by projecting $\boldsymbol{\alpha}$ orthogonally onto S. It turns out that we obtain the same result for finite-dimensional subspaces in any vector space $\mathcal{V}$.

(2.2) Best Approximation Theorem.† *The approximation problem possesses a unique solution $\boldsymbol{\alpha}_s \in S$ for each $\boldsymbol{\alpha} \in \mathcal{V}$. This vector, which is called the (best) S-approximator to $\boldsymbol{\alpha}$, is simply the orthogonal projection of $\boldsymbol{\alpha}$ on S:*

(a) $\boldsymbol{\alpha}_s = P\boldsymbol{\alpha}$.

---

†Sometimes called the "theorem on least squares."

Proof. Recall the definition of the projection of $\boldsymbol{\alpha}$ on S. We showed that when S is finite-dimensional we can decompose any $\boldsymbol{\alpha} \in \mathcal{V}$ in the form

(b) $\boldsymbol{\alpha} = P\boldsymbol{\alpha} + \boldsymbol{\beta}$,

where $P\boldsymbol{\alpha}$, the projection on S, is in S and $\boldsymbol{\beta} = \boldsymbol{\alpha} - P\boldsymbol{\alpha}$ is orthogonal to every vector in S. Now let us calculate $\|\boldsymbol{\alpha} - \mathbf{x}\|^2$ for an arbitrary $\mathbf{x} \in S$. By (b)

$$\text{(c)} \quad \begin{aligned} \|\boldsymbol{\alpha} - \mathbf{x}\|^2 &= \|[P\boldsymbol{\alpha} - \mathbf{x}] + \boldsymbol{\beta}\|^2 \\ &= ([P\boldsymbol{\alpha} - \mathbf{x}] + \boldsymbol{\beta}) \cdot ([P\boldsymbol{\alpha} - \mathbf{x}] + \boldsymbol{\beta}) \\ &= \|P\boldsymbol{\alpha} - \mathbf{x}\|^2 + 2[P\boldsymbol{\alpha} - \mathbf{x}] \cdot \boldsymbol{\beta} + \|\boldsymbol{\beta}\|^2. \end{aligned}$$

Since S is a subspace and $P\boldsymbol{\alpha}$ and $\mathbf{x}$ are in S, so is the vector $P\boldsymbol{\alpha} - \mathbf{x}$. However, $\boldsymbol{\beta}$ is orthogonal to everything in S and hence is orthogonal to $P\boldsymbol{\alpha} - \mathbf{x}$. Thus $[P\boldsymbol{\alpha} - \mathbf{x}] \cdot \boldsymbol{\beta} = 0$, and (c) reduces to

(d) $\|\boldsymbol{\alpha} - \mathbf{x}\|^2 = \|\boldsymbol{\beta}\|^2 + \|P\boldsymbol{\alpha} - \mathbf{x}\|^2 \qquad \mathbf{x} \in S.$

Since $\boldsymbol{\beta}$ is a fixed vector it is clear from (d) that $\|\boldsymbol{\alpha} - \mathbf{x}\|^2$ achieves its smallest value among vectors $\mathbf{x} \in S$ when and only when $\|P\boldsymbol{\alpha} - \mathbf{x}\| = \mathbf{0}$. Thus $\mathbf{x} = P\boldsymbol{\alpha}$ is the best approximator $\boldsymbol{\alpha}_S$. ▮

An important application of the best approximation theorem is to the treatment of solutionless systems of linear equations. SLE's in which there are more equations than unknowns are frequently of this type. Such systems arise in the process of fitting curves to experimental points by the method of least squares. We illustrate with an example.

(2.3) Example. Method of Least Squares. It is known that the resistance $y(x)$ in a certain electrical circuit is a linear function of temperature x:

$$(1) \qquad y(x) = c_1 x + c_2.$$

Determine the constants c_1 and c_2, given the following series of measurements:

x	-200	-100	$+300$
$y(x)$	2	3	4

If we substitute the given values into (1) we obtain the equations

$$(2) \qquad \begin{aligned} -200c_1 + c_2 &= 2 \\ -100c_1 + c_2 &= 3 \\ 300c_1 + c_2 &= 4. \end{aligned}$$

Application of our algorithm quickly reveals that (2) has no solutions! Hence either the measurements are in error or (1) is an oversimplified formula. Note that in any event (2) is the *same* system of equations we would get in attempting to expand the vector $\boldsymbol{\alpha} = (2, 3, 4)$ of right sides as a linear combination of the "coefficient" vectors $\boldsymbol{\beta}_1 = (-200, -100, 300)$ and $\boldsymbol{\beta}_2 = (1, 1, 1)$. This fact can be read off by rewriting (2) as

$$(3) \qquad c_1\begin{pmatrix} -200 \\ -100 \\ 300 \end{pmatrix} + c_2\begin{pmatrix} 1 \\ 1 \\ 1 \end{pmatrix} = \begin{pmatrix} 2 \\ 3 \\ 4 \end{pmatrix}$$

or, equivalently,

$$(4) \qquad c_1\boldsymbol{\beta}_1 + c_2\boldsymbol{\beta}_2 = \boldsymbol{\alpha}.$$

The fact that (4) has no solutions means that

$$\boldsymbol{\alpha} \notin \langle \boldsymbol{\beta}_1, \boldsymbol{\beta}_2 \rangle = S.$$

We now define "best" values for c_1 and c_2 to be those for which $c_1\boldsymbol{\beta}_1 + c_2\boldsymbol{\beta}_2$ is the best approximator to $\boldsymbol{\alpha}$. That is, c_1 and c_2 are required to satisfy

$$(5) \qquad c_1\boldsymbol{\beta}_1 + c_2\boldsymbol{\beta}_2 = \boldsymbol{\alpha}_s.$$

Noting that in this example $\boldsymbol{\beta}_1 \cdot \boldsymbol{\beta}_2 = 0$, we can produce an orthonormal basis for S very simply:

$$E\colon\ \boldsymbol{\epsilon}_1 = \frac{\boldsymbol{\beta}_1}{\|\boldsymbol{\beta}_1\|} = \sqrt{\tfrac{1}{14}}\,(-2, -1, 3),\ \boldsymbol{\epsilon}_2 = \frac{\boldsymbol{\beta}_2}{\|\boldsymbol{\beta}_2\|} = \sqrt{\tfrac{1}{3}}\,(1, 1, 1).$$

Then by the projection theorem $\boldsymbol{\alpha}_s = P\boldsymbol{\alpha}$ is given by

$$\begin{aligned}(6) \qquad \boldsymbol{\alpha}_s = P\boldsymbol{\alpha} &= (\boldsymbol{\alpha} \cdot \boldsymbol{\epsilon}_1)\boldsymbol{\epsilon}_1 + (\boldsymbol{\alpha} \cdot \boldsymbol{\epsilon}_2)\boldsymbol{\epsilon}_2 \\ &= \frac{5}{\sqrt{14}}\frac{1}{\sqrt{14}}(-2, -1, 3) + \frac{9}{\sqrt{3}}\frac{1}{\sqrt{3}}(1, 1, 1) \\ &= (\tfrac{16}{7}, \tfrac{37}{14}, \tfrac{57}{14}).\end{aligned}$$

Inserting this into (5) is equivalent to replacing the right sides of (2) by the numbers 16/7, 37/14, and 57/14:

$$\begin{aligned} -200c_1 + c_2 &= 16/7 \\ (2') \qquad -100c_1 + c_2 &= 37/14 \\ 300c_1 + c_2 &= 57/14. \end{aligned}$$

The system (2′) *can* be solved, as the Gauss-algorithm shows, and the result is,

$$c_1 = 1/280 \qquad c_2 = 3.$$

We call these the *best* c_1 and c_2 values.

The preceding example is often described as the problem of "fitting a line" to the given measurements. This geometric interpretation is made clear by plotting the measurements on a graph (Figure 6.9). We remark that if the points A, B, and C actually were collinear, then (2) would be solvable. That is, we would have $\boldsymbol{\alpha} \in S$. For this situation $P\boldsymbol{\alpha} = \boldsymbol{\alpha}$, so that the method would still give the correct result. In general, the method is equivalent to the following procedure. Compute the sums of the squares of the differences between the value of y, as given by (1), and the observed values at x equal to -200, -100, and 300. In the present example this sum is

$$(7) \qquad (c_1(-200) + c_2 - 2)^2 + (c_1(-100) + c_2 - 3)^2 + (c_1(300) + c_2 - 4)^2.$$

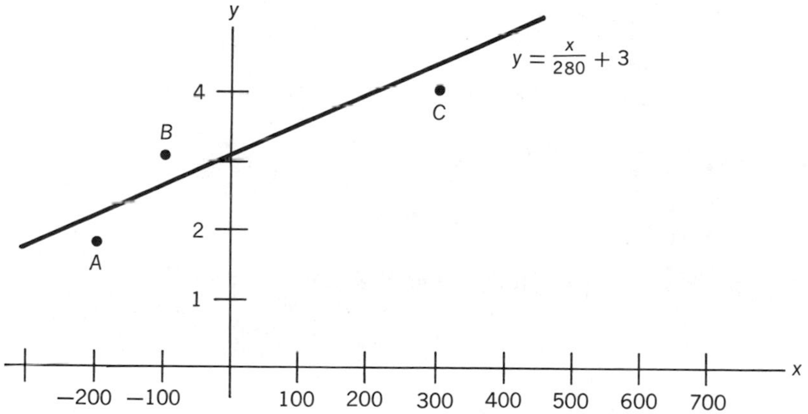

Figure 6.9

Then our choice of c_1 and c_2, as required by (5), makes the sum (7)—which equals $\|c_1\boldsymbol{\beta}_1 + c_2\boldsymbol{\beta}_2 - \boldsymbol{\alpha}\|^2$—as small as possible. This is why the method is called the method of least squares.

We shall now amplify the results obtained in solving the approximation problem. We begin by noting that for each finite-dimensional subspace S of $\mathcal{V}$ and for each $\boldsymbol{\alpha} \in \mathcal{V}$ the S-approximator to $\boldsymbol{\alpha}$, $\boldsymbol{\alpha}_s = P\boldsymbol{\alpha}$, is shorter than $\boldsymbol{\alpha}$

itself (see Figure 6.10). That is,

$$\|\alpha\| \geq \|\alpha_s\|. \tag{2.4}$$

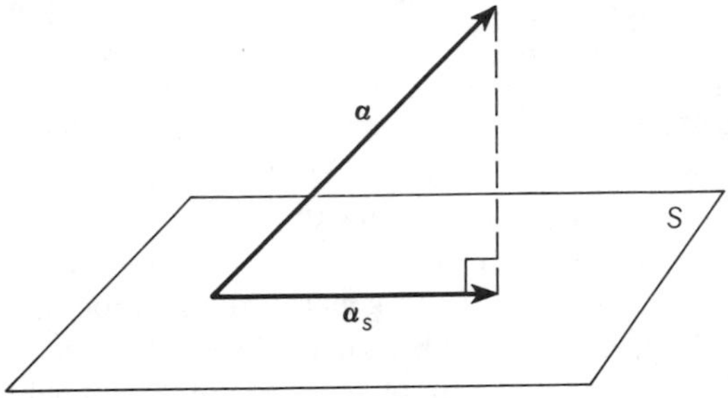

$\|\alpha_S\| \leq \|\alpha\|$

Figure 6.10

This is a consequence of the following computation:

$$\begin{aligned}\|\alpha\|^2 &= \|\alpha_s + (\alpha - \alpha_s)\|^2 \\ &= (\alpha_s + (\alpha - \alpha_s)) \cdot (\alpha_s + (\alpha - \alpha_s)) \\ &= \alpha_s \cdot \alpha_s + 2(\alpha - \alpha_s) \cdot \alpha_s + (\alpha - \alpha_s) \cdot (\alpha - \alpha_s).\end{aligned}$$

The middle term on the right side is zero, since $\alpha_s \in S$ while

$$\alpha - \alpha_s = \alpha - P\alpha$$

is perpendicular to S [see (1.8)]; hence the equation reduces to

$$\|\alpha\|^2 = \|\alpha_s\|^2 + \|\alpha - \alpha_s\|^2, \tag{2.4$'$}$$

from which (2.4) obviously follows.

It will be useful to rewrite (2.4) and (2.4′) in terms of the E-coordinates of $\alpha_s = P\alpha$, where E: $\epsilon_1, \epsilon_2, \ldots, \epsilon_k$ denotes an orthonormal basis for S. Using the expansion in (1.8b),

$$P\alpha = (\alpha \cdot \epsilon_1)\epsilon_1 + \cdots + (\alpha \cdot \epsilon_k)\epsilon_k,$$

we find that

$$\begin{aligned}\|\alpha_s\|^2 &= ((\alpha \cdot \epsilon_1)\epsilon_1 + \cdots + (\alpha \cdot \epsilon_k)\epsilon_k) \cdot ((\alpha \cdot \epsilon_1)\epsilon_1 + \cdots + (\alpha \cdot \epsilon_k)\epsilon_k) \\ &= (\alpha \cdot \epsilon_1)^2 + \cdots + (\alpha \cdot \epsilon_k)^2.\end{aligned}$$

Hence (2.4) and (2.4′) can be written in the form

$$(2.5)\qquad \begin{aligned} &(B) \qquad \|\boldsymbol{\alpha}\|^2 \geq (\boldsymbol{\alpha}\cdot\boldsymbol{\epsilon}_1)^2 + \cdots + (\boldsymbol{\alpha}\cdot\boldsymbol{\epsilon}_k)^2 \\ &(P) \qquad \|\boldsymbol{\alpha}\|^2 = (\boldsymbol{\alpha}\cdot\boldsymbol{\epsilon}_1)^2 + \cdots + (\boldsymbol{\alpha}\cdot\boldsymbol{\epsilon}_k)^2 + \|\boldsymbol{\alpha} - \boldsymbol{\alpha}_s\|^2. \end{aligned}$$

Formula (B) is called BESSEL'S INEQUALITY and can be summarized in words as: *the squared length of a vector in $\mathcal{V}$ exceeds the sum of the squares of its components relative to any orthonormal basis of any finite-dimensional subspace of* $\mathcal{V}$. Formula (P) is called PARSEVAL'S RELATION. It can be summarized: *the squared distance from a vector to its S-approximator is equal to the amount by which the squared length of the vector exceeds the sum of the squares of its components relative to any orthonormal basis of S.*

(2.6) Example. Parseval's Relation. Find the distance of $\boldsymbol{\alpha} = (1, 1, 2, -1)$ from the subspace S of $\mathcal{R}^4$ consisting of all vectors of the form

$$(a + b,\quad a - 2b + c,\quad a + c,\quad a + b - 2c)$$

for all scalars a, b, c.

By writing

$$\begin{aligned}(a + b, a - 2b + c, a + c, a + b - 2c) = a(1, 1, 1, 1) &+ b(1, -2, 0, 1) \\ &+ c(0, 1, 1, -2),\end{aligned}$$

we see that $S = \langle\boldsymbol{\beta}_1, \boldsymbol{\beta}_2, \boldsymbol{\beta}_3\rangle$, where $\boldsymbol{\beta}_1 = (1, 1, 1, 1)$, $\boldsymbol{\beta}_2 = (1, -2, 0, 1)$, $\boldsymbol{\beta}_3 = (0, 1, 1, -2)$. In order to find the vector $\boldsymbol{\alpha}_s = P\boldsymbol{\alpha}$ we proceed to obtain an orthonormal basis for S by the Gram–Schmidt procedure. This yields

$$E\colon \boldsymbol{\epsilon}_1 = \tfrac{1}{2}(1, 1, 1, 1),\ \boldsymbol{\epsilon}_2 = \sqrt{\tfrac{1}{6}}\,(1, -2, 0, 1),\ \boldsymbol{\epsilon}_3 = \sqrt{\tfrac{1}{30}}\,(2, -1, 3, -4).$$

Therefore $\boldsymbol{\alpha}\cdot\boldsymbol{\epsilon}_1 = 3/2$, $\boldsymbol{\alpha}\cdot\boldsymbol{\epsilon}_2 = -2/\sqrt{6}$, $\boldsymbol{\alpha}\cdot\boldsymbol{\epsilon}_3 = 11/\sqrt{30}$. According to the relation (P) we deduce that

$$\begin{aligned}\|\boldsymbol{\alpha} - \boldsymbol{\alpha}_s\|^2 &= \|\boldsymbol{\alpha}\|^2 - \left(\frac{3}{2}\right)^2 - \left(\frac{-2}{\sqrt{6}}\right)^2 - \left(\frac{11}{\sqrt{30}}\right)^2 \\ &= 7 - \tfrac{9}{4} - \tfrac{2}{3} - \tfrac{121}{30} = \tfrac{1}{20},\end{aligned}$$

so that the desired distance from $\boldsymbol{\alpha}$ to S is

$$\|\boldsymbol{\alpha} - \boldsymbol{\alpha}_s\| = \sqrt{\frac{1}{20}}\cdot$$

PROBLEMS

1. (a) Find the value of c in the equation $y = cx$ which best fits the following data:

x	-1	0	1	2
$y(x)$	-1	1	3	5

(b) Show on a diagram that the measurement points are collinear. Would any simple geometric relation between the fitted line and the actual line be expected? Justify.

2. In the sense of least squares find the best values for the unknowns in the following SLE's.

(a) $\begin{aligned} x_1 + \ x_2 &= 3 \\ x_1 + \ x_2 &= 4 \\ x_1 - 2x_2 &= 1 \end{aligned}$ (b) $\begin{aligned} x_1 + x_2 &= 1 \\ x_1 - x_2 &= 2 \\ 3x_1 - x_2 &= 5 \end{aligned}$

(*Hint:* Each system can be obtained by attempting to expand an appropriate vector $\boldsymbol{\alpha} \in \mathcal{R}^3$ as a linear combination of two other vectors in $\mathcal{R}^3$ [see (2.3)–(3)].)

3. (a) Find those coefficient values in the following formulas which best fit the given data. Sketch the results. (*Hint:* In each case write the equations obtained by substituting the measurements into the given formula. This SLE will also represent the attempt to express an appropriate vector $\boldsymbol{\alpha} \in \mathcal{R}^4$ as a linear combination of certain other vectors in $\mathcal{R}^4$ [see (2.3)–(3)].)

x	-2	-1	1	2
y	1	0	2	3

(i) $y = c_1x + c_2$
(ii) $y = c_1x^2 + c_2x + c_3$
(iii) $y = c_1x + c_2 + c_3/x$

(b) Using Parseval's relation, judge which of the formulas (i), (ii), (iii) is most successful in fitting the given data.

4. For each of the following functions H, find the coefficient values which yield the best approximation to the prescribed h.

(a) $\mathcal{C}[-1, 1]$ $\left(f \cdot g = \int_{-1}^{1} f(t)g(t)\, dt\right)$

$$H(t) = c_1t^2 + c_2t + c_3, \qquad h(t) = t^3.$$

(b) $\mathcal{C}[-\pi, \pi]$ $\left(f \cdot g = \int_{-\pi}^{\pi} f(t)g(t)\, dt\right)$

$$H(t) = c_0 + c_1 \cos t + d_1 \sin t, \qquad h(t) = t.$$

(c) $\mathcal{C}[-1, 1]$ $\left(f \cdot g = \int_{-1}^{1} f(t)g(t)t^2\, dt\right)$

$$H(t) = c_1t^2 + c_2t + c_3, \qquad h(t) = t^3.$$

5. Check the result obtained in (2.6): find $\boldsymbol{\alpha}_s$ and then compute $\|\boldsymbol{\alpha} - \boldsymbol{\alpha}_s\|$ directly.

6. Suppose that in $\mathcal{C}[-\pi, \pi]$ one is to find the coefficient values for

$$H(t) = c_0 + c_1 \cos t + d_1 \sin t + c_2 \cos 2t$$

which furnish the best approximation to $h(t) = t$. Using the result in problem 4(b) evaluate c_0, c_1, d_1. Do *not* evaluate c_2, but give an upper estimate on its magnitude. (*Hint:* Use Bessel's inequality.)

7. Find the solution of

$$\ddot{y} + 2\dot{y} + y = 0$$

which best approximates $h(t) = t$ in the vector space $\mathcal{C}[-1, 1]$, with

$$f \cdot g = \int_{-1}^{1} f(t)g(t)\, dt.$$

3. "Bases" in Infinite-Dimensional Spaces; Fourier Series

In this section we shall utilize the results obtained earlier to introduce a notion of coordinates into infinite-dimensional vector spaces. It is important to note that there *are* such spaces. [The fact that $\mathcal{C}[a, b]$ is one will be demonstrated in the problems.]

Consider an infinite-dimensional space $\mathcal{V}$ on which an inner product has been prescribed. For example, the various spaces $\mathcal{C}[a, b]$ with

$$f \cdot g = \int_a^b f(t)g(t)\, dt$$

are of this type. $\mathcal{V}$ must contain orthonormal systems B: $\boldsymbol{\beta}_1, \ldots, \boldsymbol{\beta}_m$ of m vectors for arbitrarily large m; otherwise $\mathcal{V}$ would be finite-dimensional (problem 9). In fact, as we shall see by way of examples, $\mathcal{V}$ contains orthonormal systems of infinitely many vectors. Let E: $\boldsymbol{\epsilon}_1, \boldsymbol{\epsilon}_2, \ldots, \boldsymbol{\epsilon}_n, \ldots$ denote one such system (Figure 6.11). That is, the $\boldsymbol{\epsilon}_i$ satisfy

$$\text{(ON)} \qquad \begin{aligned} \boldsymbol{\epsilon}_i \cdot \boldsymbol{\epsilon}_j &= 0 \qquad i \neq j \\ \boldsymbol{\epsilon}_i \cdot \boldsymbol{\epsilon}_i &= 1 \qquad i = 1, 2, \ldots . \end{aligned}$$

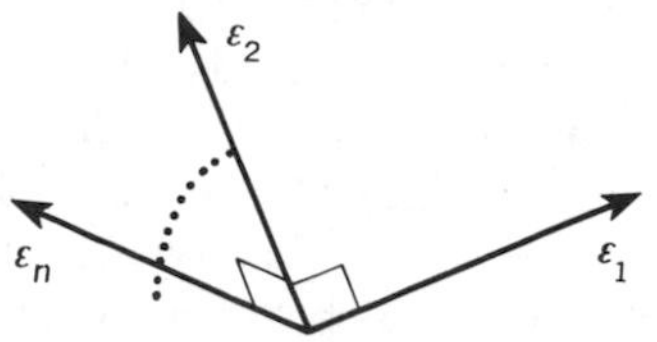

Figure 6.11

Now consider the subspace $S_1 = \langle \epsilon_1 \rangle$. S_1 is obviously finite-dimensional, so each $\alpha \in \mathcal{V}$ possesses a best S_1-approximator α_{S_1} which we write as α_1:

$$(\mathrm{A}_1) \qquad \alpha_1 = P\alpha = (\alpha \cdot \epsilon_1)\epsilon_1.$$

In other words, the vector of the form $c\epsilon_1$ which is closest to α is the one for which $c = \alpha \cdot \epsilon_1$ (Figure 6.12). Next, consider the best S_2-approximator to α, where $S_2 = \langle \epsilon_1, \epsilon_2 \rangle$ (Figure 6.13). Since ϵ_1, ϵ_2 is an orthonormal basis for S_2, the S_2-approximator to α is, according to the projection theorem, simply

$$(\mathrm{A}_2) \qquad \alpha_2 = (\alpha \cdot \epsilon_1)\epsilon_1 + (\alpha \cdot \epsilon_2)\epsilon_2.$$

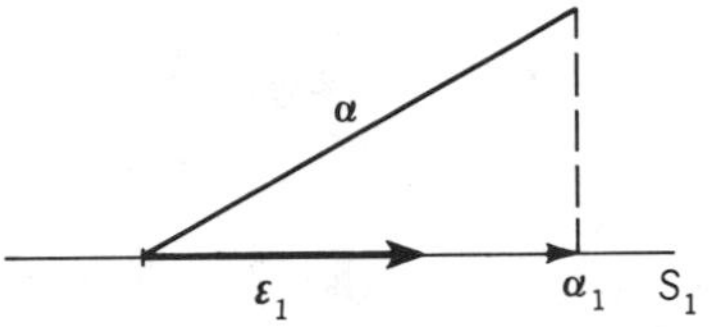

Figure 6.12

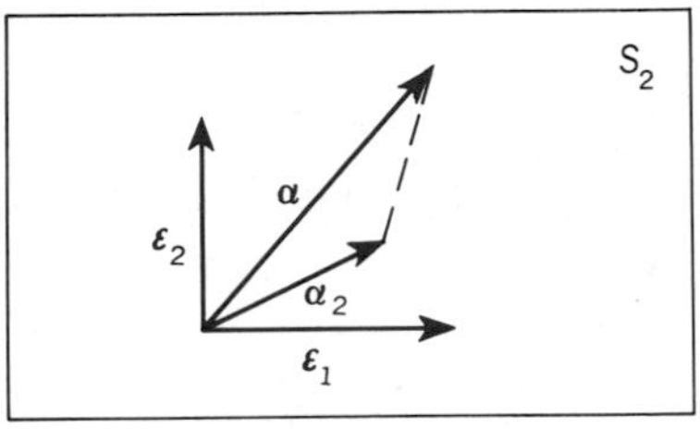

Figure 6.13

Since $\epsilon_1, \epsilon_2, \epsilon_3$ is an orthonormal basis for $S_3 = \langle \epsilon_1, \epsilon_2, \epsilon_3 \rangle$, we obtain the S_3-approximator to α in the same manner:

$$(\mathrm{A}_3) \qquad \alpha_3 = (\alpha \cdot \epsilon_1)\epsilon_1 + (\alpha \cdot \epsilon_2)\epsilon_2 + (\alpha \cdot \epsilon_3)\epsilon_3.$$

Indeed it is by now clear that for a general index k we will find that the best S_k-approximator to α, where $S_k = \langle \epsilon_1, \ldots, \epsilon_k \rangle$, is the vector

$$(\mathrm{A}_k) \qquad \alpha_k = (\alpha \cdot \epsilon_1)\epsilon_1 + (\alpha \cdot \epsilon_2)\epsilon_2 + \cdots + (\alpha \cdot \epsilon_k)\epsilon_k.$$

Let us now make a very important observation, which can be read off from equations (A_1) to (A_k), concerning the structure of the above formulas.

(3.1) Remark. *The coefficient of ϵ_i in the expansion for α_k is the same for every $k \geq i$.*

In other words, once we have computed the coefficient of a given ϵ_i in any one α_{k_0} $(k_0 \geq i)$, there is no need to recompute this coefficient for later α_k's—these α_k's differ from α_{k_0} only by the inclusion of *additional* terms $c_j\epsilon_j$ with $j > k_0$. This fact permits us to record *all* the S_k-approximations to α in a convenient manner. We simply write down the following unending expression:

$$(3.2) \qquad (\alpha \cdot \epsilon_1)\epsilon_1 + (\alpha \cdot \epsilon_2)\epsilon_2 + \cdots + (\alpha \cdot \epsilon_n)\epsilon_n + \cdots.$$

This leads to an important definition.

(3.3) Definition. Let an infinite orthonormal system E: $\epsilon_1, \ldots, \epsilon_n, \ldots$ and a vector $\boldsymbol{\alpha}$ in $\mathcal{V}$ be given. The **Fourier E-expansion** corresponding to $\boldsymbol{\alpha}$ is that expression

$$(1) \qquad c_1\epsilon_1 + c_2\epsilon_2 + \cdots + c_n\epsilon_n + \cdots$$

possessing the property:

(∗) For each $k = 1, 2, \ldots$ the vector $c_1\epsilon_1 + \cdots + c_k\epsilon_k$ formed by the sum of first k terms of (1) is the best S_k-approximator to $\boldsymbol{\alpha}$, where $S_k = \langle \epsilon_1, \ldots, \epsilon_k \rangle$.

It is easily checked [see proposition (1.3)] that (∗) uniquely determines the c's to be

$$(2) \qquad c_n = \boldsymbol{\alpha} \cdot \epsilon_n, \qquad n = 1, 2, \ldots.$$

Hence the Fourier E-expansion for $\boldsymbol{\alpha}$ is precisely (3.2). These c's are known as the **Fourier E-coefficients** of $\boldsymbol{\alpha}$.

Note that the S_k-approximations to $\boldsymbol{\alpha}$ form an infinite sequence in the sense of the Review of Calculus. This sequence is of the "series" form (3.5) noted in that chapter except that here the terms a_k and b_k—that is, $\boldsymbol{\alpha}_k$ and $(\boldsymbol{\alpha} \cdot \epsilon_k)\epsilon_k$—are *vectors* rather than real numbers.

We wish to emphasize that the unending expansion (3.2) is given a meaning *only* by its possession of property (∗). We cannot ask whether the "sum" of (3.2) "actually is" $\boldsymbol{\alpha}$, since no notion of sum for infinitely many vectors has been defined. To study that question we shall have to introduce a notion of *convergence* in $\mathcal{V}$ just as we did for real numbers in the Review of Calculus. We shall say more about this presently.

(3.4) Example. An Infinite Orthonormal System (E_s). Let $\mathcal{V} = \mathcal{C}[0, L]$, with $f \cdot g = \int_0^L f(t)g(t)\,dt$ as inner product. Then it is easy to show (problem 5) that the system F_s: $f_1, f_2, \ldots$ such that

$$f_1(t) = \sin\frac{\pi t}{L}, \qquad f_2(t) = \sin\frac{2\pi t}{L}, \ldots, \qquad f_n(t) = \sin\frac{n\pi t}{L}, \ldots$$

consists of mutually orthogonal vectors. That is,

$$\text{(i)} \quad f_m \cdot f_n = \int_0^L \sin\frac{n\pi t}{L}\sin\frac{m\pi t}{L}\,dt = 0, \qquad m \neq n.$$

However, F_s is not an orthonormal system; in fact,

$$\text{(ii)}\quad \|f_m\|^2 = f_m \cdot f_m = \int_0^L \sin^2 \frac{m\pi t}{L}\, dt = L/2.$$

Using this information we can modify F_s to obtain an orthonormal system E_s: $e_1, e_2, \ldots$ by dividing each f_m by its length $\|f_m\|$:

$$e_1(t) = \sqrt{\frac{2}{L}} \sin \frac{\pi t}{L}, \quad e_2(t) = \sqrt{\frac{2}{L}} \sin \frac{2\pi t}{L}, \ldots, \quad e_k(t) = \sqrt{\frac{2}{L}} \sin \frac{k\pi t}{L}, \ldots.$$

It is now possible to apply our preceding work to the vector space $\mathcal{V} = \mathcal{C}[0, L]$. For any function $f \in \mathcal{V}$ the Fourier E_s-expansion corresponding to f is given by

$$\text{(F)}\ c_1 \left(\sqrt{\frac{2}{L}} \sin \frac{\pi t}{L}\right) + c_2 \left(\sqrt{\frac{2}{L}} \sin \frac{2\pi t}{L}\right) + \cdots + c_k \left(\sqrt{\frac{2}{L}} \sin \frac{k\pi t}{L}\right) + \cdots,$$

where, by (3.3)–(2),

$$c_m = f \cdot \left(\sqrt{\frac{2}{L}} \sin \frac{m\pi t}{L}\right) = \sqrt{\frac{2}{L}} \int_0^L f(t) \sin \frac{m\pi t}{L}\, dt, \qquad m = 1, 2, \ldots.†$$

When we insert these values into (F) we see that the expansion can be conveniently written in the form

$$\text{(F}'\text{)}\quad \frac{2}{L}\left(f \cdot \sin \frac{\pi t}{L}\right) \sin \frac{\pi t}{L} + \frac{2}{L}\left(f \cdot \sin \frac{2\pi t}{L}\right) \sin \frac{2\pi t}{L} + \cdots.$$

---

†In this text we have consistently distinguished between the symbol for a *function*, for example, f, and the symbol for the *value* it assumes at a given argument, for example, $f(t_0)$. It is desirable to maintain this explicit notational distinction between functions and their values, but there are certain situations in which this would be quite awkward. For instance, if the function f satisfies

$$f(t) = \sin t$$

for all t, then we could write $f = \sin$; but how would we denote the function f satisfying

$$f(t) = \sin \tfrac{3}{2}t$$

for all t? It is customary in a situation of this sort just to give the formula for $f(t)$, thus relying on the reader to grasp from context that what is actually being referred to is the *function* satisfying that formula, not the *value* given by the formula. Our use of formula (F) and of the notation

$$f \cdot \left(\sqrt{\frac{2}{L}} \sin \frac{m\pi t}{L}\right)$$

to denote the inner product of f with a certain sinusoidal *function* is the first appearance of this device. Others will occur from time to time. However we shall minimize this practice so as not to put too heavy a burden on the reader.

We do a specific example. On $\mathcal{V} = \mathcal{C}[0, \pi]$ the system E_s: $e_1, e_2, \ldots$ involves

$$e_1(t) = \sqrt{\frac{2}{\pi}} \sin t, \qquad e_2(t) = \sqrt{\frac{2}{\pi}} \sin 2t, \ldots .$$

Consider the function f defined by $f(t) \equiv 1$. To obtain its Fourier E_s-expansion we compute the integrals

$$f \cdot \sin mt = \int_0^\pi 1 \sin mt\, dt = -\left.\frac{\cos mt}{m}\right|_0^\pi = \frac{1}{m} - \frac{\cos m\pi}{m}.$$

When m is an even integer this quantity is zero; when m is an odd integer it is $2/m$. Thus we can write the Fourier expansion of $f(t) \equiv 1$ as

$$\left(\sqrt{\frac{2}{\pi}}\, 2\right)\sqrt{\frac{2}{\pi}} \sin t + (0)\sqrt{\frac{2}{\pi}} \sin 2t + \left(\sqrt{\frac{2}{\pi}}\, \frac{2}{3}\right)\sqrt{\frac{2}{\pi}} \sin 3t$$
$$+ (0)\sqrt{\frac{2}{\pi}} \sin 4t + \cdots$$

or, as it is usually expressed,

(iii) $\dfrac{4}{\pi} \sin t + \dfrac{4}{3\pi} \sin 3t + \dfrac{4}{5\pi} \sin 5t + \cdots .$

In a similar way it can be shown (problem 14) that the Fourier E_s-expansion for $f(t) = t$ is

(iv) $2 \sin t - \sin 2t + \frac{2}{3} \sin 3t - \cdots + (-1)^{n+1}(2/n) \sin nt + \cdots .$

Now the expansion (iii) implies in particular that the function g of the form

(v) $g(t) = c \sin t + d \sin 2t + e \sin 3t$

which best approximates $f(t) \equiv 1$ in thc lcast-squares sense is given by

$$f_3(t) = \frac{4}{\pi} \sin t + \frac{4}{3\pi} \sin 3t, \qquad 0 \le t \le \pi.$$

Similarly, according to (iv), that function of the form (v) which best approximates $f(t) = t$ is given by

$$f_3(t) = 2 \sin t - \sin 2t + \tfrac{2}{3} \sin 3t.$$

Let us turn next to the general question of exactly how well the approximators $\boldsymbol{\alpha}_1, \boldsymbol{\alpha}_2, \boldsymbol{\alpha}_3, \ldots$ in a space $\mathcal{V}$ actually approximate the vector $\boldsymbol{\alpha}$. Inasmuch as S_1 is one-dimensional, S_2 is two-dimensional, and so on, it is certainly plausible that the later $\boldsymbol{\alpha}_k$'s give better approximations to $\boldsymbol{\alpha}$ than the early $\boldsymbol{\alpha}_k$'s. One way to show that this is actually the case (see problem 16 for another) is to make use of (P), the Parseval relation [(2.5)]. This yields the formulas

$$
(3.5)\qquad
\begin{aligned}
\|\boldsymbol{\alpha} - \boldsymbol{\alpha}_1\|^2 &= \|\boldsymbol{\alpha}\|^2 - (\boldsymbol{\alpha}\cdot\boldsymbol{\epsilon}_1)^2\\
\|\boldsymbol{\alpha} - \boldsymbol{\alpha}_2\|^2 &= \|\boldsymbol{\alpha}\|^2 - (\boldsymbol{\alpha}\cdot\boldsymbol{\epsilon}_1)^2 - (\boldsymbol{\alpha}\cdot\boldsymbol{\epsilon}_2)^2\\
&\ \vdots\\
\|\boldsymbol{\alpha} - \boldsymbol{\alpha}_k\|^2 &= \|\boldsymbol{\alpha}\|^2 - (\boldsymbol{\alpha}\cdot\boldsymbol{\epsilon}_1)^2 - (\boldsymbol{\alpha}\cdot\boldsymbol{\epsilon}_2)^2 - \cdots - (\boldsymbol{\alpha}\cdot\boldsymbol{\epsilon}_k)^2.\\
&\ \vdots
\end{aligned}
$$

It is clear by inspection of (3.5) that the distance between $\boldsymbol{\alpha}$ and its S_k-approximator $\boldsymbol{\alpha}_k$ steadily decreases as the index k grows:

$$
(3.6)\qquad \|\boldsymbol{\alpha} - \boldsymbol{\alpha}_1\|^2 \geq \|\boldsymbol{\alpha} - \boldsymbol{\alpha}_2\|^2 \geq \cdots \geq \|\boldsymbol{\alpha} - \boldsymbol{\alpha}_k\|^2 \geq \cdots.
$$

What we would like to have happen is that there should be here a "convergence" of the $\boldsymbol{\alpha}_k$'s to $\boldsymbol{\alpha}$ in some sense analogous to convergence of sequences of real numbers as described in the Review of Calculus. Thus we extend the definition of convergence to arbitrary vector spaces. All we have to do is to replace the absolute value by the norm, just as with continuity and differentiability in Chapter 2.

(3.7) Definition. An infinite sequence of vectors $\boldsymbol{\alpha}_1, \boldsymbol{\alpha}_2, \ldots$, denoted by $\{\boldsymbol{\alpha}_n\}$, **converges**† to a vector $\boldsymbol{\alpha}$ if given any number $\varepsilon > 0$ there exists an integer N such that for *all* $n \geq N$ one has the inequality

$$\|\boldsymbol{\alpha} - \boldsymbol{\alpha}_n\| < \varepsilon.$$

That is, $\{\boldsymbol{\alpha}_n\}$ converges to $\boldsymbol{\alpha}$ if and only if the sequence of real numbers $\{\|\boldsymbol{\alpha} - \boldsymbol{\alpha}_n\|\}$ converges to zero:

$$\lim_{n\to\infty} \|\boldsymbol{\alpha} - \boldsymbol{\alpha}_n\| = 0.$$

If this is so we write

$$\lim_{n\to\infty} \boldsymbol{\alpha}_n = \boldsymbol{\alpha}.$$

†Unfortunately, if we try to extend the Cauchy criterion [theorem (3.4) of the Review of Calculus] to general vector spaces, using this definition of convergence, we shall fail. The theorem simply is not always true. In particular, it is not always true for $\mathcal{C}[a, b]$ with the inner product we have used. (We remark that it is precisely this difficulty which causes the trouble, to which we alluded in Chapter 2, concerning notion of integration in infinite dimensional vector spaces.)

We have noted above that in the case of S_k-approximators the distance $\|\boldsymbol{\alpha} - \boldsymbol{\alpha}_k\|$ from $\boldsymbol{\alpha}_k$ to $\boldsymbol{\alpha}$ steadily decreases as k increases. If, in fact, this distance gets arbitrarily small, then, in the language of definition (3.7), we would say that the $\boldsymbol{\alpha}_k$'s converge to $\boldsymbol{\alpha}$. Using (3.5) we can express this convergence requirement as follows:

$$\text{(3.8)} \qquad \lim_{k\to\infty} \|\boldsymbol{\alpha} - \boldsymbol{\alpha}_k\|^2 = \lim_{k\to\infty} [\|\boldsymbol{\alpha}\|^2 - ((\boldsymbol{\alpha}\cdot\boldsymbol{\epsilon}_1)^2 + (\boldsymbol{\alpha}\cdot\boldsymbol{\epsilon}_2)^2 + \cdots + (\boldsymbol{\alpha}\cdot\boldsymbol{\epsilon}_k)^2)] = 0.$$

Now, partly because of the difficulty mentioned in the footnote, it will *not* be true for all orthonormal systems that the $\boldsymbol{\alpha}_k$'s necessarily converge to $\boldsymbol{\alpha}$. There are, however, certain special orthonormal systems for which the $\boldsymbol{\alpha}_k$'s *will* always converge to $\boldsymbol{\alpha}$. Such systems are called *complete*.

(3.9) Definition. An orthonormal system E: $\boldsymbol{\epsilon}_1, \boldsymbol{\epsilon}_2, \ldots, \boldsymbol{\epsilon}_n, \ldots$ is said to be a **complete** orthonormal system provided that for every $\boldsymbol{\alpha} \in \mathcal{V}$ the distance between $\boldsymbol{\alpha}$ and its S_k-approximator $\boldsymbol{\alpha}_k$ tends to zero as $k \to \infty$. By (3.8) this "completeness condition" can be written in an equivalent form:

$$\text{(C)} \qquad \lim_{k\to\infty} [(\boldsymbol{\alpha}\cdot\boldsymbol{\epsilon}_1)^2 + \cdots + (\boldsymbol{\alpha}\cdot\boldsymbol{\epsilon}_k)^2] = \|\boldsymbol{\alpha}\|^2.$$

When a Fourier expansion for $\boldsymbol{\alpha}$ involves an E which is complete, we shall indicate this fact by writing

$$\text{(a)} \qquad \boldsymbol{\alpha} \sim c_1\boldsymbol{\epsilon}_1 + c_2\boldsymbol{\epsilon}_2 + \cdots + c_m\boldsymbol{\epsilon}_m + \cdots.$$

From now on we shall restrict our attention to *complete* orthonormal systems E. It will be seen that for such systems the Fourier E-coefficients $c_i(\boldsymbol{\alpha}) = \boldsymbol{\alpha}\cdot\boldsymbol{\epsilon}_i$ play a role entirely analogous to B-coordinates in finite-dimensional spaces.

(3.10) Proposition. *If E: $\boldsymbol{\epsilon}_1, \ldots, \boldsymbol{\epsilon}_n, \ldots$ is a complete orthonormal system in $\mathcal{V}$, then:*

(i) *Two vectors $\boldsymbol{\alpha}, \boldsymbol{\alpha}' \in \mathcal{V}$ are equal if and only if their Fourier E-coefficients, $c_1, c_2, \ldots$ and $c_1', c_2', \ldots$, are identical:*

$$c_i = \boldsymbol{\alpha}\cdot\boldsymbol{\epsilon}_i = \boldsymbol{\alpha}'\cdot\boldsymbol{\epsilon}_i = c_i', \qquad i = 1, 2, \ldots.$$

(ii) *Fourier E-coefficients are linear functions:*

$$c_i(\boldsymbol{\alpha} + \boldsymbol{\alpha}') = c_i + c_i', \qquad c_i(k\boldsymbol{\alpha}) = kc_i, \qquad i = 1, 2, \ldots$$

(iii) *Fourier E-coefficients suffice to compute inner products:*

$$\begin{aligned}\boldsymbol{\alpha} \cdot \boldsymbol{\alpha}' &= \lim_{k\to\infty} \boldsymbol{\alpha}_k \cdot \boldsymbol{\alpha}_k = \lim_{k\to\infty} [c_1c_1' + \cdots + c_kc_k'] \\ &= \lim_{k\to\infty} \sum_{i=1}^{k} c_ic_i'.\end{aligned}$$

[In this formula the limit has the meaning given in (3.3) of the Review of Calculus.]

The analogy of equations (ii) and (iii) to results on B-coordinates in finite-dimensional spaces will be emphasized if we write schematically

$$[\boldsymbol{\alpha}]_E = \begin{bmatrix} c_1 \\ c_2 \\ \cdot \\ \cdot \\ \cdot \\ c_n \\ \cdot \\ \cdot \\ \cdot \end{bmatrix}, \qquad [\boldsymbol{\alpha}']_E = \begin{bmatrix} c_1' \\ c_2' \\ \cdot \\ \cdot \\ \cdot \\ c_n' \\ \cdot \\ \cdot \\ \cdot \end{bmatrix}.$$

Then (ii) becomes [see (2.5) of Chapter 5]

$$[\boldsymbol{\alpha} + \boldsymbol{\alpha}']_E = \begin{bmatrix} c_1 + c_1' \\ c_2 + c_2' \\ \cdot \\ \cdot \\ \cdot \\ c_n + c_n' \\ \cdot \\ \cdot \\ \cdot \end{bmatrix}, \qquad [k\boldsymbol{\alpha}]_E = \begin{bmatrix} kc_1 \\ kc_2 \\ \cdot \\ \cdot \\ \cdot \\ kc_n \\ \cdot \\ \cdot \\ \cdot \end{bmatrix},$$

while (iii) corresponds to (1.3b):

$$\boldsymbol{\alpha} \cdot \boldsymbol{\alpha}' = c_1c_1' + c_2c_2' + \cdots + c_nc_n' + \cdots.$$

Proof of Proposition (3.10). (i) If $\boldsymbol{\alpha} = \boldsymbol{\alpha}'$, the equality of their Fourier E-coefficients is obvious. Now suppose that we are only given that

$$(1) \qquad c_i = c_i', \qquad i = 1, 2, \ldots$$

By the definition of Fourier E-coefficients, it then follows that the coefficients corresponding to the vector $\boldsymbol{\gamma} = \boldsymbol{\alpha} - \boldsymbol{\alpha}'$ are

$$(2) \qquad c_i(\boldsymbol{\gamma}) = \boldsymbol{\gamma} \cdot \boldsymbol{\epsilon}_i = \boldsymbol{\alpha} \cdot \boldsymbol{\epsilon}_i - \boldsymbol{\alpha}' \cdot \boldsymbol{\epsilon}_i = 0, \qquad i = 1, 2, \ldots.$$

Thus for each k the S_k-approximator to γ is given by

$$(3) \qquad \gamma_k = (\gamma \cdot \epsilon_1)\epsilon_1 + \cdots + (\gamma \cdot \epsilon_k)\epsilon_k = \mathbf{0}.$$

On the other hand, since E is complete, we know by (3.9) that

$$(4) \qquad \|\gamma\|^2 = \lim_{k\to\infty} [0 + \cdots + 0] = 0.$$

Thus $\|\gamma\| = 0$, whereby

$$(5) \qquad \alpha - \alpha' = \gamma = \mathbf{0}.$$

This completes the proof of (i). Proofs of (ii) and (iii) are left as problems. ▮

The problem of determining whether a given orthonormal system is complete is a very difficult one which we cannot treat here [see W. Kaplan, *Advanced Calculus*, Addison-Wesley, Reading, Mass. (1952), pp. 420–422]. There are, however, three useful systems which are known to be complete. They appear in the following examples.

(3.11) Examples. Complete Orthonormal Systems (E_s, E_c, E_t)

(a) E_s. The system E_s of example (3.4), that is, E_s: $e_1, e_2, \ldots$ where

$$e_1(t) = \sqrt{\frac{2}{L}} \sin \frac{\pi t}{L}, \qquad e_2(t) = \sqrt{\frac{2}{L}} \sin \frac{2\pi t}{L}, \ldots,$$

is complete in the space $\mathcal{V} = \mathcal{C}[0, L]$.

(b) E_c. The system E_c: $e_0^*, e_1^*, e_2^*, \ldots$, defined by

$$e_0^*(t) = \frac{1}{\sqrt{L}}, \qquad e_1^*(t) = \sqrt{\frac{2}{L}} \cos \frac{\pi t}{L}, \qquad e_2^*(t) = \sqrt{\frac{2}{L}} \cos \frac{2\pi t}{L}, \ldots,$$

$$e_k^*(t) = \sqrt{\frac{2}{L}} \cos \frac{k\pi t}{L}, \ldots$$

is also a complete orthonormal system for $\mathcal{V} = \mathcal{C}[0, L]$. The proof that E_c is orthonormal will be obtained in the problems.

(c) E_t. In the space $\mathcal{V} = \mathcal{C}[-L, L]$ $\left(f \cdot g = \int_{-L}^{L} f(t)g(t)\,dt\right)$ there is an orthonormal system containing both sines and cosines. To see this let us deal with the system F_t: $f_0^*, f_1^*, f_1, f_2^*, f_2, \ldots$, where

$$f_1^*(t) = 1, \qquad f_1^*(t) = \cos\frac{\pi t}{L}, \qquad f_0(t) = \sin\frac{\pi t}{L},$$

$$f_2^*(t) = \cos\frac{2\pi t}{L}, \qquad f_2(t) = \sin\frac{2\pi t}{L}, \ldots.$$

The following computations (see problems 6 and 7) show that F_t is an orthogonal system:

$$
\begin{aligned}
f_m^* \cdot f_n^* &= \int_{-L}^{L} \cos\frac{\pi mt}{L} \cos\frac{\pi nt}{L}\, dt = 0 \qquad \text{if } m \neq n \\
(1) \qquad f_m \cdot f_n &= \int_{-L}^{L} \sin\frac{\pi mt}{L} \sin\frac{\pi nt}{L}\, dt = 0 \qquad \text{if } m \neq n \\
f_m^* \cdot f_n &= \int_{-L}^{L} \cos\frac{\pi mt}{L} \sin\frac{\pi nt}{L}\, dt = 0 \qquad \text{for all } m \text{ and } n.
\end{aligned}
$$

The reader can verify by the same methods that

$$
\begin{aligned}
f_m^* \cdot f_m^* &= \int_{-L}^{L} \cos^2\frac{\pi mt}{L}\, dt = L, \qquad m = 1, 2, \ldots \\
(2) \qquad f_0^* \cdot f_0^* &= \int_{-L}^{L} 1^2\, dt = 2L \\
f_m \cdot f_m &= \int_{-L}^{L} \sin^2\frac{\pi mt}{L}\, dt = L, \qquad m = 1, 2, \ldots.
\end{aligned}
$$

Hence by dividing each f_m and f_m^*, by $\|f_m\|$ and $\|f_m^*\|$, respectively, we obtain the system E_t: $h_0^*, h_1^*, h_1, h_2^*, h_2 \ldots$, where

$$h_0^*(t) = \frac{1}{\sqrt{2L}}, \qquad h_1^*(t) = \frac{1}{\sqrt{L}}\cos\frac{\pi t}{L}, \qquad h_1(t) = \frac{1}{\sqrt{L}}\sin\frac{\pi t}{L}, \ldots,$$

$$h_k^*(t) = \frac{1}{\sqrt{L}}\cos\frac{\pi kt}{L}, \qquad h_k(t) = \frac{1}{\sqrt{L}}\sin\frac{\pi kt}{L}, \ldots,$$

which forms an orthonormal system for $\mathcal{V} = \mathcal{C}[-L, L]$. This system is also complete in $\mathcal{V}$ (see Kaplan, *op. cit.*, p. 422).

(3.12) Examples. Incomplete Orthonormal Systems

(a) If we take the collection E: $h_1, h_2, h_3, \ldots$ in the system E_t of example (3.11c) it is still orthonormal, as follows from formulas (1) and (2) of (3.11c). However, it is *not* complete. To see this it suffices by (3.10)–(i) to exhibit two *distinct* functions in $\mathcal{C}[-L, L]$ having identical Fourier E-coefficients. Let

$$g_1(t) \equiv 0, \qquad g_2(t) = \cos \frac{\pi t}{L}.$$

The E-coefficients of g_1 are obviously zero. Moreover, by formula (1) of (3.11c)

$$g_2 \cdot h_n = \frac{1}{\sqrt{L}} \int_{-L}^{L} \cos \frac{\pi t}{L} \sin \frac{2\pi n t}{L}\, dt = 0, \qquad n = 1, 2, \ldots.$$

Hence we have two distinct functions g_1 and g_2 in $\mathcal{C}[-\pi, \pi]$ which possess identical Fourier E-coefficients, so E: $h_1, h_2, h_3, \ldots$ is not complete.

(b) If we take the collection E^*: $h_0^*, h_1^*, h_2^*, \ldots$ in the system E_t of example (3.11c), then it, too, is orthonormal but not complete in $\mathcal{C}[-L, L]$. We see this in the same way as in (a), the only difference being that our choice for g_2 is now

$$g_2(t) - \sin \frac{\pi t}{L}.$$

The system E_t of example (3.11c) is usually called the "trigonometric system on $-L \leq t \leq L$." Let us see how to obtain the Fourier E_t-expansion for a function $f \in \mathcal{C}[-L, L]$. By (3.3) and (3.9) we write

$$(3.13) \qquad f \sim c_0 h_0^* + c_1 h_1^* + d_1 h_1 + c_2 h_2^* + d_2 h_2 + \cdots,$$

where

$$c_0 = f \cdot \frac{1}{\sqrt{2L}}$$

$$c_m = f \cdot \left(\frac{1}{\sqrt{L}} \cos \frac{2\pi m t}{2L} \right), \qquad d_m = f \cdot \left(\frac{1}{\sqrt{L}} \sin \frac{\pi m t}{L} \right), \qquad m = 1, 2, \ldots.$$

(Note that the indexing used for the h's in E_t is a little different from that used for earlier systems.) When we insert these values into (3.13) we see that the expansion can conveniently be written in the form

$$
\begin{aligned}
f \sim \frac{1}{2L}(f\cdot 1)1 &+ \frac{1}{L}\left(f\cdot\cos\frac{\pi t}{L}\right)\cos\frac{\pi t}{L} + \frac{1}{L}\left(f\cdot\sin\frac{\pi t}{L}\right)\sin\frac{\pi t}{L} \\
&+ \frac{1}{L}\left(f\cdot\cos\frac{2\pi t}{L}\right)\cos\frac{2\pi t}{L} + \frac{1}{L}\left(f\cdot\sin\frac{2\pi t}{L}\right)\sin\frac{2\pi t}{L} + \cdots.
\end{aligned} \tag{3.14}
$$

This is frequently written with the use of sigma notation as

$$
f \sim a_0 + \sum_{m=1}^{\infty}\left(a_m\cos\frac{2\pi mt}{L} + b_m\sin\frac{2\pi mt}{L}\right), \tag{3.15}
$$

where of course the a's and b's can be read off from (3.14):

$$
a_0 = \frac{1}{2L}(f\cdot 1)
$$

$$
a_m = \frac{1}{L}\left(f\cdot\cos\frac{2\pi mt}{L}\right), \qquad b_m = \frac{1}{L}\left(f\cdot\sin\frac{2\pi mt}{L}\right), \qquad m = 1, 2, \ldots.
$$

We illustrate with an example involving $\mathcal{C}[-\pi, \pi]$. Consider the function $f(t) = t, \quad -\pi \le t \le \pi$. To obtain its Fourier E_t-expansion we compute the integrals

$$
f\cdot 1 = \int_{-\pi}^{\pi} t\,dt = 0,
$$

$$
f\cdot\cos mt = \int_{-\pi}^{\pi} t\cos mt\,dt = 0,
$$

$$
f\cdot\sin mt = \int_{-\pi}^{\pi} t\sin mt\,dt = \left(-t\,\frac{\cos mt}{m} + \frac{\sin mt}{m^2}\right)\Bigg|_{-\pi}^{\pi} = -2\pi\,\frac{\cos m\pi}{m}.
$$

When m is an even integer this last quantity is $-2\pi/m$; when m is an odd integer it is $2\pi/m$. Inserting these computations into (3.14) we find that the Fourier E_t-expansion of $f(t) = t$ is

$$
\begin{aligned}
f \sim 0\cdot 1 &+ 0\cos t + 2\sin t + 0\cos 2t - \tfrac{2}{2}\sin 2t \\
&+ 0\cos 3t + \tfrac{2}{3}\sin 3t + \cdots
\end{aligned}
$$

or, as it is usually expressed,

$$
f \sim 2\sin t - \sin 2t + \tfrac{2}{3}\sin 3t - \tfrac{2}{5}\sin 5t + \cdots. \tag{3.16}
$$

The expression (3.16) implies for instance that the function g of the form

$$g(t) = a + b \cos t + c \sin t$$

which best approximates $f(t) = t$ is given by

$$f_1(t) = 2 \sin t, \qquad -\pi \leq t \leq \pi.$$

Note that all the orthonormal systems studied in examples (3.11) and (3.12) include only sine and cosine functions (and constants). This does not mean that sines and cosines are the *only* terms which can appear in a complete orthonormal system. Indeed we shall discuss in the problems a complete orthonormal system consisting of polynomials and there are also complete orthonormal systems consisting of other types of functions. However, the particular complete orthonormal systems E_s, E_c, and E_t do have some special features which we will study in §4.

PROBLEMS

1. Compute the Fourier E_c-expansion of each of the following functions over the indicated interval. In addition, sketch f and the S_2-approximator of f on the same diagram.

(a) $f(t) = t, 0 \leq t \leq 1$

(b) $f(t) = t, 0 \leq t \leq 2$

(c) $f(t) = 1 + \cos t, 0 \leq t \leq \pi$

(d) $f(t) = \sin t, 0 \leq t \leq \pi$

(e) $f(t) = \begin{cases} 0, & 0 \leq t \leq 1 \\ t - 1, & 1 \leq t \leq 2 \end{cases}$

[*Hint:* Split integrals of the form $\int_0^2$ into $\int_0^1$ and $\int_1^2$ and insert the appropriate formula for the integrand $f(t)$ into each of these.]

(f) $f(t) = |t - 1|, 0 \leq t \leq 2$ [*Hint:* See hint above.]

2. Compute the Fourier E_s-expansion of each of the functions in problem 1. In each case sketch f and the S_2-approximator of f on the same diagram.

3. Compute the Fourier E_t-expansion of each of the following functions over the indicated interval. Sketch f, the best approximator to f in $\langle h_0^*, h_1^* \rangle$, and sketch the best S^2-approximator ($S^2 = \langle h_0^*, h_1^*, h_1, h_2^*, h_2 \rangle$) to f on the same diagram.

(a) $f(t) = t, -1 \leq t \leq 1$

(b) $f(t) = t, -2 \leq t \leq 2$

(c) $f(t) = 1 + \cos t, -\pi \leq t \leq \pi$

(d) $f(t) = \sin (t/2), -\pi \leq t \leq \pi$

(e) $f(t) = |t|, -\pi/2 \leq t \leq \pi/2$

(f) $f(t) = \begin{cases} t, & -2 \leq t \leq 0 \\ 0, & 0 \leq t \leq 2 \end{cases}$

4. FOURIER EXPANSION ON SHIFTED INTERVALS.

(a) Show that the system $\tilde{E}_s$: $e_1, e_2, \ldots$, where

$$(1) \qquad e_1(t) = \sqrt{\frac{2}{L}}\sin\frac{\pi(t-a)}{L},\; e_2(t) = \sqrt{\frac{2}{L}}\sin\frac{2\pi(t-a)}{L},$$
$$e_3(t) = \sqrt{\frac{2}{L}}\sin\frac{3\pi(t-a)}{L}, \ldots$$

is an orthonormal system in $\mathcal{C}[a, a+L]$. [*Hint:* Under the change of variables $x = t - a$ the interval $a \le t \le a + L$ corresponds to

$$0 \le x \le L.$$

The orthonormal system E_s for this interval is known (expressed as functions of x). Inverting the change of variables gives (1). One way to show orthonormality is simply to change the variable of integration from t to $x = t - a$.]

(b) Derive an orthonormal system in $\mathcal{C}[a, a+L]$ corresponding to E_c in $\mathcal{C}[0, L]$ by the method used in part (a). Prove that this new system is orthonormal.

*(c) Derive an orthonormal system in $\mathcal{C}[a, a+2L]$ corresponding to the system E_t in $\mathcal{C}[-L, L]$.

5. (a) Verify (3.4)–(i) and (3.4)–(ii) by computing

$$\int_0^L \sin\frac{\pi n t}{L}\sin\frac{\pi m t}{L}\,dt$$

both for $m \ne n$ and for $m = n$. [*Hint:* Use the identity

$$\sin\alpha\sin\beta = \tfrac{1}{2}\cos(\alpha-\beta) - \tfrac{1}{2}\cos(\alpha+\beta).]$$

(b) Verify that the system E_c in (3.11b) is orthonormal. [*Hint:* Use the identity $\cos\alpha\cos\beta = \frac{1}{2}\cos(\alpha-\beta) + \frac{1}{2}\cos(\alpha+\beta)$.]

6. (a) Prove that when $m \ne n$ the integral of the products

$$\cos\frac{\pi m t}{L}\cos\frac{\pi n t}{L}, \qquad \sin\frac{\pi m t}{L}\sin\frac{\pi n t}{L}, \qquad \cos\frac{\pi m t}{L}\sin\frac{\pi n t}{L}$$

over $-L \le t \le L$ is zero.

(b) Evaluate the integral over $-L \le t \le L$ of the following functions:

$$\cos^2\frac{\pi m t}{L}, \qquad \sin^2\frac{\pi m t}{L}, \qquad \cos\frac{\pi m t}{L}\sin\frac{\pi m t}{L}.$$

7. Show that for every integer n the system $f_0, f_1, \ldots, f_n \in \mathcal{C}[-1, 1]$ defined by

$$f_0(t) = 1, \qquad f_1(t) = t, \ldots, \qquad f_n(t) = t^n$$

is linearly independent. [*Hint:* By problem 15 of §1 of Chapter 5, if $f_0, \ldots, f_n$ were dependent, then there would exist constants $d_0, \ldots, d_n$, *not all zero*, such that

$$(1) \qquad f(t) = d_0 f_0(t) + d_1 f_1(t) + \cdots + d_n f_n(t) \equiv 0, \qquad -1 \le t \le 1.$$

However (1) implies that all d's *are* zero, since

$$d_0 = f(0), d_1 = f'(0), \ldots, d_n = f^{(n)}(0)/n!.]$$

This result shows that there are arbitrarily large linearly independent systems in $\mathcal{C}[-1, 1]$, which certainly *suggests* that $\mathcal{C}[-1, 1]$ is infinite dimensional. The full proof of this fact occurs next.

***8.** $\mathcal{C}[a, b]$ IS INFINITE-DIMENSIONAL.

(a) Show that any SLE with all right sides zero which possesses fewer equations than unknowns has infinitely many solutions. [*Hint:* What possibilities are there for the reduced form?]

(b) Prove that $\mathcal{C}[a, b]$ is infinite-dimensional. [*Hint:* If there were some collection $f_1, \ldots, f_n$ spanning $\mathcal{C}[a, b]$, then in particular we would have coefficients $c_i^{(j)}$ such that

$$1 = c_1^{(0)} f_1 + \cdots + c_n^{(0)} f_n, \qquad t = c_1^{(1)} f_1 + \cdots + c_n^{(1)} f_n,$$
$$t^2 = c_1^{(2)} f_1 + \cdots + c_n^{(2)} f_n, \qquad \ldots, t^j = c_1^{(j)} f_1 + \cdots + c_n^{(j)} f_n, \cdots$$

By forming a linear combination of the first $n + 1$ of these equations with respective coefficients $b_0, b_1, \ldots, b_n$ (not all zero), it is possible to make the coefficients of all f_i equal to zero [use part (a)]. Hence we get

$$(1) \qquad b_0 1 + b_1 t + \cdots + b_n t^n = 0 f_1 + \cdots + 0 f_n = 0.$$

But by a known theorem a nonzero polynomial of degree n has at most n roots. Thus the polynomial in t on the left side of (1) *cannot* be identically zero unless all the coefficients b_j are zero, contrary to fact.]

9. Prove that $\mathcal{V}$ is finite-dimensional if there is an upper limit m_0 to the number of vectors in orthonormal systems of $\mathcal{V}$. [*Hint:* Let B: $\boldsymbol{\beta}_1, \ldots, \boldsymbol{\beta}_{m_0}$ denote an orthonormal system in $\mathcal{V}$ with the maximum number, m_0, of vectors. If $\langle \boldsymbol{\beta}_1, \ldots, \boldsymbol{\beta}_{m_0} \rangle \neq \mathcal{V}$, then there are vectors $\boldsymbol{\alpha} \in \mathcal{V}$ such that $\boldsymbol{\alpha} \notin \langle \boldsymbol{\beta}_1, \ldots, \boldsymbol{\beta}_{m_0} \rangle$. Now apply the projection theorem to construct from $\boldsymbol{\alpha}$ a unit vector $\boldsymbol{\beta}_{m_0+1}$ orthogonal to $\boldsymbol{\beta}_1, \ldots, \boldsymbol{\beta}_{m_0}$. The system $\boldsymbol{\beta}_1, \ldots, \boldsymbol{\beta}_{m_0+1}$ is orthonormal and has more than m_0 vectors, which is a contradiction.]

Fourier Expansion for Piecewise Continuous Functions

10. Let f be the function indicated in Figure 6.14. That is,

$$f(t) = t, \qquad -1 < t < 1,$$

and f satisfies the identity

$$f(t + 2) = f(t), \qquad -2 < t < 2.$$

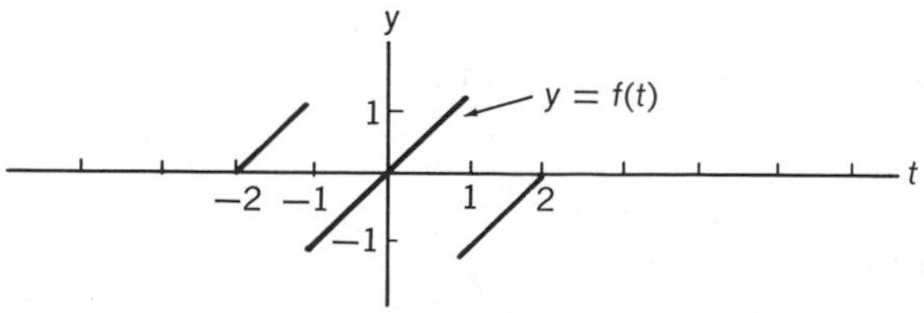

Figure 6.14

Compute the Fourier E_t-expansion for f relative to the interval $-2 \leq t \leq 2$. [Note that $f \notin \mathcal{C}[-2, 2]$, since it possesses a "finite jump" discontinuity at $t = 1$ and $t = -1$. Functions whose only discontinuities are finite jumps are called *piecewise continuous functions*. It is possible to get Fourier expansions for such functions. In fact, all results we obtain for the expansions of continuous functions will also apply to expansions of piecewise continuous functions.]

11. (a) Sketch the piecewise continuous function which satisfies

$$f(t) = t + |t|, \qquad -\pi < t < \pi$$

and

$$f(t + 2\pi) = f(t), \qquad -\infty < t < \infty.$$

(b) Compute the E_s-expansion for f relative to the interval $0 \leq t \leq 2\pi$.

(c) Compute the E_c-expansion for f relative to the above interval.

12. A COMPLETE ORTHONORMAL SYSTEM WITHOUT SINES AND COSINES.
Let $\mathcal{V} = \mathcal{C}[-1, 1]$ $(f \cdot g = \int_{-1}^{1} f(t)g(t)\,dt)$ and consider the following infinite system of vectors in $\mathcal{V}$, B: $f_0, f_1, f_2, \ldots$, where

$$f_0(t) = 1, f_1(t) = t, f_2(t) = t^2, \ldots, f_m(t) = t^m, \ldots.$$

(a) Show that B fails to be orthonormal, in fact is not even orthogonal, but that f's with even index *are* orthogonal to f's with odd index.

(b) Show that if the Gram–Schmidt procedure is applied to subsystems B_k: $f_0, f_1, \ldots, f_k$ of B, then the resulting orthonormal systems E_k: e_0, $e_1, \ldots, e_k$ are subsystems of a fixed orthonormal system $E_{\mathcal{L}}$: $e_0, e_1, e_2, \ldots$, $e_m, \ldots$. [*Hint:* What is the relation between two E_k's for different values of k?]

(c) Compute e_0, e_1, e_2, e_3 explicitly.

*(d) Show that the e's are polynomials, those with even index containing only even powers of t and those with odd index containing only odd powers of t.

The orthonormal system $E_{\mathcal{L}}$ can be shown to be complete [see W. Kaplan, *Advanced Calculus*, Addison-Wesley, Reading, Mass., 1952, p. 428]. It is called *Legendre's complete orthonormal system.*

13. The infinite system B: $f_0, f_1, \ldots, f_m, \ldots$ of problem 12 fails also to be orthonormal relative to the inner product

$$f \cdot g = \int_{-\infty}^{\infty} f(t)g(t)e^{-t^2}\,dt.$$

(a) Show that $f \cdot g$ is indeed an inner product on the subspace $\mathcal{P}^\infty$ of $\mathcal{C}(-\infty, \infty)$ which consists of all polynomials.

(b) Discuss how it is possible, using the Gram–Schmidt process, to construct from B an orthonormal system of polynomials

$$E_{\mathcal{H}}: e_0, e_1, \ldots, e_m, \ldots$$

relative to *this* inner product.

(c) Compute e_0 and e_1 explicitly.
This system is called *Hermite's complete orthonormal system*. It can be shown to be complete in $\mathcal{P}^\infty$.

14. (a) By computing coefficients show that the Fourier E_o-expansion for $f(t) = t$, $0 \leq t \leq \pi$, is given by

$$f \sim c_1\left(\sqrt{\frac{2}{\pi}}\sin t\right) + c_2\left(\sqrt{\frac{2}{\pi}}\sin 2t\right) + \cdots + c_m\left(\sqrt{\frac{2}{\pi}}\sin mt\right) + \cdots$$

$$\sim 2\sin t - \sin 2t + \cdots + (-1)^m \frac{2}{m}\sin mt + \cdots.$$

(b) Compute the "approximation errors" $\|f - f_k\|$ for $k = 1, 2, 3, 4$.

15. Find the Fourier E_t-expansion for the function f having the value -1 for $-\pi \leq t < 0$ and the value 1 for $0 \leq t \leq \pi$.

16. (a) Show that $S' \subset S''$ implies that for every $\boldsymbol{\alpha} \in \mathcal{V}$

$$\|\boldsymbol{\alpha} - \boldsymbol{\alpha}''\| \leq \|\boldsymbol{\alpha} - \boldsymbol{\alpha}'\|,$$

where $\boldsymbol{\alpha}'$ and $\boldsymbol{\alpha}''$ are the S'- and S''-approximators to $\boldsymbol{\alpha}$.

[*Hint:* $\|\boldsymbol{\alpha} - \boldsymbol{\alpha}''\| \leq \|\boldsymbol{\alpha} - \boldsymbol{\gamma}\|$ for all $\boldsymbol{\gamma} \in S''$, and the vector $\boldsymbol{\alpha}'$ is in $S' \subset S''$.]

(b) Using part (a) deduce that for any orthonormal system E,

$$\|\boldsymbol{\alpha} - \boldsymbol{\alpha}_1\| \geq \|\boldsymbol{\alpha} - \boldsymbol{\alpha}_2\| \geq \|\boldsymbol{\alpha} - \boldsymbol{\alpha}_3\| \geq \cdots.$$

17. (a) Show that in $\mathcal{C}[0, \pi]$ the orthonormal system E: $e_2, e_4, \ldots,$ where

$$e_2(t) = \sqrt{\frac{2}{\pi}}\cos 2t, \quad e_4(t) = \sqrt{\frac{2}{\pi}}\cos 4t, \ldots, \quad e_{2m}(t) = \sqrt{\frac{2}{\pi}}\cos 2mt, \ldots,$$

is not complete. [*Hint:* Examine $f(t) = \cos t - \cos 2t$.]

(b) What can be proved about completeness for the orthonormal system E: $e_1, e_3, e_4, \ldots,$ where

$$e_1(t) = \sqrt{\frac{2}{\pi}}\cos t, \quad e_3(t) = \sqrt{\frac{2}{\pi}}\cos 3t, \quad e_4(t) = \sqrt{\frac{2}{\pi}}\cos 4t, \ldots,$$

$$e_m(t) = \sqrt{\frac{2}{\pi}}\cos mt, \ldots ?$$

Try to find a larger system which is orthonormal and complete.

18. (a) Prove (ii) of proposition (3.10).

(b) Prove (iii) of proposition (3.10).

[*Hint:* $\lim_{k\to\infty} \|\boldsymbol{\alpha} - \boldsymbol{\alpha}_k\|^2 = 0$ and $\lim_{k\to\infty} \|\boldsymbol{\beta} - \boldsymbol{\beta}_k\|^2 = 0$, while $\|\boldsymbol{\alpha}_k\|^2 \leq \|\boldsymbol{\alpha}\|^2$ and $\|\boldsymbol{\beta}_k\|^2 \leq \|\boldsymbol{\beta}\|^2$. Now write $\boldsymbol{\alpha} = \boldsymbol{\alpha}_k + (\boldsymbol{\alpha} - \boldsymbol{\alpha}_k)$, $\boldsymbol{\beta} = \boldsymbol{\beta}_k + (\boldsymbol{\beta} - \boldsymbol{\beta}_k)$. Then

$$\boldsymbol{\alpha} \cdot \boldsymbol{\beta} = \boldsymbol{\alpha}_k \cdot \boldsymbol{\beta}_k + [\boldsymbol{\alpha}_k \cdot (\boldsymbol{\beta} - \boldsymbol{\beta}_k) + (\boldsymbol{\alpha} - \boldsymbol{\alpha}_k) \cdot \boldsymbol{\beta}_k + (\boldsymbol{\alpha} - \boldsymbol{\alpha}_k) \cdot (\boldsymbol{\beta} - \boldsymbol{\beta}_k)].$$

By use of Schwarz's inequality it can be shown that each term inside the brackets becomes arbitrarily small as $k \to \infty$, whereby we have $\lim_{k\to\infty} (\boldsymbol{\alpha} \cdot \boldsymbol{\beta} - \boldsymbol{\alpha}_k \cdot \boldsymbol{\beta}_k) = 0$.]

***19.** Using the E_s-expansion obtained in problem 14, show that

$$1 + \frac{1}{4} + \frac{1}{9} + \cdots = \sum_{m=1}^{\infty} \frac{1}{m^2} = \lim_{k\to\infty} \sum_{m=1}^{k} \frac{1}{m^2} = \pi^2/6.$$

[*Hint:* Use (C), the completeness condition [(3.9)] for the system E_s in $\mathcal{C}[0, \pi]$.]

*4. Fourier Series (Continued)†

In the present section we will study some further properties of Fourier expansions relative to E_s, E_c, and E_t. Let us begin by observing that the rather tedious computation of Fourier E_t-coefficients can sometimes be simplified. Recall first that for any $f \in \mathcal{C}[-L, L]$ the E_t-expansion of f,

$$f \sim c_0h_0^* + c_1h_1^* + d_1h_1 + c_2h_2^* + d_2h_2 + \cdots$$

can be written in the modified form

$$f \sim a_0 + \sum_{m=1}^{\infty} \left(a_m \cos \frac{\pi mt}{L} + b_m \sin \frac{\pi mt}{L}\right),$$

where

$$a_0 = \frac{1}{2L}(f \cdot 1) = \frac{1}{2L}\int_{-L}^{L} f(t)1\,dt = \frac{c_0}{\sqrt{2L}}$$

$$a_m = \frac{1}{L}\left(f \cdot \cos \frac{\pi mt}{L}\right) = \frac{1}{L}\int_{-L}^{L} f(t) \cos \frac{\pi mt}{L}\,dt = \frac{c_m}{\sqrt{L}}, \quad m = 1, 2, \ldots,$$

$$b_m = \frac{1}{L}\left(f \cdot \sin \frac{\pi mt}{L}\right) = \frac{1}{L}\int_{-L}^{L} f(t) \sin \frac{\pi mt}{L}\,dt = \frac{d_m}{\sqrt{L}}, \quad m = 1, 2, \ldots.$$

Suppose that the continuous function f is an odd function; that is,

$$f(-t) = -f(t).$$

Then for each a_m the integrand, being the product of $f(t)$ with $\cos(2\pi mt/2L)$, is also an odd function. Hence the integral giving a_m is zero for each m (including $m = 0$), and the E_t-expansion for f simplifies to

$$f \sim \sum_{m=1}^{\infty} b_m \sin \frac{\pi mt}{L}.$$

†The material in §4 and §5, although of importance in many physical problems is, in our experience, rather difficult. This stems both from technical and conceptual matters. Later material in this book does not depend essentially on these sections.

An analogous simplification takes place when f is an even function. This time for each b_m the integrand, being the product of $f(t)$ with $\sin(2\pi mt/2L)$, is an odd function. Hence the integral giving b_m is zero for each m, and the E_t-expansion for f simplifies to

$$f \sim a_0 + \sum_{m=1}^{\infty} a_m \cos \frac{\pi mt}{L}.$$

Summarizing, we have the following result:

(4.1) Proposition. *For each* ***odd*** *function f in $\mathcal{C}[-L, L]$ the E_t-expansion of f contains only sine terms:*

$$\text{(0)} \qquad f \sim b_1 \sin \frac{\pi t}{L} + b_2 \sin \frac{2\pi t}{L} + b_3 \sin \frac{3\pi t}{L} + \cdots,$$

where

$$b_m = \frac{1}{L}\left(f \cdot \sin \frac{\pi mt}{L}\right) = \frac{1}{L}\int_{-L}^{L} f(t) \sin \frac{\pi mt}{L}\, dt, \qquad m = 1, 2, \ldots.$$

For each ***even*** *function f in $\mathcal{C}[-L, L]$ the E_t-expansion of f contains only cosine terms (and a constant):*

$$\text{(E)} \qquad f \sim a_0 + a_1 \cos \frac{\pi t}{L} + a_2 \cos \frac{2\pi t}{L} + a_3 \cos \frac{\pi t}{L} + \cdots,$$

where

$$a_0 = \frac{1}{2L}(f \cdot 1) = \frac{1}{2L}\int_{-L}^{L} f(t)\, dt,$$

$$a_m = \frac{1}{L}\left(f \cdot \cos \frac{\pi mt}{L}\right) = \frac{1}{L}\int_{-L}^{L} f(t) \cos \frac{\pi mt}{L}\, dt, \qquad m = 1, 2, \ldots.$$

We now proceed to examine a feature of the system E_t (also of E_s and E_c) which makes it particularly useful. To examine this feature it is necessary to introduce the notion of periodic function. A function f defined on $-\infty < t < \infty$ is said to be *periodic of period p* if its graph has the property that a shift of p units to the left (or right) leaves it unaltered (Figure 6.15). We state this more precisely.

(4.2) Definition. A function f defined on $-\infty < t < \infty$ is said to be **periodic** of period p if it satisfies the following identity:

(a) $f(t \pm p) = f(t)$ for all t.

The **period** of f denotes the *smallest* number $p = p_0$ for which (a) holds.

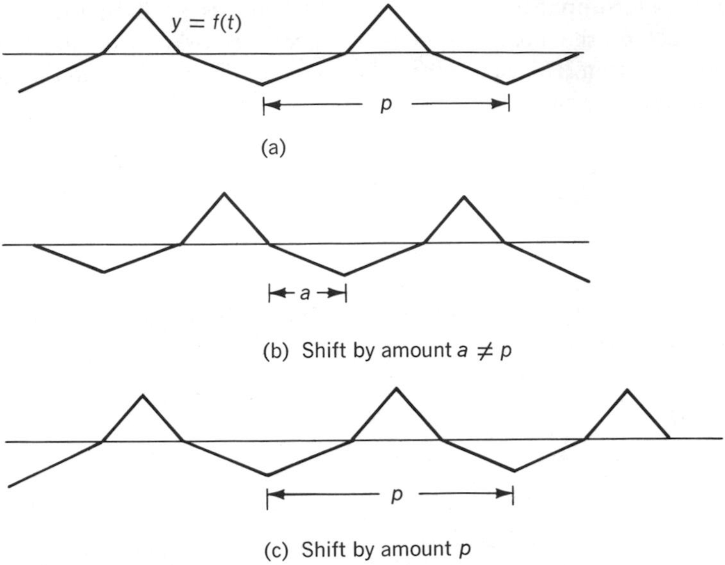

Figure 6.15

The relation (4.2a) can be observed in Figure 6.15. The reader should convince himself, by trying a few points, that if one chooses *any* two values t_1 and t_2 of t which differ by the quantity p, then f has the same value at t_1 as it has at t_2. Moreover, from (4.2a) we have in addition

$$\begin{aligned} f(t + 2p) &= f(t + p + p) = f(t + p) = f(t) \\ f(t - 3p) &= f(t - 2p - p) = f(t - 2p) = f(t - p - p) \\ &= f(t - p) = f(t). \end{aligned}$$

In general one deduces from (4.2a) that f not only is the same at points which are p units apart but also at points which are np units apart for any integer n. Thus (4.2a) implies the relations

$$f(t \pm np) = f(t), \qquad n = 1, 2, 3, \ldots. \tag{4.3}$$

Our interest here in periodic functions stems mainly from the fact that in a great variety of situations physical systems are subjected to periodic disturbances. For instance, a particle attached to a spring and constrained to move in one dimension might be subjected to a periodic external force F along the line of motion (see Figure 6.16). By formula (4.2) of Chapter 5 the equation governing the motion is then given by

$$m\ddot{z}(t) + l\dot{z}(t) + k\big(z(t) - z_0\big) = F(t). \tag{4.4}$$

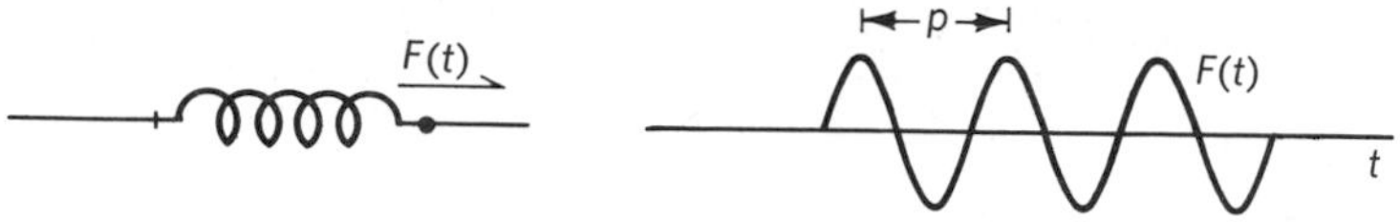

Figure 6.16

As another example, consider the *LCR* circuit discussed in example (3.2b) of Chapter 5. A periodic potential might be impressed on the circuit (see Figure 6.17). By formula (4.3) of Chapter 5 the equation governing the charge on the capacitor is then given by

(4.5) $$L\ddot{y}(t) + R\dot{y}(t) + \frac{1}{C}\,y(t) = E(t).$$

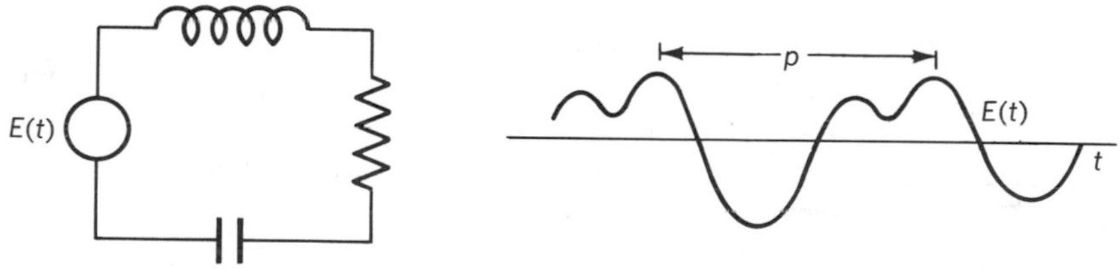

Figure 6.17

We will see in §5 that the use of Fourier E_t-expansions is a great convenience in analyzing such problems.

Let us now fix $p = 2L$ for some prescribed L and examine the set $\mathcal{P}^{2L}$ of continuous† periodic functions of period $2L$ (Figure 6.18). $\mathcal{P}^{2L}$ is a subset of $\mathcal{C}(-\infty, \infty)$, and it is not difficult to discern that the subset $\mathcal{P}^{2L}$ is actually a

†The methods to follow apply equally well to many functions having discontinuities. Therefore, we shall not hesitate to use discontinuous functions in the examples and problems. For example, the function f satisfying $f(t) = 0$ for $-L \le t < 0$, $f(t) = 1$ for $0 \le t \le L$ has a "Fourier series". Observe that the formulas for Fourier coefficients can be applied to such functions. For the function just given, for instance, the Fourier coefficients a_m are defined as follows:

$$a_0 = \frac{1}{2L}\int_{-L}^{L} f(t)\,dt = \frac{1}{2L}\left\{\int_{-L}^{0} f(t)\,dt + \int_{0}^{L} f(t)\,dt\right\} = \frac{1}{2L}\left\{\int_{-L}^{0} 0\cdot dt + \int_{0}^{L} 1\cdot dt\right\}$$

$$a_m = \frac{1}{L}\int_{-L}^{L} f(t)\cos\frac{\pi mt}{L}\,dt = \frac{1}{L}\left\{\int_{-L}^{0} f(t)\cos\frac{\pi mt}{L}\,dt + \int_{0}^{L} f(t)\cos\frac{\pi mt}{L}\,dt\right\}$$
$$= \frac{1}{L}\left\{\int_{-L}^{0} 0\cos\frac{\pi mt}{L}\,dt + \int_{0}^{L} 1\cdot\cos\frac{2\pi mt}{2L}\,dt\right\}, \quad m \ge 1.$$

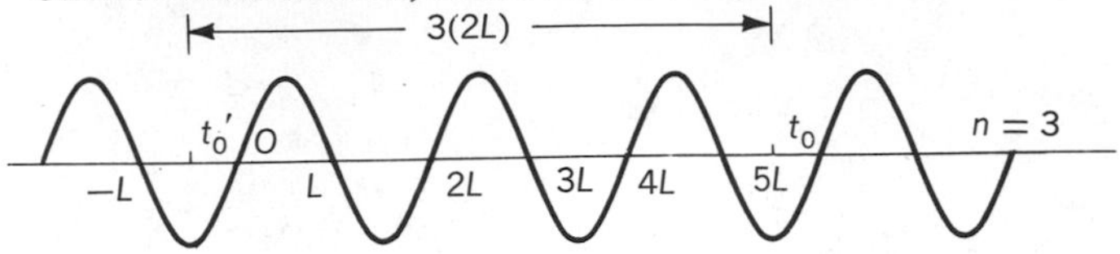

Figure 6.18

subspace of $\mathcal{C}(-\infty, \infty)$ (see problem 9). Functions f in $\mathcal{P}^{2L}$ share the following property: knowledge of the values of f on the interval $-L \leq t \leq L$ (or on any given t interval of length $2L$) suffices to determine all values which f assumes for *all* t. To understand this statement suppose the values on $-L \leq t \leq L$ are known. Let t_0 be any value of t. Then we can find a t_0', $-L \leq t_0' \leq L$ and an integer n, positive or negative, such that $t_0 = t_0' + n \cdot 2L$. But then by (4.3) we have

$$f(t_0) = f(t_0' + n \cdot 2L) = f(t_0'), \tag{4.6}$$

and since we know $f(t_0')$, $f(t_0)$ is determined.

Consider now any function $f \in \mathcal{P}^{2L}$. By what we have just said, f is completely determined by its values on $-L \leq t \leq L$. But if we look at f just on the interval $-L \leq t \leq L$, it is a function $\bar{f} \in \mathcal{C}[-L, L]$ (Figure 6.19). Now $\bar{f}$ has a Fourier series; that is,

$$\bar{f} \sim c_0 h_0^* + c_1 h_1^* + d_1 h_1 + c_2 h_2^* + d_2 h_2 + \cdots$$

or, equivalently,

$$\bar{f} \sim a_0 + \sum_{m=1}^{\infty} \left(a_m \cos \frac{\pi m t}{L} + b_m \sin \frac{\pi m t}{L} \right), \tag{4.7}$$

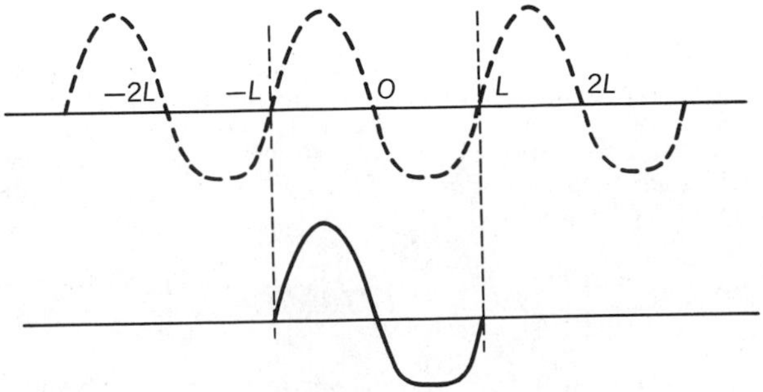

Figure 6.19

where

$$a_0 = \frac{1}{2L}\int_{-L}^{L} f(t)\,dt = \frac{c_0}{\sqrt{2L}},$$

(4.8)
$$a_m = \frac{1}{L}\int_{-L}^{L} f(t)\cos\frac{\pi m t}{L}\,dt = \frac{c_m}{\sqrt{L}}, \qquad m = 1, 2, \ldots,$$

$$b_m = \frac{1}{L}\int_{-L}^{L} f(t)\sin\frac{\pi m t}{L}\,dt = \frac{d_m}{\sqrt{L}}, \qquad m = 1, 2, \ldots.$$

One way often used to describe the relation of $\bar{f}$ to f is to say that the function $f \in \mathcal{P}^{2L}$ is the *periodic extension* of the function $\bar{f} \in \mathcal{C}[-L, L]$.

(4.9) Definition. For any $f \in \mathcal{P}^{2L}$ the series (4.7) is called the **Fourier E_t-expansion** for f.

Concerning the Fourier E_t-expansion for f we have the following result.

(4.10) Proposition. *Suppose f and g are two functions in $\mathcal{P}^{2L}$ which have the same Fourier E_t-expansion. Then f and g are identical.*

Proof. We know that both f and g are determined completely by their values on $-L \leq t \leq L$. These values form functions $\bar{f}$ and $\bar{g}$ belonging to $\mathcal{C}[-L, L]$, and the series (4.7) for f and g are simply the Fourier E_t-expansions for $\bar{f}$ and $\bar{g}$. If these Fourier expansions are the same, then, by proposition (3.2), $\bar{f} = \bar{g}$. Hence f and g agree everywhere on $-L \leq t \leq L$ and thus agree for all t. ∎

In analogy to the results for $\mathcal{C}[-L, L]$, we also make the following definition.

(4.11) Definition. If $f \in \mathcal{P}^{2L}$, then the functions f_k defined by

$$f_k = c_0h_0^* + c_1h_1^* + d_1h_1 + c_2h_2^* + d_2h_2 + \cdots + c_kh_k^* + d_kh_k$$

or, equivalently,

$$f_k(t) = a_0 + \sum_{m=1}^{k}\left(a_m \cos\frac{\pi m}{L}t + b_m \sin\frac{\pi m}{L}t\right), \qquad k = 1, 2, \ldots$$

are called the **S^k-approximators** of f (for E_t).

Observe that the relations

$$\cos \frac{\pi m}{L}(t + 2L) = \cos \frac{\pi m t}{L}, \qquad m = 0, 1, \ldots$$

$$\sin \frac{\pi m}{L}(t + 2L) = \sin \frac{\pi m t}{L}, \qquad m = 1, 2, \ldots$$

show that the functions $\cos(\pi m t/L)$ and $\sin(\pi m t/L)$ all belong to $\mathcal{P}^{2L}$. Since $\mathcal{P}^{2L}$ is a subspace, we deduce from this that the S^k-approximators to any $f \in \mathcal{P}^{2L}$ all belong to $\mathcal{P}^{2L}$.

We now give an application.

(4.12) Example. A Linear Nonhomogeneous Differential Equation with Periodic Forcing Term. We seek to obtain a solution of the nonhomogeneous differential equation

$$(1) \qquad \ddot{y}(t) - y(t) = f(t),$$

where f is a continuous function having period $p = 2\pi$.

CASE A, $f = h_m^*$ OR $f = h_m$. For such f's we can find a solution of (1) by the method of undetermined coefficients (4.1.17). That is, we can solve each of the differential equations:

$$\ddot{y}(t) - y(t) = \frac{1}{\sqrt{2L}} = h_0^*(t)$$

$$(2) \qquad y(t) - y(t) = \frac{1}{\sqrt{L}} \cos \frac{\pi m t}{L} = h_m^*(t), \qquad m = 1, 2, \ldots$$

$$\ddot{y}(t) - y(t) = \frac{1}{\sqrt{L}} \sin \frac{\pi m t}{L} = h_m(t), \qquad m = 1, 2, \ldots$$

by the method of undetermined coefficients. The reader can verify that the resulting solutions can be tabulated as follows:

$$(3) \qquad y = \begin{cases} \dfrac{-1}{m^2 + 1} h_m^* \\ \\ \dfrac{-1}{m^2 + 1} h_m \end{cases} \quad \text{for } f = \begin{cases} h_m^* \\ \\ h_m \end{cases} \qquad m = 0, 1, 2, \ldots.$$

CASE B, $f =$ A FINITE LINEAR COMBINATION OF h'S AND h^*'S. Using (3) it is easy to construct a solution of (1). That is, if

$$(4_1) \qquad f = c_0 h_0^* + c_1 h_1^* + d_1 h_1 + \cdots + c_k h_k^* + d_k h_k,$$

then it is easily checked by means of (3) that the function

$$(4_2)\quad y = -c_0h_0^* - \frac{1}{2}c_1h_1^* - \frac{1}{2}d_1h_1 - \cdots - \frac{1}{k^2+1}c_kh_k^* - \frac{1}{k^2+1}d_kh_k$$

satisfies (1).

CASE C, f AN ARBITRARY ELEMENT OF $\mathcal{C}[-\pi, \pi]$. We can utilize (4) to construct a solution of (1) whenever f is replaced by one of its S^k-approximators. Namely, for

$$(5_1)\qquad \begin{aligned} f_k &= c_0h_0^* + c_1h_1^* + d_1h_1 + \cdots + c_kh_k^* + d_kh_k \\ &= a_0 + a_1\cos t + b_1 \sin t + \cdots + a_k\cos kt + b_k\sin kt \end{aligned}$$

there corresponds the solution

$$(5_2)$$

$$\begin{aligned} y_k &= -c_0h_0 - \frac{c_1}{2}h_1 - \frac{d_1}{2}h_1^* - \cdots \frac{c_k}{k^2+1}h_k - \frac{d_k}{k^2+1}h_k^* \\ &= -a_0 - \frac{a_1}{2}\cos t - \frac{b_1}{2}\sin t - \cdots - \frac{a_k}{k^2+1}\cos kt - \frac{b_k}{k^2+1}\sin kt \end{aligned}$$

of the differential equation

$$(6)\qquad \ddot{y}_k(t) - y_k(t) = f_k(t), \qquad k = 0, 1, 2, \ldots.$$

Now note that in formula (5_2) *the coefficient of* h_i [*or* h_i^*] *in* y_k *is the same for all* y_k *with* $k \geq i$. This fact suggests that the solutions y_k to the approximating problems (6) are themselves S^k-approximators to some function $y \in \mathcal{P}^{2\pi}$. This happens to be the case, and moreover the function y is a solution of (1).

Observe that the E_t-coefficients of y appear in (5_2) and thus can be read off from those of f:

$$f \sim c_0h_0^* + c_1h_1^* + d_1h_1 + \cdots + c_mh_m^* + d_mh_m + \cdots$$

implies

$$\begin{aligned} y \sim -c_0h_0^* - \left(\frac{c_1}{2}\right)h_1^* - \left(\frac{d_1}{2}\right)h_1 - \cdots \\ - \left(\frac{c_m}{m^2+1}\right)h_m^* - \left(\frac{d_m}{m^2+1}\right)h_m + \cdots. \end{aligned}$$

Equivalently, we have the correspondence,

$$(7)\qquad \begin{aligned} f &\sim a_0 + \sum_{m=1}^{\infty} (a_m \cos mt + b_m \sin mt) \\ y &\sim -a_0 + \sum_{m=1}^{\infty} \left(-\frac{a_m}{m^2+1} \cos mt - \frac{b_m}{m^2+1} \sin mt \right) \end{aligned}$$

We know by Chapter 4 that there are infinitely many solutions of (1), yet the method above yields only *one* solution for each $f \in \mathcal{P}^{2\pi}$. The reason is that the solution we have obtained is periodic and it can be shown that there is only one solution in $\mathcal{P}^{2\pi}$ for each $f \in \mathcal{P}^{2\pi}$. The ideas encountered in the above example form the basis for the work in §5.

To close this section let us reexamine the way in which the Fourier expansion of a function represents that function. To simplify the writing we will utilize the orthonormal system E_s: $e_1, e_2, \ldots$:

$$e_1(t) = \sqrt{\frac{2}{L}} \sin \frac{\pi t}{L}, \quad e_2(t) = \sqrt{\frac{2}{L}} \sin \frac{2\pi t}{L}, \ldots, \quad e_m(t) = \sqrt{\frac{2}{L}} \sin \frac{\pi m t}{L}, \ldots .$$

It will be recalled that for an $f \in \mathcal{C}[0, L]$ the formula

$$f \sim c_1 e_1 + c_2 e_2 + \cdots$$

or, equivalently,

$$(4.13)\qquad f \sim \left(\sqrt{\frac{2}{L}}\, c_1\right) \sin \frac{\pi t}{L} + \left(\sqrt{\frac{2}{L}}\, c_2\right) \sin \frac{2\pi t}{L} + \cdots$$

is taken to mean that for each k the closest S_k-approximation to f in the subspace

$$S_k = \langle e_1, \ldots, e_k \rangle = \left\langle \sqrt{\frac{2}{L}} \sin \frac{\pi t}{L}, \ldots, \sqrt{\frac{2}{L}} \sin \frac{k\pi t}{L} \right\rangle$$

is the function

$$f_k(t) = \left(\sqrt{\frac{2}{L}}\, c_1\right) \sin \frac{\pi t}{L} + \left(\sqrt{\frac{2}{L}}\, c_2\right) \sin \frac{2\pi t}{L} + \cdots + \left(\sqrt{\frac{2}{L}}\, c_k\right) \sin \frac{k\pi t}{L}.$$

Moreover, the symbol $\sim$ indicates that the system is complete; hence (4.13) is also intended to imply that the f_k's converge to f in the sense of definition (3.7). This means that

$$(4.14)\qquad \lim_{k\to\infty} \int_0^L (f(t) - f_k(t))^2 \, dt = 0.$$

One might wonder whether more than (4.14) is true. Thus one might ask whether the f_k's would not approximate f in the same sense that the successive approximations y_k in Chapter 4 approximated the solution of the differential equation studied there. That is, will it be true that for a fixed value of t the sequence of *real numbers* $\{f_k(t)\}$ converges to the real number $f(t)$? The answer is a qualified yes. Whenever f is a function having a continuous derivative, then for any t_0 in $-L < t_0 < L$ the sequence of numbers $\{f_k(t_0)\}$ will converge to $f(t_0)$. We illustrate in Figure 6.20. In general, the sequences $\{f_k(-L)\}$ or $\{f_k(L)\}$ need *not* converge to $f(-L)$ or $f(L)$. They will, however, do so whenever f satisfies the additional conditions

$$f(-L) = f(L) \quad \text{and} \quad \dot{f}(-L) = \dot{f}(L).$$

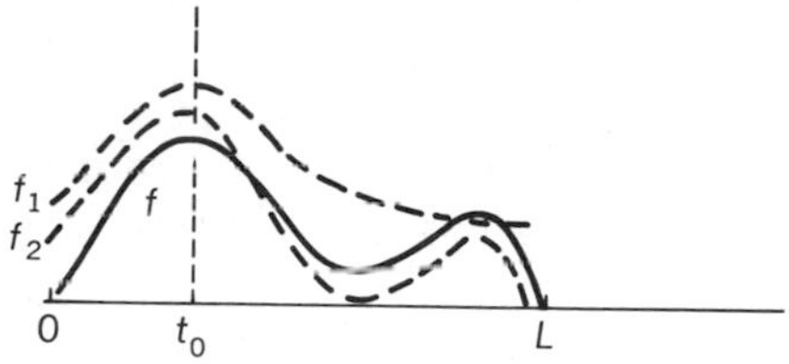

$\lim_{k\to\infty} f_k(t_0) = f(t_0) \qquad -L < t_0 < L$

Figure 6.20

Similar comments apply to other complete orthonormal systems such as E_c and E_t.

There is a similar result for the space $\mathcal{P}^{2L}$. That is, if f is in $\mathcal{P}^{2L}$ and satisfies certain differentiability conditions, then if t_0 is chosen as *any* value it will be true that

$$(4.15) \qquad \lim_{k\to\infty}\left[a_0 + \sum_{m=1}^{k}\left(a_m \cos\frac{\pi m t_0}{L} + b_m \sin\frac{\pi m t_0}{L}\right)\right] = f(t_0),$$

where the a_m and b_m are defined by (4.8). Note that equation (4.15) can be rewritten

$$(4.16) \qquad \lim_{k\to\infty} f_k(t_0) = f(t_0),$$

where the f_k's are the S^k-approximators of f (for E_t).

PROBLEMS

1. Compute the Fourier E_t-expansion for each of the following functions. Sketch f and its S^2-approximator f_2 and compute $\|f - f_2\|$.

(a) $f(t) = |t|, \quad -\pi \leq t \leq \pi$

(b) $f(t) = t, \quad -\pi \leq t \leq \pi$

(c) $f(t) = \sin 2t, \quad -1 \leq t \leq 1$

(d) $f(t) = |\sin t|, \quad -\pi \leq t \leq \pi$

(e) $f(t) = \begin{cases} 0, & |t| < 1 \\ t, & 1 \leq |t| \leq 2 \end{cases}$

(f) $f(t) = \begin{cases} 1, & -2 \leq t < -1, 0 \leq t < 1 \\ -1, & -1 \leq t < 0, 1 \leq t \leq 2 \end{cases}$

(g) $f(t) = \sin(t - 1), \quad -\pi \leq t \leq \pi$

(h) $f(t) = \cos^2 t, \quad -\pi \leq t \leq \pi$

2. Verify that each of the functions f below belongs to the given space $\mathcal{P}^{2L}$. Compute the Fourier E_t-expansion for *the prescribed* $\mathcal{P}^{2L}$ for each function. Sketch f and give the number p which is its (smallest) period.

(a) $f(t) = \sin t, \quad \mathcal{P}^{2\pi}$

(b) $f(t) = \sin t, \quad \mathcal{P}^{4\pi}$

(c) $f(t) = \sin^2 t, \quad \mathcal{P}^{2\pi}$

(d) $f(t) = \begin{cases} 0, & |t| < 1 \\ |t|, & 1 \leq t \leq 2 \end{cases}$
and $f(t + 4) = f(t)$, $\mathcal{P}^4$

(e) $f(t) = \cos^2 t, \quad \mathcal{P}^{\pi}$

(f) $f(t) = \begin{cases} -1, & -2 \leq t < -1, \quad 0 \leq t < 1 \\ 1, & -1 \leq t < 0, \quad 1 \leq t \leq 2 \end{cases}$
and $f(t + 4) = f(t)$, $\mathcal{P}^4$

(g) $f(t) = |\sin t + \cos t|, \quad \mathcal{P}^{2\pi}$

(h) $f(t) = e^t, \quad -1 \leq t \leq 1$
and $f(t + 2) = f(t)$, $\mathcal{P}^2$

3. Which of the following functions are periodic? Determine the period of each function which is periodic. [*Hint:* $g(t)$ periodic *implies* $|g(t)|$ is periodic. Why?]

(a) $f(t) = \sin(e^t)$

(b) $f(t) = |1 + \sin t|$

(c) $f(t) = \cos^2 \frac{1}{2}t$

(d) $f(t) = \sin t + \cos \frac{1}{2}t$

(e) $f(t) = \sin t + \cos \sqrt{2}\, t$

(f) $f(t) = |\cos t - \sin^2 \frac{1}{2}t|$

4. Show that there is a unique choice of the constants y_0 and $\dot{y}_0$ such that the solution of the problem

$$\ddot{y}(t) - y(t) = \cos \omega t, \qquad y(0) = y_0, \dot{y}(0) = \dot{y}_0$$

will be of the form

$$y(t) = A\cos\omega t + B\sin\omega t$$

for some constants A and B.

5. Show that if

$$f(t) = a_0 + a_1\cos\frac{\pi t}{L} + b_1\sin\frac{\pi t}{L},$$

then there exists a unique choice of y_0 and $\dot{y}_0$ such that the problem

$$\ddot{y}(t) - y(t) = f(t), \qquad y(0) = y_0,\ \dot{y}(0) = \dot{y}_0$$

will have a solution of the form

$$y(t) = A_0 + A_1\cos\frac{\pi t}{L} + B_1\sin\frac{\pi t}{L}.$$

6. Find the Fourier E_t-expansion (in $\mathcal{P}^4$) of a periodic solution to

$$\ddot{y}(t) - y(t) = f(t),$$

where f is the function defined by

$$f(t) = \begin{cases} 0, & |t| \le 1 \\ t-1, & 1 \le t \le 2 \\ -t-1, & -2 \le t \le -1, \end{cases} \qquad f(t+4) = f(t).$$

7. Find the Fourier E_t-expansion (in $\mathcal{P}^{2\pi}$) of a periodic solution to

$$\ddot{y}(t) - y(t) = |\sin \pi t|.$$

8. Find the Fourier E_t-expansion of the periodic motion which is possible for a particle attached to a spring and constrained to move in one dimension, when subjected to the following periodic external force [see formula (4.4)]

$$F(t) = \begin{cases} 1+t, & -1 \le t < 0 \\ 1-t, & 0 \le t \le 1, \end{cases} \qquad F(t+2) = F(t).$$

Assume that $m = 1, l = 0, k = 1, z_0 = 0$.

9. Every function in the complete system E_t in $\mathcal{C}[-\pi, \pi]$ is defined for t-values *outside* the interval $-\pi \le t \le \pi$. In fact, these functions are periodic functions of t with a common period of 2π.

(a) Show that the system E_t is a complete orthonormal system in $\mathcal{C}[(r-1)\pi, (r+1)\pi]$ for any integer r, where

$$f\cdot g = \int_{(r-1)\pi}^{(r+1)\pi} f(t)g(t)\,dt.$$

[*Hint:* A function f is in $\mathcal{C}[(r-1)\pi, (r+1)\pi]$ if and only if the function $\hat{f}$ defined by

$$\hat{f}(t) = f(t - r\pi)$$

is in $\mathcal{C}[-\pi, \pi]$.]

(b) Show that if f is a periodic function of period 2π, then the Fourier E_t-expansion for f on $-\pi \le t \le \pi$ is *simultaneously* the Fourier E_t-expansion for f on $(r-1)\pi \le t \le (r+1)\pi$, $r = 1, 2, \ldots$.

5. Black Boxes

We will now give an application of Fourier series to a situation which arises often in physics, one involving systems we call *black boxes*. This term denotes systems into which one puts certain inputs and out of which one obtains corresponding results. More precisely, the input data are to be such that they can be described as functions of time t and the outputs must have the same form.

The prototype of a black box is simply a box containing some system of electric circuits. The input will then be some potential f and the output will be the charge y on some capacitor, say (Figure 6.21). The circuits inside may be very complicated, or even unknown in advance. The idea is to avoid having to make a complicated, theoretical analysis of those particular circuits. Rather one wishes to experimentally determine the outputs for a few inputs and then be able to *predict* all other outputs.

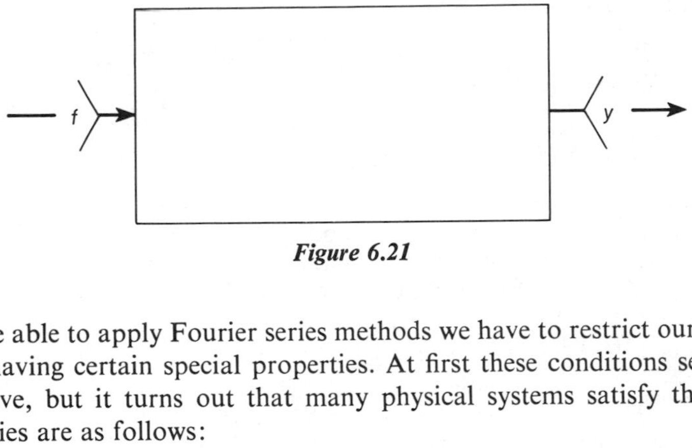

Figure 6.21

To be able to apply Fourier series methods we have to restrict ourselves to boxes having certain special properties. At first these conditions seem very restrictive, but it turns out that many physical systems satisfy them. The properties are as follows:

(1) *If the input f is a continuous† function which is periodic of period $p = 2L$, that is,*

$$f(t \pm p) = f(t), \tag{5.1}$$

then the output y is a continuous function which is periodic with the same period; that is, $y(t \pm p) = y(t)$.

(2) *If the input f has the form $f(t) = \cos \omega t$, then the output y is of the form*

$$y(t) = C_1(\omega) \cos \omega t + C_2(\omega) \sin \omega t, \tag{5.2}$$

†More generally the input can be piecewise continuous and then the output might also be piecewise continuous. We shall not pursue this in the text, but in some of the problems the f's given will be piecewise continuous.

where $C_1(\omega)$, $C_2(\omega)$ *are scalars. If the input is* $f(t) = \sin \omega t$, *then the output is*

$$y(t) = S_1(\omega) \cos \omega t + S_2(\omega) \sin \omega t, \tag{5.3}$$

where $S_1(\omega)$, $S_2(\omega)$ *are scalars.*

(3) *If* $f_1, f_2, \ldots, f_n$ *are continuous functions all of the same period p and* $y_1, y_2, \ldots, y_n$, *respectively, are the outputs corresponding to the f's as inputs, then the output y for a combined input of the form*

$$f = A_1 f_1 + A_2 f_2 + \cdots + A_n f_n$$

is given by

$$y = A_1 y_1 + A_2 y_2 + \cdots + A_n y_n.$$

(Note that this is assumed *only* for functions $f_1, \ldots, f_n$ which have the same period.)

Now we are in a position to introduce Fourier series into the analysis of a black box. Suppose the box satisfies (1), (2), and (3) and that the input is a continuous function satisfying (5.1). We saw in §4 that such a function has a Fourier E_t-expansion of the form

$$f(t) \sim a_0 + a_1 \cos \frac{\pi t}{L} + b_1 \sin \frac{\pi t}{L} + a_2 \cos \frac{2\pi t}{L} + \cdots, \tag{5.4}$$

where

$$a_0 = \frac{1}{2L} \int_{-L}^{L} f(t)\, dt, \qquad a_m = \frac{1}{L} \int_{-L}^{L} f(t) \cos \frac{m\pi t}{L}\, dt, \qquad m = 1, 2, \ldots$$

$$b_m = \frac{1}{L} \int_{-L}^{L} f(t) \sin \frac{m\pi t}{L}\, dt, \qquad m = 1, 2, \ldots.$$

The first step in finding the output y for the input f is to find the outputs for each of the S^k-approximators of f. Recall that the S^k-approximator f_k for f is given by

$$f_k(t) = a_0 + a_1 \cos \frac{\pi t}{L} + \cdots + a_k \cos \frac{k\pi t}{L} + b_k \sin \frac{k\pi t}{L}. \tag{5.5}$$

Each of the terms

$$1, \qquad \cos \frac{\pi t}{L}, \qquad \sin \frac{\pi t}{L}, \ldots, \qquad \cos \frac{k\pi t}{L}, \qquad \sin \frac{k\pi t}{L}$$

is periodic with period $2L$; hence we can apply condition (3). Let u_m be the output for an input of $\cos(m\pi t/L)$, $m = 0, 1, \ldots, k$ and v_m be the output for an input of $\sin(m\pi t/L)$, $m = 1, 2, \ldots, k$. The u_m's and v_m's are given by the formulas (5.2) and (5.3). These formulas yield (the ω for both u_m and v_m is $m\pi/L$)

(5.6)
$$u_m(t) = C_1\left(\frac{m\pi}{L}\right)\cos\frac{m\pi t}{L} + C_2\left(\frac{m\pi}{L}\right)\sin\frac{m\pi t}{L}$$
$$v_m(t) = S_1\left(\frac{m\pi}{L}\right)\cos\frac{m\pi t}{L} + S_2\left(\frac{m\pi}{L}\right)\sin\frac{m\pi t}{L}.$$

Now condition (3) states that the output corresponding to the input f_k is

$$y_k = a_0u_0 + a_1u_1 + b_1v_1 + a_2u_2 + \cdots + a_ku_k + b_kv_k$$

or

(5.7)
$$\begin{aligned} y_k(t) = {} & C_1(0)a_0 + \left(C_1\left(\frac{\pi}{L}\right)a_1 + S_1\left(\frac{\pi}{L}\right)b_1\right)\cos\frac{\pi t}{L} \\ & + \left(C_2\left(\frac{\pi}{L}\right)a_1 + S_2\left(\frac{\pi}{L}\right)b_1\right)\sin\frac{\pi t}{L} + \cdots \\ & + \left(C_1\left(\frac{k\pi}{L}\right)a_k + S_1\left(\frac{k\pi}{L}\right)b_k\right)\cos\frac{k\pi t}{L} \\ & + \left(C_2\left(\frac{k\pi}{L}\right)a_k + S_2\left(\frac{k\pi}{L}\right)b_k\right)\sin\frac{k\pi t}{L}. \end{aligned}$$

We recall that the output y corresponding to f is itself a continuous function which is periodic of period $p = 2L$ whenever f is such a function. It then follows that this solution must have S^k-approximators $\tilde{y}_k$ of the same form as (5.5); that is,

(5.8)
$$\tilde{y}_k(t) = \tilde{a}_0 + \tilde{a}_1\cos\frac{\pi t}{L} + \tilde{b}_1\sin\frac{\pi t}{L} + \cdots + \tilde{a}_k\cos\frac{k\pi t}{L} + \tilde{b}_k\sin\frac{k\pi t}{T}.$$

What is true of most physical systems is that these approximators $\tilde{y}_k$ are the same as the outputs y_k of (5.7). Thus for our analysis to be meaningful, the system must have the following additional property:

(4) *If the input f is a continuous function of period $p = 2L$ and y is the corresponding output, then the S^k-approximator of y is identical with the output y_k corresponding to an input f_k which is the S^k-approximator of f.*

The point of all this analysis is that it reduces the study of black boxes satisfying (1), (2), (3), and (4) to the determination of the functions C_1, C_2,

S_1, and S_2. In some simple situations this can be done theoretically. In any event one can always obtain *approximate* values by performing a series of simple experiments. One simply puts in f's of the form $\cos \omega t$ and $\sin \omega t$, for various choices of ω. Then by measuring the outputs, which must have the form (5.2) and (5.3), one can determine C_1, C_2, S_1, and S_2 at those frequencies.

(5.9) Examples. Black Boxes Satisfying (1), (2), (3), and (4).

(a) Suppose we have several particles moving along a line and connected by springs (Figure 6.22). Suppose each particle is subject to a frictional force, proportional to the velocity, as in example (3.2a). A force f is applied to particle (1) and no other external forces are applied. Then it is always possible to start the motion in such a way that if y denotes the position of particle (3), say, relative to its equilibrium position, then f and y will be the input and output of a system satisfying (1), (2), (3), and (4).

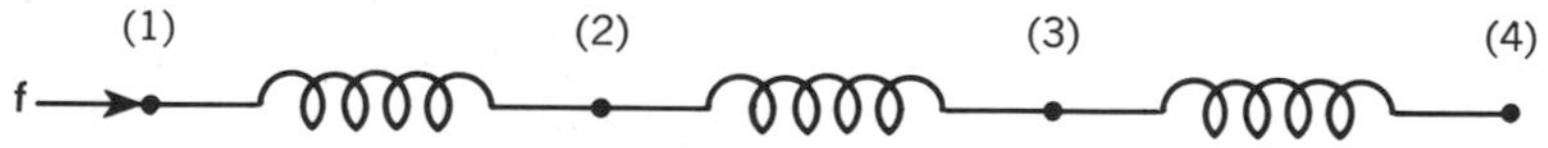

Figure 6.22

(b) Suppose we have an electric circuit consisting of several loops, which may be connected through mutual inductances as shown in Figure 6.23. Suppose a potential f is applied at some point in one of the loops. Once again it is always possible to start the system in such a way that if y is the charge on a capacitor in some loop then f and y form a system satisfying (1), (2), (3), and (4).

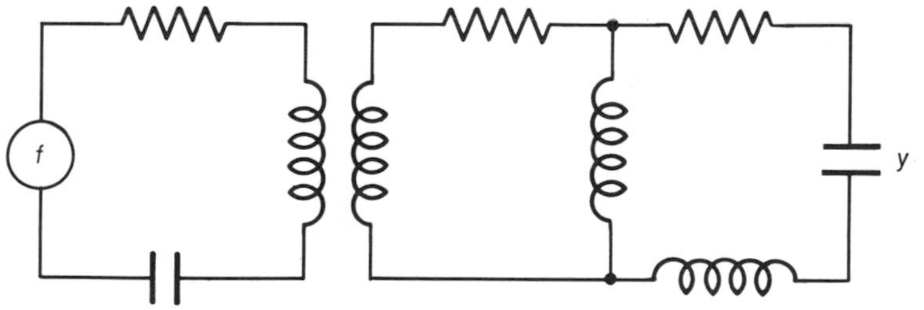

Figure 6.23

Next we give two examples in which we can be somewhat more explicit.

(c) Consider the differential equation

$$\text{(i)} \qquad \dot{y}(t) + y(t) = f(t).$$

Let f have the form $f(t) = \cos \omega t$. Then we can obtain a particular solution of (i) of the form (3.2) by the method of undetermined coefficients,

$$\text{(ii)} \qquad y(t) = \frac{1}{1 + \omega^2} \cos \omega t + \frac{\omega}{1 + \omega^2} \sin \omega t.$$

Similarly, a solution for $f(t) = \sin \omega t$ is

$$\text{(iii)} \qquad y(t) = \frac{-\omega}{1 + \omega^2} \cos \omega t + \frac{1}{1 + \omega^2} \sin \omega t.$$

Hence we have

$$\text{(iv)} \qquad \begin{aligned} C_1(\omega) &= \frac{1}{1 + \omega^2}, & C_2(\omega) &= \frac{\omega}{1 + \omega^2} \\ S_1(\omega) &= -\frac{\omega}{1 + \omega^2}, & S_2(\omega) &= \frac{1}{1 + \omega^2}. \end{aligned}$$

It is true (but hard to prove) that for any continuous f which is periodic of period p there will exist a unique solution y of (i) which is periodic of period p. [This is condition (1).] Moreover, this solution will satisfy conditions (3) and (4). In the particular cases $f(t) = \cos \omega t$ or $f(t) = \sin \omega t$ this solution is given by (ii) and (iii), respectively.

(d) Consider the differential equation

$$\text{(i)} \qquad \ddot{y}(t) + a\dot{y}(t) + by(t) = f(t), \qquad a > 0, b > 0.$$

Let f have the form $f(t) = \cos \omega t$. Then, as we saw in Chapter 5, it is possible to find, by the method of undetermined coefficients, a particular solution which has the form

$$\text{(ii)} \qquad y(t) = C_1(\omega) \cos \omega t + C_2(\omega) \sin \omega t.$$

In fact, we obtain

$$\text{(iii)} \qquad C_1(\omega) = \frac{b - \omega^2}{(b - \omega^2)^2 + a^2\omega^2}, \qquad C_2(\omega) = \frac{a\omega}{(b - \omega^2)^2 + a^2\omega^2}.$$

Similarly, for $f(t) = \sin \omega t$ there is a solution of the form

$$\text{(iv)} \qquad y(t) = S_1(\omega) \cos \omega t + S_2(\omega) \sin \omega t.$$

Here

$$\text{(v)} \qquad S_1(\omega) = \frac{-a\omega}{(b - \omega^2)^2 + a^2\omega^2}, \qquad S_2(\omega) = \frac{b - \omega^2}{(b - \omega^2)^2 + a^2\omega^2}.$$

Once again for any continuous f of period p there is a unique solution y of period p. This y satisfies (3) and (4) and reduces to (ii) or (iv) when

$$f(t) = \cos \omega t \quad \text{or } f(t) = \sin \omega t.$$

We shall now apply the results obtained in the above examples.

(5.10) Example. Fourier Series Analysis. Let f be defined as follows:

$$(1) \qquad \begin{aligned} f(t) &= \begin{cases} 0 & \text{for } -\pi \leq t \leq 0 \\ t & \text{for } 0 \leq t \leq \pi/2 \\ \pi - t & \text{for } \pi/2 \leq t \leq \pi \end{cases} \\ f(t + 2\pi) &= f(t) \qquad\qquad \text{for all } t. \end{aligned}$$

Thus f has the form shown in Figure 6.24. For this f we shall apply Fourier series to obtain approximate solutions of the differential equations occurring in examples (5.9c) and (5.9d). We write down the first three terms in the Fourier series for f. Since f is periodic of period 2π we have

$$(2) \qquad f(t) \sim a_0 + a_1 \cos t + b_1 \sin t + \cdots,$$

where

$$a_0 = \frac{1}{2\pi} \int_{-\pi}^{\pi} f(t)\, dt = \frac{\pi}{8}$$

$$a_1 = \frac{1}{\pi} \int_{-\pi}^{\pi} f(t) \cos t\, dt = 0$$

$$b_1 = \frac{1}{\pi} \int_{-\pi}^{\pi} f(t) \sin t\, dt = \frac{2}{\pi}.$$

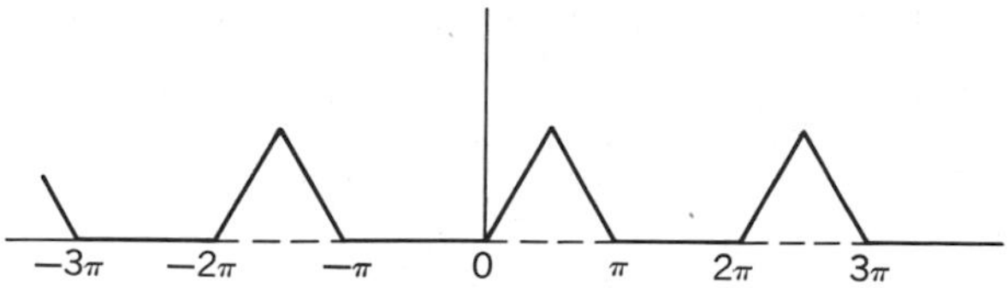

Figure 6.24

Formula (5.7) tells us how to calculate the S^1-approximator of the solution of the differential equations in examples (5.9c) and (5.9d). The solutions have the form

$$\begin{aligned} y_1(t) = C_1(0)a_0 &+ \big(C_1(1)a_1 + S_1(1)b_1\big) \cos t \\ &+ \big(C_2(1)a_1 + S_2(1)b_1\big) \sin t. \end{aligned}$$

Thus all we need do is read off the values of $C_1(0)$, $C_1(1)$, $S_1(1)$, $C_2(1)$, and $S_2(1)$ from formula (iv) in example (5.9c) or formulas (iii) and (v) in example (5.9d). We obtain in this way the following values for y_1 in the two cases.

CASE 1 [(5.9c)]

$$y_1(t) = \frac{\pi}{4} + \left(\frac{1}{2}\cdot 0 - \frac{1}{2}\cdot\frac{2}{\pi}\right)\cos t + \left(\frac{1}{2}\cdot 0 + \frac{1}{2}\cdot\frac{2}{\pi}\right)\sin t.$$

CASE 2 [(5.9d)]

$$y_1(t) = \frac{1}{b}\cdot\frac{\pi}{4} + \left(\frac{b-1}{(b-1)^2+a^2}\cdot 0 - \frac{a}{(b-1)^2+a^2}\,\frac{2}{\pi}\right)\cos t$$
$$+ \left(\frac{a}{(b-1)^2+a^2}\cdot 0 + \frac{b-1}{(b-1)^2+a^2}\,\frac{2}{\pi}\right)\sin t.$$

PROBLEMS

1. For each of the differential equations below, show that one can find solutions of the form (5.2) and (5.3) for $f(t) = \cos\omega t$ and $f(t) = \sin\omega t$. Calculate C_1, C_2, S_1, and S_2 as function of ω.

(a) $\dot{y}(t) - y(t) = f(t)$

(b) $\dot{y}(t) + 2y(t) = f(t)$

(c) $\ddot{y}(t) + 2\dot{y}(t) + y(t) = f(t)$

(d) $\ddot{y}(t) - y(t) = f(t)$

2. Show that one *cannot* find solutions of the form (5.2) and (5.3), for all values of ω, for the equation

$$\ddot{y}(t) + y(t) = \cos\omega t.$$

3. Find the S^1-approximator of the periodic solution of each of the equations in problem (1) for f as in example (5.10).

4.† Let f be the piecewise continuous function which is defined by $f(t) = t$ on $-1 < t \le 1$ and is periodic of period 2; that is, $f(t+2) = f(t)$. Find the S^1- and S^2-approximators for the periodic solution of $\dot{y}(t) - 2y(t) = f(t)$ for this f.

5. Let f be the function which is defined by $f(t) = |t|$ on $-\pi \le t < +\pi$ and is periodic of period 2π. Find the S^1- and S^2-approximators of the periodic solution of $\ddot{y}(t) + \dot{y}(t) + y(t) = f(t)$ for this f.

---

†As a technical point the periodic "solutions" of the equation in this example will be continuous functions, but their first derivatives will have jumps wherever f does. Except at these points the equation will be satisfied.

6. In a black box satisfying (1), (2), (3), and (4), the functions C_1, C_2, S_1, and S_2 are found to satisfy the formulas

$$C_1(\omega) = 2\omega, \qquad C_2(\omega) = 0$$
$$S_1(\omega) = 0, \qquad S_2(\omega) = -\omega.$$

(a) Find the S^2-approximators for the output with the following inputs:

(i) $f(t) = -t$ on $-2 \leq t < 0$, t on $0 < t < 2$
$f(t + 4) = f(t)$

(ii) $f(t) = 1$ on $-1 < t < 0$, t on $0 < t < 1$
$f(t + 2) = f(t)$

(b) Find the full E_t-expansion of the outputs in part (a).

7

Partial Differential Equations

0. Introduction

In this chapter we study equations which relate partial derivatives of a function of more than one variable. Such equations are called *partial differential equations*. (We shall use the abbreviation PDE.) Actually we restrict ourselves to the case of functions of two variables.

The study of PDE's is a very complicated one. All we propose to do in this chapter is study two rather simple PDE's which allow us to make use of some of the ideas we have developed in the preceding chapters. These equations are important in physics. The *derivation* of the equations from physical principles comes later. However, since solving the equations will afford us a good example of the utility of the methods of Chapter 6, we obtain the solutions in this chapter.

This introductory section is intended to acquaint the reader with some of the difficulties that can arise. Consider first the equation

$$u_t(x, t) = 0.\dagger \tag{0.1}$$

†We use subscripts to denote partial derivatives; that is,

$$u_t(x, t) = \frac{\partial u(x, t)}{\partial t}, \qquad u_{xx}(x, t) = \frac{\partial^2 u(x, t)}{\partial x^2}, \qquad \text{and so on.}$$

This is an analog of the ordinary differential equation $\dot{y}(t) = 0$. That equation has as its only solutions constants c. Observe, however, that there are many other solutions of (0.1): *Any* function of x *alone* has a zero partial derivative with respect to t and hence is a solution of (0.1). Thus x, e^x, and $\sin x$, for example, when considered as functions of x and t, are all solutions of (0.1). Note that in a similar way the equation $u_x(x, t) = 0$ has any arbitrary function of t as a solution.

Consider next the equation

$$u_t(x, t) = tx. \tag{0.2}$$

One can see by inspection that one solution is $u(x, t) = (t^2/2)x$. However, observe that we can add to this any arbitrary function of x and still have a solution.

Now let us look at the equation

$$u_{tt}(x, t) = tx. \tag{0.3}$$

By inspection, one solution is $(t^3/6)x$. Note, however, that $(t^3/6)x + te^x$ is another. Moreover anything of the form $(t^3/6)x + t\varphi(x) + \psi(x)$, where φ and ψ are arbitrary functions of x is also a solution.

Here is a still more complicated example.

$$u_t(x, t) + u_x(x, t) = 0. \tag{0.4}$$

Let f be *any* differentiable function of one variable s and consider the function u *of* x *and* t defined by $u(x, t) = f(x - t)$. By the chain rule [(1.4) of the Review of Calculus] we have

$$u_x(x, t) = f'(x - t)\frac{\partial}{\partial x}(x - t) = f'(x - t)$$

$$u_t(x, t) = f'(x - t)\frac{\partial}{\partial t}(x - t) = -f'(x - t),$$

where $f'(x - t)$ means the derivative f' evaluated at $s = x - t$. Thus u is a solution of (0.4).

These examples demonstrate why PDE's are hard to study. Their solutions contain arbitrary *functions* to be determined, not just arbitrary constants as with ordinary differential equations.

We recall that in ordinary differential equations arbitrary constants were connected with the existence and uniqueness of solutions. These same questions of existence and uniqueness are of fundamental importance in the study of PDE's and are related to the presence of arbitrary functions in the solutions. We illustrate with an example.

(0.5) Example. Existence and Uniqueness. Find a function u such that

$$u_t(x, t) = tx, \qquad u(x, 1) = 3x.$$

We saw that any function of the form $u(x, t) = (t^2/2)x + \varphi(x)$ satisfies the equation. We substitute this function into $u(x, 1) = 3x$ and obtain

$$3x = \tfrac{1}{2}x + \varphi(x) \qquad \text{or} \qquad \varphi(x) = \tfrac{5}{2}x.$$

Thus $u(x, t) = (t^2/2)x + \frac{5}{2}x$ is a solution and existence is established. Can there be more than one solution? Let u^1 and u^2 be solutions and let $u = u^1 - u^2$. Then

$$u_t(x, t) = u_t^1(x, t) - u_t^2(x, t) = tx - tx = 0.$$

But if a function of x and t has its partial derivative with respect to t identically equal to zero, then it must be a function only of x; that is, $u(x, t) = \psi(x)$. However this gives $\psi(x) = u(x, 1) = u^1(x, 1) - u^2(x, 1) = 3x - 3x$. Hence $\psi(x)$ is zero, and

$$u(x, t) \equiv 0 \qquad \text{or} \qquad u^1(x, t) \equiv u^2(x, t).$$

Thus we have proved uniqueness.

It will be recalled that there is a special class of ordinary differential equations which is relatively easy to handle. These are the s-linear equations, defined as those having the property that linear combinations of solutions are again solutions. The same notion occurs for PDE's and is of fundamental importance for the work in this chapter.

(0.6) Definition. A PDE is called **s-linear** if whenever $u^1, u^2, \ldots, u^n$ are solutions, then the function

$$u = \alpha_1 u^1 + \alpha_2 u^2 + \cdots + \alpha_n u^n,$$

where $\alpha_1, \alpha_2, \ldots, \alpha_n$ are constants, is also a solution.

Observe that equations (0.1) and (0.4) are s-linear. For example, suppose that $u^1, \ldots, u^n$ are solutions of (0.4) and set $u = \alpha_1 u^1 + \cdots + \alpha_n u^n$. Then

$$\begin{aligned} u_t + u_x &= (\alpha_1 u^1 + \cdots + \alpha_n u^n)_t + (\alpha_1 u^1 + \cdots + \alpha_n u^n)_x \\ &= \alpha_1(u_t^1 + u_x^1) + \alpha_2(u_t^2 + u_x^2) + \cdots + \alpha_n(u_t^n + u_x^n) \\ &= \alpha_1 \cdot 0 + \alpha_2 \cdot 0 + \cdots + \alpha_n \cdot 0 = 0. \end{aligned}$$

On the other hand, equations (0.2) and (0.3) are not s-linear. For example, $u^1 = (t^3/6)x$ and $u^2 = (t^3/6)x + tx$ are both solutions of (0.3), but their sum $u^1 + u^2$ is not.

PROBLEMS

1. Find the most general solution for each of the following equations:

(a) $u_x(x, t) = 0$
(b) $u_{tt}(x, t) = 0$
(c) $u_{xt}(x, t) = 0$
(d) $u_{ttt}(x, t) = 0$

2. Find the most general solution for each of the following equations:

(a) $u_x(x, t) = t$
(b) $u_{xx}(x, t) = xt$
(c) $u_{xt}(x, t) = t + x$

3. Find the solution of each of the following problems:

(a) $u_x(x, t) = t, \;\; u(1, t) = 0$

(b) $u_{tt}(x, t) = 0, \;\; u(x, 0) = x, \;\; u_t(x, 0) = x^2$

(c) $u_{xx}(x, t) = tx, \;\; u(1, t) = t, \;\; u_x(1, t) = 0$

4. Find a solution of the problem

$$u_t(x, t) + u_x(x, t) = 0, \qquad u(x, -x) = 2x.$$

[*Hint:* Use the result for equation (0.4).]

5. Show that any function of the form $f(x + 2t)$, where f is a differentiable function of s, is a solution of

$$u_t(x, t) - 2u_x(x, t) = 0.$$

6. Show that x/t, x^2/t^2, $\sin(x/t)$, and $e^{x/t}$ are all solutions of the equation $xu_x(x, t) - tu_t(x, t) = 0$. Show, in fact, that if f is any differentiable function of s, then $u(x, t) = f(x/t)$ is a solution of the same equation.

7. Show that $x + t$, $(x + t)^2$, $\sin(x + t)$, and e^{x+t} are all solutions of the equation $u_{tt}(x, t) = u_{xx}(x, t)$. Show that if f is any twice differentiable function of s, then $u(x, t) = f(x + t)$ and $u(x, t) = f(x - t)$ are solutions of this equation.

8. Find functions f and g of s such that

$$u(x, t) = f(x + t) + g(x - t)$$

is a solution of $u_{tt}(x, t) = u_{xx}(x, t)$ satisfying

$$u(x, 0) = x, \qquad u_t(x, 0) = 1, \qquad -\infty < x < \infty.$$

9. Which of the following differential equations are s-linear?

(a) $u_{tx}(x, t) = 0$
(b) $u_{tt}(x, t) + u_{xx}(x, t) = 0$
(c) $u_t(x, t) - u_x(x, t) = 1$
(d) $u_t(x, t) = ku_{xx}(x, t)$
(e) $u_t(x, t) = ku_{xx}(x, t) + f(x, t)$
(f) $u_t(x, t) + u(x, t)u_x(x, t) = 0$

1. The Heat Equation

The particular equation we study in this section is

$$u_t(x, t) = Ku_{xx}(x, t), \qquad K = k^2 \text{ a positive constant.} \tag{1.1}$$

This is called the *one-dimensional heat equation.* We will see later how this equation arises in certain physical processes. For now we simply state that in certain important situations it governs the flow of heat in materials. The particular problem we study is one which has physical interest and also is one for which there are existence and uniqueness theorems.

We seek solutions of (1.1) defined for all x, t in the region R specified by $0 < x < L, 0 < t < \infty$ (Figure 7.1). (In physical problems t represents the time and x is a measure of position.) We shall impose not only an *initial* condition (at $t = 0$) but also what are referred to as "boundary conditions":

(1.2) $$u(x, 0) = \varphi(x), \qquad 0 \leq x \leq L$$

(1.3) $$u(0, t) = 0, \qquad u(L, t) = 0, \qquad 0 \leq t < \infty.$$

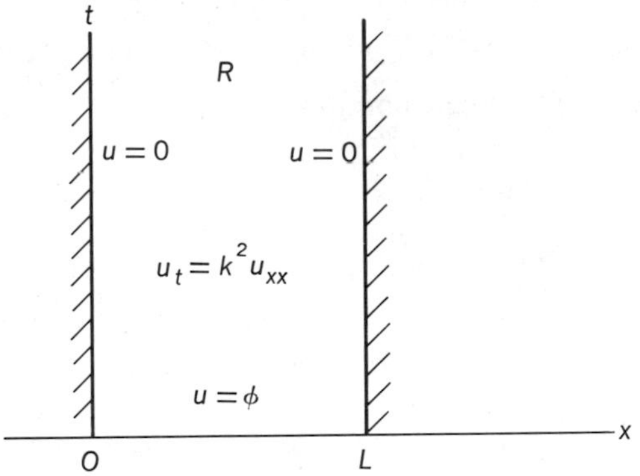

Figure 7.1

It is useful in PDE problems to depict the problem geometrically. Thus the problem we are considering is fully indicated in Figure 7.1. Our first observation is that equation (1.1) is s-linear. That is, if $u^1, u^2, \ldots, u^n$ are solutions, then the function $u = \alpha_1 u^1 + \cdots + \alpha_n u^n$ for any constants $\alpha_1, \ldots, \alpha_n$ is also a solution [see problem 9(d) of the Introduction].

It will be recalled that for ordinary differential equations there was a relation between the fact that an equation is s-linear and the fact that a kind of linearity with respect to the initial data holds. This is illustrated best in proposition (1.19) of Chapter 4, which we now summarize. The equation

$$\dot{y}(t) + p(t)y(t) = 0$$

is an s-linear one. As a consequence, if we have solutions y_1 and y_2 of this equation with initial values $y_1(t_0) = a_1$ and $y_2(t_0) = a_2$, then the solution

y such that $y(t_0) = \alpha_1 a_1 + \alpha_2 a_2$, where α_1 and α_2 are constants, is given by $y = \alpha_1 y_1 + \alpha_2 y_2$. An analogous result holds for the problem (1.1)–(1.3) and is basic to our approach.

(1.4) Proposition. *Let* $u^1, u^2, \ldots, u^n$ *be solutions of* (1.1)–(1.3) *for initial functions* φ *equal to* $\varphi^1, \varphi^2, \ldots, \varphi^n$, *respectively. Then the function*

$$u = \alpha_1 u^1 + \alpha_2 u^2 + \cdots + \alpha_n u^n$$

is a solution of the same problem for initial function

$$\varphi = \alpha_1 \varphi^1 + \alpha_2 \varphi^2 + \cdots + \alpha_n \varphi^n.$$

Proof. The first observation is that u is, in fact, a solution of (1.1). This follows, as above, from the fact that (1.1) is s-linear. Next we have

$$u(x, 0) = \alpha_1 u^1(x, 0) + \cdots + \alpha_n u^n(x, 0) = \alpha_1 \varphi^1(x) + \cdots + \alpha_n \varphi^n(x) = \varphi(x).$$

Also we have

$$u(0, t) = \alpha_1 u^1(0, t) + \alpha_n u^n(0, t) = \alpha_1 \cdot 0 + \cdots + \alpha_n \cdot 0 = 0.$$

Similarly, $u(L, t) = 0$. ∎

The procedure we are going to follow to solve the problem (1.1)–(1.3) is based on proposition (1.4) and closely follows the ideas of §4 of Chapter 6. We are going to show first how to obtain a solution u^m of this problem when φ is chosen as one of the special functions $f_m(x) = \sin(m\pi x/L)$. Then by proposition (1.4) we can also find the solution for any φ which is of the form $\alpha_1 f_1 + \cdots + \alpha_n f_n$. Since we know that sums of this form approximate any continuous function φ on $0 \leq x \leq L$ we can thus hope to obtain *approximate* solutions of (1.1)–(1.3) for any such φ. Let us carry out the details.

We seek solutions u^m of (1.1)–(1.3) with initial values $f_m(x) = \sin(m\pi x/L)$, $m = 1, 2, 3, \ldots$. We shall find that it is possible to obtain solutions of these problems in the form

$$u^m(x, t) = a_m(t) \sin \frac{m\pi x}{L}, \qquad m = 1, 2, 3, \ldots. \tag{1.5}$$

Observe that since $\sin(m\pi 0/L) = \sin(m\pi L/L) = 0$ all functions of the form given in (1.5) certainly satisfy condition (1.3) no matter what $a_m(t)$ is. The problem is to choose the functions $a_m(t)$ so that (1.1) and (1.2) are also satisfied. Note first that if $a_m(0) = 1$ for all m, then

$$u^m(x, 0) = a_m(0) \sin \frac{m\pi x}{L} = \varphi^m(x);$$

hence (1.2) is satisfied. Next observe that

$$u_t^m(x, t) - Ku_{xx}^m(x, t) = \dot{a}_m(t) \sin \frac{m\pi x}{L} + (Km^2\pi^2/L^2)a_m(t) \sin \frac{m\pi x}{L}.$$

Hence the u^m's will satisfy (1.1) if

$$\text{(1.6)} \qquad \dot{a}_m(t) + \frac{Km^2\pi^2}{L^2} a_m(t) = 0, \qquad m = 1, 2, 3, \ldots.$$

We can solve these first-order differential equations subject to the condition $a_m(0) = 1$ thereby obtaining

$$a_m(t) = e^{-Km^2\pi^2t/L^2}.$$

Thus the required functions u^m are given by

$$\text{(1.7)} \qquad u^m(x, t) = e^{-Km^2\pi^2t/L^2} \sin \frac{m\pi x}{L}.$$

From proposition (1.4) we have now the following result.

(1.8) Corollary. *If*

$$\varphi(x) = \alpha_1 \sin \frac{\pi x}{L} + \alpha_2 \sin \frac{2\pi x}{L} + \cdots + \alpha_n \sin \frac{n\pi x}{L},$$

then the function $u = \alpha_1 u^1 + \cdots + \alpha_n u^n$ *is a solution of* (1.1)–(1.3).

Now we connect the above results with the ideas of Chapter 6. Observe that the functions $f_1, f_2, \ldots$ appearing above are precisely the ones occurring in the orthogonal system F_s of Chapter 6, (3.4), namely

$$F_s\colon\ f_1(x) = \sin \frac{\pi x}{L}, \qquad f_2(x) = \sin \frac{2\pi x}{L}, \ldots.$$

The corresponding orthonormal system E_s is,

$$E_s\colon\ e_1(x) = \sqrt{\frac{2}{L}} \sin \frac{\pi x}{L}, \qquad e_2(x) = \sqrt{\frac{2}{L}} \sin \frac{2\pi x}{L}, \ldots.$$

Then we saw that given any function $\varphi \in \mathcal{C}[0, L]$, its best approximation φ^n in the subspace spanned by $e_1, \ldots, e_n$ could be written in the form

$$\varphi_n = \alpha_1 f_1 + \cdots + \alpha_n f_n, \tag{1.9}$$

where

$$\alpha_1 = \frac{2}{L}\int_0^L \varphi(x)\sin\frac{\pi x}{L}\,dx, \ldots, \qquad \alpha_n = \frac{2}{L}\int_0^L \varphi(x)\sin\frac{n\pi x}{L}\,dx. \tag{1.10}$$

We expressed this by saying that the Fourier E_s-expansion of φ is

$$\alpha_1 \sin\frac{\pi x}{L} + \alpha_2 \sin\frac{2\pi x}{L} + \cdots. \tag{1.11}$$

Using what we have learned already, we can solve (1.1)–(1.3) whenever φ is replaced by its best n-approximator φ_n. Indeed the solution, which we denote by $U_n(x, t)$, is given by

$$\begin{aligned} U_n(x, t) &= \alpha_1 u^1(x, t) + \cdots + \alpha_n u^n(x, t) \\ &= \alpha_1 e^{-\pi^2 t/L^2} \sin\frac{\pi x}{L} + \cdots + \alpha_n e^{-n^2\pi^2 t/L^2} \sin\frac{n\pi x}{L}, \\ &\qquad n = 1, 2, 3, \ldots; \end{aligned} \tag{1.12}$$

or, if we insert the values of the α's from (1.10),

$$\begin{aligned} U_n(x, t) = {} & \left(\frac{2}{L}\int_0^L \varphi(x)\sin\frac{\pi x}{L}\,dx\right) e^{-\pi^2 t/L^2} \sin\frac{\pi x}{L} + \cdots \\ & + \left(\frac{2}{L}\int_0^L \varphi(x)\sin\frac{n\pi x}{L}\,dx\right) e^{-n^2\pi^2 t/L^2} \sin\frac{n\pi x}{L}, \\ & \qquad n = 1, 2, 3, \ldots. \end{aligned} \tag{1.12'}$$

Let us examine formula (1.12). For each fixed t, $U_n(x, t)$ is a function just of x. It will be different functions for different choices of t. Think of t as fixed. Then (1.12) can be written in the form

$$U_n(x, t) = \beta_1(t) \sin\frac{\pi x}{L} + \beta_2(t) \sin\frac{2\pi x}{L} + \cdots + \beta_n(t) \sin\frac{n\pi x}{L},$$

where

$$\beta_m(t) = \alpha_m e^{-m^2\pi^2 t/L^2}.$$

Observe that *the coefficient* $\beta_k(t)$ *of* $\sin(k\pi x/L)$ *is the same in each* U_n *for* $n \geq k$. This suggests that *for each fixed* t the U_n's, considered as functions of x, are themselves the best approximators, in $\langle e_1, \ldots, e_n \rangle$, of some continuous function of x. This is in fact true under certain conditions on the function φ. These conditions are rather technical and we simply state that they will be satisfied in problems of physical interest. When these conditions hold, one has the following result:

(1.13) Theorem. *There exists one and only one solution u of* (1.1)–(1.3). *Moreover, for a fixed value of t, $u(x, t)$ is a continuous function of x, and for $n = 1, 2, \ldots$ the function $U_n(x, t)$ in* (1.12) *is its best approximator in the space spanned by $e_1, \ldots, e_n$.*

The uniqueness of the solution u will be proved a little later. The existence of u is a hard theorem which will not be proved. It is, however, important to understand what it says. On the one hand, we have shown how to solve (1.1)–(1.3) *exactly* if φ has the form $\varphi = \alpha_1 f_1 + \cdots + \alpha_n f_n$. On the other hand, we have shown how to obtain, for each t, the best n-approximators U_n of the actual solution u. We point out that the approximators U_n all satisfy the differential equation (1.1) and the boundary conditions (1.3) *exactly*. It is the initial condition (1.2) which they only approximately satisfy.

Observe that the fact that the U_n's are the best n-approximators of the solution u means that the coefficients of $\sin(m\pi x/L)$ in (1.12) are precisely the coefficients of $\sin(m\pi x/L)$ in the Fourier E_s-expansion of u for fixed t. That is, the Fourier expansion of u is

$$e^{-\pi^2 t/L^2}\alpha_1 \sin\frac{\pi x}{L} + e^{-4\pi^2 t/L^2}\alpha_2 \sin\frac{2\pi x}{L} + \cdots. \tag{1.14}$$

If we compare (1.14) with (1.11) we obtain the following rule which makes the process easier to remember.

(1.15) Rule. *To obtain the Fourier expansion of the solution at time t, multiply the term $\alpha_m \sin(\pi m x/L)$ in the expansion of the initial function φ by $e^{-m^2\pi^2 t/L^2}$.*

(1.16) Examples

(a) Find a solution of the problem

$$u_t = u_{xx}, \qquad u(x, 0) = 2\sin x - \sin 3x, \qquad u(0, t) = u(\pi, t) = 0.$$

Here $K = 1$ and $L = \pi$ and $\varphi(x) = 2\sin x - \sin 3x$. We can solve this problem *exactly*, since φ is a finite combination of the functions $f_k(x) = \sin kx$

appropriate to $L = \pi$, that is $\varphi = 2f_1 - f_3$. A solution is $u = 2u^1 - u^3$, or

$$u = 2e^{-t}\sin x - e^{-9t}\sin 3x.$$

(b) Find a solution of the problem

$$u_t = 2u_{xx}, \qquad u(x, 0) = \sin 4x \cos 4x, \qquad u(0, t) = u\left(\frac{\pi}{2}, t\right) = 0.$$

Here $K = 2$ and $L = \pi/2$. The functions f_k appropriate to this interval are $f_k(x) = \sin 2kx$, $k = 1, 2, 3, \ldots.$ Although $\varphi(x) = \sin 4x \cos 4x$ looks more complicated than the f_k's, we observe that it can be written

$$\varphi(x) = \tfrac{1}{2}\sin 8x = \tfrac{1}{2}f_4(x).$$

Hence the problem can again be solved exactly and the solution is

$$u = \tfrac{1}{2}e^{-64t}\sin 8x.$$

(c) Find a solution of

$$u_t = u_{xx}, \qquad u(x, 0) \equiv 1, \qquad u(0, t) = u(\pi, t) = 0.$$

Here $K = 1$ and $L = \pi$. The appropriate f_k's are $f_k(x) = \sin kx$, $k = 1, 2, 3, \ldots.$ The function $\varphi(x) \equiv 1$ is *not* a combination of the f_k's. Because of this we cannot find the solution in the same way we did above. Rather we shall find its best n-approximators for $n = 1, 2, 3, \ldots.$ In example (3.4) of Chapter 6 we found the Fourier expansion of $\varphi(x) = 1$ in $\mathcal{C}[0, \pi]$ to be

$$\frac{4}{\pi}\sin x + \frac{4}{3\pi}\sin 3x + \frac{4}{5\pi}\sin 5x + \cdots.$$

Hence by rule (1.15) the Fourier expansion of the solution is

$$\frac{4}{\pi}e^{-t}\sin x + \frac{4}{3\pi}e^{-9t}\sin 3x + \frac{4}{5\pi}e^{-25t}\sin 5x + \cdots.$$

Thus its first six n-approximators are

$$U_1(x, t) = U_2(x, t) = \frac{4}{\pi}e^{-t}\sin x$$

$$U_3(x, t) = U_4(x, t) = \frac{4}{\pi}e^{-t}\sin x + \frac{4}{3\pi}e^{-9t}\sin 3x$$

$$U_5(x, t) = U_6(x, t) = \frac{4}{5}e^{-t}\sin x + \frac{4}{3\pi}e^{-9t}\sin 3x + \frac{4}{5\pi}e^{-25t}\sin 5x.$$

We recall from Chapter 6 that the set E_s

$$E_s\colon\ e_1(x) = \sqrt{\frac{2}{L}}\sin\frac{\pi x}{L}, \qquad e_2(x) = \sqrt{\frac{2}{L}}\sin\frac{2\pi x}{L}, \ldots$$

is complete. This means that if g is any continuous function and g_n represents its best n-approximator, then

$$\|g - g_n\| = \left(\int_0^L (g(x) - g_n(x))^2\,dx\right)^{1/2} \to 0 \qquad \text{as } n \to \infty.$$

Hence in view of theorem (1.13) we have the result that

$$(1.17) \qquad \int_0^L (u(x, t) - U_n(x, t))^2\,dx \to 0 \qquad \text{as } n \to \infty \text{ for each fixed } t.$$

Here u is the true solution and the U_n's are as in (1.12). Actually more is true in any reasonable situation. If one fixes one's attention on a particular t and x, the $U_n(x, t)$'s form a sequence of numbers. What is true is that this sequence converges to the value $u(x, t)$ of the true solution at x and t. Thus for a given value of t, say t_1, one would have the situation depicted in Figure 7.2.

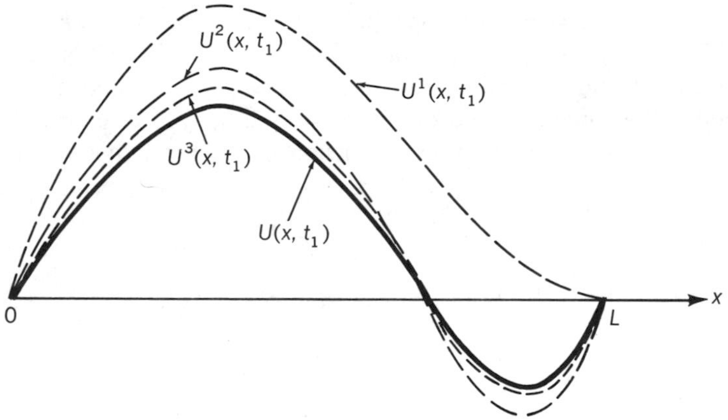

Figure 7.2

PROBLEMS

1. Find exact solutions of the following problems:

(a) $u_t = u_{xx}$, $u(x, 0) = \sin 2x$, $u(0, t) = u(\pi, t) = 0$

(b) $u_t = 2u_{xx}$, $u(x, 0) = \sin 2x$, $u(0, t) = u(\pi, t) = 0$

(c) $u_t = u_{xx}$, $u(x, 0) = \sin \pi x$, $u(0, t) = u(1, t) = 0$

(d) $u_t = u_{xx}$, $u(x, 0) = \sin 2x - 3 \sin 3x$, $u(0, t) = u(\pi, t) = 0$

(e) $u_t = 4u_{xx}$, $u(x, 0) = 2 \sin 2\pi x - 4 \sin 4\pi x$, $u(0, t) = u(\frac{1}{2}, t) = 0$

(f) $u_t = u_{xx}$, $u(x, 0) = \sin 3x \cos x + \cos 3x \sin x$, $u(0, t) = u(\pi, t) = 0$

2. For each of the following problems find the most general functions φ for which an *exact* solution can be obtained.

(a) $u_t = u_{xx}$, $u(x, 0) = \varphi(x)$, $u(0, t) = u(2, t) = 0$

(b) $u_t = 4u_{xx}$, $u(x, 0) = \varphi(x)$, $u(0, t) = u(2\pi, t) = 0$

(c) $u_t = 2u_{xx}$, $u(x, 0) = \varphi(x)$, $u(0, t) = u(3, t) = 0$

3. Find the first three terms in the Fourier series for the solution of each of the following problems:

(a) $u_t = 2u_{xx}$, $u(x, 0) = x$, $u(0, t) = u(\pi, t) = 0$

(b) $u_t = u_{xx}$, $u(x,0) = 1$, $u(0, t) = u(2\pi, t) = 0$

(c) $u_t = 2u_{xx}$, $u(x, 0) = \begin{Bmatrix} x \text{ for } 0 \leq x \leq \frac{1}{2} \\ 1 - x \text{ for } \frac{1}{2} \leq x \leq 1 \end{Bmatrix}$, $u(0, t) = u(1, t) = 0$

4. What changes in the procedure would have been necessary if equation (1.1) were replaced by

$$u_t(x, t) = t u_{xx}(x, t)$$

with the conditions (1.2) and (1.3) remaining the same?

2. Separation of Variables (The Method of Product Solutions)

The key to success in studying the problem of §1 was the use of the special solutions u^m of equation (1.1). It turns out that there are similar special solutions for *other* equations which can be used to construct the solutions of various PDE problems. Indeed, there even exist other special solutions of (1.1). The general method of constructing and using such solutions is called *separation of variables.* We illustrate it here and in §3.

One thing that is special about the functions u^m in (1.7) is that by construction, each of these solutions is a function of x and t which has the form of a function of x alone—$f_m(x) = \sin (m\pi x/L)$—multiplied by a function of t alone—$a_m(t) = e^{-Km^2\pi^2 t/L^2}$. There are other such product solutions of (1.1), and as a first step we determine *all* such solutions. Thus we seek to find all functions X and T such that the product

$$u(x, t) = T(t)X(x) \tag{2.1}$$

is a solution of equation (1.1); that is, $u_t = Ku_{xx}$. Since

$$u_t(x, t) = \dot{T}(t)X(x), \qquad u_{xx}(x, t) = T(t)X''(x),$$

we find by substitution into the PDE that

$$\dot{T}(t)X(x) = KT(t)X''(x), \qquad 0 < x < L,\ 0 < t < \infty. \tag{2.2}$$

We divide equation (2.2) by the product $u = TX$ and obtain

$$\frac{\dot{T}(t)}{T(t)} = K\frac{X''(x)}{X(x)}, \qquad 0 < x < L, 0 < t < \infty. \tag{2.3}$$

Equation (2.3) is an identity to be satisfied for all x and t values indicated. To investigate the function T we fix the value of x and let t vary, $0 < t < \infty$. The *right* side of (2.3) is obviously fixed as t varies; that is, it is a constant α. Hence by (2.3) we have

$$\frac{\dot{T}(t)}{T(t)} = \alpha \qquad \text{or} \qquad \dot{T}(t) - \alpha T(t) = 0, \qquad 0 < t < \infty,\ \alpha \text{ a constant.} \tag{2.4}$$

To investigate the function X we could similarly fix the value of t and let x vary, but it is simpler merely to insert (2.4) into (2.3). This yields

$$K\frac{X''(x)}{X(x)} = \alpha \qquad \text{or} \qquad X''(x) - \frac{\alpha}{K}X(x) = 0, \qquad 0 < x < L. \tag{2.5}$$

Thus if (2.1) is to yield a solution of $u_t = Ku_{xx}$, then the functions T and X must satisfy (2.4) and (2.5), respectively. Conversely, if T and X are *any* solutions of (2.4) and (2.5), then TX satisfies (2.2), so this product will, in fact, be a solution of $u_t = Ku_{xx}$. Hence we can find *all* product solutions of the form (2.1) by finding all possible solutions of (2.4) and (2.5). But this is simple to do by our previous work. We know that no matter what value α has, all solutions of (2.4) have the form

$$T(t) = Ce^{\alpha t} \qquad \text{for some constant } C. \tag{2.6}$$

Solutions of (2.5) are a little more complicated in that we have to distinguish three cases:

CASE 1, $\alpha/K > 0$. In this case solutions of (2.5) have the form

$$X(x) = Ae^{\sqrt{(\alpha/K)}\,x} + Be^{-\sqrt{(\alpha/K)}\,x}, \qquad A \text{ and } B \text{ constants.} \tag{2.7}$$

CASE 2, $\alpha/K < 0$. In this case the solutions are

$$X(x) = A\cos\sqrt{(-\alpha/K)}\,x + B\sin\sqrt{(-\alpha/K)}\,x. \tag{2.8}$$

CASE 3, $\alpha/K = 0$. In this case the solutions are

$$X(x) = A + Bx. \tag{2.9}$$

We have now a large variety of product solutions at our disposal. We can give the constant α arbitrarily and then for each choice of α we can specify A, B, and C arbitrarily.

The functions u^m of (1.7) correspond to special choices of the various constants. In particular, to get u^m we chose $\alpha = -Km^2\pi^2/L^2$, $A = 0$, $B = 1$, and $C = 1$. Why were *these* choices made in (1.7)? The answer is that they were essentially the *only* choices that *could* be made once we required the product solutions to satisfy the boundary conditions (1.3);

$$u(0, t) = 0, \qquad u(L, t) = 0 \qquad \text{for all } t. \tag{2.10}$$

Let us confirm this statement. Conditions (2.10) for the product solutions require that

$$T(t)X(0) = 0, \qquad T(t)X(L) = 0 \qquad \text{for all } t.$$

By (2.6) we see that $T(t)$ is never zero unless we choose $C = 0$, in which case the whole product is identically zero. Hence we deduce that necessarily

$$X(0) = 0, \qquad X(L) = 0. \tag{2.11}$$

Let us try each of the three possible choices of sign of α/K to see if A and B can be chosen so that (2.11) is satisfied. In Case 3 we would have

$$A + B\cdot 0 = 0, \qquad A + B\cdot L = 0.$$

Hence $A = B = 0$ is the only possibility and this gives $u \equiv 0$. In Case 1 we would have

$$A + B = 0, \qquad Ae^{\sqrt{(\alpha/K)}\,L} + Be^{-\sqrt{(\alpha/K)}\,L} = 0,$$

and one can check again that the only possible solution satisfying (2.11) is $u \equiv 0$. Finally in Case 2 we obtain

$$\begin{aligned} A\cos 0 + B\sin 0 &= 0 \\ A\cos\sqrt{(-\alpha/K)}\,L + B\sin\sqrt{(-\alpha/K)}\,L &= 0, \end{aligned} \qquad \text{or} \qquad \begin{aligned} A &= 0 \\ B\sin\sqrt{(-\alpha/K)}\,L &= 0. \end{aligned}$$

Now there *are* choices of α which will make these equations satisfied without A and B both being zero. We can choose α so that $\sqrt{(-\alpha/K)}\,L = m\pi$, where m is a positive integer (and these are the only α choices). Then

$$(2.12) \qquad -\frac{\alpha}{K}L^2 = m^2\pi^2 \quad \text{or} \quad \alpha = -\frac{Km^2\pi^2}{L^2}, \qquad m = 1, 2, \ldots .$$

If we make the choices (2.12) for α, then we do obtain functions $X(x)$, namely $B \sin (m\pi x/L)$ for any B, which satisfy both equation (2.5) and conditions (2.11). Thus the functions

$$(2.13) \qquad CBe^{-Km^2\pi^2 t/L^2} \sin \frac{m\pi x}{L}$$

are product solutions which satisfy (2.10) and they are the only ones. Note that the product CB is just some other arbitrary constant. The only specialization we made to get the functions u^m of (1.7) was to choose $CB = 1$ for each m.

The above procedure can be extended in two ways. We can either change the equation (1.1) or we can change the boundary conditions (1.3). The only prerequisite is that product solutions must be available. In all such cases these product solutions can be combined, using Fourier series methods as in §1, to form solutions of various problems. This technique will be discussed in detail in §3. Here we simply show how to obtain other product solutions. We do this by means of examples.

(2.14) Examples. Product Solutions. In each case we seek solutions of the form (2.1) which satisfy the given equation and boundary conditions.

(a) $u_t = u_{xx}$, $u_x(0, t) = 0$, $u_x(\pi, t) = 0$. Since the equation is still of the form (1.1) (with $K = 1$), T and X are still given by (2.1) together with (2.7), (2.8) or (2.9). The boundary conditions require

$$\text{(i)} \qquad X'(0) = X'(\pi) = 0.$$

The reader should check that in Case 1 no choice of A and B except $A = 0$, $B = 0$, will satisfy condition (i). Next he should verify that if α is chosen as zero, then the only choice is $B = 0$, so this product solution is simply CA, a constant. Finally, if α is chosen so that $\alpha < 0$, as in Case 2, then

$$X = A \cos \sqrt{-\alpha}\, x + B \sin \sqrt{-\alpha}\, x$$

and (i) requires

$$\text{(ii)} \qquad \begin{aligned} -\sqrt{-\alpha}\, A \sin 0 + \sqrt{-\alpha}\, B \cos 0 &= 0 \\ -\sqrt{-\alpha}\, A \sin \sqrt{-\alpha}\, \pi + \sqrt{-\alpha}\, B \cos \sqrt{-\alpha}\, \pi &= 0, \end{aligned}$$

that is

$$B = 0 \qquad \text{and} \qquad -\sqrt{-\alpha}\, A \sin \sqrt{-\alpha}\, \pi = 0.$$

The only choices, other than $A = 0$, $B = 0$, are

$$\sqrt{-\alpha}\, \pi = m\pi \qquad \text{or} \qquad \alpha = -m^2, \qquad m \text{ an integer;}$$

hence the product solutions are

$$e^{-m^2 t} \cos mx.$$

(b) $u_t = u_{xx}$, $u_x(0, t) = 0$, $u(\pi, t) = 0$. The only change over the preceding case is that (i) is replaced by

$$\text{(i}'\text{)} \qquad X'(0) = X(\pi) = 0.$$

Here the reader should check that cases 1 and 3 offer no possibilities except $A = 0$, $B = 0$. In case 2 we obtain instead of (ii),

$$\text{(ii}'\text{)} \qquad \begin{aligned} -\sqrt{-\alpha}\, A \sin 0 + \sqrt{-\alpha}\, B \cos 0 &= \sqrt{-\alpha}\, B = 0 \\ A \cos \sqrt{-\alpha}\, \pi + B \sin \sqrt{-\alpha}\, \pi &= A \cos \sqrt{-\alpha}\, \pi = 0. \end{aligned}$$

The only possibilities are

$$\sqrt{-\alpha}\, \pi = \frac{\pi}{2}, \frac{3\pi}{2}, \frac{5\pi}{2}, \ldots \qquad \text{or} \qquad \alpha = \frac{1}{4}, \frac{9}{4}, \frac{25}{4}, \ldots,$$

and the product solutions are

$$e^{-t/4} \cos \frac{\pi}{2} x, \qquad e^{-9t/4} \cos \frac{3\pi}{2} x, \qquad e^{-25t/4} \cos \frac{5\pi}{2} x, \ldots$$

(c) $u_t = u_{xx} + u$, $u(0, t) = 0$, $u(\pi, t) = 0$. Here the equation has changed and we must repeat the calculation which led to (2.4) and (2.5). We substitute the product (2.1) into the equation and obtain

$$\dot{T}(t)X(x) = T(t)X''(x) + T(t)X(x).$$

Once again we divide by TX and obtain

$$\text{(i)} \qquad \frac{\dot{T}(t)}{T(t)} = \frac{X''(x)}{X(x)} + 1.$$

The left side depends only on t and the right side only on x. Hence by the argument given before each must be equal to a constant α. Thus we obtain the two ordinary differential equations

$$\text{(ii)} \quad \frac{\dot{T}(t)}{T(t)} = \alpha \quad \text{or} \quad \dot{T}(t) - \alpha T(t) = 0$$

$$\text{(iii)} \quad \frac{X''(x)}{X(x)} + 1 = \alpha \quad \text{or} \quad X''(x) - (\alpha - 1)X(x) = 0.$$

These equations have the same solutions as before except that the three cases become $\alpha - 1 > 0$, $\alpha - 1 < 0$, $\alpha - 1 = 0$ and in formulas (2.7), (2.8), and (2.9) we have to replace α by $\alpha - 1$. Thus to obtain solutions which satisfy the boundary conditions we must choose $\alpha - 1 = -m^2$ or $\alpha = 1 - m^2$. The appropriate functions X are still $\sin mx$ but now the product solutions are

$$e^{\alpha t} \sin mx = e^{(1-m^2)t} \sin mx.$$

Let us summarize the steps in the method of separation of variables.

(2.15) Summary

STEP 1. Substitute $u(x, t) = T(t)X(x)$ into the equation and divide by $T(t)X(x)$. If the method is to be successful, the variables should be "separated"; that is, one side should be a function only of t and the other side only of x.

STEP 2. If the variables are separated, set each side equal to a constant α. This gives two ordinary differential equations for T and X. Find all solutions of these.

STEP 3. Substitute $T(t)X(x)$ into the boundary conditions. This will give conditions on X at $x = 0$ and $x = L$.

STEP 4. Choose the constant α and the arbitrary constants in the solution X so that the conditions in step 3 are satisfied.

PROBLEMS

1. In each of the following problems determine all product solutions of the form $u(x, t) = T(t)X(x)$.

   (a) $u_t = u_{xx}$, $u(0, t) = u(1, t) = 0$

   (b) $u_t = 4u_{xx}$, $u(0, t) = u(2, t) = 0$

(c) $u_t = -u_{xx}, \quad u(0, t) = u(\pi, t) = 0$

(d) $u_t = -u_{xx}, \quad u_x(0, t) = u_x(1, t) = 0$

(e) $u_t = 3u_{xx}, \quad u(0, t) = u_x(\pi, t) = 0$

(f) $u_t = 2u_{xx}, \quad u_x(0, t) = u(1, t) = 0$

(g) $u_t = u_{xx} + u_x, \quad u(0, t) = u(\pi, t) = 0$

(h) $u_t = u_{xx} + u, \quad u_x(0, t) = u_x(2\pi, t) = 0$

(i) $(1 + t^2)u_t = u_{xx}, \quad u(0, t) = u(\pi, t) = 0$

(j) $u_{tt} = u_{xx}, \quad u(0, t) = u(\pi, t) = 0$

2. In each of the following problems find all possible product solutions, if any, of the given equation (no boundary conditions).

(a) $u_t + u_x = 0$

(b) $u_{tt} + xu_x = 0$

(c) $tu_t + xu_x = 0$

(d) $xu_t + tu_x = 0$

(e) $e^{x+t}u_t + u_x = 0$

(f) $e^{xt}u_t + u_x = 0$

(g) $u_t = e^t u_{xx}$

(h) $u_t - e^{xt}u_{xx}$

3. Separation of Variables (Fourier Series Solutions)

In this section we shall use the product solutions obtained in §2 to determine the solution of various PDE problems. We give an example before discussing the method in general.

(3.1) Example. Fourier Expansion of a Solution. Consider example (2.14a). We showed there that the functions

$$u^m(x, t) = e^{-m^2 t} \cos mx, \qquad m = 0, 1, 2, \ldots$$

are solutions of $u_t = u_{xx}$ satisfying the boundary conditions (iii) $u_x(0, t) = 0$, $u_x(\pi, t) = 0$. Observe that at $t = 0$ $u^m(x, 0) = f_m^*(x) = \cos mx$. Now these f_m^*'s are multiples of the functions which make up the system E_c of example (3.11b) of Chapter 6. For recall that E_c is given by (here $L = \pi$)

$$E_c\colon\ e_0^*(x) = \frac{1}{\sqrt{\pi}}, \qquad e_1^*(x) = \sqrt{\frac{2}{\pi}}\cos x, \qquad e_2^*(x) = \sqrt{\frac{2}{\pi}}\cos 2x, \ldots.$$

We stated there that this system is orthonormal and complete in $\mathcal{C}[0, \pi]$. This means that *every* function $\varphi \in \mathcal{C}[0, \pi]$ has a Fourier E_c-expansion:

$$\varphi \sim (\varphi \cdot e_0^*)e_0^* + (\varphi \cdot e_1^*)e_1^* + (\varphi \cdot e_2^*)e_2^* + \cdots$$

or

$$\varphi \sim \frac{1}{\pi}\int_0^\pi \varphi(x)\,dx + \frac{2}{\pi}\left(\int_0^\pi \varphi(x)\cos x\,dx\right)\cos x$$
$$+ \frac{2}{\pi}\left(\int_0^\pi \varphi(x)\cos 2x\,dx\right)\cos 2x + \cdots.$$

Now we are in a position to imitate what was done in §1. Consider the PDE problem of finding a function u satisfying

(a) $u_t(x, t) = u_{xx}(x, t),\ 0 < x < \pi,\ 0 < t < \infty.$

(b) $u(x, 0) = \varphi(x),\ \varphi \in \mathcal{C}[0, \pi].$

(c) $u_x(0, t) = 0,\ u_x(\pi, t) = 0.$

The only significant change from the problem considered in §1 is that the boundary conditions (1.3) are here replaced by (c). There is an analog of proposition (1.4) available for the present problem.

Proposition. *Let* $u^1, \ldots, u^n$ *be solutions of* (a), (b), (c) *for initial functions equal to* $\varphi^1, \varphi^2, \ldots, \varphi^n$, *respectively. Then the function* $u = \alpha_1 u^1 + \cdots + \alpha_n u^n$ *is a solution of the same problem for initial function* $\varphi = \alpha_1\varphi^1 + \cdots + \alpha_n\varphi^n$.

This result is proved just like proposition (1.4) [see proposition (3.10)]. Using it we see that one can obtain an *explicit* solution of problem (a), (b), (c) if φ is replaced by its best n-approximator φ_n in the system E_c, that is, by the function

(d)
$$\begin{aligned}\varphi_n(x) &= (\varphi\cdot \overset{*}{e}_0)\overset{*}{e}_0(x) + (\varphi\cdot \overset{*}{e}_1)\overset{*}{e}_1(x) + \cdots + (\varphi\cdot \overset{*}{e}_n)\overset{*}{e}_n(x)\\ &= \frac{1}{\pi}\left(\int_0^\pi \varphi(x)\,dx\right) + \cdots + \frac{2}{\pi}\left(\int_0^\pi \varphi(x)\cos nx\,dx\right)\cos nx.\end{aligned}$$

Indeed the solution U_n is simply

(e)
$$\begin{aligned}U_n(x, t) &= \left(\frac{1}{\pi}\int_0^\pi \varphi(x)\,dx\right)u^0(x, t) + \cdots\\ &\qquad + \left(\frac{2}{\pi}\int_0^\pi \varphi(x)\cos nx\,dx\right)u^n(x, t)\\ &= \frac{1}{\pi}\left(\int_0^\pi \varphi(x)\,dx\right) + \cdots\\ &\qquad + \frac{2}{\pi}\left(\int_0^\pi \varphi(x)\cos nx\,dx\right)e^{-n^2 t}\cos nx.\end{aligned}$$

Furthermore, just as in §1, the above facts can be used to analyze (a), (b), (c) for *all* reasonable† functions φ. It will again be true, as in theorem (1.13), that corresponding to each such φ the problem (a), (b), (c) has a unique solution u and that the U_n's of (e) are the best n-approximators of that solution. That is, for each fixed t, the Fourier E_c-expansion of the solution is given by

$$\text{(f)}\qquad \begin{aligned} u \sim \frac{1}{\pi}\left(\int_0^\pi \varphi(x)\,dx\right) + \left(\frac{2}{\pi}\int_0^\pi \varphi(x)\cos x\,dx\right)e^{-t}\cos x \\ + \left(\frac{2}{\pi}\int_0^\pi \varphi(x)\cos 2x\,dx\right)e^{-4t}\cos 2x + \cdots. \end{aligned}$$

Observe that we again obtain the Fourier expansion for the solution at time t simply by multiplying the nth term of the expansion for φ by e^{-n^2t}, $n = 0, 1, 2, \ldots$.

It is no coincidence that in the above example, as well as in the example in §1, the special product solutions happened to be connected to a complete orthonormal system of initial functions and thus could be used to obtain approximate solutions for *all* reasonable $\varphi \in \mathcal{C}[0, \pi]$. Rather the two examples are special cases of a general principle. We shall not even attempt to formulate the complete result (which is called the *Sturm Liouville Principle*). However, we do want to carry it far enough to show that it is applicable to the product solutions of each PDE problem occurring in problem 1 of §2. We first sketch a general result and then give some specific examples.

We seek to find a function u such that

$$r(t)u_t(x, t) = Ku_{xx}(x, t) + Mu(x, t) \tag{3.2}$$

$$u(x, 0) = \varphi(x) \tag{3.3}$$

$$u(0, t) = u(L, t) = 0. \tag{3.4}$$

In (3.2) r is continuous for all $t \geq 0$ and $r(t) > 0$. The quantities K, L, and M are constants, with $K \neq 0$. In (3.3) φ is continuous on $0 \leq x \leq L$. Let us begin by finding product solutions $u = T(t)X(x)$. We substitute in (3.2) and find

$$r(t)\dot{T}(t)X(x) = T(t)\{KX''(x) + MX(x)\}.$$

Hence if we divide by TX we obtain

$$\frac{r(t)\dot{T}(t)}{T(t)} = \frac{1}{X(x)}\{KX''(x) + MX(x)\}.$$

†*Reasonable* here again has a technical meaning.

The variables are separated so that each side must equal a constant α; hence we obtain the two ordinary differential equations

$$(3.5)\qquad \frac{r(t)\dot{T}(t)}{T(t)} = \alpha \qquad \text{or} \qquad \dot{T}(t) - \frac{\alpha}{r(t)}T(t) = 0$$

$$(3.6)\qquad \frac{1}{X(x)}\{KX''(x) + MX(x)\} = \alpha \qquad \text{or} \qquad X''(x) + \frac{M-\alpha}{K}X(x) = 0.$$

We also substitute $u = TX$ into the boundary conditions (3.4) and find

$$(3.7)\qquad X(0) = X(L) = 0.$$

The general result we need is contained in the following theorem.

(3.8) Theorem

(i) *There exist infinitely many distinct values of* α, $\alpha_1, \alpha_2, \alpha_3, \ldots$, *such that for these choices of* α, *and only these choices,* (3.6) *has nonzero solutions X which satisfy conditions* (3.7).†

(ii) *For each such value* α_m *all solutions of* (3.6) *and* (3.7) *have the form*

$$X(x) = CX_m(x),$$

where X_m *is a fixed solution and C is a constant.*

(iii) *The functions* X_m *in* (ii) *form a complete orthonormal system in* $\mathcal{C}[0, L]$ *provided they have been chosen to have unit norm.*

The examples and problems will serve to demonstrate the existence of α_m's and X_m's as well as the truth of statement (ii). The orthogonality of the X_m's is also discussed in the problems. However, the completeness of this system is a hard result which we do not prove.

Once we have Theorem (3.8) we can proceed exactly as before. First we let $T_m(t)$ denote the solutions of the first-order s-linear differential equation (3.5) for $\alpha = \alpha_m$ with the initial condition $T_m(0) = 1$. These solutions are

$$T_m(t) = e^{\int_0^t (\alpha_m/r(\tau))d\tau}, \qquad m = 1, 2, \ldots.$$

Then we define functions u^m by

$$(3.9)\qquad u^m(x, t) = T_m(t)X_m(x).$$

†In certain cases such as example (3.1), it is more usual to denote the smallest α value by α_0 rather than α_1, but this is just a matter of convenience.

By construction these satisfy (3.2) and (3.4). Moreover,

$$u^m(x, 0) = X_m(x).$$

The reader should convince himself that (3.2) is again an s-linear equation and thus that there is available the following analog of proposition (1.4).

(3.10) Proposition. *Let* $u^1, \ldots, u^n$ *be solutions of* (3.2), (3.3), *and* (3.4) *for* $\varphi = \varphi^1, \ldots, \varphi = \varphi^n$. *Then for any constants* $\alpha_1, \ldots, \alpha_n$, *the function,*

$$u = \alpha_1 u^1 + \cdots + \alpha_n u^n$$

is a solution of (3.2), (3.3) *and* (3.4) *for,*

$$\varphi = \alpha_1 \varphi^1 + \cdots + \alpha_n \varphi^n.$$

Now we proceed just as before. Since the X_m's form an orthonormal system $\mathfrak{X}$ for $\mathcal{C}[0, L]$,

$$\mathfrak{X}: X_1, X_2, X_3, \ldots,$$

any continuous function φ has a Fourier $\mathfrak{X}$-expansion,

$$\varphi \sim (\varphi \cdot X_1)X_1 + (\varphi \cdot X_2)X_2 + \cdots, \tag{3.11}$$

where

$$\varphi \cdot X_1 = \int_0^L \varphi(x)X_1(x)\,dx, \qquad \varphi \cdot X_2 = \int_0^L \varphi(x)X_2(x)\,dx, \ldots. \tag{3.12}$$

By proposition (3.10) we can obtain an explicit solution of (3.2), (3.3), and (3.4) if we replace φ in (3.3) by its best n-approximator φ_n, given by

$$\varphi_n(x) = (\varphi \cdot X_1)X_1(x) + \cdots + (\varphi \cdot X_n)X_n(x).$$

This solution U_n is simply

$$\begin{aligned} U_n(x, t) &= (\varphi \cdot X_1)u^1(x, t) + \cdots + (\varphi \cdot X_n)u^n(x, t) \\ &= (\varphi \cdot X_1)T_1(t)X_1(x) + \cdots + (\varphi \cdot X_n)T_n(t)X_n(x). \end{aligned} \tag{3.13}$$

As before, the original problem (3.2)–(3.4) has a solution $u(x, t)$ and, for each *fixed* t, the functions U_n of (3.13) are its best n-approximators in the system $\mathfrak{X}$. That is for each fixed t the Fourier $\mathfrak{X}$-expansion of the solution corresponding to the actual initial function φ is given by

$$u \sim (\varphi \cdot X_1)T_1(t)X_1 + (\varphi \cdot X_2)T_2(t)X_2 + \cdots. \tag{3.14}$$

Observe that, once again, the expansion (3.14) is obtained from that of φ [that is, (3.11)] simply by multiplying the mth term by $T_m(t)$, $m = 1, 3, \ldots$.

The above principle is still more general than we have indicated. The boundary conditions (3.4) can be replaced by any set of conditions of the form

$$\begin{aligned} au_x(0, t) + bu(0, t) &= 0 \\ cu_x(L, t) + du(L, t) &= 0, \end{aligned} \tag{3.4'}$$

where the constants (a, b, c, d) are one of the following sets†:

$$(0, 1, 0, 1), \qquad (1, 0, 1, 0), \qquad (0, 1, 1, 0), \qquad (1, 0, 0, 1).$$

Thus for example by choosing the set (0, 1, 1, 0) we obtain the conditions $u(0, t) = u_x(L, t) = 0$. All that changes under (3.4′) is that equations (3.7) are now replaced by

$$\begin{aligned} aX'(0) + bX(0) &= 0 \\ cX'(L) + dX(L) &= 0. \end{aligned} \tag{3.7'}$$

A number of examples of the α_m's and X_m's are already contained in problem 1 of §2. We point out that all those equations and boundary conditions fit the form (3.2) and (3.4) or (3.4′) save for problems 1(g) and 1(j), which we discuss shortly. For example, for problem 1(e) we take $L = \pi$, $r(t) \equiv 1$, $K = 3$, $M = 0$, $a = 0$, $b = 1$, $c = 1$, $d = 0$. In 1(h) we take $L = 2\pi$, $r(t) \equiv 1$, $K = 1$, $M = 1$, $a = 0$, $b = 1$, $c = 0$, $d = 1$.

(3.15) Examples

(a) $u_t = u_{xx}$, $u(x, 0) = 1$, $u(0, t) = u_x(\pi/2, t) = 0$. Here $L = \pi/2$, $r(t) \equiv 1$, $K = 1$, $M = 0$, $a = 0$, $b = 1$, $c = 1$, $d = 0$. Equation (3.6) becomes $X''(x) - \alpha X(x) = 0$, while (3.7′) becomes $X(0) = X'(\pi/2) = 0$. Solutions are obtained only if $\alpha = \alpha_1, \alpha_2, \alpha_3, \ldots$, where $\alpha_1 = -(1)^2$, $\alpha_2 = -(3)^2$, $\alpha_3 = -(5)^2, \ldots$. These solutions have the form $c_1 \sin x$, $c_2 \sin 3x$, $c_3 \sin 5x, \ldots$, where the c_k's are constants. We choose the con-

†Actually the principle holds for *all* sets (a, b, c, d) in which neither $(a, b) = (0, 0)$ nor $(c, d) = (0, 0)$, but the sets given above are the easiest to treat and suffice for our purposes.

stants $c_1, c_2, c_3, \ldots$ so that the corresponding functions have norm 1. For example, c_1 is chosen by

$$\int_0^{\pi/2} c_1^2 \sin^2 x \, dx = \frac{\pi}{4} c_1^2 = 1 \qquad \text{or} \qquad c_1 = \frac{2}{\sqrt{\pi}}.$$

Then we get the *orthonormal* system $\mathfrak{X}$ as†

$$\mathfrak{X}: \ X_1 = \frac{2}{\sqrt{\pi}} \sin x, \qquad X_2 = \frac{2}{\sqrt{\pi}} \sin 3x, \qquad X_3 = \frac{2}{\sqrt{\pi}} \sin 5x, \ldots.$$

The functions $T_m(t)$ are given by

$$T_1(t) = e^{-t}, \qquad T_2(t) = e^{-9t}, \qquad T_3(t) = e^{-25t}, \ldots.$$

Now to obtain the Fourier $\mathfrak{X}$-expansion of the solution we proceed as follows. We first find the Fourier $\mathfrak{X}$-expansion of the function $\varphi(x) = 1$. This is

$$\begin{aligned}
&\left(\int_0^{\pi/2} X_1(x)\,dx\right) X_1(x) + \left(\int_0^{\pi/2} X_2(x)\,dx\right) X_2(x) \\
&\qquad + \left(\int_0^{\pi/2} X_3(x)\,dx\right) X_3(x) + \cdots \\
&= \left(\frac{2}{\sqrt{\pi}} \int_0^{\pi/2} dx\right) \frac{2}{\sqrt{\pi}} \sin x + \left(\frac{2}{\sqrt{\pi}} \int_0^{\pi/2} \sin 3x\,dx\right) \frac{2}{\sqrt{\pi}} \sin 3x \\
&\quad + \left(\frac{2}{\sqrt{\pi}} \int_0^{\pi} \sin 5x\,dx\right) \frac{2}{\sqrt{\pi}} \sin 5x + \cdots \\
&= \sqrt{\pi}\left(\frac{2}{\sqrt{\pi}} \sin x\right) + \frac{2}{3\sqrt{\pi}}\left(\frac{2}{\sqrt{\pi}} \sin 3x\right) + \frac{2}{5\sqrt{\pi}}\left(\frac{2}{\sqrt{\pi}} \sin 5x\right) + \cdots.
\end{aligned}$$

Then the Fourier $\mathfrak{X}$-expansion of the solution is

$$u \sim \sqrt{\pi}\, u^1(x, t) + \frac{2}{3\sqrt{\pi}} u^2(x, t) + \frac{2}{5\sqrt{\pi}} u^3(x, t) + \cdots;$$

that is,

$$u \sim 2e^{-t} \sin x + \frac{4}{3\pi} e^{-9t} \sin 3x + \frac{4}{5\pi} e^{-25t} \sin 5x + \cdots.$$

---

†One can verify directly that if the X_k's are so chosen, then $\int_0 X_k(x) X_l(x)\,dx = 0$ if $k \neq l$. Note, however, that this fact is guaranteed automatically by theorem (3.8).

(b) $e^{-t}u_t(x, t) = u_{xx}(x, t) - u(x, t)$, $u(x, 0) = x$, $u_x(0, t) = u_x(1, t) = 0$. Here $L = 1$, $r(t) = e^{-t}$, $K = 1$, $M = -1$, $a = 1$, $b = 0$, $c = 1$, $d = 0$. Equation (3.6) becomes

$$\text{(i)} \qquad X''(x) - (1 + \alpha)X(x) = 0,$$

while equations (3.7′) become

$$\text{(ii)} \qquad X'(0) = X'(1) = 0.$$

It is easy to check that one can obtain solutions of (i) satisfying (ii) only if α is one of the values $\alpha_0, \alpha_1, \ldots,$ where $1 + \alpha_0 = 0$, $1 + \alpha_1 = -\pi^2$, $1 + \alpha_2 = -4\pi^2, \ldots, 1 + \alpha_m = -m^2\pi^2 \ldots.$ Then the solutions are

$$c_0, \qquad c_1 \cos \pi x, \qquad c_2 \cos 2\pi x, \qquad c_3 \cos 3\pi x, \ldots.$$

Once again we choose $c_0, c_1, c_2, \ldots$ so as to make the corresponding functions have norm 1. Thus

$$\int_0^1 c_0^2\, dx = 1 \quad \text{or} \quad c_0 = 1, \qquad \int_0^1 c_1^2 \cos^2 \pi x\, dx = 1 \quad \text{or} \quad c_1 = \sqrt{2}, \ldots,$$

and the required orthonormal system $\mathfrak{X}$ is

$$\mathfrak{X}\colon\ X_0 = 1, \qquad X_1 = \sqrt{2} \cos x, \qquad X_2 = \sqrt{2} \cos 2x, \ldots.$$

The corresponding functions $T_0, T_1, \ldots$ are

$$\begin{aligned} T_0(t) &= e^{\int_0^t \alpha_0 e^\tau d\tau} &&= e^{-(e^t - 1)} \\ T_1(t) &= e^{\int_0^t \alpha_1 e^\tau d\tau} &&= e^{-(1+\pi^2)(e^t - 1)} \\ T_2(t) &= e^{\int_0^t \alpha_2 e^\tau d\tau} &&= e^{-(1+4\pi^2)(e^t - 1)} \\ &\vdots && \vdots \end{aligned}$$

Now the Fourier $\mathfrak{X}$-expansion of the function $\varphi(x) = x$ is

$$\begin{aligned} &\int_0^1 x\, dx + \left(\sqrt{2} \int_0^1 x \cos \pi x\, dx\right) \sqrt{2} \cos \pi x \\ &\qquad + \left(\sqrt{2} \int_0^1 x \cos 2\pi x\, dx\right) \sqrt{2} \cos 2\pi x + \cdots \\ &\qquad = \frac{1}{2} - \frac{4}{\pi^2} \cos \pi x + 0 \cos 2\pi x + \cdots. \end{aligned}$$

Hence the Fourier expansion of the solution u is

$$T_0(t) - \frac{4}{\pi^2} T_1(t) \cos \pi x + 0T_2(t) \cos 2\pi x + \cdots$$

$$= \frac{1}{2} e^{-(e^t-1)} - \frac{4}{\pi^2} e^{-(1+\pi^2)(e^t-1)} \cos \pi x + \cdots.$$

We still have to deal with the equations in problems 1(g) and 1(j) of §2. We deal with 1(g) in the problems (see problem 9). As for 1(j), this equation is sufficiently different and important that we devote §4 to it.

PROBLEMS

For each of the following problems determine an appropriate orthonormal system $\mathfrak{X}$ in which the solution has a Fourier expansion and find the first two nonzero terms of the expansion.

1. $u_t = 2u_{xx}, \;\; u(x, 0) = x, \;\; u_x(0, t) = u(\pi, t) = 0.$

2. $u_t = 2u_{xx}, \;\; u(x, 0) = x, \;\; u_x(0, t) = u(2, t) = 0.$

3. $u_t = u_{xx} + 2u, \;\; u(x, 0) = 1, \;\; u_x(0, t) = u_x(1, t) = 0.$

4. $u_t = u_{xx},$
$u(x, 0) = \sin 2x \cos x + \cos 2x \sin x + \sin 3x \cos 2x + \cos 3x \sin 2x,$
$u(0, t) = u_x(\pi, t) = 0.$

5. $(1 + t^2)u_t = u_{xx}, \;\; u(x, 0) = x^2, \;\; u_x(0, t) = u(1, t) = 0.$

6. $u_t = -u_{xx} + u, \;\; u(x, 0) = 1, \;\; u(0, t) = u_x(2\pi, t) = 0.$

7. $3u_t = 2u_{xx} - u, \;\; u(x, 0) = x, \;\; u_x(0, t) = u(1, t) = 0.$

8. $u_t = (1 + e^t)u_{xx}, \;\; u(x, 0) = 1, \;\; u(0, t) = u(2, t) = 0.$

9. Solve the following problem which is related to problem 1(g) of §2:

$$u_t(x, t) = u_{xx}(x, t) + u_x(x, t),$$

$$u(x, 0) = \varphi(x), \qquad u(0, t) = 0, \qquad u(\pi, t) = 0.$$

[*Hint:* This differential equation does not have the form (3.2) because of the presence of the u_x term, but it can be reduced to that form by a change of variable. Substitute $u(x, t) = e^{ax}v(x, t)$ into the PDE and note that if a is chosen appropriately there results a PDE in v with no v_x term. The equation in v is now of the form (3.2). Moreover, the initial conditions and boundary conditions on u go over into initial conditions and boundary conditions on v. The PDE problem for v is now of our standard form. Once it is solved by our methods u can be recovered by the change of variable relating u and v.]

Reduce the following two problems to standard form (see problem 9) and obtain the first two nonzero terms of the expansion of their solutions.

10. $u_t = 2u_{xx} + 3u_x, \;\; u(x, 0) = e^{-3x/4}, \;\; u_x(0, t) = u_x(\pi, t) = 0.$

11. $u_t = u_{xx} - 3u_x + u,\ u(x, 0) = 1,\ u_x(0, t) = u(1, t) = 0.$

12. Prove proposition (3.10).

13. Prove the following result, which is a part of theorem (3.8).

Let α_1 and α_2 be two distinct values of α such that equations (3.6) and (3.7) have solutions. Let X_1 and X_2 be corresponding solutions. Then

$$\int_0^L X_1(x)X_2(x)\,dx = 0.$$

[*Hint:* Write down the differential equations satisfied by X_1 and X_2. Multiply the differential equation for X_1, by X_2, and the equation for X_2, by X_1. Subtract the two equations and integrate the result from 0 to L. Integrate by parts and make use of the fact that both X_1 and X_2 satisfy (3.7) to show that

$$(\alpha_1 - \alpha_2)\int_0^L X_1(x)X_2(x)\,dx = 0.$$

Since $\alpha_1 \neq \alpha_2$, the result follows.]

14. Prove the following proposition. If K and M in (3.6) are positive and if the constants a, b, c, d of equation (3.7′) satisfy the conditions

$$\frac{d}{c} < 0 \quad \text{and} \quad \frac{b}{a} > 0,$$

then the values of α for which (3.6) and (3.7′) have nonzero solutions X are all positive. [*Hint:* Suppose X is a nonzero solution. Multiply the equation (3.6) for X by $X(x)$ and integrate from 0 to L. Integrate one term by parts and use (3.7′) to show that

$$\frac{\alpha}{K}\int_0^L X^2(x)\,dx = \frac{M}{K}\int_0^L X^2(x)\,dx - \frac{d}{c}\,X(L)^2 + \frac{b}{a}\,X(0)^2.]$$

4. The Wave Equation

In this section we extend our methods to the study of what is called the *one-dimensional wave equation.* Again the equation involves a function u of two variables x and t. It has the form [see problem 1(j) of §2]

$$(4.1) \qquad u_{tt}(x, t) = c^2u_{xx}(x, t), \qquad c \text{ a constant.}$$

This equation occurs several places in physics. We mention one. Suppose a string is stretched under tension and fastened at two points A and B. Let x measure horizontal distance from A toward B and let t denote the time. Suppose the string is set in motion, say by bowing. Let $u(x, t)$ denote the vertical displacement of the string at position x, at time t (see Figure 7.3).

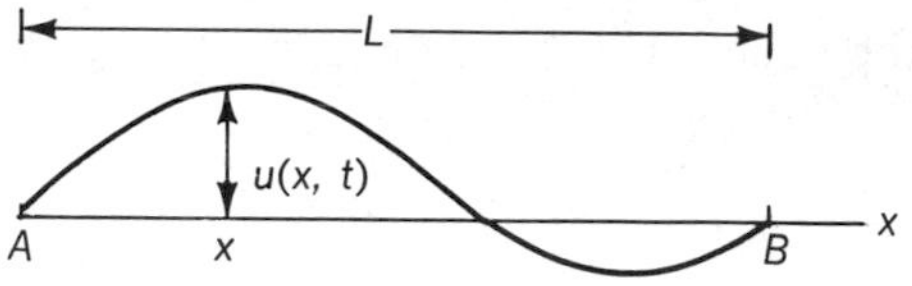

Figure 7.3

Then if the motions are small, one can show that u will satisfy (4.1) (approximately). Here $c^2 = T/\rho$, where T denotes the tension and ρ is the mass per unit length.

The physical problem discussed above involves not only equation (4.1) but boundary conditions as well. The fact that the string is fastened at A and B means that u must vanish at these points:

(4.2) $$u(0, t) = 0, \qquad u(L, t) = 0, \qquad 0 < t < \infty.$$

Note that the boundary conditions (4.2) are identical with those we first studied when analyzing the one-dimensional heat equation. For the heat equation we also had to give an initial condition of the form

(4.3) $$u(x, 0) = \varphi(x).$$

Shortly we shall use the method of separation of variables to tell us whether (4.3) provides appropriate initial data for the wave equation, but the reader should be able to anticipate the result on physical grounds. Is the motion of the string completely determined if we give its initial displacement? The answer is no.

Let us proceed to study solutions of (4.1) subject to (4.2). We use the methods of the previous sections. First we seek product solutions

(4.4) $$u(x, t) = T(t)X(x), \qquad 0 < x < L, \qquad 0 < t < \infty$$

of (4.1). If we substitute (4.4) into (4.1) and divide by TX we obtain

$$\frac{\ddot{T}(t)}{T(t)} = c^2 \frac{X''(x)}{X(x)}.$$

The reasoning of the earlier sections tells us that each side must be constant. Denoting the constant by α we get

(4.5) $$\frac{X''(x)}{X(x)} = \frac{\alpha}{c^2}$$

(4.6) $$\frac{\ddot{T}(t)}{T(t)} = \alpha.$$

Let us examine the equation for $X(x)$. In order that TX satisfy the edge condition we must have

$$X(0) = X(L) = 0.$$

As in §2, this requires that $\alpha/c^2 = -m^2\pi^2/L^2$ (m an integer). The desired solutions of (4.5) can accordingly be taken as the family

$$X_m(x) = \sin\frac{m\pi x}{L}, \qquad m = 1, 2, \ldots. \tag{4.7}$$

So far everything has gone just as for the heat equation. The difference between the wave equation and the heat equation shows up when we study (4.6). With α determined as above, this reduces to

$$\ddot{T}(t) = \frac{-m^2c^2\pi^2}{L^2}T(t), \qquad m = 1, 2, \ldots. \tag{4.6$'$}$$

The solutions of the constant coefficient ordinary equation (4.6′) are of the form:

$$T(t) = A\cos\frac{mc\pi t}{L} + B\sin\frac{mc\pi t}{L}, \qquad m = 1, 2, \ldots, \tag{4.8}$$

where A and B are constants. That is, we have *two* arbitrary constants available in each product solution TX, rather than one, as formerly. To say this another way, recall that we need two items to single out a solution of the second-order equation (4.6′). Not only must we give the value of T at some initial time, $t_0 = 0$, say, but also the value of $\dot{T}$. This observation affords the clue as to appropriate initial data for the wave equation; in addition to (4.3) we specify the initial value of u_t:

$$u_t(x, 0) = \psi(x), \qquad 0 < x < L. \tag{4.9}$$

Note that $u_t(x, 0)$ is the initial vertical velocity of the string in Figure 7.3. Thus the conditions on u are as indicated in Figure 7.4.

For each m we introduce two special solutions of (4.1). These correspond to choosing first B and then A equal to zero in (4.8). Thus we define u^m and v^m by the formulas

(4.10)

$$u^m(x, t) = \cos\frac{mc\pi t}{L}X_m(x) = \cos\frac{mc\pi t}{L}\sin\frac{m\pi x}{L}$$

$$v^m(x, t) = \frac{L}{mc\pi}\sin\frac{mc\pi t}{L}X_m(x) = \frac{L}{mc\pi}\sin\frac{mc\pi t}{L}\sin\frac{m\pi x}{L}, \quad m = 1, 2, \ldots.$$

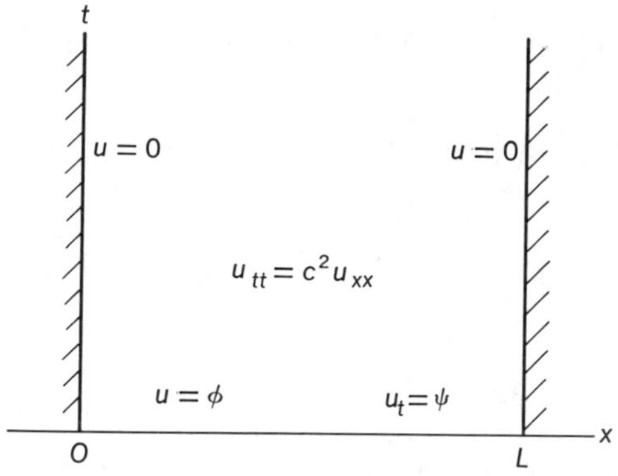

Figure 7.4

By construction both u^m and v^m satisfy (4.1) and (4.2). Moreover, we have

$$u^m(x, 0) = X_m(x), \qquad u_t^m(x, 0) = 0$$
$$v^m(x, 0) = 0, \qquad v_t^m(x, 0) = X_m(x).$$

To make use of these functions we need an analog of some earlier propositions for the heat equation. Observe that (4.1) is again an s-linear equation. Because of this one can prove the following result (see the problems).

(4.11) Proposition. *Suppose the functions* φ *and* ψ *in* (4.3) *and* (4.9) *have the form*

$$(*) \qquad \begin{aligned} \varphi(x) &= \alpha_1 X_1(x) + \alpha_2 X_2(x) + \cdots + \alpha_n X_n(x) \\ \psi(x) &= \beta_1 X_1(x) + \beta_2 X_2(x) + \cdots + \beta_n X_n(x). \end{aligned}$$

Then the function

$$u = \alpha_1 u^1 + \alpha_2 u^2 + \cdots + \alpha_n u^n + \beta_1 v^1 + \cdots + \beta_n v^n,$$

where the u^k's *and* v^k's *are given by* (4.10) *is a solution of the problem* (4.1), (4.2), (4.3), *and* (4.9).

According to this result we can obtain an *exact* solution whenever φ and ψ have the form (*). Once again, we can go further by noting that the X_m's are just the elements of the orthogonal system F_s: $f_1, f_2, \ldots$, where

$$f_1(x) = \sin \frac{\pi x}{L}, \qquad f_2(x) = \sin \frac{2\pi x}{L}, \ldots.$$

Hence any functions φ and ψ in $\mathcal{C}[0, L]$ have best n-approximators of the form

(4.12a)

$$\varphi_n(x) = \left(\frac{2}{L}\int_0^L \varphi(x)\sin\frac{\pi x}{L}\,dx\right)\sin\frac{\pi x}{L} + \cdots + \left(\frac{2}{L}\int_0^L \varphi(x)\sin\frac{n\pi x}{L}\,dx\right)\sin\frac{n\pi x}{L}$$

$$\psi_n(x) = \left(\frac{2}{L}\int_0^L \psi(x)\sin\frac{\pi x}{L}\,dx\right)\sin\frac{\pi x}{L} + \cdots + \left(\frac{2}{L}\int_0^L \psi(x)\sin\frac{n\pi x}{L}\,dx\right)\sin\frac{n\pi x}{L}.$$

If we replace φ and ψ in (4.3) and (4.9) by these approximators, then by proposition (4.11) we can obtain the corresponding solution U_n of (4.1), (4.2), (4.3), and (4.9):

(4.12b)

$$\begin{aligned} U_n(x, t) = {} & \left(\frac{2}{L}\int_0^L \varphi(x)\sin\frac{\pi x}{L}\,dx\right)u^1(x, t) + \cdots \\ & + \left(\frac{2}{L}\int_0^L \varphi(x)\sin\frac{n\pi x}{L}\,dx\right)u^n(x, t) \\ & + \left(\frac{2}{L}\int_0^L \psi(x)\sin\frac{\pi x}{L}\,dx\right)v^1(x, t) + \cdots \\ & + \left(\frac{2}{L}\int_0^L \psi(x)\sin\frac{\pi x}{L}\,dx\right)v^n(x, t). \end{aligned}$$

Once again it will be true that there is a unique solution $u(x, t)$ of problem (4.1), (4.2), (4.3), and (4.9) for all reasonable functions φ and ψ and that the functions U_n of (4.12) are its best n-approximators. Observe that we can rewrite (4.12b) as

(4.13)

$$\begin{aligned} U_n(x, t) = {} & \left\{\left(\frac{2}{L}\int_0^L \varphi(x)\sin\frac{\pi x}{L}\,dx\right)\cos\frac{\pi ct}{L} \right. \\ & \left. + \left(\frac{2}{L}\int_0^L \psi(x)\sin\frac{\pi x}{L}\,dx\right)\frac{L}{c\pi}\sin\frac{\pi ct}{L}\right\}\sin\frac{\pi x}{L} + \cdots \\ & + \left\{\left(\frac{2}{L}\int_0^L \varphi(x)\sin\frac{n\pi x}{L}\,dx\right)\cos\frac{n\pi ct}{L} \right. \\ & \left. + \left(\frac{2}{L}\int_0^L \psi(x)\sin\frac{\pi x}{L}\,dx\right)\frac{L}{nc\pi}\sin\frac{n\pi ct}{L}\right\}\sin\frac{n\pi x}{L}. \end{aligned}$$

In this form we can see that the Fourier expansion of the actual solution is obtained according to the following rule.

(4.14) Rule. *Let the Fourier expansions of the initial functions* φ *and* ψ *of* (4.3) *and* (4.9) *be of the form*

$$\varphi \sim \alpha_1 \sin \frac{\pi x}{L} + \alpha_2 \sin \frac{2\pi x}{L} + \cdots$$

$$\psi \sim \beta_1 \sin \frac{\pi x}{L} + \beta_2 \sin \frac{2\pi x}{L} + \cdots.$$

Then the Fourier expansion of the solution for each fixed t is

$$u \sim \left(\alpha_1 \cos \frac{\pi ct}{L} + \beta_1 \frac{L}{\pi c} \sin \frac{\pi ct}{L}\right) \sin \frac{\pi x}{L} + \left(\alpha_2 \cos \frac{2\pi ct}{L} + \beta_2 \frac{L}{2\pi c} \sin \frac{2\pi ct}{L}\right) \sin \frac{2\pi x}{L} + \cdots.$$

(4.15) Examples

(a) Find a solution of the problem

$$u_{tt} = 4u_{xx}, \qquad u(x, 0) = \sin \pi x - \sin 3\pi x, \qquad u_t(x, 0) = 2 \sin 2\pi x,$$
$$u(0, t) = u(1, t) = 0.$$

Here $c = 2$ and $L = 1$; hence the functions X_m are $\sin m\pi x$. We have

$$\varphi(x) = \sin \pi x - \sin 3\pi x = X_1(x) - X_3(x)$$
$$\psi(x) = 2 \sin 2\pi x = 2X_2(x).$$

By proposition (4.11) we can find an exact solution. It is

$$u(x, t) = 1 \cdot u^1(x, t) - 1 \cdot u^3(x, t) + 2v^2(x, t)$$
$$= \cos 2\pi t \sin \pi x - \cos 6\pi t \sin 3\pi x + \frac{2}{4\pi} \cos 4\pi t \sin 2\pi x.$$

(b) Find a solution of the problem

$$u_{tt} = 4u_{xx}, \qquad u(x, 0) = 1, \qquad u_t(x, 0) = x, \qquad u(0, t) = u(1, t) = 0.$$

Here the functions X_m, u^m, and v^m are the same as in example (a). However, $\varphi(x) = 1$ and $\psi(x) = x$. Neither of these is a finite linear combination of the X_m's; hence in this case we cannot find the solution explicitly. Rather we find the Fourier expansion of the solution using rule (4.14). The expansions of φ and ψ are given by (4.12a) as

$$\begin{aligned}\varphi &\sim \left(2\int_0^1 \sin \pi x\, dx\right) \sin \pi x + \left(2\int_0^1 \sin 2\pi x\, dx\right) \sin 2\pi x + \cdots \\ &= \frac{4}{\pi} \sin \pi x + 0 \cdot \sin 2\pi x + \cdots \\ \psi &\sim \left(2\int_0^1 x \sin \pi x\, dx\right) \sin \pi x + \left(2\int_0^1 x \sin 2\pi x\, dx\right) \sin 2\pi x + \cdots \\ &= \frac{2}{\pi} \sin \pi x - \frac{1}{\pi} \sin 2\pi x + \cdots .\end{aligned}$$

Hence the expansion of the solution is

$$u \sim \left(\frac{4}{\pi} \cos 2\pi t + \frac{2}{2\pi^2} \sin 2\pi t\right) \sin \pi x - \left(\frac{1}{4\pi^2} \sin 4\pi t\right) \sin 2\pi x + \cdots .$$

It should be fairly clear that the method can be extended to other boundary conditions and to variations of equation (4.1). These notions are to be carried out in the problems.

PROBLEMS

1. Find all product solutions of the following problems.

(a) $u_{tt} = 2u_{xx}, \quad u(0, t) = u(\pi, t) = 0$

(b) $u_{tt} = u_{xx}, \quad u(0, t) = u(2\pi, t) = 0$

(c) $u_{tt} = u_{xx}, \quad u_x(0, t) = u_x(\pi, t) = 0$

(d) $u_{tt} = 9u_{xx}, \quad u_x(0, t) = u_x(1, t) = 0$

(e) $u_{tt} = u_{xx}, \quad u(0, t) = u_x(\pi, t) = 0$

(f) $u_{tt} = u_{xx} + u, \quad u(0, t) = u(\pi, t) = 0$

(g) $u_{tt} = u_{xx} - u, \quad u_x(0, t) = u(2, t) = 0$

*(h) $u_{tt} = u_{xx} + u_x, \quad u(0, t) = u(\pi, t) = 0$

2. Find exact solutions of the following problems.

(a) $u_{tt} = 2u_{xx}, \quad u(0, t) = u(2, t) = 0,$

$u(x, 0) = -\sin \frac{\pi}{2} x + 2 \sin \pi x,$

$u_t(x, 0) = 4 \sin \pi x - 3 \sin 2\pi x$

(b) $u_{tt} = u_{xx}$, $u_x(0, t) = u_x(1, t) = 0$,
$u(x, 0) = 2 \cos 2\pi x - \cos 3\pi x$,
$u_t(x, 0) = \cos \pi x$

(c) $u_{tt} = 2u_{xx} + u$, $u(0, t) = u(\pi, t) = 0$,
$u(x, 0) = \sin x - \sin 3x$,
$u_t(x, 0) = 0$

(d) $u_{tt} = u_{xx} + 2u$, $u_x(0, t) = u(1, t) = 0$,
$u(x, 0) = 0$,
$u_t(x, 0) = -\cos \frac{\pi}{2} x - 3 \cos \frac{3\pi}{2} x$

(e) $u_{tt} = 4u_{xx} - u$, $u_x(0, t) = u(2, t) = 0$,
$u(x, 0) = \cos \frac{3\pi}{4} x$,
$u_t(x, 0) = \cos \frac{\pi}{4} x - 2 \cos \frac{3\pi x}{4}$

3. In each of the following determine the first two nonzero terms in the appropriate Fourier expansion of the solution.

(a) $u_{tt} = u_{xx}$, $u(0, t) = u(\pi, t) = 0$,
$u(x, 0) = x$,
$u_t(x, 0) = 1$

(b) $u_{tt} = 4u_{xx}$, $u_x(0, t) = u_x(1, t) = 0$,
$u(x, 0) = 0$,
$u_t(x, 0) = 2x$

(c) $u_{tt} = u_{xx} + u$, $u(0, t) = u_x(\pi, t) = 0$,
$u(x, 0) = 1$,
$u_t(x, 0) = 1$

(d) $u_{tt} = 9u_{xx} - u$, $u_x(0, t) = u(2, t) = 0$,
$u(x, 0) = x$,
$u_t(x, 0) = x$

*(e) $u_{tt} = 4u_{xx} + u_x$, $u(0, t) = u(\pi, t) = 0$,
$u(0, t) = 1$,
$u_t(0, t) = 0$

4. Prove proposition (4.11).

5. Establish the following result: Suppose one wants a solution of the problem $u_{tt} = u_{xx}$, $u(0, t) = u(L, t) = 0$, $u(x, 0) = \varphi(x)$, $u_t(x, 0) = 0$. Let $v(x, t)$ be a solution of the problem $v_{tt} = v_{xx}$, $v(0, t) = v(L, t) = 0$, $v(x, 0) = 0$, $v_t(x, 0) = \varphi(x)$. Then one obtains a solution of the first problem by means of the formula

$$u(x, t) = v_t(x, t).$$

5. Nonhomogeneous Equations

All the partial differential equations studied so far in this chapter are what are called "linear homogeneous" equations. This refers to the fact that each of them can be written in the form

$$Lu = 0, \tag{5.1}$$

where Lu is a certain linear combination of u and some of its partial derivatives. "Nonhomogeneous" linear partial differential equations are ones which have the form

$$Lu = g, \tag{5.2}$$

where $g(x, t) \not\equiv 0$ is a prescribed function.

In the present section we are going to illustrate the treatment of nonhomogeneous equations by studying the particular example

$$u_t(x, t) = Ku_{xx}(x, t) + g(x, t). \tag{5.3}$$

This is called the *nonhomogeneous one-dimensional heat equation.* We will search for solutions of (5.3) satisfying the same edge and initial conditions as were prescribed in §1 for the one-dimensional heat equation (1.1). That is,

$$u(0, t) = 0, \qquad u(L, t) = 0 \tag{5.4}$$

$$u(x, 0) = \varphi(x). \tag{5.5}$$

This problem is illustrated in Figure 7.5.

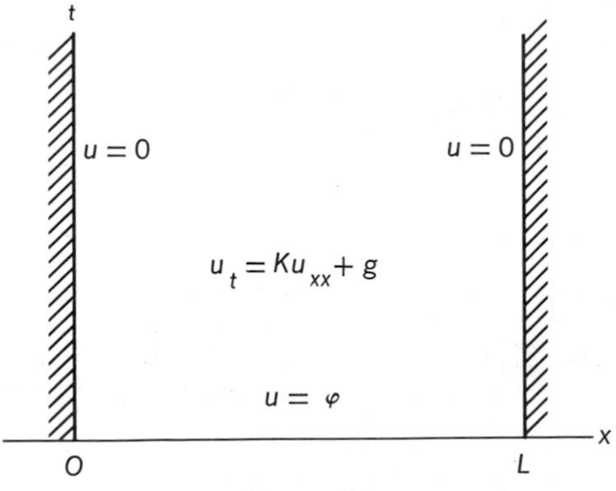

Figure 7.5

Once again we want to exploit notions from Fourier series to reduce the problem above to the solution of several simpler problems. Also as before, the particular orthonormal set

$$E_s\colon\ e_1(x) = \sqrt{\frac{2}{L}}\sin\frac{\pi x}{L},\ e_2(x) = \sqrt{\frac{2}{L}}\sin\frac{2\pi x}{L},\dots$$

is going to play a central role, the reason being that all these e's satisfy the edge conditions (5.4). Our first step is to obtain the Fourier E_s-series for the function g, as a function of x, for each t. This has the form

(5.6) $$g \sim g^1(t)e_1 + g^2(t)e_2 + \cdots,$$

where

(5.7)
$$g^m(t) = \int_0^L g(x, t)e_m(x)\,dx = \sqrt{\frac{2}{L}}\int_0^L g(x, t)\sin\frac{m\pi x}{L}\,dx, \quad m = 1, 2, \dots.$$

Note that the g^m's actually are functions of t since for different t values the integrands, $g(x, t)\sin(m\pi x/L)$, are different functions of x.

The second step is to find the Fourier E_s-series for φ. This is,

(5.8) $$\varphi \sim \alpha_1 e_1 + \alpha_2 e_2 + \cdots,$$

where

(5.9)
$$\alpha_m = \int_0^L \varphi(x)e_m(x)\,dx = \sqrt{\frac{2}{L}}\int_0^L \varphi(x)\sin\frac{m\pi x}{L}\,dx, \qquad m = 1, 2, \dots.$$

Now the idea is to find functions $\hat{u}^m(x, t)$† which satisfy (5.3), (5.4), and (5.5) with the following *simplified* φ and g choices:

(5.3′) $$\hat{u}^m_t(x, t) = K\hat{u}^m_{xx}(x, t) + g^m(t)e_m(x)$$

(5.4′) $$\hat{u}^m(0, t) = 0, \qquad \hat{u}^m(L, t) = 0$$

(5.5′) $$\hat{u}^m(x, 0) = \alpha_m e_m(x), \qquad m = 1, 2, \dots.$$

†When $g^m(t) = 0$ the function $\hat{u}^m$ is just the function $\alpha_m u^m$, where the u^m's are defined as in equation (1.7).

This is not too difficult to do. In fact, we can find these solutions in the form of products:

$$\hat{u}^m(x, t) = b_m(t)e_m(x) = \sqrt{\frac{2}{L}}\, b_m(t) \sin \frac{m\pi x}{L}. \tag{5.10}$$

Note first that these functions surely satisfy (5.4′), no matter what choice is made for $b_m(t)$, since $e_m(0) = e_m(L) = 0$. Also we have for these functions the initial values $\hat{u}^m(x, 0) = b_m(0)e_m(x)$, so that (5.5′) will be satisfied if we require

$$b_m(0) = \alpha_m, \qquad m = 1, 2, \ldots. \tag{5.11}$$

It remains only to choose $b_m(t)$, so that (5.3′) is satisfied. We have, by (5.10),

$$\hat{u}_t^m = \dot{b}_m(t)e_m(x), \qquad \hat{u}_{xx}^m = b_m(t)e_m''(x) = -\frac{m^2\pi^2}{L^2}\, b_m(t)e_m(x).$$

It follows by substitution in (5.3)′ that the functions $\hat{u}^m(x, t)$ will satisfy (5.3′) only if

$$\dot{b}_m(t) = -m^2\beta^2 b_m(t) + g^m(t), \qquad \beta^2 = \frac{K\pi^2}{L^2}. \tag{5.12}$$

Now (5.12) is a first-order ordinary differential equation of a type we learned how to solve in Chapter 4. In fact, the solution of (5.12), subject to (5.11), is

$$b_m(t) = e^{-m^2\beta^2 t}\int_0^t e^{m^2\beta^2 s} g^m(s)\, ds + \alpha_m e^{-m^2\beta^2 t}, \qquad m = 1, 2, \ldots. \tag{5.13}$$

Hence we have obtained solutions of (5.3′), (5.4′), and (5.5′) for each $m = 1, 2, \ldots$.

Now we are in the same position as we were in earlier sections of this chapter. We can solve (5.3), (5.4), and (5.5) *exactly* with g and φ taken to be finite sums of e's. In particular, we can solve (5.3), (5.4), and (5.5) when these functions are best n-approximators to a prescribed g and φ:

$$\begin{aligned} g_n(x, t) &= g^1(t)e_1(x) + \cdots + g^n(t)e_n(x) \\ \varphi_n(x) &= \alpha_1 e_1(x) + \cdots + \alpha_n e_n(x). \end{aligned} \tag{5.14}$$

The solutions, $U_n(x, t)$, obtained for these choices of g and φ, are simply the sums of the first n of the $\hat{u}^m$'s. That is,

$$U_n(x, t) = \hat{u}^1(x, t) + \hat{u}^2(x, t) + \cdots + \hat{u}^n(x, t). \tag{5.15}$$

We note that the functions U_n in (5.15) all have the form

$$U_n(x, t) = b_1(t)e_1(x) + \cdots + b_n(t)e_n(x), \qquad n = 1, 2, \ldots,$$

where, by (5.13),

$$b_m(t) = e^{-m^2\beta^2 t}\int_0^t e^{m^2\beta^2 s} g^m(s)\,ds + \alpha_m e^{-m^2\beta^2 t}, \qquad m = 1, 2, \ldots.$$

Once again, the coefficient of $e_i(x)$ in $U_n(x, t)$ is the same for each $n \geq i$, and this suggests that the $U_n(x, t)$, for each fixed t, are the best n-approximators of some function $u(x, t)$. This plausible statement is actually true for wide classes of functions φ and g and, in fact, $u(x, t)$ is the (unique) solution of (5.3), (5.4), and (5.5).

(5.16) Example. We seek the solution of the problem

$$u_t = u_{xx} + g, \qquad u(x, 0) = \varphi(x), \qquad u(0, t) = u(\pi, t) = 0,$$

where

$$g(x, t) = xt - t^2$$

$$\varphi(x) = \begin{cases} x & \text{for } 0 \leq x \leq \frac{\pi}{2} \\ \pi - x & \text{for } \frac{\pi}{2} \leq x \leq \pi. \end{cases}$$

Here $K = 1$ and $L = \pi$. We begin by finding the Fourier series for the function g. Equations (5.6) and (5.7) yield

$$g \sim \left(\sqrt{\frac{2}{\pi}}\int_0^\pi (xt - t^2)\sin x\,dx\right)\sqrt{\frac{2}{\pi}}\sin x$$
$$+ \left(\sqrt{\frac{2}{\pi}}\int_0^\pi (xt - t^2)\sin 2x\,dx\right)\sqrt{\frac{2}{\pi}}\sin 2x + \cdots.$$

We have

$$\int_0^\pi (xt - t^2)\sin x\,dx = \pi t - 2t^2,$$

$$\int_0^\pi (xt - t^2)\sin 2x\,dx = -\frac{\pi t}{2}, \ldots.$$

Hence

$$\text{(i)} \qquad xt - t^2 \sim \frac{2}{\pi}(\pi t - 2t^2)\sin x - t\sin 2x + \cdots.$$

Next we calculate the Fourier series for φ, that is,

$$\varphi \sim \left(\sqrt{\frac{2}{\pi}}\int_0^\pi \varphi(x)\sin x\,dx\right)\sqrt{\frac{2}{\pi}}\sin x + \left(\sqrt{\frac{2}{\pi}}\int_0^\pi \varphi(x)\sin 2x\,dx\right)\sqrt{\frac{2}{\pi}}\sin 2x + \cdots.$$

We have

$$\int_0^\pi \varphi(x)\sin x\,dx = \int_0^{\pi/2} x\sin x\,dx + \int_{\pi/2}^\pi (\pi - x)\sin x\,dx = 2$$

$$\int_0^\pi \varphi(x)\sin 2x\,dx = \int_0^{\pi/2} x\sin 2x\,dx + \int_{\pi/2}^\pi (\pi - x)\sin 2x\,dx = 0$$

and hence

$$\text{(ii)} \qquad \varphi \sim \frac{4}{\pi}\sin x + 0\cdot\sin 2x + \cdots.$$

We can now calculate the first two of the functions $\hat{u}^m$. We have $\hat{u}^1(x, t) = \sqrt{2/\pi}\, b_1(t)\sin x$ and by (i) and (ii) we have

$$g^1(t) = \sqrt{\frac{2}{\pi}}(\pi t - 2t^2) \qquad \text{and} \qquad \alpha_1 = 2\sqrt{\frac{2}{\pi}}\cdot$$

Hence, by (5.11) and (5.12), b_1 is a solution of the problem

$$\dot{b}_1(t) = -b_1(t) + \sqrt{\frac{2}{\pi}}(\pi t - 2t^2), \qquad b_1(0) = 2\sqrt{\frac{2}{\pi}}\cdot$$

The reader can verify that the solution of this problem is

$$\text{(iii)} \qquad b_1(t) = \sqrt{\frac{2}{\pi}}\{-2t^2 + (\pi + 4)(t - 1) + (\pi + 6)e^{-t}\}.$$

We also have $g^2(t) = -\sqrt{(\pi/2)}\,t, \quad \alpha_2 = 0$. Hence

$$\hat{u}^2(x, t) = \sqrt{\frac{2}{\pi}}\, b_2(t)\sin 2x,$$

where

$$\dot{b}_2(t) = -4b_2(t) - \sqrt{\frac{\pi}{2}}\,t, \qquad b_2(0) = 0.$$

The solution of this problem is

$$b_2(t) = -\frac{1}{4}\sqrt{\frac{\pi}{2}}\,t + \frac{1}{16}\sqrt{\frac{\pi}{2}}\,(1 - e^{-4t}).$$

Thus we have determined the first two terms in the Fourier expansion of the solution.

It should be fairly clear that the method of this section can be extended to other nonhomogeneous equations and other boundary conditions. Some examples are given in the problems.

As a final topic, we wish to point out that one can now replace the edge conditions (5.4) by nonhomogeneous ones. For instance, suppose we want to find a solution of (1.1), (1.2) satisfying not (1.3) but instead

$$(5.17) \qquad u(0, t) = k(t), \qquad u(\pi, t) = m(t), \qquad 0 < t < \infty,$$

where $k(t)$, $m(t)$ are prescribed functions. Define a function $u^0(x, t)$ as follows:

$$(5.18) \qquad u^0(x, t) = k(t) + \big(m(t) - k(t)\big)\frac{x}{\pi}, \qquad 0 < x < \pi,\ 0 < t < \infty.$$

Then u^0 is generally *not* a solution of (1.1), but it does satisfy the edge conditions (5.17):

$$u^0(0, t) = k(t), \qquad u^0(\pi, t) = m(t), \qquad 0 < t < \infty.$$

Therefore, if u denotes a solution of (1.1), (1.2), and (5.17), then the difference

$$v = u - u^0$$

satisfies the following conditions:

$$(5.19) \qquad \begin{aligned} v_t - k^2 v_{xx} &= (u_t - k^2 u_{xx}) - (u_t^0 - k^2 u_{xx}^0) \\ &= 0 - \Big(\dot{k}(t) + \big(\dot{m}(t) - \dot{k}(t)\big)\frac{x}{\pi} - 0\Big) = \tilde{g}(x, t) \end{aligned}$$

$$(5.20) \qquad \begin{aligned} v(0, t) &= u(0, t) - u^0(0, t) = k(t) - k(t) = 0 \\ v(\pi, t) &= u(\pi, t) - u^0(\pi, t) = m(t) - m(t) = 0 \end{aligned}$$

$$(5.21) \qquad \begin{aligned} v(x, 0) = u(x, 0) - u^0(x, 0) &= \varphi(x) - \Big(k(0) + \big(m(0) - k(0)\big)\frac{x}{\pi}\Big) \\ &= \tilde{\varphi}(x). \end{aligned}$$

Thus v is a solution of (5.3), (5.4), and (5.5) with the indicated functions $\tilde{g}$ and $\tilde{\varphi}$.

The point of this remark is that since we can solve the problem (5.3)–(5.5) we will also be able to solve (1.1) and (1.2) with edge conditions (5.17). For to solve the latter problem we merely solve (5.3)–(5.5) with

$$g(x, t) = \tilde{g}(x, t), \qquad \varphi(x) = \tilde{\varphi}(x)$$

taken as in (5.19) and (5.21), and then add $u^0(x, t)$ to the result. That is,

$$u(x, t) = v(x, t) + u^0(x, t).$$

A completely analogous procedure permits us to handle the problem (5.3), (5.5), and (5.17) by determining the solution of (5.3)–(5.5) and adding the result to u^0. Thus we could treat the problem indicated in Figure 7.6.

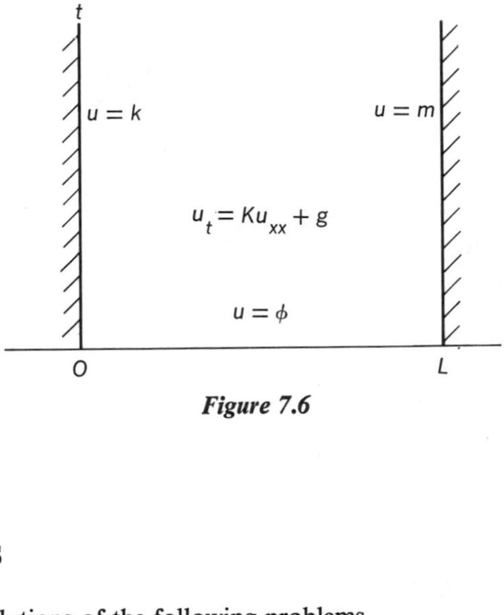

Figure 7.6

PROBLEMS

1. Find *exact* solutions of the following problems.

   (a) $u_t = u_{xx} + 2t \sin 2x, \quad u(0, t) = u(\pi, t) = 0, \quad u(x, 0) = \sin x - 3 \sin 3x$

   (b) $u_t = 2u_{xx} + \sin x, \quad u(0, t) = u(2\pi, t) = 0, \quad u(x, 0) = 2 \sin \frac{1}{2}x$

   (c) $u_t = u_{xx} + 2t \cos 2x, \quad u_x(0, t) = u_x(\pi, t) = 0,$
   $u(x, 0) = \cos x - 3 \cos 3x$

   (d) $u_t = u_{xx} - u + \sin 2\pi x, \quad u(0, t) = u(1, t) = 0, \quad u(x, 0) = 3 \sin \pi x$

   (e) $u_t = u_{xx} + \sin \frac{3}{2}x, \quad u(0, t) = u_x(\pi, t) = 0, \quad u(x, 0) = \sin \frac{1}{2}x$

   (f) $u_{tt} = u_{xx} + \sin x, \quad u(0, t) = u(\pi, t) = 0,$
   $u(x, 0) = \sin 2x, \quad u_t(x, 0) = 2 \sin x$

2. For each of the following problems find the first two nonzero terms in the appropriate Fourier expansion of the solution.

(a) $u_t = u_{xx} + 1, \quad u(0, t) = u(\pi, t) = 0, \quad u(x, 0) = 1$

(b) $u_t = 4u_{xx} + t, \quad u(0, t) = u(1, t) = 0, \quad u(x, 0) = 1 - x$

(c) $u_t = u_{xx} + t, \quad u_x(0, t) = u_x(\pi, t) = 0, \quad u(x, 0) = x$

(d) $u_t = u_{xx} - u + t, \quad u_x(0, t) = u(\pi, t) = 0, \quad u(x, 0) = 1$

(e) $u_{tt} = u_{xx} + e^t, \quad u(0, t) = u(1, t) = 0, \quad u(x, 0) = x$

(f) $u_{tt} = 2u_{xx} + u + 1, \quad u(0, t) = u_x(2, t) = 0, \quad u(x, 0) = x$

3. Reduce each of the following problems to one with homogeneous boundary conditions.

(a) $u_t = u_{xx} + 2x, \quad u(0, t) = t, u(1, t) = 0, \quad u(x, 0) = x$

(b) $u_t = u_{xx}, \quad u_x(0, t) = t, \quad u_x(\pi, t) = 1, \quad u(x, 0) = 0$

(c) $u_{tt} = u_{xx}, \quad u(0, t) = u_x(\pi, t) = t, \quad u(x, 0) = 0, \quad u_t(x, 0) = 1$

6. Uniqueness Theorems

In the preceding sections we have found expansions approximating solutions to certain problems. We tacitly assumed in our analysis that each of the problems really had a solution and in fact that it had exactly one. It is quite difficult to prove *existence* for any of those problems, but the question of uniqueness can be resolved rather easily in a number of cases. We discuss this in the present section.

The techniques we use are related to those in Chapter 4. They exploit the fact that we are dealing with s-linear equations. The basic idea is the same in all problems. We suppose that u^1 and u^2 are solutions of the problem in question. Then we form $u = u^1 - u^2$ and look at the problem that u solves. This will turn out to be a problem involving a homogeneous equation with boundary conditions and initial conditions which are identically zero. From this we will be able to conclude that $u(x, t) \equiv 0$, that is, that u^1 and u^2 are identical. Let us give some examples. We will need the following result from calculus:

(6.1) Proposition. *Suppose f has a continuous partial derivative with respect to t for $0 \le x \le L$ and $a < t < b$. Then the function I defined by*

$$I(t) = \int_0^L f(x, t)\, dx$$

is a differentiable function of t in $a < t < b$ and

$$\dot{I}(t) = \int_0^L f_t(x, t)\, dx.$$

(6.2) Examples

(a) Show that there is at most one solution of the problem

$$u_t = u_{xx}, \qquad u(x, 0) = \varphi(x), \qquad u(0, t) = u(L, t) = 0.$$

Suppose u^1 and u^2 are solutions and set $u = u^1 - u^2$. Since the equation is s-linear u also satisfies that equation. Moreover, u vanishes at $x = 0$ and $x = L$ and finally

$$u(x, 0) = u^1(x, 0) - u^2(x, 0) = \varphi(x) - \varphi(x) = 0.$$

Thus u is a solution of the problem

$$\text{(i)} \qquad u_t = u_{xx}, \qquad u(x, 0) = 0, \qquad u(0, t) = u(L, t) = 0.$$

We show now that a solution of problem (i) must be zero. For this we use a trick. Multiply the equation by u and integrate with respect to x from 0 to L. We have

$$\int_0^L u(x, t)u_t(x, t)\, dx = \int_0^L u(x, t)u_{xx}(x, t)\, dx.$$

Now integrate the right side by parts, leaving the left side unchanged:

$$\int_0^L u(x, t)u_t(x, t)\, dx = u(x, t)u_x(x, t)\Big|_0^L - \int_0^L u_x(x, t)^2\, dx$$

$$= u(L, t)u_x(L, t) - u(0, t)u_x(0, t) - \int_0^L u_x(x, t)^2\, dx.$$

Since $u(0, t) = u(L, t) = 0$, the first two terms on the right side are zero; hence

$$\text{(ii)} \qquad \int_0^L u(x, t)u_t(x, t)\, dx = -\int_0^L u_x(x, t)^2\, dx \leq 0.$$

Observe that

$$\frac{1}{2}\frac{\partial}{\partial t}(u(x, t))^2 = u(x, t)u_t(x, t).$$

Hence by proposition (6.1) the left side of (ii) is

$$\int_0^L \frac{1}{2}\frac{\partial}{\partial t}(u(x, t))^2\,dx = \dot{I}(t),$$

where

$$\text{(iii)} \qquad I(t) = \tfrac{1}{2}\int_0^L u(x, t)^2\,dx.$$

Since $u(x, 0) = 0$ we have $I(0) = 0$. By (ii) we have

$$\dot{I}(t) \leq 0.$$

But by (iii) $I(t)$ is necessarily nonnegative, since the integrand $u(x, t)^2$ can never be negative. But then what kind of function can $I(t)$ be? It is zero at $t = 0$, can never be negative, and, since its derivative is ≤ 0, it can never increase. Hence it must be identically zero. Thus for *all* t, $0 \leq t < \infty$,

$$\text{(iv)} \qquad \int_0^L u(x, t)^2\,dx = 0.$$

Since $u^2(x, t) \geq 0$, (iv) requires that $u(x, t)$ must be identically zero. This completes the proof of uniqueness.

(b) Show that there is at most one solution of the problem,

$$u_t = u_{xx} + g(x, t), \qquad u(x, 0) = \varphi(x), \qquad u(0, t) = u(L, t) = 0.$$

Again let u^1 and u^2 be solutions and form $u = u^1 - u^2$. We have $u_t^1(x, t) = u_{xx}^1(x, t) + g(x, t)$ and $u_t^2(x, t) = u_{xx}^2(x, t) + g(x, t)$. If we subtract, the functions g cancel and we find

$$\text{(i)} \qquad u_t(x, t) = u_{xx}(x, t).$$

Thus we make the important observation that although the equations for u^1 and u^2 are each nonhomogeneous, their difference satisfies a homogeneous equation. We have, as in example (a),

$$\text{(ii)} \qquad u(0, t) = u(L, t) = 0, \qquad u(x, 0) = \varphi(x) - \varphi(x) = 0.$$

Equations (i) and (ii) show that u is again a solution of problem (i) of example (a); hence u is zero or $u^1 = u^2$.

(c) Show that there is at most one solution of the problem

$$u_{tt} = u_{xx}, \qquad u(x, 0) = \varphi(x), \qquad u_t(x, 0) = \psi(x),$$
$$u(0, t) = u(L, t) = 0.$$

Let u^1 and u^2 be solutions. Then their difference $u = u^1 - u^2$ is a solution of the problem

$$\text{(i)} \qquad u_{tt} = u_{xx}, \qquad u(x, 0) = 0, \qquad u_t(x, 0) = 0,$$
$$u(0, t) = u(L, t) = 0.$$

Again we show that such a function must be zero for *all* t. This time we multiply the equation by u_t and integrate from 0 to L. We find

$$\text{(ii)} \qquad \int_0^L u_t(x, t)u_{tt}(x, t)\,dx = \int_0^L u_t(x, t)u_{xx}(x, t)\,dx$$
$$= u_t(L, t)u_x(L, t) - u_t(0, t)u_x(0, t)$$
$$- \int_0^L u_{xt}(x, t)u_x(x, t)\,dx$$

(after we integrate by parts). Once again the first two terms on the right vanish. For if we differentiate, with respect to t, the relations $u(0, t) = 0$, $u(L, t) = 0$, $0 < t < \infty$, then we deduce that $u_t(0, t) = 0$ and $u_t(L, t) = 0$. Now we can apply proposition (6.1) to each of the remaining terms. We have

$$\frac{1}{2}\frac{\partial}{\partial t}\left(u_t^2(x, t)\right) = u_t(x, t)u_{tt}(x, t)$$

$$\frac{1}{2}\frac{\partial}{\partial t}\left(u_x^2(x, t)\right) = u_x(x, t)u_{xt}(x, t).$$

Hence

$$\int_0^L u_{tt}(x, t)u_t(x, t)\,dx = \dot{I}_1(t)$$

$$\int_0^L u_x(x, t)u_{xt}(x, t)\,dx = \dot{I}_2(t),$$

where

$$\text{(iii)} \qquad I_1(t) = \tfrac{1}{2}\int_0^L u_t(x, t)^2\,dx, \qquad I_2(t) = \tfrac{1}{2}\int_0^L u_x(x, t)^2\,dx.$$

Thus we can write (ii) in the form

$$\text{(iv)} \qquad \dot{I}_1(t) + \dot{I}_2(t) = 0 \qquad \text{or} \qquad I_1(t) + I_2(t) = c \text{ (a constant).}$$

The constant c must be zero, since

$$I_1(0) = \int_0^L u_t(x, 0)^2\,dx = 0 \qquad \text{and} \qquad I_2(0) = \int_0^L u_x(x, 0)^2\,dx = 0$$

[$u(x, 0) = 0$ implies $u_x(x, 0) = 0$].

Note that both I_1 and I_2 are nonnegative. Their sum is now known to be zero, hence *each* is zero; that is,

$$\int_0^L u_t(x, t)^2\,dx = \int_0^L u_x(x, t)^2\,dx = 0.$$

As before, we deduce that $u_t(x, t) \equiv 0$ and $u_x(x, t) \equiv 0$, which means that u is a constant. However, we know that u is zero when $t = 0$; hence $u(x, t) \equiv 0$ or $u^1(x, t) = u^2(x, t)$.

The procedures discussed in these two examples can be extended to situations involving other boundary conditions and other equations. We present some of these in the problems.

PROBLEMS

1. Show that there exists at most one solution of each of the following problems. [In each case let u be the difference of two solutions, multiply the equation by u, and integrate from 0 to L. Use integration by parts and the boundary conditions to show that the quantity

$$I(t) = \int_0^L u(x, t)^2\,dx$$

has nonnegative derivative. Show that $I(0) = 0$; hence deduce that $u = 0$.]

(a) $u_t = u_{xx} + xt,\quad u(x, 0) = x,\quad u_x(0, t) = u_x(L, t) = 0$

(b) $u_t = u_{xx} + xt,\quad u(x, 0) = 1,\quad u(0, t) = u_x(L, t) = 0$

(c) $u_t = 4u_{xx},\quad u(x, 0) = x,\quad u_x(0, t) = u(L, t) = 0$

(d) $u_t = u_{xx} - u,\quad u(x, 0) = x,\quad u(0, t) = u(L, t) = 0$

(e) $u_t = e^t u_{xx} - e^{2t}u,\quad u(x, 0) = 1,\quad u(0, t) = u(L, t) = 0$

(f) $u_t = u_{xx} + u_x,\quad u(x, 0) = 1,\quad u(0, t) = u(L, t) = 0$

2. Show that the method of proof in problem 1 does not work here:

$$u_t = u_{xx} + au, \quad a > 0, \qquad u(x, 0) = \psi(x), \qquad u(0, t) = u(L, t) = 0.$$

3. Show that there exists at most one solution of the following problem:

$$u_t = u_{xx}, \qquad u(x, 0) = 0, \qquad u(0, t) = t^2, \qquad u(L, t) = e^t.$$

4. Show there exists at most one solution of each of the following problems. Use the proof in example (6.2c) as a model.

(a) $u_{tt} = u_{xx}, \quad u(x, 0) = 1, u_t(x, 0) = 0, \quad u_x(0, t) = u_x(L, t) = 0$

(b) $u_{tt} = u_{xx}, \quad u(x, 0) = x, u_t(x, 0) = 1, \quad u(0, t) = u(L, t) = 0$

(c) $u_{tt} = u_{xx} + e^t, \quad u(x, 0) = 0, u_t(x, 0) = x, \quad u_x(0, t) = u(L, t) = 0$

(d) $u_{tt} = u_{xx} - u, \quad u(x, 0) = 0, u_t(x, 0) = 1, \quad u(0, t) = u(L, t) = 0$

[*Hint:* For (d) show that

$$\dot{I}_1(t) + \dot{I}_2(t) + \dot{I}(t) = 0,$$

where I_1 and I_2 are as in (iii) of example (6.2c) and I is as in example (6.2a).]

8

Linear Transformations

1. Range and Nullspace of Transformations

In our analysis of partial differential equations in Chapter 7 we made use, over and over again, of the heuristic principle: *Solutions obtained for simplified problems can be superposed to provide the solution of a complex problem.* In the present chapter we shall show that this and other related ideas become quite transparent when viewed from the appropriate vector space format. For this purpose it will be necessary for us to study new kinds of vector functions in which the *arguments* as well as the values belong to suitable vector spaces. That is, an argument of such a function need not be a *scalar* as in Chapter 2, but can be a pair (t_1, t_2) in $\mathcal{R}^2$, a triple (t_1, t_2, t_3) in $\mathcal{R}^3$, or even a vector $\boldsymbol{\alpha}$ in some other specified vector space. For clarity we shall use the term "transformation" to describe vector functions of this sort.

(1.1) Examples. Transformations

(a) Consider the arrows which are parallel to a fixed plane Π. A familiar notion in geometry is that of rotation through a fixed angle. Now under a rotation of 90° each arrow $\boldsymbol{\alpha}$ parallel to Π goes into an arrow $\boldsymbol{\beta}$ parallel to Π which is perpendicular to, and of the same length as, $\boldsymbol{\alpha}$ (Figure 8.1). Thus this rotation can be interpreted as a transformation f whose arguments $\boldsymbol{\alpha}$ *and* values $\boldsymbol{\beta}$ are both arrows parallel to Π.

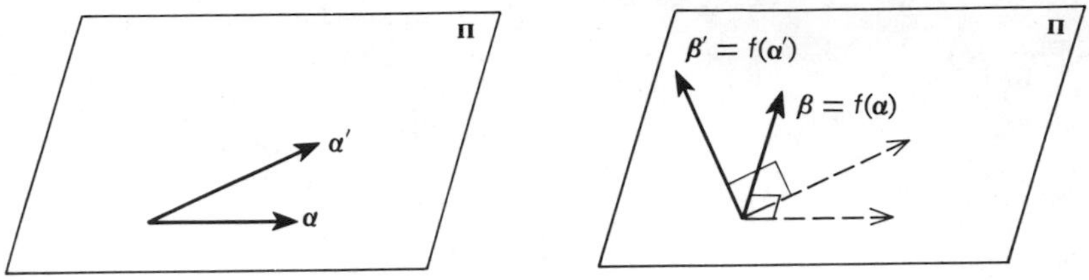

Figure 8.1

(b) Consider the equations

$$\text{(i)}\qquad \begin{aligned} t_1 + 0t_2 &= w_1 \\ 0t_1 + t_2 &= w_2 \\ t_1^2 + t_2^2 &= w_3. \end{aligned}$$

These equations can be regarded as a formula which gives for each pair of numbers (t_1, t_2) a triple of numbers (w_1, w_2, w_3):

$$\text{(ii)}\qquad f(t_1, t_2) = (t_1, t_2, t_1^2 + t_2^2) = (w_1, w_2, w_3).$$

Thus we interpret f as a transformation whose arguments (t_1, t_2) are vectors in $\mathcal{R}^2$ and whose values (w_1, w_2, w_3) are vectors in $\mathcal{R}^3$. Figure 8.2 gives a simple geometric interpretation of this transformation.

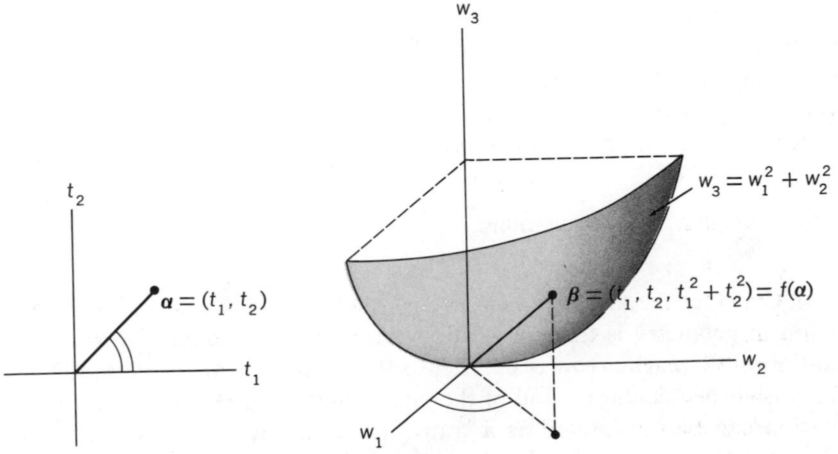

Figure 8.2

(c) Consider the formula

$$\text{(i)} \qquad \dot{y}(t) - y(t) = w(t) \qquad \text{for all } t.$$

This formula gives, for each function y which is continuously differentiable for all t, a function $w \in \mathcal{C}(-\infty, \infty)$. It is possible here, too, to describe the situation in terms of a transformation. Let $f(y) = \dot{y} - y$. That is, f is a transformation whose arguments y are certain vectors in $\mathcal{C}(-\infty, \infty)$ and whose values w also belong to the space $\mathcal{C}(-\infty, \infty)$. [More precisely, the arguments of f belong to the vector space $\mathcal{C}^1(-\infty, \infty)$ consisting of continuously differentiable functions, while the values of f belong to $\mathcal{C}(-\infty, \infty)$.] Then equation (i) can be interpreted as a specification of this transformation f. In the present example there is no *geometric* description of the transformation.

To introduce an appropriate terminology for the study of transformations we make the following definition.

(1.2) Definition. A transformation, or *mapping*, of a vector space $\mathfrak{D}$ into a vector space $\mathcal{W}$ is a rule T by which each vector $\mathbf{y}$ of $\mathfrak{D}$ is assigned a single element $\mathbf{w}$ of $\mathcal{W}$. The vector $\mathbf{w}$ is called the *T-image of* $\mathbf{y}$, and this correspondence between the vectors $\mathbf{y}$ of $\mathfrak{D}$ and their T images in $\mathcal{W}$ is written briefly $\mathbf{w} = T\mathbf{y}$. The space $\mathfrak{D}$ is called the **domain** of T, while the set of all T-images of the vectors of $\mathfrak{D}$ is called the **range** of T and is denoted by R_T. Thus as $\mathbf{y}$ varies throughout $\mathfrak{D}$, $T\mathbf{y}$ varies throughout R_T (Figure 8.3).

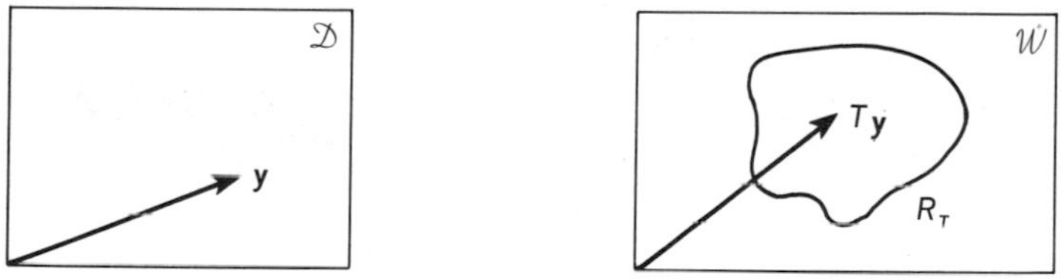

Figure 8.3

It is often helpful to think of the vector space $\mathfrak{D}$ as being transformed or carried into $\mathcal{W}$ by T, and so we denote the entire process by the formula $T\colon \mathfrak{D} \rightarrow \mathcal{W}$.

(1.3) Examples. Transformations

(a) Let $\mathfrak{D} = (-\infty, \infty)$, the vector space of all real numbers. For $y \in \mathfrak{D}$ define $Ty = y^2$ (Figure 8.4). In this case we likewise have $\mathcal{W} = (-\infty, \infty)$.

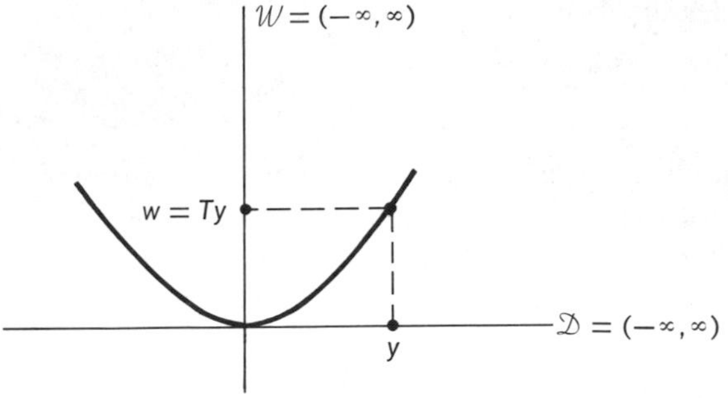

Figure 8.4

Now as y varies throughout $\mathfrak{D}$, Ty varies throughout $[0, \infty)$, the set of all nonnegative numbers. Thus $R_T = [0, \infty)$. Note that R_T in this case is only part of $\mathfrak{W}$.

(b) Let $\mathfrak{D} = (-\infty, \infty)$, and for $y \in \mathfrak{D}$ define $Ty = y^3$ (Figure 8.5).

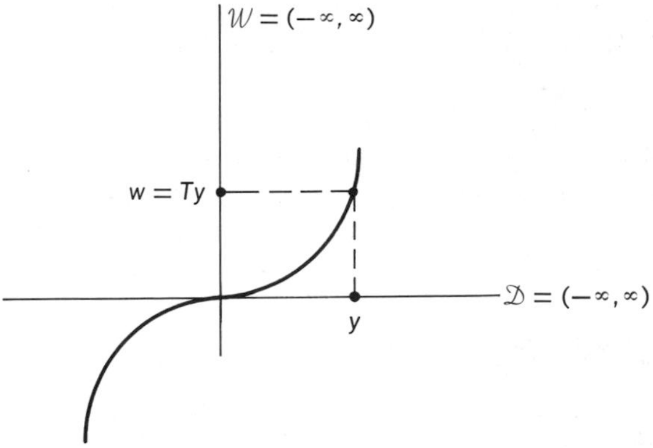

Figure 8.5

Then as y varies from $-\infty$ to ∞, Ty also varies from $-\infty$ to ∞ and $R_T = (-\infty, \infty)$. In this example we again have $\mathfrak{W} = \mathfrak{D} = (-\infty, \infty)$, but this time R_T is all of $\mathfrak{W}$, not a smaller subset as in (a). This latter fact is conveniently emphasized by saying that T transforms $\mathfrak{D}$ *onto* $\mathfrak{W}$, or occasionally simply by stating, *T is onto*.

(c) Let $\mathfrak{D} = \mathfrak{R}^3$, the vector space of all triples (a, b, c) of real numbers. For $\mathbf{y} = (y_1, y_2, y_3)$ in $\mathfrak{D}$ define $T\mathbf{y} = (y_1^2 + y_2^2, y_1^2 + 2y_2^2)$. Then T is a mapping from $\mathfrak{D} = \mathfrak{R}^3$ into $\mathfrak{W} = \mathfrak{R}^2$. Note that the range of T (Figure 8.6) is the first quadrant of $\mathfrak{R}^2$ (origin included).

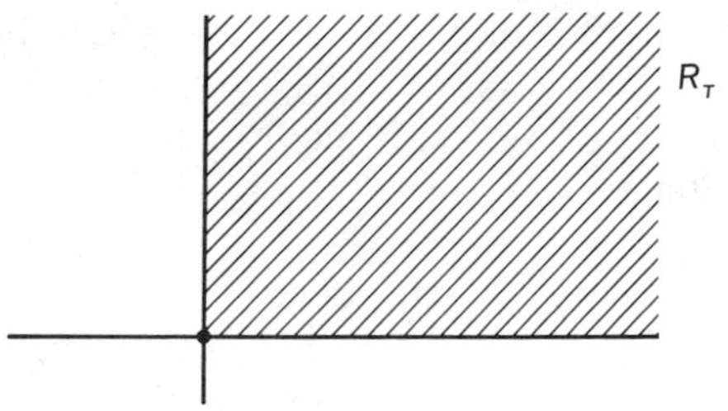

Figure 8.6

(d) Let $\mathfrak{D} = \mathcal{C}[0, \pi]$, the vector space of functions continuous over $0 \leq t \leq \pi$. For $f \in \mathfrak{D}$ define $Tf = \int_0^\pi f(t)\,dt$; that is, Tf is a scalar. Thus $\mathcal{W}$ is the vector space $(-\infty, \infty)$. It is easy to convince oneself that as f varies throughout $\mathfrak{D}$, Tf varies throughout all of $\mathcal{W}$. Thus we have here another example of a transformation from $\mathfrak{D}$ onto $\mathcal{W}$.

One reason for our interest in transformations is that problems of mathematics and mathematical physics often find their most natural formulation in terms of transformations. They take the form of **conditional equations**:

$$\text{(CE)} \qquad T\mathbf{y} = \mathbf{w}.$$

Here T denotes some known transformation from the vector space $\mathfrak{D}$ into the vector space $\mathcal{W}$ and (CE) poses the problem of finding, for the prescribed vector $\mathbf{w} \in \mathcal{W}$, all vectors $\mathbf{y} \in D$ whose T-image is $\mathbf{w}$. These vectors $\mathbf{y}$ are, of course, called *solutions* of (CE).

One can make some general comments about such problems even in terms of the little we have covered thus far. For instance, if the vector $\mathbf{w} \in \mathcal{W}$ is not in R_T, then (CE) has no solutions whatsoever. This follows from the definition of R_T. Likewise, even when $\mathbf{w} \in R_T$, there is no reason to expect only one solution of (CE) unless the transformation T is of a special nature. Aside from these observations, however, the analysis of equations of the form (CE) for all or even most transformations from a vector space $\mathfrak{D}$ into another vector space $\mathcal{W}$ is much too difficult for our purposes. Hence in this chapter we shall restrict attention to a special class of transformations. These transformations are far easier to analyze than others, and yet occur over and over again in applications. They are the *linear* transformations.

(1.4) Definition. A transformation T of the vector space $\mathfrak{D}$ into the vector space $\mathcal{W}$ is called a **linear transformation** if it carries vectors $\mathbf{y} \in \mathfrak{D}$ to vectors $\mathbf{w} \in \mathcal{W}$ in such a manner that the *linearity identity*

$$\text{(L)} \qquad T(c_1\mathbf{y}_1 + c_2\mathbf{y}_2) = c_1T\mathbf{y}_1 + c_2T\mathbf{y}_2$$

is maintained for all $\mathbf{y}_1, \mathbf{y}_2 \in \mathfrak{D}$ and all scalars c_1, c_2. That is, if $\mathbf{w}_1$ is the T-image of $\mathbf{y}_1$ and $\mathbf{w}_2$ is the T-image of $\mathbf{y}_2$, then for all c_1, c_2 the T-image of the linear combination $c_1\mathbf{y}_1 + c_2\mathbf{y}_2$ is required to be the exactly corresponding linear combination $c_1\mathbf{w}_1 + c_2\mathbf{w}_2$.

As special cases of (L) we have the identities

$$\text{(1.5a)} \qquad \begin{aligned} &(\mathrm{L}_1) \qquad T(\mathbf{y}_1 + \mathbf{y}_2) = T\mathbf{y}_1 + T\mathbf{y}_2 \\ &(\mathrm{L}_2) \qquad T(c\mathbf{y}_1) = cT\mathbf{y}_1, \end{aligned}$$

and conversely it can be shown that (L_1) and (L_2) together imply (L) (see problem 10). Moreover it is easy to prove by induction that (L) also implies similar identities for more than two vectors:

$$\text{(1.5b)} \qquad T(c_1\mathbf{y}_1 + \cdots + c_n\mathbf{y}_n) = c_1T\mathbf{y}_1 + \cdots + c_nT\mathbf{y}_n.$$

(1.6) Examples. Linear Transformations

(a) Let $\mathfrak{D} = (-\infty, \infty)$ and for $y \in \mathfrak{D}$ define $Ty = y^2$. In this case the linearity identity $T(c_1y_1 + c_2y_2) = c_1Ty_1 + c_2Ty_2$ reduces to the statement

$$(c_1y_1 + c_2y_2)^2 = c_1y_1^2 + c_2y_2^2.$$

This equation is obviously invalid except in special cases. Thus T is *not* a linear transformation or, stated another way, T is a *nonlinear* transformation.

(b) Let $\mathfrak{D} = \mathcal{C}[0, \pi]$ and for $f \in \mathfrak{D}$ define $Tf = \int_0^\pi f(t)\,dt$. In this case $\mathcal{W} = (-\infty, \infty)$ and the linearity identity

$$T(c_1f_1 + c_2f_2) = c_1Tf_1 + c_2Tf_2$$

reduces to the statement

$$\int_0^\pi [c_1f_1(t) + c_2f_2(t)]\,dt = c_1\int_0^\pi f_1(t)\,dt + c_2\int_0^\pi f_2(t)\,dt,$$

which is known to be true from calculus. Thus T *is* a linear transformation in this case.

(c) Let $\mathfrak{D} = \mathcal{C}[0, \pi]$ and define Tf for $f \in \mathfrak{D}$ by $Tf = g$, where the function g is given by

$$g(t) = \int_0^t f(s)\,ds, \qquad 0 \le t \le \pi.$$

In this example we can take $\mathcal{W} = \mathcal{C}[0, \pi] = \mathcal{D}$. The linearity identity reduces to the requirement

$$\int_0^t [c_1 f_1(s) + c_2 f_2(s)]\, ds = c_1 \int_0^t f_1(s)\, ds + c_2 \int_0^t f_2(s)\, ds, \qquad 0 \le t \le \pi,$$

which is a standard fact from calculus. The precise determination of the range R_T for this transformation is an interesting exercise (see the problems).

(d) Let $\mathcal{D} = \mathcal{R}^2$ and for $\mathbf{x} = (x_1, x_2)$ in $\mathcal{D}$ define

$$T\mathbf{x} = (x_1 + x_2, x_1 - x_2, x_1 + 2x_2).$$

In this example, $\mathcal{W} = \mathcal{R}^3$. We leave to the reader the task of determining whether or not T is linear. To determine R_T we proceed as follows. By rewriting the given formula for $T\mathbf{x}$ we have

$$T\mathbf{x} = x_1(1, 1, 1) + x_2(1, -1, 2).$$

This makes it clear that for each $\mathbf{x} \in \mathcal{D}$, $T\mathbf{x}$ is in the span of (1, 1, 1) and (1, −1, 2):

$$T\mathbf{x} \in \langle(1, 1, 1), (1, -1, 2)\rangle = S.$$

That is, $R_T \subset S$. Conversely, if $\boldsymbol{\alpha}$ is any vector in S, then for certain scalars c, d we have $\boldsymbol{\alpha} = c(1, 1, 1) + d(1, -1, 2)$. It follows that for

$$\mathbf{x} = (c, d) \in \mathcal{D}, \qquad T\mathbf{x} = c(1, 1, 1) + d(1, -1, 2) = \boldsymbol{\alpha},$$

so that $\boldsymbol{\alpha}$ is the T-image of $\mathbf{x}$. In other words,

$$R_T = S = \langle(1, 1, 1), (1, -1, 2)\rangle.$$

(e) Let $\mathcal{D} = \mathcal{R}^3$, and for $\mathbf{x} = (x_1, x_2, x_3)$ in $\mathcal{D}$ define

$$T\mathbf{x} = (x_1 - x_2 + 2x_3,\ x_1 + 2x_2 - x_3,\ x_1 - 4x_2 + 5x_3).$$

Here $\mathcal{W} = \mathcal{R}^3 = \mathcal{D}$. If we wished to determine R_T we could imitate the ideas of (d). Since $T\mathbf{x} = x_1(1, 1, 1) + x_2(-1, 2, -4) + x_3(2, -1, 5)$ it is obvious that $R_T \subset S = \langle(1, 1, 1), (-1, 2, -4), (2, -1, 5)\rangle$. As a matter of fact, one can show by the technique used in (d) that $R_T = S$.

Although we have seen that a conditional equation has no solutions unless $\mathbf{w} \in R_T$, the two sets of examples above indicate that it is not always an easy matter to determine the precise range of a transformation. In some examples we found that R_T is a subspace of $\mathcal{W}$. Indeed for *linear* transformations this is always the case (see problem 8), so that for them the search for R_T narrows down to a search among those subsets of $\mathcal{W}$ which are subspaces.

Hereafter the term transformation will denote a *linear* transformation unless stated otherwise. The observation in the preceding paragraph then helps to identify R_T and thereby to determine those $\mathbf{w} \in \mathcal{W}$ for which there *exist* solutions of

$$\text{(CE)} \qquad T\mathbf{y} = \mathbf{w}.$$

[By the convention above, the T appearing in (CE) is assumed to be linear.] Now there is one $\mathbf{w} \in \mathcal{W}$ which belongs to R_T for *every* linear transformation T, namely $\mathbf{w} = \mathbf{0}$. (***Proof.*** For $\mathbf{y} \in \mathcal{D}$ we have by (L_2) of (1.5a),

$$\mathbf{0} = 0T\mathbf{y} = T(0\mathbf{y}) = T(\mathbf{0}),$$

so that $\mathbf{0}$ is the T-image of the vector $\mathbf{0} \in \mathcal{D}$.) It follows from this that the "homogeneous" conditional equation defined by

$$(\text{CE}_0) \qquad T\mathbf{y} = \mathbf{0}$$

is guaranteed to have at least one solution, no matter what linear transformation T is involved.

Our next theorem gives an idea of the total number of solutions $\mathbf{y}$ to a homogeneous conditional equation (CE_0).

(1.7) Theorem. *If T is a linear transformation from $\mathcal{D}$ into $\mathcal{W}$, then the set N_T consisting of all vectors* $\mathbf{y}$ *whose T-image is $\mathbf{0} \in \mathcal{W}$ is a subspace of $\mathcal{D}$.*

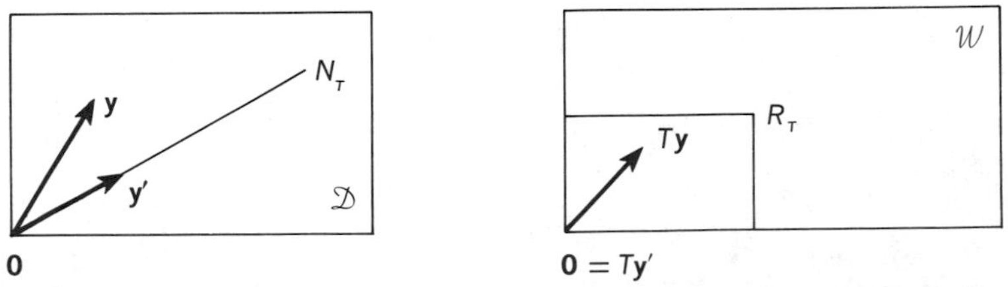

Figure 8.7

Proof. Let $\mathbf{y}_1$, $\mathbf{y}_2$ be arbitrarily chosen in N_T; that is, $T\mathbf{y}_1 = \mathbf{0}$ and $T\mathbf{y}_2 = \mathbf{0}$. Then, by (1.5a),

$$T(\mathbf{y}_1 + \mathbf{y}_2) = T\mathbf{y}_1 + T\mathbf{y}_2 = \mathbf{0} + \mathbf{0} = \mathbf{0},$$

which proves that $\mathbf{y}_1 + \mathbf{y}_2 \in N_T$. Likewise, for any scalar c we have

$$T(c\mathbf{y}_1) = cT\mathbf{y}_1 = c\mathbf{0} = \mathbf{0},$$

which proves that $c\mathbf{y}_1 \in N_T$. Since N_T is closed under addition and scalar multiplication, N_T is a subspace of $\mathfrak{D}$. ▮

The subspace N_T is called the **nullspace** of the operator T. Note that if N_T contains any nonzero vector $\mathbf{y}$, then it also contains all the vectors $c\mathbf{y}$ for all scalars c. Thus N_T either contains infinitely many vectors or else contains only the zero vector.

(1.8) Examples. Range and Nullspace

(a) Consider the transformation $T: \mathbb{R}^3 \to \mathbb{R}^2$ defined by

$$T\mathbf{y} = (y_1 - y_2 + y_3,\ y_1 + 2y_2 - y_3) \qquad \text{for } \mathbf{y} = (y_1, y_2, y_3).$$

Let us find R_T first. By definition R_T consists of those vectors

$$\mathbf{w} = (w_1, w_2) \in \mathbb{R}^2$$

which are the T-image of some $\mathbf{y} \in \mathbb{R}^3$:

$$\text{(i)} \qquad T\mathbf{y} = (y_1 - y_2 + y_3, y_1 + 2y_2 - y_3) = (w_1, w_2).$$

Now the equality of the vectors occurring in (i) is equivalent to equality of their corresponding entries:

$$\text{(ii)} \qquad \begin{aligned} y_1 - y_2 + y_3 &= w_1 \\ y_1 + 2y_2 - y_3 &= w_2. \end{aligned}$$

Hence in order to find R_T it suffices to find all w_1, w_2 such that the system of equations (ii) has a solution. By Gauss reduction (ii) is equivalent to

$$\text{(iii)} \qquad \begin{aligned} y_1 + \tfrac{1}{3}y_3 &= \tfrac{2}{3}w_1 + \tfrac{1}{3}w_2 \\ y_2 - \tfrac{2}{3}y_3 &= -\tfrac{1}{3}w_1 + \tfrac{1}{3}w_2. \end{aligned}$$

Obviously (iii) has solutions no matter what choices are made for the entries w_1 and w_2. Hence R_T is the set of *all* vectors $\mathbf{w} \in \mathbb{R}^2$. That is, $R_T = \mathbb{R}^2$, so that the transformation T takes $\mathbb{R}^3$ *onto* $\mathbb{R}^2$.

To find the null space of T we must find all $\mathbf{y} \in \mathbb{R}^3$ whose T-image is (0, 0):

$$\text{(iv)} \qquad T\mathbf{y} = (y_1 - y_2 + y_3,\ y_1 + 2y_2 - y_3) = (0, 0).$$

This is of course equivalent to the system of equations

$$\text{(v)}\qquad \begin{aligned} y_1 - y_2 + y_3 &= 0 \\ y_1 + 2y_2 - y_3 &= 0. \end{aligned}$$

By (iii), the Gauss reduced form of (v) is

$$\text{(vi)}\qquad \begin{aligned} y_1 + \tfrac{1}{3}y_3 &= 0 \\ y_2 - \tfrac{2}{3}y_3 &= 0 \end{aligned}$$

By selecting y_3 arbitrarily, $y_3 = c$ say, we obtain a formula for all solutions $\mathbf{y}$ of (iv):

$$\mathbf{y} = (-\tfrac{1}{3}c, \tfrac{2}{3}c, c) \qquad \text{for all scalars } c.$$

It is easily verified that these vectors $\mathbf{y}$ form a subspace of $\mathcal{R}^3$. In fact, we have $N_T = \langle(-\frac{1}{3}, \frac{2}{3}, 1)\rangle$, so that N_T is a one-dimensional subspace of $\mathcal{R}^3$.

(b) Let $\mathcal{D} = \mathcal{C}^1(-\infty, \infty)$, the vector space of functions having a continuous first derivative for all t. For $y \in \mathcal{D}$ define, as in (1.1b), $Ty = \dot{y} - y$. Here $\mathcal{W} = \mathcal{C}(-\infty, \infty)$, the vector space of continuous functions. The reader should verify that the transformation T: $\mathcal{C}^1(-\infty, \infty) \to \mathcal{C}(-\infty, \infty)$ is linear.

Let us find N_T. That is, we must find all $y \in \mathcal{C}^1(-\infty, \infty)$ whose T-image is the zero function:

$$\text{(i)}\qquad \dot{y}(t) - y(t) = 0 \qquad \text{for all } t.$$

As we know, the solutions y of the differential equation (i) all have the form $y(t) = ce^t$ for some scalar c. Hence in the present case $N_T = \langle e^t \rangle$, and the nullspace of T is a one-dimensional subspace of $\mathcal{D}$.

To find R_T we must determine all functions $f \in \mathcal{W} = \mathcal{C}(-\infty, \infty)$ such that f is the T-image of some $y \in \mathcal{D}$:

$$\text{(ii)}\qquad \dot{y}(t) - y(t) = f(t) \qquad \text{for all } t.$$

Now (ii) is a "linear nonhomogeneous" first-order equation. Hence as we saw in Chapter 4, §1, it has solutions no matter what continuous function f enters. In fact, there is a unique solution satisfying $y(0) = c$ for each choice of the scalar c,

$$\text{(iii)}\qquad y(t) = ce^t + e^t \int_0^t e^{-s} f(s)\, ds.$$

Thus (ii) has (infinitely many) solutions $y \in \mathcal{D}$ for every $f \in \mathcal{W}$. In particular, T is onto: $R_T = \mathcal{W} = \mathcal{C}(-\infty, \infty)$.

(c) Let $\mathfrak{D} = \mathcal{C}[0 \leq x \leq \pi, 0 \leq t < \infty]$ be the vector space of continuous functions u of two variables having values $u(x, t)$ for $0 \leq x \leq \pi$, $0 \leq t < \infty$. For $u \in \mathfrak{D}$ define $E^0 u = w$, where $w(t) = u(0, t)$, $0 \leq t < \infty$. Then $\mathfrak{W} = \mathcal{C}[0, \infty)$ is the vector space of continuous functions of one variable $0 \leq t < \infty$. The reader should verify that this "evaluation" transformation $E^0: \mathcal{C}[0 \leq x \leq \pi, 0 \leq t < \infty] \to \mathcal{C}[0, \infty)$ is linear.

Finding N_{E^0} is easy. For $E^0 u = 0$ it is necessary that $u(0, t) = 0$. Hence N_{E^0} consists of all $u \in \mathfrak{D}$ which vanish identically at $x = 0$. It is left as an exercise to show that $R_{E^0} = \mathfrak{W}$.

PROBLEMS

1. For each transformation T below,

(i) Give the vector space $\mathfrak{W}$ and determine whether T is linear.

(ii) Ascertain whether there exist distinct elements $\mathbf{y}, \mathbf{y}' \in \mathfrak{D}$ having the same T-image. If there are, T is called *many to one;* if not, T is called *one to one.*

(iii) For the prescribed subset $A \subset \mathfrak{D}$ find $T(A)$, the set of T-images of elements $\mathbf{y} \in A$.

(a) $\mathfrak{D} = (-\infty, \infty)$; $Ty = \sin y$; $A = [0, \pi/2]$, the set of all real numbers between 0 and $\pi/2$ inclusive.

(b) $\mathfrak{D} = (-\infty, \infty)$; $Ty = y^n$, n a positive integer; $A = [-1, 2]$.

(c) $\mathfrak{D} = \mathcal{C}[0, \pi]$; $Tf = \int_0^\pi f(t)\, dt$; $A =$ the set of all $f \in \mathfrak{D}$ vanishing at 0 and at π.

2. For each of the problems below answer (i) and (iii) of problem 1 and also find R_T and give dim R_T when the latter is defined.

(a) $\mathfrak{D} = \mathfrak{R}^2$; $T(x_1, x_2) = (x_1^2, x_2^2)$; $A =$ unit circle, that is, all (x_1, x_2) such that $x_1^2 + x_2^2 = 1$.

(b) $\mathfrak{D} = \mathfrak{R}^2$; $T(x_1, x_2) = (3x_1 - x_2, x_1 - 3x_2)$; $A =$ the line $x_2 = mx_1 + b$.

(c) $\mathfrak{D} = \mathfrak{R}^3$;
$T(x_1, x_2, x_3) = (x_1 - x_2 + 2x_3, x_1 + 2x_1 - x_3, x_1 - 4x_2 + 5x_3)$;
$A =$ the plane $x_3 = x_1 + x_2 + b$.

*(d) $\mathfrak{D} = \mathcal{C}[0, \pi]$; $Tf = \int_0^\pi \sin (t - s) f(s)\, ds$; $A =$ set of all functions of unit length: $\int_0^\pi f(t)^2\, dt = 1$.

*(e) $\mathfrak{D} = \mathcal{C}[0, \pi]$; $Tf = g$, where $g(t) = \int_0^t f(s)\, ds$; $A =$ the set of all $f \in \mathfrak{D}$ vanishing at 0. (*Hint:* What differentiability property does every T-image possess? What is its value at 0? Show that each function with both these properties is in R_T.)

*(f) $\mathfrak{D} = \mathcal{C}^1[0, \pi]$, the vector space of functions with a continuous first derivative $0 \leq t \leq \pi$; $Tf = \dot{f}$; $A =$ the set of all $f \in \mathfrak{D}$ satisfying $f(0) = f(\pi)$.

3. For each of the problems below supply a $\mathfrak{D}, \mathfrak{W}$, and T so that the problem can be put in the form (CE) of a conditional equation. Determine in each case whether or not T is linear.

(a) $y^2 - 3y + 5 = w$

(b) $y(t)^2 - 3y(t) + 5 = \sin t$

(c) $\dot{y}(t) - 2y(t) = f(t)$

(d) $\dot{y}(t) - 2y(t) + \sin t = f(t)$

(e) $\int_0^t \sin(st)y(s)\,ds = f(t)$

4. Show that the transformation on arrows parallel to Π described in example (1.1a) is linear. [*Hint:* The proof of (L_1) and (L_2) utilizes congruent triangles. Sketch these triangles but omit detailed proofs of congruence.]

5. Let $\mathfrak{D}$ and $\mathfrak{W}$ be arbitrarily selected vector spaces. For each $\mathbf{y} \in \mathfrak{D}$ define $T\mathbf{y} = \mathbf{0} \in \mathfrak{W}$. This is called the *zero transformation*. Prove that the zero transformation is invariably linear.

6. For each $\mathbf{y} \in \mathfrak{D}$ define $T\mathbf{y} = \mathbf{y}$. This is called the *identity transformation* and is denoted by I (sometimes $I_{\mathfrak{D}}$). Prove that the identity transformation is invariably linear.

7. Let S be a finite-dimensional subspace of $\mathfrak{D}$. For each $\mathbf{y} \in \mathfrak{D}$ define $T\mathbf{y} = \mathbf{y}_s$, where $\mathbf{y}_s \in S$ denotes the best approximator to $\mathbf{y}$ (see Chapter 6, §2).

(a) Prove or disprove: T is linear.

(b) Find R_T.

8. (a) Prove that for any linear transformation T, R_T is a subspace of $\mathfrak{W}$. [*Hint:* Use (L_1) to show that R_T is closed under addition: if $\mathbf{w}_1 = T\mathbf{y}_1$ and $\mathbf{w}_2 = T\mathbf{y}_2$ are in R_T, then so is $\mathbf{w}_1 + \mathbf{w}_2$. Use ($L_2$) to show that R_T is closed under scalar multiplication.]

(b) Prove that for any subspace $S \subset \mathfrak{D}$, $T(S)$, the set of all $\mathbf{w} \in \mathfrak{W}$ such that $\mathbf{w} = T\mathbf{y}$ for some $\mathbf{y} \in S$, is a subspace of $\mathfrak{W}$.

9. Show that for any linear transformation T the T-image of any line segment in $\mathfrak{D}$, $L = \{\mathbf{y}; \mathbf{y} = (1 - r)\boldsymbol{\alpha} + r\boldsymbol{\beta}, 0 \le r \le 1\}$ [see (1.5)] is a line segment in $\mathfrak{W}$.

10. Prove that the identities (L_1) and (L_2) of (1.5a) are not only implied *by* the linearity identity (L) but together imply (L). [*Hint:* Use (L_1) first in simplifying $T(c_1\mathbf{y}_1 + c_2\mathbf{y}_2)$.]

****11.** Show that a continuous transformation T of $(-\infty, \infty)$ into itself is one to one if and only if T is either strictly increasing or strictly decreasing: For all pairs of numbers, y, y' with $y < y'$ it is always the case that $Ty < Ty'$, or else it is always the case that $Ty > Ty'$.

12. Show that for any fixed t_0, $0 \le t_0 \le \pi$, "evaluation at t_0" is a linear transformation on $\mathfrak{C}[0, \pi]$. That is, show that the transformation

$$T: \mathfrak{C}[0, \pi] \to (-\infty, \infty)$$

defined by $Tx = x(t_0)$ is linear.

13. Prove that for any fixed x_0, $0 \le x_0 \le \pi$ "evaluation at x_0" is a linear transformation on functions of two variables. That is, show that the transformation

$E^{x_0}: \mathcal{C}[0 \leq x \leq \pi, 0 \leq t < \infty] \rightarrow \mathcal{C}[0, \infty)$ defined by

$$E^{x_0}u = w,$$

where $w(t) = u(x_0, t)$, $0 < t < \infty$, is linear.

***14.** Show that the set $\mathcal{W}$ of vectors $\mathbf{w}$, which consist of three parts

$$\mathbf{w} = (g; k, m),$$

where $g \in \mathcal{C}[0 \leq x \leq \pi, 0 < t < \infty]$ is a continuous function of two variables, and $k,m \in \mathcal{C}[0, \infty)$ are continuous functions of one variable, is a vector space provided that we define addition and scalar multiplication "componentwise":

$$\mathbf{w}_1 + \mathbf{w}_2 = (g_1 + g_2; k_1 + k_2, m_1 + m_2), \qquad c\mathbf{w}_1 = (cg_1; ck_1, cm_1).$$

***15.** Prove that with $\mathcal{W}$ as in problem 14 the transformation

$$T: \mathcal{C}^2[0 \leq x \leq \pi, 0 < t < \infty] \rightarrow \mathcal{W}$$

given by

$$Tu = (u_{tt} - u_{xx}; E^0u, E^\pi u)$$

is linear.

Linear Combinations and Products of Linear Transformations

16. (a) Let T_1 and T_2 be two linear transformations taking the same domain $\mathfrak{D}$ into the vector space $\mathcal{W}$, $T_1: \mathfrak{D} \rightarrow \mathcal{W}$, $T_2: \mathfrak{D} \rightarrow \mathcal{W}$. Define their *sum* $T_1 + T_2$ to be the transformation from $\mathfrak{D}$ into $\mathcal{W}$ which assigns to each $\mathbf{y} \in \mathfrak{D}$ the sum of its T_1- and T_2-images:

$$\text{(i)} \qquad (T_1 + T_2)\mathbf{y} = T_1\mathbf{y} + T_2\mathbf{y} \qquad \text{for } \mathbf{y} \in D.$$

Prove that $T_1 + T_2$ is linear. [*Hint:* It must be shown that

$$(T_1 + T_2)(c\mathbf{y} + d\mathbf{z}) = c(T_1 + T_2)\mathbf{y} + d(T_1 + T_2)\mathbf{z}.$$

Apply (i) *first* in simplifying both sides of this formula.]

(b) For T_1 and T_2 as in part (a) define a "linear combination" $c_1T_1 + c_2T_2$ for any scalars c_1, c_2 to be the transformation from $\mathfrak{D}$ into $\mathcal{W}$ which assigns to each $\mathbf{y} \in \mathfrak{D}$ c_1 times its T_1-image plus c_2 times its T_2-image:

$$(c_1T_1 + c_2T_2)\mathbf{y} = c_1(T_1\mathbf{y}) + c_2(T_2\mathbf{y}) \qquad \text{for } \mathbf{y} \in \mathfrak{D}.$$

Prove that $c_1T_1 + c_2T_2$ is linear.

17. Let $T_1: \mathfrak{D}_1 \rightarrow \mathcal{W}_1$, $T_2: \mathfrak{D}_2 \rightarrow \mathcal{W}_2$ be two transformations such that the *range* R_1 of T_1 is equal to or contained in the *domain* $\mathfrak{D}_2$ of T_2. Define the *product* (or *composition*) T_2T_1 to be that transformation taking $\mathfrak{D}_1$ into $\mathcal{W}_2$ which assigns to each $\mathbf{y}_1 \in \mathfrak{D}_1$ the T_2-image of its T_1-image (Figure 8.8):

$$\text{(i)} \qquad (T_2T_1)\mathbf{y} = T_2(T_1\mathbf{y}) \qquad \text{for } \mathbf{y} \in \mathfrak{D}_1.$$

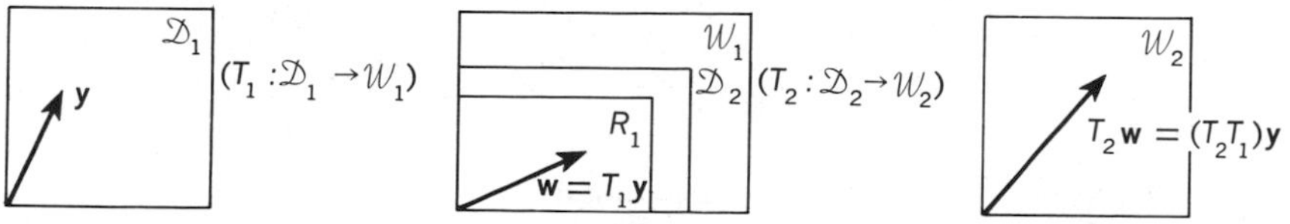

Figure 8.8

Show that T_2T_1 is linear. [*Hint:* It must be shown that

$$(T_2T_1)(c\mathbf{y} + d\mathbf{z}) = c(T_2T_1)\mathbf{y} + d(T_2T_1)\mathbf{z}.$$

Simplify both sides by use of (i), then utilize the linearity of T_1 and of T_2.]

18. (a) Let $\mathfrak{D} = \mathfrak{R}^2$, and for $\mathbf{x} = (x_1, x_2) \in \mathfrak{D}$ define

$$T_1\mathbf{x} = (x_1 + x_2, x_1 - x_2, x_1 + 2x_2)$$
$$T_2\mathbf{x} = (x_1 - x_2, x_1 + x_2, 2x_1 + x_2).$$

Give a formula for $T_1 + T_2$, and explain why T_2T_1 and T_1T_2 are not defined.

(b) Let $\mathfrak{D} = \mathcal{C}(-\infty, \infty) = \mathcal{W}$ and define T_1 and T_2 by

$$T_1 f = h_1, \qquad \text{where } h_1(t) = \int_0^t f(s)\, ds \qquad \text{for all } t$$

$$T_2 f = h_2, \qquad \text{where } h_2(t) = t f(t) \qquad \text{for all } t.$$

Give a formula for $-T_1 + T_2$. Show that $T_2T_1 \neq T_1T_2$, by computing both these transformations. *The product of two transformations, when computable in two orders, generally gives two different results.*

2. Conditional Equations

The stage has now been set for a discussion of general (linear) conditional equations from a unified point of view. First comes a key definition.

(2.1) Definition. Let $\boldsymbol{\alpha}$ and S be, respectively, a vector in and a subspace of the vector space $\mathfrak{D}$. The *sum* of $\boldsymbol{\alpha}$ and S is defined to be the set $\boldsymbol{\alpha} + S$ of all sums $\boldsymbol{\alpha} + \boldsymbol{\sigma}$ for $\boldsymbol{\sigma} \in S$ (Figure 8.9). (The set $\boldsymbol{\alpha} + S$ is *not* a subspace unless $\boldsymbol{\alpha} \in S$.) We say that $P = \boldsymbol{\alpha} + S$ is a **plane parallel to S**. If S happens to be finite-dimensional, then the *dimension* of P is defined to be the dimension of S.

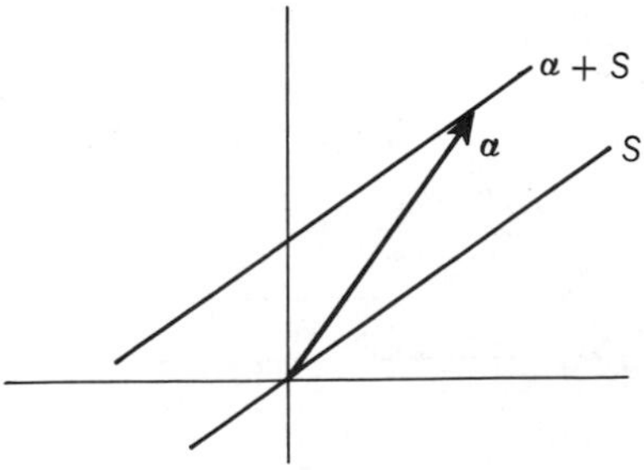

Figure 8.9

Our initial result expresses the close relation between solutions of a conditional equation (CE) and those of the homogeneous conditional equation formed with the same transformation,

$$(\mathrm{CE}_0) \qquad T\mathbf{y} = \mathbf{0}.$$

(2.2) The Splitting Theorem. *The set P of all solutions of the conditional equation*

$$(\mathrm{CE}) \qquad T\mathbf{y} = \mathbf{w}$$

may be empty. If P is not empty, P is a plane in $\mathfrak{D}$ *which is parallel to the nullspace of the linear transformation T:*

$$(\mathrm{s}) \qquad P = \mathbf{y}^* + N_T,$$

where $\mathbf{y}^*$ *is any particular solution of* (CE). *In particular,* (CE) *has a* unique *solution if and only if* $\mathbf{w} \in R_T$ *and* $N_T = \mathbf{0}$.

We shall call P the "solution plane "of (CE). Clearly N_T is the solution plane of the corresponding homogeneous equation (CE_0), so that (s) relates the solutions of (CE) to those of (CE_0), as was claimed.

Proof. Suppose that $\mathbf{w} \in R_T$. Then the set P is not empty. We will show that $P = \mathbf{y}^* + N_T$ by first showing that every vector in $\mathbf{y}^* + N_T$ is a solution of (CE), that is, $\mathbf{y}^* + N_T \subset P$, and then showing that every solution of (CE) is a vector in $\mathbf{y}^* + N_T$, that is, $P \subset \mathbf{y}^* + N_T$.

(1) $\mathbf{y}^* + N_T \subset P$. Choose a vector in $\mathbf{y}^* + N_T$. It necessarily has the form $\mathbf{y}^* + \boldsymbol{\sigma}$, where by assumption $\mathbf{y}^*$ is a solution of (CE) and $\boldsymbol{\sigma}$ is in N_T. Then by linearity of T,

$$T(\mathbf{y}^* + \boldsymbol{\sigma}) = T\mathbf{y}^* + T\boldsymbol{\sigma} = \mathbf{w} + \mathbf{0} = \mathbf{w}.$$

That is, the T-image of $\mathbf{y}^* + \boldsymbol{\sigma}$ is $\mathbf{w}$; so $\mathbf{y}^* + \boldsymbol{\sigma} \in P$, as claimed.

(2) $P \subset \mathbf{y}^* + N_T$. Choose any solution $\mathbf{y}$ of (CE). That is, $\mathbf{y} \in P$. We show that $\mathbf{y} \in \mathbf{y}^* + N_T$. By assumption $\mathbf{y}$ and $\mathbf{y}^*$ both satisfy (CE). Hence

$$T(\mathbf{y} - \mathbf{y}^*) = T\mathbf{y} - T\mathbf{y}^* = \mathbf{w} - \mathbf{w} = \mathbf{0}.$$

That is, $\mathbf{y} - \mathbf{y}^* \in N_T$. Thus the decomposition

$$\mathbf{y} = \mathbf{y}^* + (\mathbf{y} - \mathbf{y}^*)$$

reveals that $\mathbf{y} \in \mathbf{y}^* + N_T$, as claimed.

This completes the argument. ▮

The splitting theorem is the *formal* statement of a general method of attack on conditional equations. This solution technique will be restated, in (2.4), following a study of some examples.

(2.3) Examples. Applications of the Splitting Theorem

(a) Let us find the solutions of the system of equations

$$\text{(i)} \qquad \begin{aligned} y_1 - 2y_2 + y_3 &= 2 \\ y_1 + y_2 + 2y_3 &= 3. \end{aligned}$$

This system can be interpreted as an equation of the form (CE). We simply write it in the form

$$(y_1 - 2y_2 + y_3, y_1 + y_2 + 2y_3) = (2, 3).$$

If we define $T\mathbf{x}$ for $\mathbf{x} = (x_1, x_2, x_3) \in \mathcal{R}^3$ as

$$T\mathbf{x} = (x_1 - 2x_2 + x_3, x_1 + x_2 + 2x_3),$$

then T is a linear transformation taking $\mathcal{R}^3$ into $\mathcal{R}^2$, and (i) has the form

$$\text{(ii)} \qquad T\mathbf{y} = (2, 3).$$

Since (ii) is a conditional equation we know that its solutions, therefore the solutions of (i), form a plane P in $\mathcal{R}^3$.

Gauss reduction of the system (i) gives

$$\text{(iii)} \qquad \begin{aligned} y_1 &= -\tfrac{5}{3}y_3 + \tfrac{8}{3} \\ y_2 &= -\tfrac{1}{3}y_3 + \tfrac{1}{3}. \end{aligned}$$

Here we can choose y_3 arbitrarily. Taking $y_3 = 1$, say, yields the solution

$$\mathbf{y}^* = (1, 0, 1).$$

Since $\mathbf{y}^*$ is a particular solution of (i), it only remains to determine N_T. Now the equation $T\mathbf{y} = \mathbf{0}$ is clearly equivalent to

$$\text{(iv)} \qquad \begin{aligned} y_1 - 2y_2 + y_3 &= 0 \\ y_1 + y_2 + 2y_3 &= 0. \end{aligned}$$

Hence for an arbitrary scalar c, $y_3 = c$ leads to the following solution of (iv):

$$\sigma = (-\tfrac{5}{3}c, -\tfrac{1}{3}c, c) = c(-\tfrac{5}{3}, -\tfrac{1}{3}, 1).$$

This implies that $N_T = \langle(-\tfrac{5}{3}, -\tfrac{1}{3}, 1)\rangle$.

Combining the results obtained above we see by the splitting theorem that the solution plane of (ii) is

$$\mathbf{y}^* + N_T = (1, 0, 1) + \langle(-\tfrac{5}{3}, -\tfrac{1}{3}, 1)\rangle.$$

Note that Gauss reduction of (iv) is almost the same task as Gauss reduction of (i), the only difference being that in (i) the nonzero constant terms have to be carried along. Hence it is possible to accomplish the second Gauss reduction by merely omitting the constant terms $\tfrac{8}{3}$ and $\tfrac{1}{3}$ in formula (iii).

(b) Let us find the solutions of the ordinary differential equation

$$\text{(i)} \qquad \ddot{y}(t) - \dot{y}(t) - 2y(t) = 1 + t, \qquad -\infty < t < \infty.$$

Equation (i) can be interpreted as a conditional equation. Let

$$\mathfrak{D} = \mathcal{C}^2(-\infty, \infty),$$

the vector space of functions having two continuous derivatives for all t. Then define Ly for $y \in \mathfrak{D}$ as follows:

$$Ly = \ddot{y} - \dot{y} - 2y.$$

Here $\mathcal{W} = \mathcal{C}(-\infty, \infty)$, and it is easy to verify that the transformation L is linear. (This is simply the statement that equation (iii) below is s-linear.) Equation (i) now takes the form

$$\text{(ii)} \qquad Ly = 1 + t.$$

Since (ii) is a conditional equation we know that its solutions, therefore the solutions of (i), form a plane P in $\mathfrak{D} = \mathcal{C}^2(-\infty, \infty)$. Let us insert $y(t) = A + Bt$ into (i). This gives

$$0 - B - 2(A + Bt) = 1 + t, \qquad -\infty < t < \infty.$$

Simplifying, we deduce that $B = -\tfrac{1}{2}$, $A = -\tfrac{1}{4}$. Thus

$$y^*(t) = -\tfrac{1}{4} - \tfrac{1}{2}t,$$

is a solution. Since y^* is a particular solution we now concentrate on finding N_L. The equation $Ly = 0$ is equivalent to

$$\text{(iii)} \qquad \ddot{y}(t) - \dot{y}(t) - 2y(t) = 0, \qquad -\infty < t < \infty.$$

By (3.15) of Chapter 5, solutions of (iii) have the form

$$c_1 e^{2t} + c_2 e^{-t}, \qquad c_1, c_2 \text{ arbitrary constants.}$$

That is,

$$N_L = \langle e^{2t}, e^{-t} \rangle.$$

Thus the solution plane for (ii) is given by

$$y^* + N_L = -\tfrac{1}{4} - \tfrac{1}{2}t + \langle e^{2t}, e^{-t} \rangle.$$

The above manipulations are, of course, identical with the method for solution of (i) already used in Chapter 5, §4. What our example emphasizes is that this method is a particular application of the splitting theorem.

The following is a more sophisticated application of the splitting theorem.

*(c) Find all solutions of the partial differential equation

$$\text{(i)} \qquad u_{tt} - u_{xx} = 0 \qquad 0 \le x \le \pi, \qquad 0 \le t < \infty$$

which satisfy the edge conditions

$$\text{(ii)} \qquad u(0, t) = t, \qquad u(\pi, t) = t^2, \qquad 0 \le t < \infty.$$

Equations (i) and (ii) can be interpreted together as a conditional equation provided that we use a little ingenuity. Let $\mathfrak{D} = \mathcal{C}^2[0 \le x \le \pi, 0 \le t < \infty]$ be the vector space of functions u having continuous first- and second-order partial derivatives at all points of the strip $0 \le x \le \pi$, $0 \le t < \infty$. Then define Lu for $u \in \mathfrak{D}$ as follows:

$$Lu = u_{tt} - u_{xx}.$$

Likewise, define $E^0 u$ and $E^\pi u$ for $u \in \mathfrak{D}$ as follows:

$$E^0 u = k,$$

where $k(t) = u(0, t)$, $0 \le t < \infty$,

$$E^\pi u = m,$$

where $m(t) = u(\pi, t)\ 0 \leq t < \infty$. Now L transforms $\mathfrak{D}$ into the vector space $\mathcal{C}[0 \leq x \leq \pi, 0 \leq t < \infty]$ consisting of functions which are continuous at all points (x, t) of the strip; E^0 and E^π each transform $\mathfrak{D}$ into the vector space $\mathcal{C}[0, \infty)$.

Let us define $\mathcal{W}$ to be the vector space whose vectors consist of three terms,

$$\mathbf{w} = (g; k; m),$$

where $g \in \mathcal{C}[0 \leq x \leq \pi, 0 \leq t < \infty]$ is a function of x, t continuous at each point of the strip, and $k,m \in \mathcal{C}[0, \infty)$ are continuous functions of t, $0 \leq t < \infty$.

Then we may define the following transformation from $\mathfrak{D}$ into $\mathcal{W}$:

$$\text{(iii)} \qquad Tu = (Lu; E^0u; E^\pi u).$$

Taking the obvious definition for addition and scalar multiplication for vectors $\mathbf{w} = (g; k; m)$, it can be shown that T is a linear transformation (see problem 15, §1). Equations (i) and (ii) therefore take the form of a single conditional equation,

$$\text{(iv)} \qquad Tu = (0; t; t^2).$$

It follows from this that the solutions of (i) and (ii) form a plane P in

$$\mathfrak{D} = \mathcal{C}^2[0 \leq x \leq \pi, 0 \leq t < \infty].$$

To find one solution of (i) and (ii), let us note that [see formula (1.7) of Chapter 7] functions having the following form satisfy the partial differential equation (i):

$$\text{(v)} \qquad u(x, t) = f(x - t) + g(x + t),$$

where f and g are twice differentiable functions of one variable. Let us try to select f and g so that (ii) will be satisfied,

$$\text{(vi)} \quad u(0, t) = f(-t) + g(t) = t, \qquad u(\pi, t) = f(\pi - t) + g(\pi + t) = t^2.$$

Since the quantities t, t^2 are both polynomials, it is reasonable to look for an f and g which are polynomials. The most natural choices,

$$f(t) = At^2 + Bt + C, \qquad g(t) = at^2 + bt + c,$$

turn out not to work. But with a little effort we come up with the choices

$$f(t) = At^3 + Bt^2 + Ct + D, \qquad g(t) = at^3 + bt^2 + ct + d.$$

Inserting these into (vi) gives the equations

$$(-At^3 + Bt^2 - Ct + D) + (at^3 + bt^2 + ct + d) = t$$

$$\big(A(\pi - t)^3 + B(\pi - t)^2 + C(\pi - t) + D\big) + \big(a(\pi + t)^3 + b(\pi + t)^2 + c(\pi + t) + d\big) = t^2.$$

Collecting terms we get the requirement that two cubic polynomials vanish identically and hence that all their coefficients are zero. The resulting equations permit us to solve for f and g as follows:

$$f(t) = \frac{1}{6\pi}t^3 + \frac{1}{4\pi}t^2 - \left(\frac{1}{2} + \frac{\pi}{6}\right)t$$

$$g(t) = \frac{1}{6\pi}t^3 - \frac{1}{4\pi}t^2 + \left(\frac{1}{2} - \frac{\pi}{6}\right)t.$$

Thus we have by (v) a particular solution u^* of (i) and (ii):

$$u^*(x, t) = \frac{1}{6\pi}(x - t)^3 + \frac{1}{4\pi}(x - t)^2 - \left(\frac{1}{2} + \frac{\pi}{6}\right)(x - t) + \frac{1}{6\pi}(x + t)^3 - \frac{1}{4\pi}(x + t)^2 + \left(\frac{1}{2} - \frac{\pi}{6}\right)(x + t).$$

The further analysis of the solution plane P is covered in the problems.

The amount of effort we expended to put (i) and (ii) into the form of a conditional equation is rather high. On the other hand, the observation that solutions of (i), (ii) form a plane in $\mathfrak{D} = \mathcal{C}^2[0 \leq x \leq \pi, 0 \leq t < \infty]$ is very enlightening. In practice one develops an intuitive feeling for which PDE problems yield solutions forming a plane; then one doesn't bother, as we have, to describe in detail the space $\mathfrak{W}$ and transformation T. However, it is important to realize that every "linear" problem has the *potential* for being put into the form (CE).

The splitting theorem provides one of two general tactics for solving conditional equations. Before proceeding to describe the other general method let us summarize the splitting theorem in operational terms.

(2.4) Splitting Rule. *To construct the solution plane of* (CE) *find a particular solution of* (CE), *find the general solution of* (CE_0), *then add them together.*

We now discuss the other main approach to solving conditional equations. It involves expressing $\mathbf{w}$ as a linear combination of presumably simpler terms.

(2.5) Superposition Theorem. *Consider a conditional equation of the form*

$$\text{(CE)} \qquad T\mathbf{y} = a_1\mathbf{w}_1 + \cdots + a_k\mathbf{w}_k,$$

where $\mathbf{w}_i \in R_T$, $i = 1, \ldots, k$. *Let* $\mathbf{y}_1, \ldots, \mathbf{y}_k$ *be solutions of the conditional equations*

$$\text{(CE}_1\text{)} \quad T\mathbf{y} = \mathbf{w}_1, \qquad \text{(CE}_2\text{)} \quad T\mathbf{y} = \mathbf{w}_2, \ldots, \qquad \text{(CE}_k\text{)} \quad T\mathbf{y} = \mathbf{w}_k,$$

respectively. Then the vector

$$\text{(a)} \qquad \mathbf{y}^* = a_1\mathbf{y}_1 + \cdots + a_k\mathbf{y}_k$$

is a solution of (CE).

Proof. We are to show that every $\mathbf{y}^*$ of the form (a) is a solution of (CE). For this just use the linearity identity (1.4),

$$T\mathbf{y}^* = T(a_1\mathbf{y}_1 + \cdots + a_k\mathbf{y}_k) = a_1T\mathbf{y}_1 + \cdots + a_kT\mathbf{y}_k.$$

Since, by assumption, $\mathbf{y}_1$ is a solution of (CE$_1$), $\mathbf{y}_2$ is a solution of (CE$_2$), and so on, we deduce that

$$T\mathbf{y}^* = a_1\mathbf{w}_1 + \cdots + a_k\mathbf{w}_k = \mathbf{w}.$$

That is, $\mathbf{y}^*$ is a solution of (CE), as claimed. ▮

(2.6) Examples. Superposition Theorem

(a) Examine the following four systems of equations:

$$\text{(i)} \quad \begin{matrix} y_1 - 2y_2 + y_3 = 2 \\ y_1 + y_2 + 2y_3 = 3 \end{matrix} \qquad \begin{pmatrix} = 4 & = -2 & = -1 \\ = 6 & = -3 & = -\frac{3}{2} \end{pmatrix}.$$

By the method of (2.3a), each of these systems can be rewritten as a conditional equation of the form (CE) $T\mathbf{y} = \mathbf{w}$ for an appropriate linear transformation $T: \mathcal{R}^3 \to \mathcal{R}^2$ and an appropriate vector $\mathbf{w} \in \mathcal{R}^2$. Since the given systems differ only in their right sides, they all involve the *same* transformation T but differ in the choice of $\mathbf{w}$:

$$\text{(ii)} \qquad \mathbf{w}^1 = (2, 3), \quad \mathbf{w}^2 = (4, 6), \quad \mathbf{w}^3 = (-2, -3), \quad \mathbf{w}^4 = (-1, -\tfrac{3}{2}).$$

Now with the help of the superposition theorem it will be possible to obtain the solution of all four systems by solving just *one* of them. For note that

$$\text{(iii)} \qquad \mathbf{w}^2 = 2\mathbf{w}^1, \qquad \mathbf{w}^3 = -\mathbf{w}^1, \qquad \mathbf{w}^4 = -\tfrac{1}{2}\mathbf{w}^1.$$

Gauss reduction of the first system in (i) yields

$$\text{(iv)} \qquad \begin{aligned} y_1 &= -\tfrac{5}{3}y_3 + \tfrac{8}{3} \\ y_2 &= -\tfrac{1}{3}y_3 + \tfrac{1}{3}. \end{aligned}$$

Let us obtain the solution plane P_1 of this system. Taking $y_3 = 0$ gives us the particular solution

$$\mathbf{y} = (\tfrac{8}{3}, \tfrac{1}{3}, 0).$$

Moreover, N_T is easily checked to be the subspace $N_T = \langle(-\tfrac{5}{3}, -\tfrac{1}{3}, 1)\rangle$. Thus

$$\text{(v)} \qquad P_1 = (\tfrac{8}{3}, \tfrac{1}{3}, 0) + \langle(-\tfrac{5}{3}, -\tfrac{1}{3}, 1)\rangle.$$

According to (v) all vectors $\mathbf{y}_1 \in P_1$ have the form

$$\mathbf{y}_1 = (\tfrac{8}{3}, \tfrac{1}{3}, 0) + \mathbf{n}, \qquad \mathbf{n} \in \langle(-\tfrac{5}{3}, -\tfrac{1}{3}, 1)\rangle.$$

Using (iii) and applying the superposition theorem we now conclude, without further effort, that vectors of the form

$$\begin{aligned} \mathbf{y}_2 &= 2\mathbf{y}_1 = (\tfrac{16}{3}, \tfrac{2}{3}, 0) + 2\mathbf{n} \\ \mathbf{y}_3 &= -\mathbf{y}_1 = (-\tfrac{8}{3}, -\tfrac{1}{3}, 0) - \mathbf{n} \\ \mathbf{y}_4 &= -\tfrac{1}{2}\mathbf{y}_1 = (-\tfrac{4}{3}, -\tfrac{1}{6}, 0) - \tfrac{1}{2}\mathbf{n}, \qquad \mathbf{n} \in \langle(-\tfrac{5}{3}, -\tfrac{1}{3}, 1)\rangle \end{aligned}$$

are, respectively, solutions of the second, third, and fourth systems in (i). Equivalently, the solution planes P_2, P_3, P_4 of these systems are given by

$$\begin{aligned} P_2 &= (\tfrac{16}{3}, \tfrac{2}{3}, 0) + \langle(-\tfrac{5}{3}, -\tfrac{1}{3}, 1)\rangle \\ P_3 &= (-\tfrac{8}{3}, -\tfrac{1}{3}, 0) + \langle(-\tfrac{5}{3}, -\tfrac{1}{3}, 1)\rangle \\ P_4 &= (-\tfrac{4}{3}, -\tfrac{1}{6}, 0) + \langle(-\tfrac{5}{3}, -\tfrac{1}{3}, 1)\rangle. \end{aligned}$$

(b) To find the solution plane of the equation

$$\text{(i)} \qquad Ty = \ddot{y} - 3\dot{y} + 2y = 3e^{3t} - 6e^{4t},$$

we proceed as follows. The splitting theorem indicates that it will suffice to obtain a particular solution of (i), for in this problem it will be an easy matter to get N_T. Let us introduce the decomposition

$$w(t) = 3e^{3t} - 6e^{4t} = 3w_1(t) - 6w_2(t),$$

where $w_1(t) = e^{3t}$ and $w_2(t) = e^{4t}$. Then according to the superposition theorem solutions of (i) can be constructed by combining solutions of the following equations:

$$\text{(ii)} \qquad \ddot{y}(t) - 3\dot{y}(t) + 2y(t) = e^{3t} = w_1(t)$$

$$\text{(iii)} \qquad \ddot{y}(t) - 3\dot{y}(t) + 2y(t) = e^{4t} = w_2(t).$$

To find a particular solution of (ii) we make use of the fact that the function w_1 is in $\mathfrak{D}$ and that the T-image of w_1 is closely related to w_1 itself. Indeed, one can verify that

$$Tw_1 = 9e^{3t} - 9e^{3t} + 2e^{3t} = 2w_1.$$

Then by linearity of T it follows that $y_1 = \frac{1}{2}w_1 = \frac{1}{2}e^{3t}$ is a particular solution of (ii): $T(\frac{1}{2}w_1) = \frac{1}{2}Tw_1 = w_1$.

Likewise, we can obtain a solution of (iii) by noting that w_2 is in $\mathfrak{D}$ and that its T-image is closely related to w_2; that is,

$$Tw_2 = (16 - 12 + 2)e^{4t} = 6w_2.$$

Linearity of T implies here that $y_2 = \frac{1}{6}w_2 = \frac{1}{6}e^{4t}$ is a particular solution of (iii).

Now the superposition theorem implies that *every* function of the form

$$y = 3y_1 - 6y_2$$

is a solution of (i) when y_1 is a solution of (ii) and y_2 is a solution of (iii). Thus by selecting y_1 and y_2 as above, we are led to the following solution of (i):

$$y^*(t) = 3(\tfrac{1}{2}e^{3t}) - 6(\tfrac{1}{6}e^{4t}) = \tfrac{3}{2}e^{3t} - e^{4t}.$$

Moreover, by a straightforward calculation we find that

$$N_T = \langle e^t, e^{2t} \rangle.$$

Together these give the solution plane for (i) as

$$P = \tfrac{3}{2}e^{3t} - e^{4t} + \langle e^t, e^{2t} \rangle.$$

Observe that in the second of the above examples the decomposition of $w(t) = 3e^{3t} - 6e^{4t}$ in terms of $w_1(t) = e^{3t}$ and $w_2 = e^{4t}$ was a particularly advantageous move because w_1 and w_2 happen to be vectors which are proportional to their T-images. As we will see in §3, the superposition theorem plays a most useful role in situations of this sort.

We shall close this section with the observation that both the theorems discussed above are directly applicable to many *physical* systems. First we observe that the idea of superposition — that is, that the output which is produced by a given linear combination of inputs $f_1, \ldots, f_n$ will be the *same* linear combination of the outputs $y_1, \ldots, y_n$ corresponding to the *separate* inputs $f_1, f_2, \ldots, f_n$ — occurred in the definition of a black box in Chapter 6, §5 (see Figure 8.10). In fact, the reader should notice, on referring to that section, that black-box systems actually correspond to linear transformations on the spaces $\mathcal{P}^{2L}$ of periodic functions.

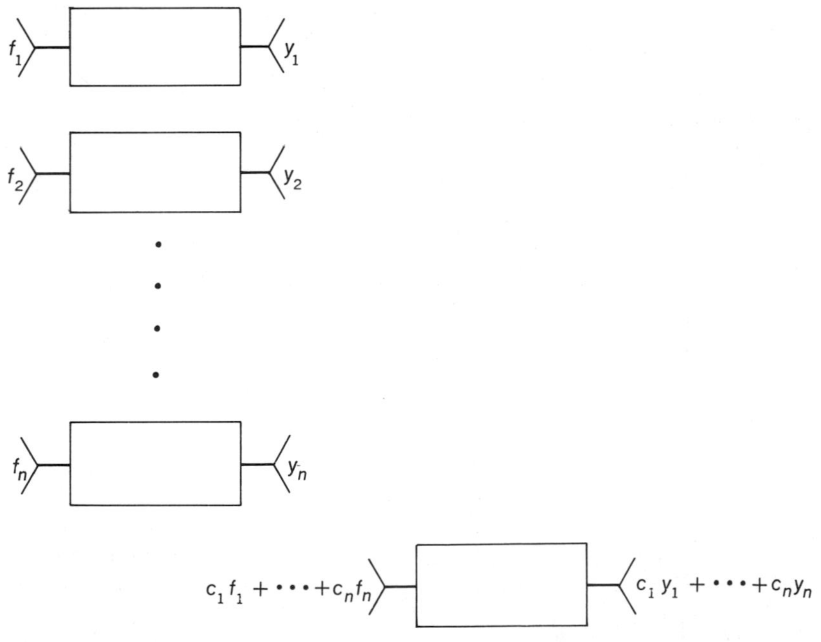

Figure 8.10

Next consider the electric circuit shown in Figure 8.11. For this circuit the splitting theorem asserts that all possible currents I which could be produced by a specific input voltage function E can be predicted as follows. Observe any *one* output for E and determine all possible outputs which can occur when the input E is zero. This idea forms a significant item among the techniques used by electrical engineers (and others) to analyze much more complicated linear systems.

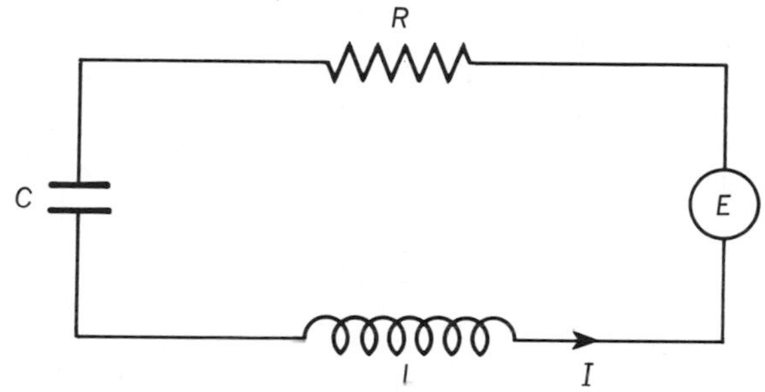

Figure 8.11

PROBLEMS

1. Solve the following conditional equations (give a formula or description for the solution plane).

(a) $y_1 + y_2 + y_3 = 2$
$y_1 - y_2 + 2y_3 = 0$

(b) $\ddot{y}(t) - y(t) = 1 - \sin t$

(c) $\ddot{y}(t) + y(t) = e^t - e^{2t}$

(d) $\int_0^{\pi} e^t y(t)\, dt = 1$

*(e) $\dot{y}(t) + \int_0^t y(s)\, ds = t$

(f) $y_1 + 2y_2 - y_3 = 1$
$2y_1 + y_2 + y_3 = 2$
$-y_1 + 4y_2 - 5y_3 = 1$

(g) $y(t) + \int_0^t sy(s)\, ds = t^2 + 2$

*(h) $u_{xx} - u_{tt} = -3 \sin x$
$u(x, 0) = 0, \quad 0 \leq x \leq \pi$
$u(0, t) = u(\pi, t) = 0, \quad 0 \leq t < \infty.$

2. Let S denote the subspace $\langle(1, 2, 1), (1, -1, 1)\rangle$ of $\mathcal{R}^3$. Solve the equation

$$P\boldsymbol{\alpha} = \boldsymbol{\alpha}_S = (1, 0, 1).$$

That is, give a formula for the set of all $\boldsymbol{\alpha} \in \mathcal{R}^3$ for which $\boldsymbol{\alpha}_S = (1, 0, 1)$. (*Hint:* This is a conditional equation.)

3. Express each of the following as a conditional equation, then find the solution plane.

(a) $\ddot{y}(t) = 0,\ y(0) = 1$ [*Hint:* Define $Ty = (Ly; y(0))$, where $Ly = \ddot{y}$. See (2.3c).]

(b) $\ddot{y}(t) = 0,\ \dot{y}(0) + y(0) = 1$

(c) $\ddot{y}(t) = 0,\ y(0) = 1, y(1) = 0$

4. Find all solutions of the following equations, using the splitting theorem.

(a)
$$\begin{aligned} y_1 - 3y_2 + y_3 &= 2 \\ 2y_1 - y_2 + y_3 &= -1 \\ y_1 + y_2 - y_3 &= 1 \\ 3y_1 - 2y_2 - 2y_3 &= 8 \end{aligned}$$

(b)
$$\ddot{y}(t) + y(t) = 0$$
$$\int_0^{\pi} y(t)\,dt = 1$$

*(c)
$$\int_0^1 \sin(\omega t) f(t)\,dt = \frac{1 - \cos\omega}{\omega}$$

(d)
$$\begin{aligned} y_1(t) + 2y_2(t) - y_3(t) &= t \\ 2y_1(t) - y_2(t) + y_3(t) &= \sin t \end{aligned}$$

5. Try to solve the following conditional equations by use of the superposition theorem with the vectors $\mathbf{w}_i$ chosen as indicated. If difficulties arise explain why.

(a)
$$\begin{aligned} 3x_1 - x_2 + x_3 + x_4 &= 4 \\ x_1 - 2x_2 + 2x_3 - x_4 &= -3, \qquad \mathbf{w}_1 = (1, 0),\ \mathbf{w}_2 = (0, 1) \end{aligned}$$

(b)
$$\begin{aligned} 3x_1 - x_2 + x_3 + x_4 &= 4 & \mathbf{w}_1 &= (1, 0, 0), \\ x_1 - 2x_2 + 2x_3 - x_4 &= -3 & \mathbf{w}_2 &= (0, 1, 0), \\ 3x_1 + 4x_2 - 4x_3 + 5x_4 &= 17, & \mathbf{w}_3 &= (0, 0, 1) \end{aligned}$$

(c) $\dot{y}(t) - y(t) = 2t - 3\sin t + 5e^t$

$w_1(t) = t,\ w_2(t) = \sin t,\ w_3(t) = e^t$

(d) $\ddot{y}(t) - \dot{y}(t) + y(t) = 2e^t + 5e^{-t}$

$w_1(t) = e^t,\ w_2(t) = e^{-t}$

(e) $\ddot{y}(t) - \dot{y}(t) + y(t) = t$

$y(0) = 10 \qquad \mathbf{w}_1 = (t; 0),\ \mathbf{w}_2 = (0, 1)$

[The *first* entry in $\mathbf{w}_i$ is a function of t, the second is a scalar denoting the value $y(0)$.]

(f)
$$\int_0^{\pi} (\sin t) y(t)\,dt = 2$$
$$\int_0^{\pi} (\cos t) y(t)\,dt = -5 \qquad \mathbf{w}_1 = (1, 0),\ \mathbf{w}_2 = (0, 1)$$

(g) $\dot{y}(t) + \int_0^t y(s)\,ds = 3t + 5\sin t \qquad w_1(t) = t,\ w_2(t) = \sin t$

*(h) $y(t) + \int_0^t sy(s)\,ds = 2t^2 + 5te^t \qquad w_1(t) = t^2,\ w_2(t) = e^t$

*(i) $u_{xx} - u_t = -3 \sin x$
$u(x, 0) = 2 \sin 2x,\ 0 \le x \le \pi$
$u(0, t) = u(\pi, t) = 0,\ 0 \le t < \infty \qquad \mathbf{w}_1 = (\sin x; 0),\ \mathbf{w}_2 = (0; \sin 2x)$

6. Solve the following conditional equations by use of the superposition theorem as indicated.

(a) $\ddot{y}(t) = 5t$
$y(0) = e^2 \quad \mathbf{w}_1 = (t; 0),\ \mathbf{w}_2 = (0; 1)$
[See problem 5(e) for the notation.]

(b) $\dddot{y}(t) = 0$
$\dot{y}(0) + y(0) = 2$
$\ddot{y}(0) = -5 \qquad \mathbf{w}_1 = (0; 1, 0),\ \mathbf{w}_2 = (0; 0, 1)$

(c) $\ddot{y}(t) = 0$
$y(0) = 1$
$y(1) = -2 \quad \mathbf{w}_1 = (0; 1, 0),\ \mathbf{w}_2 = (0; 0, 1)$

(d) $\dot{y}(t) = 2t$

$\int_0^1 y(t)\,dt = -3 \quad \mathbf{w}_1 = (t; 0),\ \mathbf{w}_2 = (0; 1)$

7. (a) Show that it is possible to solve all systems having the form

$$\text{(i)} \qquad \begin{aligned} y_1 - 5y_2 &= w_1 \\ 3y_1 + y_2 &= w_2 \end{aligned}$$

by applying the following method. Use Gauss reduction to simplify the system of equations (actually, a pair of systems) given by

$$\begin{aligned} y_1 + 5y_2 &= 1 \;\vdots\; 0 \\ 3y_1 + y_2 &= 0 \;\vdots\; 1. \end{aligned}$$

That is, handle the cases $\mathbf{w} = (1, 0)$ and $\mathbf{w} = (0, 1)$ simultaneously by manipulating each such right side independently of the other. For instance, the first two steps become

$$\begin{aligned} y_1 + 5y_2 &= 1 \;\vdots\; 0 \\ 3y_1 + y_2 &= 0 \;\vdots\; 1 \end{aligned} \xrightarrow{[2] - 3[1]} \begin{aligned} y_1 + 5y_2 &= 1 \;\vdots\; 0 \\ 0y_1 - 14y_2 &= -3 \;\vdots\; 1 \end{aligned} \xrightarrow{-\frac{1}{14}[2]}$$

$$\begin{aligned} y_1 - 5y_2 &= 1 \;\vdots\; 0 \\ 0y_1 + y_2 &= \tfrac{3}{14} \;\vdots\; -\tfrac{1}{14}. \end{aligned}$$

The information gained from completing this simultaneous Gauss reduction now permits one to solve (i) by inspection for any w_1 and w_2.

(b) Apply the technique in part (a) to the solution of the system

$$\begin{aligned} 2y_1 - 3y_2 &= w_1 \\ 3y_1 + 2y_2 &= w_2. \end{aligned}$$

8. (a) Is the technique discussed in problem 7 applicable to systems in three unknowns? Verify by applying it to the following systems.

$$\text{(i)}\quad \begin{aligned} 2y_1 - y_2 + y_3 &= w_1 \\ 3y_1 - y_2 - y_3 &= w_2 \\ 2y_1 + 3y_2 - 2y_3 &= w_3. \end{aligned} \qquad \text{(ii)}\quad \begin{aligned} 2y_1 - y_2 + 2y_3 &= w_1 \\ 2y_1 - 2y_2 + y_3 &= w_2. \end{aligned}$$

(b) Solve the following system by an analogous method:

$$\begin{aligned} y_1 + 2y_2 - y_3 + y_4 &= w_1 \\ 2y_1 - y_2 + 2y_3 - y_4 &= w_2 \\ y_1 + 8y_2 - 7y_3 + 5y_4 &= w_3. \end{aligned}$$

***9.** Solve the problem

$$y(t) - \int_0^t sy(s)\,ds = 2 - t^2 + 2t^3 - \tfrac{1}{2}t^4.$$

(*Hint:* Use both the splitting theorem and the superposition theorem.)

3. Eigenvectors, Inverses

In the present section we shall discuss two other methods for conditional equations. These lack the generality of the splitting theorem and superposition theorem, but provide an enormous simplification in those problems to which they do apply. Furthermore the first of these methods introduces the notion of eigenvectors, which is of outstanding importance in other situations. In particular this notion will form the basis of Chapters 9 and 10.

A. Eigenvectors

We found in the final example of §2 that the solution of

$$Ty = \ddot{y} - 3\dot{y} + 2y = 3e^{3t} - 6e^{4t} \tag{3.1}$$

by use of the superposition theorem is greatly facilitated because the functions $w_1(t) = e^{3t}$ and $w_2(t) = e^{4t}$ are proportional to their T-images: $Tw_1 = 2w_1, Tw_2 = 6w_2$. A result to follow will show that the superposition theorem is particularly effective *whenever* the $\mathbf{w}$ in a conditional equation consists of terms possessing such proportionality. First we give an important definition.

(3.2) Definition. Let T be a linear transformation from $\mathfrak{D}$ into $\mathfrak{W}$. A nonzero vector $\mathbf{y} \in \mathfrak{D}$ whose T-image is a scalar multiple of itself, that is,

$$T\mathbf{y} = \lambda\mathbf{y}, \qquad \lambda \text{ a scalar,} \tag{3.3}$$

is called an **eigenvector** of T ("eigen" = "self"). The number λ which gives the factor of proportionality between $\mathbf{y}$ and its T-image is called the **eigenvalue** of T associated with the eigenvector $\mathbf{y}$. The set of all eigenvalues of T is called the *spectrum* of T.

One thing that should be noted about an eigenvector is that (if $\lambda \neq 0$) it necessarily belongs both to $\mathfrak{D}$ and to $\mathfrak{W}$. It is an element of $\mathfrak{D}$ by definition, while (3.3) implies that it belongs to R_T. Hence definition (3.2) is only applicable when $\mathfrak{D}$ and $\mathfrak{W}$ have some vectors in common (Figure 8.12).

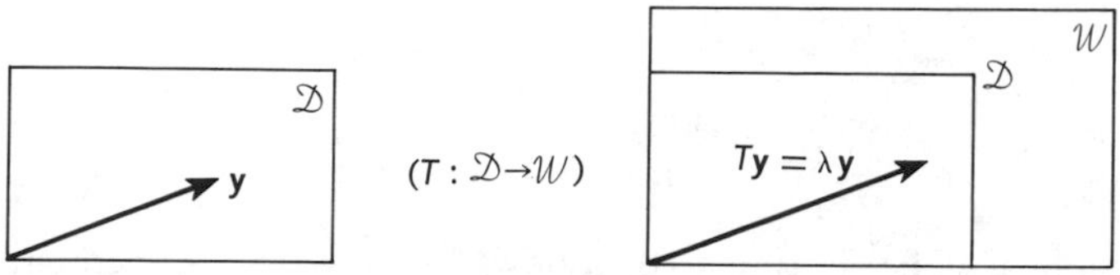

Figure 8.12

Note, too, that although an eigen*vector* is by definition nonzero, there is no such restriction on eigen*values*. In fact, if the eigenvalue associated with $\mathbf{y}$ is $\lambda = 0$ then, by (3.3), $T\mathbf{y} = 0$, which implies that $\mathbf{y} \in N_T$; conversely, every nonzero vector in N_T is an eigenvector of T with the eigenvalue $\lambda = 0$. In other words, N_T can be described as "the set of eigenvectors of T corresponding to $\lambda = 0$" (this omits $\mathbf{0} \in N_T$).

We can now apply this idea to conditional equations.

(3.4) Eigenvector Formula. *Consider a conditional equation of the form*

$$\text{(CE)} \qquad T\mathbf{y} = \mathbf{w} = a_1\mathbf{w}_1 + \cdots + a_k\mathbf{w}_k,$$

where the vectors $\mathbf{w}_i$ *are eigenvectors of* T *associated with* nonzero *eigenvalues* $\lambda_1, \ldots, \lambda_k$. *Then* $\mathbf{w}$ *is in* R_T, *and the following vector is a solution of* (CE):

$$\text{(a)} \qquad \mathbf{y}^* = \frac{a_1}{\lambda_1}\mathbf{w}_1 + \cdots + \frac{a_k}{\lambda_k}\mathbf{w}_k.$$

That is, the solution plane of (CE) *is given by the relation*

$$\text{(b)} \qquad P = \left(\frac{a_1}{\lambda_1}\mathbf{w}_1 + \cdots + \frac{a_k}{\lambda_k}\mathbf{w}_k\right) + N_T.$$

Proof. By assumption, $\mathbf{w}_1$ satisfies $T\mathbf{w}_1 = \lambda_1\mathbf{w}_1$. Since T is linear and $\lambda_1 \neq 0$, it follows that $\mathbf{y}_1 = \mathbf{w}_1/\lambda_1$ is a solution of

$$(\text{CE}_1) \qquad T\mathbf{y} = \mathbf{w}_1.$$

In a similar fashion we deduce that

$$\mathbf{y}_2 = \frac{\mathbf{w}_2}{\lambda_2}, \quad \ldots, \quad \mathbf{y}_k = \frac{\mathbf{w}_k}{\lambda_k},$$

are solutions, respectively, of the conditional equations

$$(\mathrm{CE}_2) \qquad T\mathbf{y} = \mathbf{w}_2, \quad \ldots, \quad (\mathrm{CE}_k) \qquad T\mathbf{y} = \mathbf{w}_k.$$

The superposition theorem then asserts that the vector

$$\begin{aligned} \mathbf{y}^* &= a_1\mathbf{y}_1 + \cdots + a_k\mathbf{y}_k \\ &= \frac{a_1}{\lambda_1}\mathbf{w}_1 + \cdots + \frac{a_k}{\lambda_k}\mathbf{w}_k \end{aligned}$$

is a solution of (CE). Formula (b) follows by the splitting theorem. ▌

Observe that the above result should find its maximum utility with transformations T for which *every* $\mathbf{w} \in R_T$ is a linear combination of T-eigenvectors with nonzero eigenvalues. Although not stressed earlier, the fact is that our analysis of black boxes in Chapter 6, §5, succeeds primarily because the transformation T associated with any black box is essentially of that sort. Likewise, the method of separation of variables is based on the fact that transformations T of the form

$$TX = X'' + CX, \qquad C = \frac{M}{K} \text{ (a constant)},$$

very nearly have the above property (Chapter 7, (3.8)). We will see below a much simpler example of a transformation whose range is spanned by eigenvectors with nonzero eigenvalues.

(3.5) Examples. Eigenvectors and Spectrum

(a) Let $T: \mathbb{R}^2 \to \mathbb{R}^2$ be defined by

$$T(y_1, y_2) = (-2y_1 + \tfrac{3}{2}y_2, 6y_1 - 2y_2).$$

To obtain the eigenvectors and associated eigenvalues of T let us write the vector equation $T\mathbf{y} = \lambda\mathbf{y}$ as a system of two scalar equations

$$\text{(A)} \qquad \begin{aligned} -2y_1 + \tfrac{3}{2}y_2 &= \lambda y_1 \\ 6y_1 - 2y_2 &= \lambda y_2. \end{aligned}$$

This system actually involves three unknowns: the quantities y_1, y_2, and the parameter λ. Thus solutions of (A) are triples of scalars (λ, y_1, y_2) which, when inserted into (A), satisfy both equations. To solve (A) let us rewrite it, by transposing terms, as

$$(\mathrm{A}') \qquad \begin{aligned} (-2-\lambda)y_1 + \tfrac{3}{2}y_2 &= 0 \\ 6y_1 - (2+\lambda)y_2 &= 0. \end{aligned}$$

Then the following scheme presents itself: Arbitrarily select a value for λ, $\lambda = c$ say, and insert it into (A′); then solve the resulting system of equations in *two* unknowns. By varying the choice of c we could obtain all solutions of (A′) in this manner. To illustrate, the choice $\lambda = -1$ results in the system

$$\begin{aligned} -y_1 + \tfrac{3}{2}y_2 &= 0 \\ 6y_1 - y_2 &= 0. \end{aligned}$$

By Gauss reduction we find that

$$\begin{aligned} y_1 &= 0 \\ y_2 &= 0, \end{aligned}$$

so that with $\lambda = -1$ the only solution of (A′) is the triple $(-1, 0, 0)$. Actually $(y_1, y_2) = (0, 0)$ will be the only y values we obtain for *most* values of the scalar λ. Those values of λ which produce from (A′) a system having nonzero y values are quite exceptional. It is possible to find these exceptional λ-values by doing Gauss reduction in a careful way (see the problems), but we shall instead rely on the familiar fact that a homogeneous pair of equations has *nonzero* solutions if and only if the determinant of its coefficients is zero. Applying this to (A′) we obtain the criterion

$$(\mathrm{i}) \qquad (-2-\lambda)^2 - 6\cdot\tfrac{3}{2} = \lambda^2 + 4\lambda - 5 = 0.$$

Equation (i) has as roots $\lambda = 1$, $\lambda = -5$. Hence these are the only λ values associated with *nonzero* vectors satisfying $T\mathbf{y} = \lambda\mathbf{y}$; that is, $\lambda = 1$ and $\lambda = -5$ are the eigenvalues of T. To find the eigenvectors associated with these eigenvalues we merely insert $\lambda = 1$ and $\lambda = -5$ into (A′) and then solve. Thus we must solve the systems,

$$(\mathrm{A}'_1) \quad \begin{aligned} -3y_1 + \tfrac{3}{2}y_2 &= 0 \\ 6y_1 - 3y_2 &= 0, \end{aligned} \qquad\qquad (\mathrm{A}'_{-5}) \quad \begin{aligned} 3y_1 + \tfrac{3}{2}y_2 &= 0 \\ 6y_1 + 3y_2 &= 0. \end{aligned}$$

Gauss reduction now leads to

$$(A_1'')\quad \begin{aligned} y_1 - \tfrac{1}{2}y_2 &= 0 \\ 0y_1 + 0y_2 &= 0, \end{aligned} \qquad (A_{-5}'')\quad \begin{aligned} y_1 + \tfrac{1}{2}y_2 &= 0 \\ 0y_1 + 0y_2 &= 0. \end{aligned}$$

In the first of these formulas we may select y_2 arbitrarily, $y_2 = k$, say. Then to obtain a solution of (A_1'') [hence of (A_1')] we must choose $y_1 = \frac{1}{2}k$. Thus the solutions corresponding to $\lambda = 1$ are

$$\lambda = 1: \quad \mathbf{y} = (y_1, y_2) = k(\tfrac{1}{2}, 1), \qquad k \text{ a scalar.}$$

In a similar way we find that the solutions corresponding to $\lambda = -5$ are

$$\lambda = -5: \quad \mathbf{y} = (y_1, y_2) = k(-\tfrac{1}{2}, 1), \qquad k \text{ a scalar.}$$

To summarize, we have found that, aside from scalar multiples, the vectors $\gamma_1 = (\frac{1}{2}, 1)$ and $\gamma_2 = (-\frac{1}{2}, 1)$ are the only eigenvectors of T. They correspond to $\lambda_1 = 1$ and $\lambda_2 = -5$, respectively. Observe that γ_1, γ_2 are a basis for $\mathcal{R}^2$. Thus the above transformation is an example of a transformation T whose range (that is, $\mathcal{R}^2$) is spanned by eigenvectors with nonzero eigenvalues. This fact will be pursued in the problems.

(b) Let us find the eigenvalues and eigenvectors for the differential operator $T: \mathcal{C}^1[0, \pi] \to \mathcal{C}[0, \pi]$ defined by

$$Ty = \dot{y} - 2y.$$

Here the equation $Ty = \lambda y$ takes the form

$$\text{(i)} \qquad \dot{y}(t) - 2y(t) = \lambda y(t).$$

Rewriting this as

$$\dot{y}(t) - (2 + \lambda)y(t) = 0,$$

we observe that for each value of λ this is a first-order ordinary differential equation and hence is guaranteed to have solutions $y \neq 0$. In fact, we can give all its solutions explicitly,

$$\text{(ii)} \qquad y(t) = ke^{(2+\lambda)t}, \qquad k \text{ a scalar.}$$

For this transformation *all scalars* λ *are eigenvalues*. Moreover, since the eigenvectors for $\lambda = 0$ all have the form $y(t) = ke^{2t}$, it follows that

$N_T = \langle e^{2t} \rangle$. The eigenvector formula now permits us to write down — by inspection — the solution plane of

$$Ty = \dot{y} - 2y = w$$

whenever w is a linear combination of finitely many exponentials e^{at}, $a \neq 2$. For by (ii) each of these exponentials e^{at} is an eigenvector corresponding to the nonzero eigenvalue $\lambda = a - 2$. Hence theorem (3.4) shows that the solution plane for the differential equation

$$\dot{y} - 2y = c_1 e^{a_1 t} + c_2 e^{a_2 t} + \cdots + c_k e^{a_k t}, \qquad a_i \neq 2,$$

is

$$P = \left(\frac{c_1}{a_1 - 2} e^{a_1 t} + \frac{c_2}{a_2 - 2} e^{a_2 t} + \cdots + \frac{c_k}{a_k - 2} e^{a_k t} \right) + \langle e^{2t} \rangle.$$

B. Inverses

The second method for solving conditional equations will apply only if T is a "one-to-one" transformation, that is, if the T-images of distinct vectors are always distinct (problem 1, §1). The basic idea of this approach is to construct for T a second transformation $\tilde{T}$ which "inverts" T in the following sense: For every $\mathbf{w} \in R_T$, $\tilde{T}\mathbf{w}$ is that unique vector $\mathbf{y} \in \mathfrak{D}$ which is the solution of $T\mathbf{y} = \mathbf{w}$ (Figure 8.13). Let us begin by considering an example.

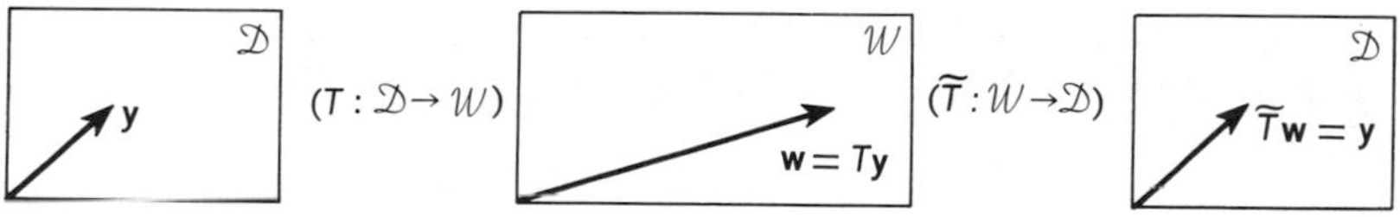

Figure 8.13

(3.6) Example. Inverse of *T*. Let T denote the transformation on

$$\mathfrak{D} = \mathcal{C}(-\infty, \infty)$$

such that $Tf = g$ where $g \in \mathcal{C}^1(-\infty, \infty)$ is defined by

$$\text{(i)} \qquad g(t) = \int_0^t f(s)\, ds, \qquad -\infty < t < \infty.$$

We have seen before that T is a linear transformation. In order to solve the conditional equation

$$\text{(ii)} \qquad Ty = w,$$

let us define a transformation $\tilde{T}$ on $\mathcal{W} = \mathcal{C}^1(-\infty, \infty)$ as follows:

$$\text{(iii)} \qquad \tilde{T}f = \dot{f}, \qquad f \in \mathcal{C}^1(-\infty, \infty).$$

That is, $\tilde{T}$ is the differentiation operator. Clearly

$$\tilde{T}: \mathcal{C}^1(-\infty, \infty) \to \mathcal{C}(-\infty, \infty)$$

is linear. We proceed to show that $\tilde{T}$ inverts† T.

Suppose that $w \in R_T$. Then by (i) there is a function $f \in \mathfrak{D} = \mathcal{C}(-\infty, \infty)$ such that

$$\text{(iv)} \qquad w(t) = \int_0^t f(s)\,ds, \qquad -\infty < t < \infty.$$

According to the fundamental theorem [theorem (3.7) of Chapter 2], both terms in (iv) are differentiable and further,

$$\text{(v)} \qquad \dot{w}(t) = f(t) \qquad \text{for all } t.$$

That is,

$$\text{(vi)} \qquad \dot{w} = \tilde{T}w = f.$$

Comparing (iv) with (vi) we see that

$$\text{(vii)} \qquad Tf = w \qquad \text{implies } f = \tilde{T}w = \dot{w}.$$

This equation indicates how to solve the conditional equation (ii). If $w \notin R_T$, there is *no* solution; if $w \in R_T$, then the function $y = \tilde{T}w$ is the (unique) solution.

To complete the analysis we should give the vector space $\tilde{\mathfrak{D}}$ which is the domain of the transformation $\tilde{T}$. For this we observe that R_T is the subspace $\mathcal{C}_0^1(-\infty, \infty)$ of $\mathcal{W} = \mathcal{C}^1(-\infty, \infty)$ consisting of those continuously differentiable functions w which satisfy $w(0) = 0$. The proof that $\mathcal{C}_0^1(-\infty, \infty)$ actually is a subspace of $\mathcal{W}$ and that $\mathcal{C}_0^1(-\infty, \infty) = R_T = \tilde{\mathfrak{D}}$ is left to the problems.

Observe that the T in the above example was a one-to-one transformation. For if $f_1, f_2 \in \mathcal{C}(-\infty, \infty)$ are not identical, then for some t values at least, $\int_0^t f_1(s)\,ds \neq \int_0^t f_2(s)\,ds$ and hence $g_1 = Tf_1$ and $g_2 = Tf_2$ are distinct. [*Proof:* Since $\dot{g}_1(t) \not\equiv \dot{g}_2(t)$, g_1 and g_2 cannot be the same function.] The

†Actually the transformation $\tilde{T}$ defined here is called a "left inverse" of T.

next result states that one-to-oneness is the *only* restriction on a linear transformation T needed for the existence of an inverse $\tilde{T}$.

(3.7) Invertibility Theorem. *Suppose that T is a one-to-one linear transformation from $\mathfrak{D}$ into $\mathfrak{W}$. Then there exists a linear transformation $\tilde{T}$ carrying the vector space $\tilde{\mathfrak{D}} = R_T$ onto $\tilde{\mathfrak{W}} = \mathfrak{D}$ such that $\tilde{T}$ inverts T:*

$$\text{(a)} \qquad T\mathbf{y} = \mathbf{w} \text{ implies } \mathbf{y} = \tilde{T}\mathbf{w}, \qquad \mathbf{w} \in R_T.$$

For obvious notational reasons the linear transformation from $\tilde{\mathfrak{D}} = R_T$ to $\tilde{\mathfrak{W}} = \mathfrak{D}$ which satisfies (3.7a) is called the **inverse** of T and will hereafter be denoted by T^{-1} rather than $\tilde{T}$.

We shall omit the proof of theorem (3.7). We note, however, the following facts. Let $\mathbf{y}$ be in $\mathfrak{D}$. Then $T\mathbf{y}$ is in R_T, hence in the domain of T^{-1}. If we apply T^{-1} to $T\mathbf{y}$ we shall obtain a vector in $\mathfrak{D}$. What vector is it? By definition it is the vector whose image under T is $T\mathbf{y}$. But this vector is obviously just $\mathbf{y}$ itself. Thus we have the formula

$$T^{-1}(T\mathbf{y}) = \mathbf{y}.$$

The reader should also interpret and verify the similar formula

$$T(T^{-1}\mathbf{w}) = \mathbf{w}.$$

(3.8) Examples. Inverses

(a) Let us find the inverse, if any, of the linear transformation

$$T: \mathcal{R}^2 \to \mathcal{R}^2, \qquad T(y_1, y_2) = (y_1 + 2y_2, 2y_1 + 3y_2).$$

The equation $T\mathbf{y} = \mathbf{w} = (w_1, w_2)$ can be written as a system of equations

$$\text{(A)} \qquad \begin{aligned} y_1 + 2y_2 &= w_1 \\ 2y_1 + 3y_2 &= w_2. \end{aligned}$$

To know whether or not T has an inverse we must check whether T is one to one. We can accomplish this task by Gauss-reducing (A),

$$\begin{aligned} y_1 + 2y_2 &= w_1 \\ 2y_2 + 3y_2 &= w_2 \end{aligned} \quad \xrightarrow{[2] - 2[1]} \quad \begin{aligned} y_1 + 2y_2 &= w_1 \\ 0y_1 - y_2 &= w_2 - 2w_1 \end{aligned} \quad \xrightarrow{-[2]}$$

$$\begin{aligned} y_1 + 2y_2 &= w_1 \\ 0y_1 + \ y_2 &= w_2 - 2w_1 \end{aligned} \quad \xrightarrow{[1] - 2[2]} \quad \text{(A}'\text{)} \quad \begin{aligned} y_1 &= -3w_1 + 2w_2 \\ y_2 &= w_2 - 2w_1. \end{aligned}$$

Inspection of (A′) reveals that each vector $\mathbf{w} = (w_1, w_2)$ determines a unique solution $\mathbf{y} = (y_1, y_2)$ of (A); namely,

$$\text{(i)} \qquad (y_1, y_2) = (-3w_1 + 2w_2, -w_2 + 2w_1).$$

It remains now to observe that since (A) has a solution for *every* $\mathbf{w}$, $R_T = \mathcal{R}^2$. Clearly the transformation $\tilde{T}: \mathcal{R}^2 \to \mathcal{R}^2$ defined by

$$\tilde{T}(x_1, x_2) = (-3x_1 + 2x_2, -x_2 + 2x_1)$$

is linear. Thus (i) can be rewritten

$$\text{(ii)} \qquad (y_1, y_2) = (-3w_1 + 2w_2, -w_2 + 2w_1) = \tilde{T}(w_1, w_2).$$

This means that the transformation $\tilde{T}$ satisfies (3.7a) and is therefore the inverse of T:

$$T^{-1}(w_1, w_2) = (-3w_1 + 2w_2, -w_2 + 2w_1).$$

(b) Let us take $\mathfrak{D} = \mathcal{C}_0^1[0, \pi]$, the vector space of continuously differentiable functions y on $0 \leq t \leq \pi$ which satisfy $y(0) = 0$. The proof that $\mathfrak{D}$ actually is a vector space is left as an exercise. Define $T: \mathfrak{D} \to \mathcal{C}[0, \pi]$ by

$$Ty = \dot{y} - y.$$

Let us find the inverse, if any, of T.

The equation $T\mathbf{y} = \mathbf{w}$ reduces to

$$\text{(i)} \qquad \dot{y}(t) - y(t) = w(t), \qquad 0 \leq t \leq \pi.$$

where $w \in \mathcal{W} = \mathcal{C}[0, \pi]$. Let us try to solve (i), leaving aside for the moment the question of whether or not T is one-to-one. The methods of Chapter 4, §1, show that any solution is of the form

$$\text{(ii)} \qquad y(t) = ce^t + e^t \int_0^t e^{-s} w(s)\, ds,$$

for some constant c.

Now there is only one function prescribed by (ii), which is in $\mathfrak{D} = \mathcal{C}_0^1[0, \pi]$. For in order to have $y(0) = 0$, it is necessary to have $c = 0$. Hence the only solution *in* $\mathfrak{D}$ is

$$\text{(iii)} \qquad y(t) = e^t \int_0^t e^{-s} w(s)\, ds.$$

This proves that T *is one-to-one:* There is at most one solution in $\mathfrak{D}$ for any $w \in \mathcal{C}[0, \pi] = \mathcal{W}$. Moreover since the function y given in (iii) is a solution of (i) for *any* choice of $w \in \mathcal{C}[0, \pi]$ [see Chapter 4, §1] we see that in this problem $R_T = \mathcal{W}$.

Observe that the right side of (iii) suggests a candidate for the transformation $\tilde{T}$:

$$\tilde{T}w = z, \qquad \text{where } z(t) = e^t \int_0^t e^{-s} w(s)\, ds, \qquad 0 \le t \le \pi.$$

It is left as an exercise (see the problems) to verify that this transformation is linear and carries every function in $\mathcal{W} = \mathcal{C}[0, \pi]$ to a function in $\mathfrak{D}$. Moreover, according to (i) and (iii) $\tilde{T}$ satisfies (3.7a). Hence $\tilde{T}$ is the inverse of T:

$$\text{(iv)} \qquad T^{-1}w = y, \qquad \text{where } y(t) = e^t \int_0^t e^{-s} w(s)\, ds, \qquad 0 \le t \le \pi.$$

One word of warning. Suppose that a transformation T has $N_T = 0$, and hence by the splitting theorem is one to one. Theorem (3.7) then guarantees that there *exists* a linear transformation $\tilde{T} = T^{-1}$ which inverts T, but it does *not* provide a systematic procedure for finding T^{-1}. In general, the calculation of T^{-1} is quite difficult; hence one does not ordinarily solve $T\mathbf{y} = \mathbf{w}$ by first finding T^{-1} and then evaluating $T^{-1}\mathbf{w}$. However, the calculation of T^{-1} happens to be quite straightforward when T is a transformation on $\mathcal{R}^n$. This will be shown in §4.

PROBLEMS

1. Find the eigenvectors and eigenvalues of the following transformations.

(a) $T(y_1, y_2) = (y_1 + y_2, y_1 + 2y_2)$

(b) $T(y_1, y_2) = (y_1 - y_2, y_1 + 2y_2)$

(c) $T(y_1, y_2) = (2y_1, 2y_2)$

(d) $Ty = \dot{y} - 2y, \; y \in \mathcal{C}^1(-\infty, \infty)$

(e) $Ty = \ddot{y} - \dot{y} + y, \; y \in \mathcal{C}^2(-\infty, \infty)$

*(f) $Ty = \ddot{y}, \; y \in \hat{\mathcal{C}}^2(-\infty, \infty)$, where $\hat{\mathcal{C}}^2(-\infty, \infty)$ is the subspace of $\mathcal{C}^2(-\infty, \infty)$ consisting of functions which satisfy $y(0) = 0, y(\pi) = 0$.

**(g) $Ty = \ddot{y}, \; y \in \check{\mathcal{C}}^2(-\infty, \infty)$, where $\check{\mathcal{C}}^2(-\infty, \infty)$ is the subspace of $\check{\mathcal{C}}^2(-\infty, \infty)$ consisting of functions which satisfy

$$y(0) = y(\pi), \qquad \dot{y}(0) = \dot{y}(\pi).$$

2. Find the eigenvectors and eigenvalues of the transformation on $\mathcal{R}^3$ defined by

$$T\boldsymbol{\alpha} = P\boldsymbol{\alpha},$$

where $P\boldsymbol{\alpha}$ is the projection of $\boldsymbol{\alpha}$ on $S = \langle(1, 2, 1), (1, -1, 1)\rangle$.

3. Find the eigenvectors and eigenvalues of the following transformations.

(a) $Ty = f$, where $f(t) = \int_0^t sy(s)\,ds;\ y \in \mathcal{C}(-\infty, \infty)$

(b) $Ty = f$, where $f(t) = \int_0^\pi \sin(s + t)y(s)\,ds;\ y \in \mathcal{C}[0, \pi]$

4. Suppose a transformation on $\mathcal{R}^2$ has two distinct eigenvalues λ_1 and λ_2 with corresponding eigenvectors $\boldsymbol{\gamma}_1, \boldsymbol{\gamma}_2$. Show that $\boldsymbol{\gamma}_1$ and $\boldsymbol{\gamma}_2$ form a basis for $\mathcal{R}^2$.

***5.** Prove that if $\boldsymbol{\gamma}_1, \boldsymbol{\gamma}_2, \boldsymbol{\gamma}_3$ are eigenvectors of a transformation T corresponding to *distinct* eigenvalues $\lambda_1, \lambda_2, \lambda_3$, then the $\boldsymbol{\gamma}$'s are linearly independent. (*Hint:* Supposing $c_1\boldsymbol{\gamma}_1 + c_2\boldsymbol{\gamma}_2 + c_3\boldsymbol{\gamma}_3 = \mathbf{0}$, apply T to both sides of this equation. Then apply T to both sides of the resulting equation. Consider the three simultaneous equations obtained in this way.)

6. Find the inverses of the transformations in problems 1(a), 1(b), and 1(c).

***7.** Find the inverse, if any, of the transformation

$$Ty = f, \qquad \text{where } f(t) = y(t) + \int_0^t y(s)\,ds,\ y \in \mathcal{C}(-\infty, \infty)$$

8. Find the inverse of the transformation

$$Ty = \ddot{y}, \qquad y \in \mathcal{C}_0^2(-\infty, \infty),$$

the space $\mathcal{C}_0^2(-\infty, \infty)$ being defined as that subspace of $\mathcal{C}^2(-\infty, \infty)$ whose vectors satisfy $y(0) = \dot{y}(0) = 0$.

9. Solve the following equations by use of the eigenvector formula.

(a) $\ddot{y}(t) + y(t) = 2e^{3t} - 3e^{2t} + 5e^{-t}$

(b) $\dot{y}(t) + y(t) = 2e^t - 2e^{3t} + e^{5t}$

(c) $\ddot{y}(t) + y(t) = 2\sin 2t - 3e^{3t}$

(d) $\ddot{y}(t) - y(t) = 2\sin 2t - 3\cos 2t + 5\cos 2t$

(e) $y(t) + \int_0^t y(s)\,ds = e^t - 2e^{-t}$

10. (a) Find the eigenvalues of $Ty = (y_1 + 2y_2, 2y_1 - 5y_2)$ as follows. The appropriate system of linear equations reads

$$\text{(A)} \qquad \begin{aligned} (1 - \lambda)y_1 + 2y_2 &= 0 \\ 2y_1 - (5 + \lambda)y_2 &= 0. \end{aligned}$$

Apply Gauss reduction to (A), the first step, for instance, being

$$(1 - \lambda)^{-1}[1].$$

The final result is

$$\text{(A')} \qquad \begin{aligned} y_1 &= 0 \\ y_2 &= 0. \end{aligned}$$

Examine those values for λ which would invalidate some of the steps; for example, the first step above would not be valid if $\lambda = 1$. The eigenvalues for T are included in this set of scalars.

(b) Use this method to find the eigenvalues and eigenvectors of

$$T\mathbf{y} = (y_1 + 3y_2, 3y_1 + 5y_2).$$

11. Use the results obtained in example (3.5a) to solve

$$T\mathbf{y} = (-2y_1 + \tfrac{3}{2}y_2, 6y_1 - 2y_2) = (2, -2)$$

by use of the eigenvector formula.

12. (a) Prove that $\mathcal{C}_0^1(-\infty, \infty)$ as defined in example (3.6) is a subspace of $\mathcal{C}^1(-\infty, \infty)$.

(b) Prove that $R_T = \mathcal{C}_0^1(-\infty, \infty)$ if T is the transformation on $\mathcal{C}(-\infty, \infty)$ defined by

$$Tf = g, \qquad \text{where } g(t) = \int_0^t f(s)\, ds.$$

13. Show that the transformation $\tilde{T}$ defined by

$$\tilde{T}w = z, \qquad w \in \mathcal{C}[0, \pi],$$

where $z(t) = e^t \int_0^t e^{-s} w(s)\, ds$, is linear and that $R_{\tilde{T}} = \mathcal{C}_0^1[0, \pi]$.

4. Transformations on $\mathcal{R}^n$ to $\mathcal{R}^n$

This section will involve the study of transformations whose domain is one of the vector spaces $\mathcal{R}^n$. Consider, for example, the transformation T defined by

$$T(y_1, y_2, y_3) = (y_1 - y_2 - y_3,\ 2y_1 + y_2 - y_3,\ y_1 + y_2 + y_3).$$

It is a simple matter to verify that $T: \mathcal{R}^3 \to \mathcal{R}^3$ is a *linear* transformation. What is not so obvious is that *all* linear transformations taking $\mathcal{R}^3$ to $\mathcal{R}^3$ (more generally, $\mathcal{R}^n$ to $\mathcal{R}^n$) have virtually the same form as T. That is the significance of our next result.

(4.1) Theorem. *The transformation $T: \mathcal{R}^n \to \mathcal{R}^n$ is linear if and only if there is a system of n^2 scalars,*

$$t_{11}, t_{12}, \ldots, t_{1n};\ t_{21}, t_{22}, \ldots, t_{2n};\ \ldots;\ t_{n1}, t_{n2}, \ldots, t_{nn}$$

such that for all $\mathbf{y} = (y_1, \ldots, y_n) \in \mathbb{R}^n$,

(a) $T(y_1, \ldots, y_n) =$

$$(t_{11}y_1 + t_{12}y_2 + \cdots + t_{1n}y_n, t_{21}y_1 + t_{22}y_2 + \cdots + t_{2n}y_n, \ldots, t_{n1}y_1 + t_{n2}y_2 + \cdots + t_{nn}y_n).$$

The proof of this result will be carried out in the problems. What we want to do here is discuss a very convenient notation suggested by theorem (4.1). According to the theorem one can keep track of any (linear) transformation T from $\mathbb{R}^n$ to $\mathbb{R}^n$ by recording the n^2 scalars $t_{11}, \ldots, t_{nn}$. Hence it is reasonable to *represent* T by merely listing these t_{ij}'s. That is, we introduce the following notation:

$$(4.2) \qquad T = \begin{pmatrix} t_{11} & t_{12} & \cdots & t_{1n} \\ t_{21} & t_{22} & \cdots & t_{2n} \\ \vdots & & & \vdots \\ t_{n1} & t_{n2} & \cdots & t_{nn} \end{pmatrix}.$$

Note that the first row of this array consists of those coefficients of $y_1, \ldots, y_n$ occurring in the first component of $T\mathbf{y}$; likewise, the second row of the array consists of those coefficients of $y_1, \ldots, y_n$ occurring in the second component of $T\mathbf{y}$, and so on.

The notation becomes particularly clear if we hereafter adopt the tactic of writing vectors in $\mathbb{R}^n$ as *vertical* rather than horizontal n-tuples. Formula (4.1a) then reads

$$(4.3) \qquad T\begin{pmatrix} y_1 \\ \vdots \\ y_n \end{pmatrix} = \begin{pmatrix} t_{11}y_1 + t_{12}y_2 + \cdots + t_{1n}y_n \\ \vdots \\ t_{n1}y_1 + t_{n2}y_2 + \cdots + t_{nn}y_n \end{pmatrix}.$$

Equivalently, by employing the symbol for T given in (4.2), we have

$$(4.4) \qquad \begin{pmatrix} t_{11} & t_{12} & \cdots & t_{1n} \\ \vdots & & & \vdots \\ t_{n1} & t_{n2} & \cdots & t_{nn} \end{pmatrix} \begin{pmatrix} y_1 \\ \vdots \\ y_n \end{pmatrix} = \begin{pmatrix} t_{11}y_1 + t_{12}y_2 + \cdots + t_{1n}y_n \\ \vdots \\ t_{n1}y_1 + t_{n2}y_2 + \cdots + t_{nn}y_n \end{pmatrix}.$$

[Note that the right sides of (4.3) and (4.4) actually *are* n-tuples of scalars despite the fact that these scalars are given as lengthy sums.]

(4.5) Definition. For any linear transformation T from $\mathcal{R}^n$ to $\mathcal{R}^n$, the array (4.2) consisting of the n^2 scalars t_{ij} which occur in computing $T\mathbf{y}$ from $\mathbf{y}$ is called the *standard matrix form* for T, or briefly the **matrix** for T.

Let us now observe that according to equation (4.4) the n-tuple $\mathbf{w} = T\mathbf{y}$ is computed from the n-tuple $\mathbf{y}$ and the matrix $\begin{pmatrix} t_{11} & & \\ & \ddots & \\ & & t_{nn} \end{pmatrix}$ as follows.

(4.6) Rule. *The* first *component of* $\mathbf{w}$ *is obtained by multiplying the components of* $\mathbf{y}$ *with the entries in the* first *row of* $\begin{pmatrix} t_{11} & & \\ & \ddots & \\ & & t_{nn} \end{pmatrix}$ *and then adding; the* second *component of* $\mathbf{w}$ *is obtained by multiplying the components of* $\mathbf{y}$ *with the entries in the* second *row of* $\begin{pmatrix} t_{11} & & \\ & \ddots & \\ & & t_{nn} \end{pmatrix}$ *and then adding; similarly for later components of* $\mathbf{w}$.

The above rule leads to the following terminology. Given any matrix $T = \begin{pmatrix} t_{11} & & \\ & \ddots & \\ & & t_{nn} \end{pmatrix}$ and any n-tuple $\mathbf{y} = \begin{pmatrix} y_1 \\ \cdot \\ \cdot \\ \cdot \\ y_n \end{pmatrix}$, we call the n-tuple $\mathbf{w}$ constructed from them by rule (4.6) the *product* of the matrix $\begin{pmatrix} t_{11} & & \\ & \ddots & \\ & & t_{nn} \end{pmatrix}$ with the column $\begin{pmatrix} y_1 \\ \cdot \\ \cdot \\ \cdot \\ y_n \end{pmatrix}$.

It should be noted that this new notation makes transparent an important fact about systems of linear equations. Suppose we are given any system of linear equations possessing as many equations as unknowns.† For instance, consider the equations

$$\text{(i)} \qquad \begin{aligned} a_{11}y_1 + a_{12}y_2 + \cdots + a_{1n}y_n &= d_1 \\ \vdots \qquad\qquad\qquad \vdots \quad &\quad \vdots \\ a_{n1}y_1 + a_{n2}y_2 + \cdots + a_{nn}y_n &= d_n. \end{aligned}$$

†Similar facts hold for systems in which the number of equations is not the same as the number of unknowns (see the problems).

By regarding the left and right sides of (i) as n-tuples, namely,

$$\begin{pmatrix} a_{11}y_1 + \cdots + a_{1n}y_n \\ \vdots \\ a_{n1}y_1 + \cdots + a_{nn}y_n \end{pmatrix} \quad \text{and} \quad \begin{pmatrix} d_1 \\ \vdots \\ d_n \end{pmatrix},$$

we can use (4.4) to rewrite equation (i) in the following equivalent form

$$\text{(ii)} \qquad \begin{pmatrix} a_{11} & a_{12} & \cdots & a_{1n} \\ \vdots & & & \vdots \\ a_{n1} & a_{n2} & \cdots & a_{nn} \end{pmatrix} \begin{pmatrix} y_1 \\ \vdots \\ y_n \end{pmatrix} = \begin{pmatrix} d_1 \\ \vdots \\ d_n \end{pmatrix}.$$

In other words, *every linear system of the form* (i) *can be interpreted as a conditional equation on* $\mathbb{R}^n$:

$$\text{(CE)} \qquad T\mathbf{y} = \mathbf{w},$$

where T is the transformation whose matrix is made up of the coefficients of $y_1, \ldots, y_n$ *in* (i).

(4.7) Examples. Matrices

(a) Find the image of the vector $\boldsymbol{\alpha} = \begin{pmatrix} 1 \\ 2 \\ 3 \end{pmatrix}$ under each of the transformations

$$T_1 = \begin{pmatrix} 1 & 0 & 1 \\ -1 & 2 & -1 \\ 1 & 1 & 1 \end{pmatrix}, \qquad T_2 = \begin{pmatrix} 3 & -1 & 2 \\ 2 & -1 & 3 \\ 2 & 0 & 0 \end{pmatrix}.$$

According to (4.6), $T_1\boldsymbol{\alpha}$ is the product

$$\begin{pmatrix} 1 & 0 & 1 \\ -1 & 2 & -1 \\ 1 & 1 & 1 \end{pmatrix} \begin{pmatrix} 1 \\ 2 \\ 3 \end{pmatrix} = \begin{pmatrix} 1 \cdot 1 + 0 \cdot 2 + 1 \cdot 3 \\ -1 \cdot 1 + 2 \cdot 2 + (-1) \cdot 3 \\ 1 \cdot 1 + 1 \cdot 2 + 1 \cdot 3 \end{pmatrix} = \begin{pmatrix} 4 \\ 0 \\ 6 \end{pmatrix}.$$

Likewise, as the reader should verify,

$$\begin{pmatrix} 3 & -1 & 2 \\ 2 & -1 & 3 \\ 2 & 0 & 0 \end{pmatrix} \begin{pmatrix} 1 \\ 2 \\ 3 \end{pmatrix} = \begin{pmatrix} 7 \\ 9 \\ 2 \end{pmatrix}.$$

(b) Find the matrix form for the identity transformation $I: \mathcal{R}^n \to \mathcal{R}^n$, defined by $I\mathbf{y} = \mathbf{y}$ for all $\mathbf{y}$. By definition,

$$\mathbf{y} = \begin{pmatrix} y_1 \\ \cdot \\ \cdot \\ \cdot \\ y_n \end{pmatrix} \quad \text{implies } I\mathbf{y} = \begin{pmatrix} y_1 \\ \cdot \\ \cdot \\ \cdot \\ y_n \end{pmatrix} = \begin{pmatrix} y_1 + 0y_2 + \cdots + 0y_n \\ \vdots \\ 0y_1 + 0y_2 + \cdots + \ y_n \end{pmatrix}.$$

Comparing with (4.4) we conclude that the desired matrix is

$$I = \begin{pmatrix} 1 & 0 & \cdots & 0 \\ 0 & 1 & \cdots & 0 \\ \cdot & & \cdot & \cdot \\ \cdot & & & \cdot \\ \cdot & & & \cdot \\ 0 & 0 & \cdots & 1 \end{pmatrix}$$

In other words, the matrix form for the identity transformation consists of 1's along the diagonal and 0's everywhere else.

Our next objective is to justify the claim made in §3 that the computation of inverses is a straightforward procedure in the case of transformations taking $\mathcal{R}^n$ to $\mathcal{R}^n$. We begin by considering an example.

(4.8) Example. Inverse. Let us find the inverse, if any, of the following transformation on $\mathcal{R}^3$:

$$T = \begin{pmatrix} 1 & 2 & 1 \\ 1 & -1 & 1 \\ 1 & 1 & 0 \end{pmatrix}.$$

By definition T^{-1}, if it exists, is that transformation which assigns to each $\mathbf{w} = \begin{pmatrix} w_1 \\ w_2 \\ w_3 \end{pmatrix} \in R_T$ the unique $\mathbf{y} = \begin{pmatrix} y_1 \\ y_2 \\ y_3 \end{pmatrix}$ satisfying

$$\text{(i)} \qquad \begin{pmatrix} 1 & 2 & 1 \\ 1 & -1 & 1 \\ 1 & 1 & 0 \end{pmatrix} \begin{pmatrix} y_1 \\ y_2 \\ y_3 \end{pmatrix} = \begin{pmatrix} w_1 \\ w_2 \\ w_3 \end{pmatrix}.$$

Now equating components of the product on the left with those of the triple on the right gives the system of equations (an SLE),

$$\text{(ii)} \qquad \begin{aligned} y_1 + 2y_2 + y_3 &= w_1 \\ y_1 - \ y_2 + y_3 &= w_2 \\ y_1 + \ y_2 \qquad &= w_3. \end{aligned}$$

We may simplify (ii) by Gauss reduction:

$$\begin{aligned} y_1 + 2y_2 + y_3 &= w_1 \\ y_1 - \ \ y_2 + y_3 &= w_2 \\ y_1 + \ \ y_2 \qquad &= w_3 \end{aligned} \quad \begin{matrix} \\ \xrightarrow{[2]-[1]} \\ \xrightarrow{[3]-[1]} \end{matrix} \quad \begin{aligned} y_1 + 2y_2 + y_3 &= w_1 \\ -3y_2 \qquad &= -w_1 + w_2 \\ -\ y_2 - y_3 &= -w_1 + w_3 \end{aligned} \quad \begin{matrix} \\ \xrightarrow{-\frac{1}{3}[2]} \\ \\ \end{matrix}$$

$$\begin{aligned} y_1 + 2y_2 + y_3 &= w_1 \\ y_2 \qquad &= \tfrac{1}{3}w_1 - \tfrac{1}{3}w_2 \\ -y_2 - y_3 &= -w_1 + w_3 \end{aligned} \quad \begin{matrix} \xrightarrow{[1]-2[2]} \\ \\ \xrightarrow{[3]+[2]} \end{matrix} \quad \begin{aligned} y_1 + y_3 &= \tfrac{1}{3}w_1 + \tfrac{2}{3}w_2 \\ y_2 \qquad &= \tfrac{1}{3}w_1 - \tfrac{1}{3}w_2 \\ -y_3 &= -\tfrac{2}{3}w_1 - \tfrac{1}{3}w_2 + w_3 \end{aligned} \quad \begin{matrix} \\ \\ \xrightarrow{-[3]} \end{matrix}$$

$$\begin{aligned} y_1 + y_3 &= \tfrac{1}{3}w_1 + \tfrac{2}{3}w_2 \\ y_2 \qquad &= \tfrac{1}{3}w_1 - \tfrac{1}{3}w_2 \\ y_3 &= \tfrac{2}{3}w_1 + \tfrac{1}{3}w_2 - w_3 \end{aligned} \quad \begin{matrix} \xrightarrow{[1]-[3]} \\ \\ \\ \end{matrix} \quad \begin{aligned} y_1 &= -\tfrac{1}{3}w_1 + \tfrac{1}{3}w_2 + w_3 \\ y_2 &= \tfrac{1}{3}w_1 - \tfrac{1}{3}w_2 \\ y_3 &= \tfrac{2}{3}w_1 + \tfrac{1}{3}w_2 - w_3. \end{aligned}$$

The final formula reveals that (ii) is uniquely solvable for *every* triple $\begin{pmatrix} w_1 \\ w_2 \\ w_3 \end{pmatrix} \in \mathcal{R}^3$ and that the solution is

$$\text{(iii)} \qquad \mathbf{y} = \begin{pmatrix} -\frac{1}{3}w_1 + \frac{1}{3}w_2 + w_3 \\ \frac{1}{3}w_1 - \frac{1}{3}w_2 \\ \frac{2}{3}w_1 + \frac{1}{3}w_2 - w_3 \end{pmatrix} \qquad \text{if } \mathbf{w} = \begin{pmatrix} w_1 \\ w_2 \\ w_3 \end{pmatrix}.$$

Referring to (4.4) we see by the above formula that the solution $\mathbf{y}$ is the image of $\mathbf{w}$ under the transformation

$$\tilde{T} = \begin{pmatrix} -\frac{1}{3} & \frac{1}{3} & 1 \\ \frac{1}{3} & -\frac{1}{3} & 0 \\ \frac{2}{3} & \frac{1}{3} & -1 \end{pmatrix}.$$

In other words [see (3.7)], we have shown that the transformation

$$T = \begin{pmatrix} 1 & 2 & 1 \\ 1 & -1 & 1 \\ 1 & 1 & 0 \end{pmatrix}$$

is invertible, and that its inverse is

$$T^{-1} = \begin{pmatrix} -\frac{1}{3} & \frac{1}{3} & 1 \\ \frac{1}{3} & -\frac{1}{3} & 0 \\ \frac{2}{3} & \frac{1}{3} & -1 \end{pmatrix}.$$

The following result reveals that example (4.8) is typical.

(4.9) Theorem. *Let T be a transformation on $\mathcal{R}^n$ to $\mathcal{R}^n$:*

$$T = \begin{pmatrix} t_{11} & t_{12} & \cdots & t_{1n} \\ \vdots & & & \vdots \\ t_{n1} & t_{n2} & \cdots & t_{nn} \end{pmatrix}.$$

Then T is invertible if and only if $R_T = \mathcal{R}^n$. In that case, and not otherwise, the system of equations corresponding to

$$\text{(a)} \qquad \begin{pmatrix} t_{11} & t_{12} & \cdots & t_{1n} \\ \vdots & & & \vdots \\ t_{n1} & t_{n2} & \cdots & t_{nn} \end{pmatrix} \begin{pmatrix} y_1 \\ \vdots \\ y_n \end{pmatrix} = \begin{pmatrix} w_1 \\ \vdots \\ w_n \end{pmatrix},$$

namely

$$\text{(b)} \qquad \begin{array}{ccccccc} t_{11}y_1 + t_{12}y_2 + \cdots + t_{1n}y_n &=& w_1 \\ \vdots & & \vdots \\ t_{n1}y_1 + t_{n2}y_2 + \cdots + t_{nn}y_n &=& w_n, \end{array}$$

has a unique solution for each $\mathbf{w} \in \mathcal{R}^n$. Moreover, the formula giving the solution of (b) *in terms of $w_1, \ldots, w_n$ has the form*

$$\text{(c)} \qquad \begin{array}{ccc} y_1 &=& u_{11}w_1 + u_{12}w_2 + \cdots + u_{1n}w_n \\ \vdots & & \vdots \\ y_n &=& u_{n1}w_1 + u_{n2}w_2 + \cdots + u_{nn}w_n, \end{array}$$

and the coefficients of $w_1, \ldots, w_n$ occurring in (c) *are the entries in the matrix for T^{-1},*

$$\text{(d)} \qquad T^{-1} = \begin{pmatrix} u_{11} & u_{12} & \cdots & u_{1n} \\ \vdots & & & \vdots \\ u_{n1} & u_{n2} & \cdots & u_{nn} \end{pmatrix}.$$

The above result gives the promised *systematic* method for computing T^{-1}. Namely, solve the system of equations in (b). If (b) fails to have a solution for some $\mathbf{w} \in \mathcal{R}^n$, then T has *no* inverse. If (b) does have a solution for every $\mathbf{w} \in \mathcal{R}^n$, then read off the matrix for T^{-1} from the formula for solutions of (b).

As the final topic in this section we study the computation of eigenvalues and eigenvectors [see (3.5)]. Let us first observe that in calculating eigenvalues the use of determinants, although convenient, is not essential.

(4.10) Example. Calculation of Eigenvectors. Let us compute the eigenvalues and eigenvectors of the transformation

$$T = \begin{pmatrix} 2 & 0 & -3 \\ 0 & 2 & 4 \\ -3 & 4 & 2 \end{pmatrix}.$$

The equation $T\mathbf{y} - \lambda\mathbf{y} = \mathbf{0}$ or

$$\text{(i)} \qquad \begin{pmatrix} 2 & 0 & -3 \\ 0 & 2 & 4 \\ -3 & 4 & 2 \end{pmatrix}\begin{pmatrix} y_1 \\ y_2 \\ y_3 \end{pmatrix} - \lambda\begin{pmatrix} y_1 \\ y_2 \\ y_3 \end{pmatrix} = \begin{pmatrix} 0 \\ 0 \\ 0 \end{pmatrix}$$

is equivalent to the system of equations

$$\text{(ii)} \qquad \begin{aligned} (2-\lambda)y_1 + 0y_2 - 3y_3 &= 0 \\ 0y_1 + (2-\lambda)y_2 + 4y_3 &= 0 \\ -3y_1 + 4y_2 + (2-\lambda)y_3 &= 0. \end{aligned}$$

We proceed to solve (ii) by Gauss reduction as follows (let $\mu = 2 - \lambda$):

$$\begin{aligned} \mu y_1 + 0y_2 - 3y_3 &= 0 \\ 0y_1 + \mu y_2 + 4y_3 &= 0 \\ -3y_1 + 4y_2 + \mu y_3 &= 0 \end{aligned} \quad \xrightarrow{\mu^{-1}[1]} \quad \begin{aligned} y_1 + 0y_2 - \frac{3}{\mu}y_3 &= 0 \\ 0y_1 + \mu y_2 + 4y_3 &= 0 \\ -3y_1 + 4y_2 + \mu y_3 &= 0 \end{aligned} \quad \xrightarrow{[3] + 3[1]}$$

$$\begin{aligned} y_1 + 0y_2 - \frac{3}{\mu}y_3 &= 0 \\ 0y_1 + \mu y_2 + 4y_3 &= 0 \\ 0y_1 + 4y_2 + \left(\mu - \frac{9}{\mu}\right)y_3 &= 0 \end{aligned} \quad \xrightarrow{\mu^{-1}[2]} \quad \begin{aligned} y_1 + 0y_2 - \frac{3}{\mu}y_3 &= 0 \\ 0y_1 + y_2 + \frac{4}{\mu}y_3 &= 0 \\ 0y_1 + 4y_2 + \frac{\mu^2 - 9}{\mu}y_3 &= 0 \end{aligned} \quad \xrightarrow{[3] - 4[2]}$$

$$\begin{aligned} y_1 + 0y_2 - \frac{3}{\mu}y_3 &= 0 \\ 0y_1 + y_2 + \frac{4}{\mu}y_3 &= 0 \\ 0y_1 + 0y_2 + \frac{\mu^2 - 25}{\mu}y_3 &= 0 \end{aligned} \quad \xrightarrow{\left(\frac{\mu^2 - 25}{\mu}\right)^{-1}[3]} \quad \begin{aligned} y_1 + 0y_2 - \frac{3}{\mu}y_3 &= 0 \\ 0y_1 + y_2 + \frac{4}{\mu}y_3 &= 0 \\ 0y_1 + 0y_2 + y_3 &= 0 \end{aligned}$$

$$\begin{aligned} &\xrightarrow{[1] + 3\mu^{-1}[3]} & y_1 + 0y_2 + 0y_3 &= 0 \\ &\xrightarrow{[2] - 4\mu^{-1}[3]} & 0y_1 + y_2 + 0y_0 &= 0 \\ & & 0y_1 + 0y_2 + y_3 &= 0 \end{aligned}$$

This calculation shows that whenever λ is such that none of the divisions occurring above involves division by zero, then the only solution to (i) is $y_1 = y_2 = y_3 = 0$. Hence, by examining those divisions, we see that every eigenvalue λ must be a root of $2 - \lambda = 0$ or of $\lambda^2 - 4\lambda - 21 = 0$. Thus the only possible eigenvalues are $\lambda_1 = 2, \lambda_2 = 7, \lambda_3 = -3$.

Let us compute the corresponding eigenvectors. If we insert $\lambda = 2$ into (ii) we obtain

$$\begin{aligned} 0y_1 + 0y_2 - 3y_3 &= 0 \\ 0y_1 + 0y_2 + 4y_3 &= 0 \\ -3y_1 + 4y_2 + 0y_3 &= 0, \end{aligned}$$

and it is clear by inspection that the solutions of the above SLE all have the form

$$\mathbf{y} = k\begin{pmatrix} 4 \\ 3 \\ 0 \end{pmatrix}.$$

Thus all eigenvectors corresponding to $\lambda_1 = 2$ are multiples of the eigenvector γ_1 given by

$$\gamma_1 = \begin{pmatrix} 4 \\ 3 \\ 0 \end{pmatrix}.$$

If we insert $\lambda = 7$ in (ii) we obtain

$$\begin{aligned} -5y_1 + 0y_2 - 3y_3 &= 0 \\ 0y_1 - 5y_2 + 4y_3 &= 0 \\ -3y_1 + 4y_2 - 5y_3 &= 0. \end{aligned}$$

Gauss reduction then leads to

$$\begin{aligned} y_1 + 0y_2 + \tfrac{3}{5}y_3 &= 0 \\ 0y_1 + y_2 - \tfrac{4}{5}y_3 &= 0 \\ 0y_1 + 0y_2 + 0y_3 &= 0, \end{aligned}$$

so all solutions have the form

$$\mathbf{y} = k\begin{pmatrix} -\frac{3}{5} \\ \frac{4}{5} \\ 1 \end{pmatrix}.$$

This time all the eigenvectors corresponding to $\lambda_2 = 7$ are multiples of the eigenvector γ_2 given by

$$\gamma_2 = \begin{pmatrix} -\frac{3}{5} \\ \frac{4}{5} \\ 1 \end{pmatrix}.$$

Finally, if we insert $\lambda = -3$ into (ii) we obtain

$$\begin{aligned} 5y_1 + 0y_2 - 3y_3 &= 0 \\ 0y_1 + 5y_2 + 4y_3 &= 0 \\ -3y_1 + 4y_2 + 5y_3 &= 0. \end{aligned}$$

Gauss reduction leads to

$$\begin{aligned} y_1 + 0y_2 - \tfrac{3}{5}y_3 &= 0 \\ 0y_1 + \quad y_2 + \tfrac{4}{5}y_3 &= 0 \\ 0y_1 + 0y_2 + 0y_3 &= 0, \end{aligned}$$

and the solutions all have the form

$$\mathbf{y} = k\begin{pmatrix} \frac{3}{5} \\ -\frac{4}{5} \\ 1 \end{pmatrix}.$$

Hence all eigenvectors are multiples of

$$\gamma_3 = \begin{pmatrix} \frac{3}{5} \\ -\frac{4}{5} \\ 1 \end{pmatrix}.$$

This completes our program of finding eigenvalues and eigenvectors for T.

Incidentally, the computation of eigenvalues in the present example would have been somewhat shortened had we avoided the initial Gauss reduction of (ii) and used instead the fact that for λ to be an eigenvalue, the determinant of the matrix

$$T - \lambda I = \begin{pmatrix} 2-\lambda & 0 & -3 \\ 0 & 2-\lambda & 4 \\ -3 & 4 & 2-\lambda \end{pmatrix}$$

must be zero. However, we warn the reader that the computation of such determinants becomes very tedious for $\mathcal{R}^n$ with $n > 3$. For this reason we shall *not require* in what follows that the reader be acquainted with determinants of size exceeding 2×2.

We can formulate the procedure used above in calculating eigenvectors and eigenvalues, in general terms.

(4.11) Rule (Eigenvector Calculations in $\mathcal{R}^n$)

(1) Compute the eigenvalues for T. Do this either by finding the roots of that polynomial which is given by the determinant of

$$\text{(a)} \qquad T - \lambda I = \begin{pmatrix} t_{11} - \lambda & t_{12} & \cdots & t_{1n} \\ t_{21} & t_{22} - \lambda & \cdots & t_{2n} \\ \vdots & \vdots & & \vdots \\ t_{n1} & t_{n2} & \cdots & t_{nn} - \lambda \end{pmatrix}$$

or else by finding all those values of λ for which Gauss reduction of the homogeneous system

$$\text{(b)} \qquad \begin{matrix} (t_{11} - \lambda)y_1 + \cdots + t_{1n}y_n = 0 \\ \vdots \qquad\qquad\qquad \vdots \quad \vdots \\ t_{n1}y_1 + \cdots + (t_{nn} - \lambda)y_n = 0 \end{matrix}$$

does *not* imply $y_1 = y_2 = \cdots = y_n = 0$.

(2) Insert each eigenvalue λ_j obtained in part (1) into (b) and Gauss-reduce the resulting system. Take any convenient basis for the solution space S of this system as the eigenvector γ_j—eigenvectors, if dim $S > 1$—corresponding to λ_j.

It will be noted that the transformation occurring in example (4.10) has eigenvectors which form a basis for its domain. In general, this property of a transformation T cannot be known until *after* its eigenvectors are *calculated.* However, the possession of such a basis of eigenvectors will be crucial for transformations entering in the study of systems of differential equations (Chapters 9 and 10). Therefore it is quite important that we can describe certain situations in which existence of such a basis is *guaranteed.* In some cases one can even tell *by inspection* that T has the above property. This is the significance of the next result.

(4.12) Spectral Theorem. *Every transformation T on $\mathcal{R}^n$ to $\mathcal{R}^n$ whose matrix is* symmetric *in the sense that entries which are symmetrically located with respect to the main diagonal are always equal,*

$$t_{ij} = t_{ji} \qquad i, j = 1, \ldots, n,$$

possesses a set of n eigenvectors $\gamma_1, \ldots, \gamma_n$ *forming a basis for* $\mathcal{R}^n$. *Moreover* $\gamma_1, \ldots, \gamma_n$ *is an* orthogonal *basis for* $\mathcal{R}^n$ *whenever T has n distinct eigenvalues.*

The proof of the above result is too complicated to be given in this book.

We comment that the matrix of the transformation T in example (4.10) was symmetric. Hence the spectral theorem assures us in advance that T *has* eigenvectors and that they are a basis for $\mathcal{R}^3$. However, the *computation* of the eigenvalues and eigenvectors can only be accomplished by actual calculation, as in the example. Incidentally, the reader is advised to verify that the eigenvectors obtained in (4.10) really do form an orthogonal basis for $\mathcal{R}^3$ as claimed.

In contrast to (4.12) our next criterion requires more than a mere inspection of the given transformation. This time the *eigenvalues* (although not the eigen*vectors*) of T must be computed.

(4.13) Eigenvalue Criterion. *Every transformation T on* $\mathcal{R}^n$ *to* $\mathcal{R}^n$ *which has n distinct eigenvalues possesses a set of eigenvectors* $\gamma_1, \ldots, \gamma_n$ *forming a basis for* $\mathcal{R}^n$.

Note that in this theorem there is no claim that the γ's are mutually orthogonal, and in fact they may *not* be orthogonal.

As with the spectral theorem we will omit the proof of the eigenvalue criterion. However, in order to give substance to both these results we shall now analyze in detail the case of transformations on $\mathcal{R}^2$. The reader is advised to study this analysis carefully since it will be used repeatedly in Chapters 9 and 10.

Suppose that T is a transformation on $\mathcal{R}^2$ having the matrix

(4.14)
$$T = \begin{pmatrix} t_{11} & t_{12} \\ t_{21} & t_{22} \end{pmatrix} = \begin{pmatrix} a & b \\ c & d \end{pmatrix}.$$

Now the equation $T\mathbf{y} - \lambda\mathbf{y} = \mathbf{0}$ or

$$\begin{pmatrix} a & b \\ c & d \end{pmatrix}\begin{pmatrix} y_1 \\ y_2 \end{pmatrix} - \lambda\begin{pmatrix} y_1 \\ y_2 \end{pmatrix} = \begin{pmatrix} 0 \\ 0 \end{pmatrix}$$

is equivalent to the system of equations

(i)
$$\begin{aligned} (a - \lambda)y_1 + by_2 &= 0 \\ cy_1 + (d - \lambda)y_2 &= 0. \end{aligned}$$

Also, the latter has solutions $(y_1, y_2) \neq (0, 0)$ if and only if its determinant is zero. Thus eigenvalues of T are roots of the quadratic equation

(ii)
$$(a - \lambda)(d - \lambda) - bc = \lambda^2 - (a + d)\lambda + ad - bc = 0.$$

Setting $t = a + d$, $D = ad - bc$, we may write this as

$$\text{(iii)} \qquad \lambda^2 - t\lambda + D = 0.$$

The quadratic formula gives us the two roots of (iii),

$$\text{(iv)} \qquad \lambda_1 = \frac{t + \sqrt{t^2 - 4D}}{2}, \qquad \lambda_2 = \frac{t - \sqrt{t^2 - 4D}}{2}.$$

These are real if and only if $t^2 - 4D \geq 0$. However, substitution for t and D and a little rearrangement shows that

$$\text{(v)} \qquad t^2 - 4D = (a - d)^2 + 4bc.$$

Observe that symmetry of T's matrix requires $b = c$. Hence by (v), *both roots of* (iii) *are real for symmetric* T.

We here consider only those cases in which $t^2 - 4D \geq 0$, so that the eigenvalues are real. (The case $t^2 - 4D < 0$ is discussed in Chapter 10.)

CASE 1, $t^2 - 4D > 0$. (The eigenvalues of T are unequal: $\lambda_1 \neq \lambda_2$.) By (iv) and (v) we have

$$\text{(4.15)} \qquad \begin{aligned} \lambda_1 &= \frac{t + \sqrt{t^2 - 4D}}{2} = \frac{a + d + \sqrt{(a - d)^2 + 4bc}}{2} \\ \lambda_2 &= \frac{t - \sqrt{t^2 - 4D}}{2} = \frac{a + d - \sqrt{(a - d)^2 + 4bc}}{2}. \end{aligned}$$

If we insert λ_1 into (i) we obtain

$$\text{(vi)} \qquad \begin{aligned} &\frac{a - d - \sqrt{(a - d)^2 + 4bc}}{2} y_1 + by_2 = 0 \\ &cy_1 + \frac{d - a - \sqrt{(a - d)^2 + 4bc}}{2} y_2 = 0. \end{aligned}$$

Assume $b \neq 0$.† Then (vi) implies

$$y_2 = \frac{d - a + \sqrt{(a - d)^2 + 4bc}}{2b} y_1,$$

†The case $b = 0$ is left to the problems.

so that all solutions of (vi) have the form

$$\mathbf{y} = k\begin{pmatrix} 1 \\ \dfrac{d - a + \sqrt{(a-d)^2 + 4bc}}{2b} \end{pmatrix}.$$

Consequently, we may take

$$\gamma_1 = \begin{pmatrix} 1 \\ \dfrac{d - a + \sqrt{(a-d)^2 + 4bc}}{2b} \end{pmatrix}. \tag{4.16}$$

Now insert λ_2 into (i). This gives

$$\text{(vii)}\qquad \begin{aligned} \frac{a - d + \sqrt{(a-d)^2 + 4bc}}{2}\, y_1 + b y_2 &= 0 \\ c y_1 + \frac{d - a + \sqrt{(a-d)^2 + 4bc}}{2}\, y_2 &= 0. \end{aligned}$$

Thus we have

$$y_2 = \frac{d - a - \sqrt{(a-d)^2 + 4bc}}{2b}\, y_1,$$

and consequently we may take

$$\gamma_2 = \begin{pmatrix} 1 \\ \dfrac{d - a - \sqrt{(a-d)^2 + 4bc}}{2b} \end{pmatrix}. \tag{4.17}$$

Note that $t^2 - 4D > 0$ implies that γ_1 and γ_2 are not parallel. Hence, as asserted by (4.13), γ_1, γ_2 form a basis for $\mathcal{R}^2$. It is also an easy matter to show that when T is symmetric, that is, $b = c$, then $\gamma_1 \cdot \gamma_2 = 0$. This condition clearly ensures that the eigenvectors γ_1, γ_2 form an orthogonal basis for $\mathcal{R}^2$.

CASE 2, $t^2 - 4D = 0$. (The eigenvalues of T are equal: $\lambda_1 = \lambda_2$.) By (4.15) this occurs if and only if

$$\text{(viii)}\qquad t^2 - 4D = (a-d)^2 + 4bc = 0,$$

and then we have

$$\lambda_1 = \lambda_2 = \frac{a+d}{2}.$$

Inserting this into (i) we obtain

$$\text{(ix)}\qquad \begin{aligned} \frac{a-d}{2}y_1 + by_2 &= 0 \\ cy_1 + \frac{d-a}{2}y_2 &= 0. \end{aligned}$$

Assuming for the moment that $b \neq 0$, we find that all solutions have the form

$$\mathbf{y} = k\begin{pmatrix} 1 \\ \dfrac{d-a}{2b} \end{pmatrix}.$$

Consequently we may take

$$\text{(x)}\qquad \gamma_1 = \begin{pmatrix} 1 \\ \dfrac{d-a}{2b} \end{pmatrix},$$

but there is no other eigenvector, hence *no basis of eigenvectors*, in this situation.

Next, let us examine Case 2 when $b = 0$. According to (viii), in this circumstance $a = d$. Hence (ix) has the form

$$\text{(xi)}\qquad \begin{aligned} 0y_1 + 0y_2 &= 0 \\ cy_1 + 0y_2 &= 0. \end{aligned}$$

We find that when $c \neq 0$, all solutions of (xi) have the form

$$\mathbf{y} = k\begin{pmatrix} 0 \\ 1 \end{pmatrix}.$$

Consequently we may take

$$\text{(xii)}\qquad \gamma_1 = \begin{pmatrix} 0 \\ 1 \end{pmatrix},$$

but there is again no basis of eigenvectors.

Finally, we examine what happens when $c = b = 0$. This means that T is symmetric and, since $a = d$, T has the form

$$T = \begin{pmatrix} a & 0 \\ 0 & a \end{pmatrix} = a\begin{pmatrix} 1 & 0 \\ 0 & 1 \end{pmatrix}.$$

Clearly since $T = cI$, *all* vectors in $\mathcal{R}^2$ are eigenvectors and in particular we may take

$$(4.18) \qquad \gamma_1 = \begin{pmatrix} 1 \\ 0 \end{pmatrix}, \qquad \gamma_2 = \begin{pmatrix} 0 \\ 1 \end{pmatrix},$$

which is obviously an orthogonal basis for $\mathcal{R}^2$.

We now wish to point out that the spectral theorem is also exceedingly useful in other vector spaces $\mathcal{V}$, not merely in $\mathcal{R}^n$. [These remarks are intended to illustrate connections with earlier work but are not essential for what follows.] First, we describe a useful property for transformations $T: \mathcal{V} \to \mathcal{V}$ which takes the place of the matrix symmetry hypothesized in theorem (4.12).

(4.19) Definition. Let $\mathcal{V}$ be a Euclidean vector space. A transformation $T: \mathcal{V} \to \mathcal{V}$ is said to be **symmetric** (or *self-adjoint*) if and only if it satisfies the identity

$$\text{(S)} \qquad \boldsymbol{\alpha} \cdot T\boldsymbol{\beta} = (T\boldsymbol{\alpha}) \cdot \boldsymbol{\beta} \qquad \text{for all } \boldsymbol{\alpha},\boldsymbol{\beta} \in \mathcal{V}.$$

In the space $\mathcal{V} = \mathcal{R}^n$ it can be shown that the symmetry property (S) is *equivalent to* the requirement that T have a symmetric matrix (see the problems), but in general spaces $\mathcal{V}$ there need not even *be* a matrix form for T—yet (S) is still meaningful.

We can now state an analog of theorem (4.12) for general spaces $\mathcal{V}$.

(4.20) Spectral Theorem (Second Version). *Let $\mathcal{V}$ be a Euclidean vector space and let $T: \mathcal{V} \to \mathcal{V}$ be a symmetric transformation. Then*

(1) *Eigenvectors of T which correspond to different eigenvalues are orthogonal to each other:*

$$T\boldsymbol{\beta} = \lambda\boldsymbol{\beta}, \qquad T\boldsymbol{\beta}' = \lambda'\boldsymbol{\beta}' \quad (\lambda \neq \lambda') \qquad \text{implies} \quad \boldsymbol{\beta} \cdot \boldsymbol{\beta}' = 0.$$

(2) *If $\mathcal{V}$ is finite-dimensional,* $\dim \mathcal{V} = m$, *then T possesses a set of m eigenvectors $\gamma_1, \ldots, \gamma_m$ forming a basis for $\mathcal{V}$. Moreover the basis $\gamma_1, \ldots, \gamma_m$ is* orthogonal *if T has m distinct eigenvalues.*

Proof. Although the proof of part (2) is too complicated for this book, the proof of part (1) is quite simple. Let $\boldsymbol{\beta}$, $\boldsymbol{\beta}'$, λ, and λ' be as in (1):

$$\text{(i)} \qquad \begin{aligned} T\boldsymbol{\beta} &= \lambda\boldsymbol{\beta}, \\ T\boldsymbol{\beta}' &= \lambda'\boldsymbol{\beta}', \end{aligned} \qquad \lambda \neq \lambda'.$$

Now take the inner product of both sides of the *first* equation in (i) with the vector $\boldsymbol{\beta}'$, and take the inner product of the *second* equation in (i) with $\boldsymbol{\beta}$. This yields the equations

$$\text{(ii)} \qquad \begin{aligned} \boldsymbol{\beta}' \cdot T\boldsymbol{\beta} &= \lambda(\boldsymbol{\beta}' \cdot \boldsymbol{\beta}) \\ \boldsymbol{\beta} \cdot T\boldsymbol{\beta}' &= \lambda'(\boldsymbol{\beta} \cdot \boldsymbol{\beta}'). \end{aligned}$$

According to (S) the *left sides* of the equations in (ii) are equal. Hence subtraction of these equations yields

$$\text{(iii)} \qquad 0 = \lambda(\boldsymbol{\beta}' \cdot \boldsymbol{\beta}) - \lambda'(\boldsymbol{\beta} \cdot \boldsymbol{\beta}') = (\lambda - \lambda')(\boldsymbol{\beta} \cdot \boldsymbol{\beta}').$$

By hypothesis $\lambda - \lambda' \neq 0$, so (iii) implies

$$\boldsymbol{\beta} \cdot \boldsymbol{\beta}' = 0,$$

which yields the desired conclusion. ▮

One final comment. We found in Chapter 7 that the solution of partial differential equation problems by the method of separation of variables hinges on the fact that such ordinary differential equation problems as

$$\text{(4.21)} \qquad X''(x) - \lambda X(x) = 0, \qquad X(0) = X(L) = 0$$

have solutions forming a complete orthonormal system **X** in $\mathcal{C}[0, L]$ [see Chapter 7, (3.8)]. Explaining the completeness of these systems is beyond our reach, but explaining the orthogonality is now possible. After all, equation (4.21) can be viewed as the requirement that X be an *eigenvector* of the "second derivative" transformation—defined on the subspace $\hat{\mathcal{C}}_0^2[0, L]$ of $\mathcal{C}[0, L]$ consisting of twice-differentiable functions which satisfy $X(0) = X(L) = 0$. In addition, it can be shown that the "second derivative" transformation on $\hat{\mathcal{C}}_0^2[0, L]$ is *symmetric*† (see problem 11). Thus the orthogonality of the functions (eigenvectors) X_n is guaranteed by theorem (4.19)–(1).† Actually, much of the development in Chapter 7 can be accomplished using these ideas. This is discussed further in §3 of Chapter 9.

†Here the transformation is not from $\mathcal{V}$ to $\mathcal{V}$ but from $\mathcal{V}$ to $\mathcal{C}[0, L]$ containing $\mathcal{V}$. However, the definition of symmetry and theorem (4.14)–(1) are still valid.

PROBLEMS

1. Find the matrix of each of the following transformations:

(a) $T: \mathcal{R}^2 \to \mathcal{R}^2$, such that T rotates every $\mathbf{y} \in \mathcal{R}^2$ counterclockwise by the angle $\frac{\pi}{3}$. [*Hint:* First compute the vectors $T\begin{pmatrix}1\\0\end{pmatrix}$ and $T\begin{pmatrix}0\\1\end{pmatrix}$.]

(b) $T: \mathcal{R}^2 \to \mathcal{R}^2$, such that T takes each $\mathbf{y} \in \mathcal{R}^2$ into its mirror image across the line $y_1 = y_2$.

(c) $T: \mathcal{R}^2 \to \mathcal{R}^2$ such that

$$T\begin{pmatrix}1\\0\end{pmatrix} = \begin{pmatrix}0\\0\end{pmatrix}, \quad T\begin{pmatrix}0\\1\end{pmatrix} = \begin{pmatrix}1\\0\end{pmatrix}.$$

(d) $T: \mathcal{R}^2 \to \mathcal{R}^2$ such that

$$T\begin{pmatrix}0\\1\end{pmatrix} = \begin{pmatrix}0\\0\end{pmatrix}, \quad T\begin{pmatrix}1\\1\end{pmatrix} = \begin{pmatrix}1\\1\end{pmatrix}.$$

(e) $T: \mathcal{R}^3 \to \mathcal{R}^3$ such that

$$T\begin{pmatrix}1\\0\\0\end{pmatrix} = \begin{pmatrix}0\\\frac{1}{2}\\\frac{4}{3}\end{pmatrix}, \quad T\begin{pmatrix}0\\1\\0\end{pmatrix} = \begin{pmatrix}0\\0\\0\end{pmatrix}, \quad T\begin{pmatrix}0\\0\\1\end{pmatrix} = \begin{pmatrix}-18\\1\\2\end{pmatrix}.$$

(f) $T: \mathcal{R}^3 \to \mathcal{R}^3$ such that

$$T\begin{pmatrix}1\\2\\3\end{pmatrix} = \begin{pmatrix}1\\1\\1\end{pmatrix}, \quad T\begin{pmatrix}0\\1\\0\end{pmatrix} = \begin{pmatrix}0\\0\\0\end{pmatrix}, \quad T\begin{pmatrix}0\\0\\1\end{pmatrix} = \begin{pmatrix}0\\0\\0\end{pmatrix}.$$

(g) $T: \mathcal{R}^3 \to \mathcal{R}^3$ such that

$$T\begin{pmatrix}1\\0\\0\end{pmatrix} = T\begin{pmatrix}0\\1\\0\end{pmatrix} = T\begin{pmatrix}0\\0\\1\end{pmatrix} = \begin{pmatrix}-1\\-1\\-1\end{pmatrix}.$$

2. In each of the following, give a necessary and sufficient condition on the matrix for T such that the stated property holds.

(a) $T\begin{pmatrix}1\\-2\end{pmatrix} = \begin{pmatrix}3\\1\end{pmatrix}$

(b) $T\begin{pmatrix}1\\-2\end{pmatrix} = \begin{pmatrix}a\\b\end{pmatrix}$

(c) $T\begin{pmatrix}1\\-2\end{pmatrix} = \begin{pmatrix}0\\0\end{pmatrix}$

3. Prove theorem (4.1).

(a) Show that the transformation defined by (5.1a) is linear no matter what the scalars $t_{11}, \ldots, t_{nn}$ are. [*Hint:* Prove that $T(\mathbf{y} + \mathbf{z}) = T\mathbf{y} + T\mathbf{z}$ and $T(c\mathbf{y}) = cT\mathbf{y}$.]

(b) Given *any* system of n vectors (repetitions permitted),

$$\gamma_1 = \begin{pmatrix} c_{11} \\ \cdot \\ \cdot \\ \cdot \\ c_{n1} \end{pmatrix}, \quad \gamma_2 = \begin{pmatrix} c_{12} \\ \cdot \\ \cdot \\ \cdot \\ c_{n2} \end{pmatrix}, \ldots, \quad \gamma_n = \begin{pmatrix} c_{1n} \\ \cdot \\ \cdot \\ \cdot \\ c_{nn} \end{pmatrix},$$

establish the general formula for $T\mathbf{y}$ which would hold *if* there existed a (linear) transformation T satisfying

$$\text{(i)} \qquad T\begin{pmatrix} 1 \\ 0 \\ \cdot \\ \cdot \\ \cdot \\ 0 \end{pmatrix} = \gamma_1, \quad T\begin{pmatrix} 0 \\ 1 \\ \cdot \\ \cdot \\ \cdot \\ 0 \end{pmatrix} = \gamma_2, \ldots, \quad T\begin{pmatrix} 0 \\ \cdot \\ \cdot \\ \cdot \\ 0 \\ 1 \end{pmatrix} = \gamma_n.$$

[*Hint:* Write

$$\mathbf{y} = \begin{pmatrix} y_1 \\ \cdot \\ \cdot \\ \cdot \\ y_n \end{pmatrix} = y_1\begin{pmatrix} 1 \\ 0 \\ \cdot \\ \cdot \\ \cdot \\ 0 \end{pmatrix} + y_2\begin{pmatrix} 0 \\ 1 \\ \cdot \\ \cdot \\ \cdot \\ 0 \end{pmatrix} + \cdots + y_n\begin{pmatrix} 0 \\ 0 \\ \cdot \\ \cdot \\ \cdot \\ 1 \end{pmatrix}$$

and utilize linearity.]

(c) Show by reference to part (a) that the formula obtained in part (b) actually defines a linear transformation T satisfying (i).

(d) Given any linear transformation T define $\gamma_1, \ldots, \gamma_n$ by (i) and thereby show that T has the form (4.1a).

4. Compute the inverse of each of the following:

(a) $T = \begin{pmatrix} 0 & 1 \\ 1 & 0 \end{pmatrix}$

(b) $T = \begin{pmatrix} 1 & 2 \\ 2 & 1 \end{pmatrix}$

(c) $T = \begin{pmatrix} 1 & 1 & 1 \\ 1 & -1 & 1 \\ 1 & 1 & -1 \end{pmatrix}$

(d) $T = \begin{pmatrix} 1 & 2 & 0 \\ 2 & 1 & 0 \\ 0 & 0 & 1 \end{pmatrix}$

(e) $T = \begin{pmatrix} 1 & 2 & 0 & 0 \\ 2 & 1 & 0 & 0 \\ 0 & 0 & 3 & 1 \\ 0 & 0 & 2 & 3 \end{pmatrix}$

5. Compute the matrix for the transformation P which projects vectors in $\mathcal{R}^3$ to the subspace $S = \langle(1, 1, 1), (1, -2, 1)\rangle$; that is,

$$P\boldsymbol{\alpha} = \boldsymbol{\alpha}_s.$$

6. Find the eigenvalues and eigenvectors of each of the following transformations. State whether or not it is symmetric. Also state whether or not its eigenvectors form a basis.

(a) $\begin{pmatrix} 0 & 1 \\ 1 & 0 \end{pmatrix}$

(b) $\begin{pmatrix} 0 & 1 \\ 2 & 0 \end{pmatrix}$

(c) $\begin{pmatrix} 1 & 2 \\ 2 & 0 \end{pmatrix}$

(d) $\begin{pmatrix} 3 & -1 \\ -1 & 3 \end{pmatrix}$

(e) $\begin{pmatrix} 4 & 1 \\ 1 & 3 \end{pmatrix}$

(f) $\begin{pmatrix} 0 & 1 & 0 \\ 1 & 0 & 0 \\ 0 & 0 & 2 \end{pmatrix}$

(g) $\begin{pmatrix} 1 & 0 & 2 \\ 0 & 0 & 0 \\ 2 & -1 & 3 \end{pmatrix}$

(h) $\begin{pmatrix} 1 & 1 & 2 \\ 1 & 2 & 1 \\ 3 & 1 & 2 \end{pmatrix}$

(i) $\begin{pmatrix} 4 & 0 & 0 \\ 0 & 3 & -1 \\ 0 & -1 & 3 \end{pmatrix}$

(j) $\begin{pmatrix} -8 & 0 & 0 \\ 0 & -6 & 2 \\ 0 & -2 & -6 \end{pmatrix}$

(k) $\begin{pmatrix} 1 & 1 & 2 \\ 1 & 0 & 1 \\ 2 & 1 & 3 \end{pmatrix}$

7. Find eigenvectors and eigenvalues of each of the following. Determine whether the eigenvectors form a basis.

(a) $\begin{pmatrix} 1 & 2 \\ 3 & 1 \end{pmatrix}$

(b) $\begin{pmatrix} 1 & 0 \\ 0 & 0 \end{pmatrix}$

(c) $\begin{pmatrix} 1 & 0 \\ 1 & 1 \end{pmatrix}$

(d) $\begin{pmatrix} 0 & 1 \\ 1 & 1 \end{pmatrix}$

(e) $\begin{pmatrix} -1 & 0 & 0 \\ 0 & 1 & 2 \\ 0 & 3 & 1 \end{pmatrix}$

(f) $\begin{pmatrix} 1 & 0 & 0 \\ 0 & 2 & 0 \\ 0 & 0 & 0 \end{pmatrix}$

(g) $\begin{pmatrix} 2 & 3 & -1 \\ 6 & 1 & 3 \\ 2 & 3 & -1 \end{pmatrix}$

(h) $\begin{pmatrix} -2 & 0 & 0 & 0 \\ 0 & 0 & 1 & 0 \\ 0 & 1 & 0 & 0 \\ 0 & 0 & 0 & 2 \end{pmatrix}$

8. Determine which of the following are symmetric.

(a) $T: \mathcal{R}^2 \to \mathcal{R}^2$ such that

$$T\begin{pmatrix} 1 \\ 1 \end{pmatrix} = \begin{pmatrix} 2 \\ 2 \end{pmatrix}, \qquad T\begin{pmatrix} 1 \\ -1 \end{pmatrix} = \begin{pmatrix} 1 \\ 1 \end{pmatrix}$$

(b) $T: \mathcal{R}^2 \to \mathcal{R}^2$ such that

$$T\begin{pmatrix} 1 \\ 1 \end{pmatrix} = \begin{pmatrix} 4 \\ 5 \end{pmatrix}, \qquad T\begin{pmatrix} 1 \\ -1 \end{pmatrix} = \begin{pmatrix} -2 \\ 1 \end{pmatrix}$$

(c) $T: \mathcal{R}^3 \to \mathcal{R}^3$ such that

$$T\begin{pmatrix}1\\0\\1\end{pmatrix} = \begin{pmatrix}4\\4\\4\end{pmatrix}, \quad T\begin{pmatrix}1\\0\\-1\end{pmatrix} = \begin{pmatrix}-2\\-2\\-2\end{pmatrix}, \quad T\begin{pmatrix}1\\2\\0\end{pmatrix} = \begin{pmatrix}5\\5\\5\end{pmatrix}$$

9. Show that the spectral theorem and eigenvalue criterion both apply to transformations

$$T = \begin{pmatrix}a & b\\c & d\end{pmatrix}$$

for which $b = c = 0$.

10. Show that a transformation $T: \mathcal{R}^n \to \mathcal{R}^n$ satisfies the identity

$$\text{(S)} \qquad \boldsymbol{\alpha} \cdot T\boldsymbol{\beta} = (T\boldsymbol{\alpha}) \cdot \boldsymbol{\beta} \qquad \text{for all } \boldsymbol{\alpha}, \boldsymbol{\beta} \in \mathcal{V},$$

if and only if T has a symmetric matrix. [*Hint:* Take $\boldsymbol{\alpha} = \mathbf{e}_i$, $\boldsymbol{\beta} = \mathbf{e}_j$, where $\mathbf{e}_1 = (1, 0, \ldots, 0)$, $\mathbf{e}_2 = (0, 1, \ldots, 0), \ldots, \mathbf{e}_n = (0, \ldots, 0, 1)$.]

***11.** (a) Show that the "second derivative" transformation **C** on $\hat{\mathcal{C}}_0^2[0, L]$ defined by

$$CX = X''$$

is symmetric in the sense that it satisfies the identity

$$X \cdot CY - (CX) \cdot Y \qquad \text{for all } X, Y \in \hat{\mathcal{C}}_0^2[0, L].$$

[Here the inner product is given by $f \cdot g = \int_0^L f(t)g(t)\,dt$.] [*Hint:* Use integration by parts.]

(b) Show that the "second derivative" transformation is also symmetric on the subspace $V = \check{\mathcal{C}}_0^2[0, L]$ of twice differentiable functions which satisfy

$$X'(0) = X'(L) = 0.$$

(c) Show that the "second derivative" transformation is *not* symmetric on $\mathcal{C}^2[0, L]$.

Transformations on $\mathcal{R}^n$ to $\mathcal{R}^m$

***12.** Prove the analog of theorem (4.1) for transformations $T: \mathcal{R}^n \to \mathcal{R}^m$; that is, show that T is linear if and only if there is a system of mn scalars,

$$t_{11}, t_{12}, \ldots, t_{1n}; t_{21}, t_{22}, \ldots, t_{2n}; \ldots; t_{m1}, t_{m2}, \ldots, t_{mn}$$

such that for all $\mathbf{y} = (y_1, \ldots, y_n) \in \mathcal{R}^n$,

$$T(y_1, \ldots, y_n)$$
$$= (t_{11}y_1 + t_{12}y_2 + \cdots + t_{1n}y_n, \ldots, t_{m1}y_1 + t_{m2}y_2 + \cdots + t_{mn}y_n).$$

[*Hint:* Proceed as in problem 3.]

13. Utilize the result in problem 12 to justify the claim that any system of linear equations, whether or not it possesses the same number of equations as unknowns, can be interpreted as a conditional equation for a transformation on $\mathcal{R}^n$.

14. Define the matrix for a transformation $T: \mathcal{R}^n \to \mathcal{R}^m$ in roughly the same way as for transformations on $\mathcal{R}^n$ to $\mathcal{R}^n$ (by problem 12 there always is a system of mn scalars determining T). That is, represent

$$T(y_1, \ldots, y_n) = (t_{11}y_1 + \cdots + t_{1n}y_n, \ldots, t_{m1}y_1 + \cdots + t_{mn}y_n)$$

by

$$T = \begin{pmatrix} t_{11} & t_{12} & \cdots & t_{1n} \\ t_{21} & t_{22} & \cdots & t_{2n} \\ \vdots & & & \vdots \\ t_{m1} & t_{m2} & \cdots & t_{mn} \end{pmatrix}.$$

(a) Identify $\mathcal{R}^n$ and $\mathcal{R}^m$ for each of the following transformations. Which of them is one to one?

(i) $$T = \begin{pmatrix} 1 & 2 & 3 \\ -1 & 1 & 0 \end{pmatrix}$$

(ii) $$T = \begin{pmatrix} 1 & -1 \\ 2 & 1 \\ 1 & 2 \end{pmatrix}$$

(iii) $$T = \begin{pmatrix} 1 & -1 & 0 \\ 2 & 1 & 1 \\ 2 & 1 & 0 \\ 0 & 2 & 1 \end{pmatrix}$$

**(b) Find T^{-1} for the one-to-one transformations in part (a).

Matrices for Products and Sums of Transformations

15. (a) Let

$$B = \begin{pmatrix} 1 & 2 \\ -2 & 3 \end{pmatrix}, \quad T = \begin{pmatrix} 4 & 3 \\ 3 & -4 \end{pmatrix}.$$

Show that for all $\mathbf{y} \in \mathcal{R}^2$ the T-image of the vector $B\mathbf{y}$ is expressible as the product of $\mathbf{y}$ with an appropriate matrix S (find S).

(b) Find $S: \mathcal{R}^3 \to \mathcal{R}^3$ such that, with

$$B = \begin{pmatrix} 1 & 2 & 1 \\ 7 & 1 & 3 \\ -3 & 3 & 1 \end{pmatrix}, \quad T = \begin{pmatrix} 4 & 2 & 1 \\ 1 & 0 & 0 \\ -1 & -2 & 1 \end{pmatrix},$$

$S\mathbf{y}$ is the T-image of $B\mathbf{y}$, for all $\mathbf{y} \in \mathcal{R}^3$.

16. (a) Show that with

$$B = \begin{pmatrix} b_{11} & b_{12} \\ b_{21} & b_{22} \end{pmatrix}, \quad T = \begin{pmatrix} t_{11} & t_{12} \\ t_{22} & t_{22} \end{pmatrix},$$

the matrix S whose first column is the T-image of the first column $\begin{pmatrix} b_{11} \\ b_{21} \end{pmatrix}$ of B and whose second column is the T-image of the second column $\begin{pmatrix} b_{12} \\ b_{22} \end{pmatrix}$ of B satisfies

$$S\mathbf{y} = T(B\mathbf{y}) \qquad \text{for } \mathbf{y} \in \mathcal{R}^2.$$

Observe by problem 17 of §1 that S is called the *product* of T and B, $S = TB$. Hence the above rule shows how to compute the matrix of the product $S = TB$ of any two linear transformations on $\mathcal{R}^2$ to $\mathcal{R}^2$.

**(b) Show that for any two transformations B, T from $\mathcal{R}^n$ to $\mathcal{R}^n$, $n \geq 2$, the matrix of $S = TB$ is that matrix whose *first* column is the T-image of the first column of B, whose *second* column is the T-image of the second column of $B, \ldots$, whose nth column is the T-image of the nth column of B. Verify that this rule leads to the correct result in problem 15(b).

17. (a) Using the definition given in problem 16 of §1, show that, with

$$B = \begin{pmatrix} b_{11} & b_{12} \\ b_{21} & b_{22} \end{pmatrix}, \qquad T = \begin{pmatrix} t_{11} & t_{12} \\ t_{21} & t_{22} \end{pmatrix},$$

the matrix of $U = B + T$ is given by

$$U = \begin{pmatrix} b_{11} + t_{11} & b_{12} + t_{12} \\ b_{21} + t_{21} & b_{22} + t_{22} \end{pmatrix}.$$

*(b) Show that for any two transformations B, T from $\mathcal{R}^n$ to $\mathcal{R}^n$, $n \geq 2$, the matrix of $U = B + T$ is that matrix each of whose entries is the *sum* of the correspondingly located entries in B and in T.

*(c) Show that for any transformations B, T from $\mathcal{R}^n$ to $\mathcal{R}^n$ and any scalars k, l, the matrix of $kB + lT$ is that matrix each of whose entries is k times the correspondingly located entry in B plus l times the correspondingly located entry in CT.

9

Linear Algebra and Differential Equations

1. Examples and Notation

In Chapter 8 we gave several examples in which we applied techniques developed for general conditional equations to the solution of ordinary differential equations. Now we want to describe in a more systematic way how the ideas of linear algebra assist in the study of differential equations.

The particular subject we wish to discuss is that of *systems* of differential equations with constant coefficients. Such systems are of great importance in physics, and we begin our discussion by giving two examples. These are extensions of the examples in (3.2) of Chapter 5.

(1.1) Examples

(a) TWO PARTICLES CONNECTED BY SPRINGS. Suppose two particles of masses m_1 and m_2, located at P_1 and P_2, are connected by springs. One spring is fastened at O as shown in Figure 9.1. Let z_1 and z_2 denote the positions of the particles relative to O. Let the unstretched length of each spring be L. In the position shown, the lengths of the two springs are

$$\overline{OP_1} = z_1(t) \qquad \text{and} \qquad \overline{P_1P_2} = z_2(t) - z_1(t),$$

The forces exerted by the springs are proportional to the changes in length.

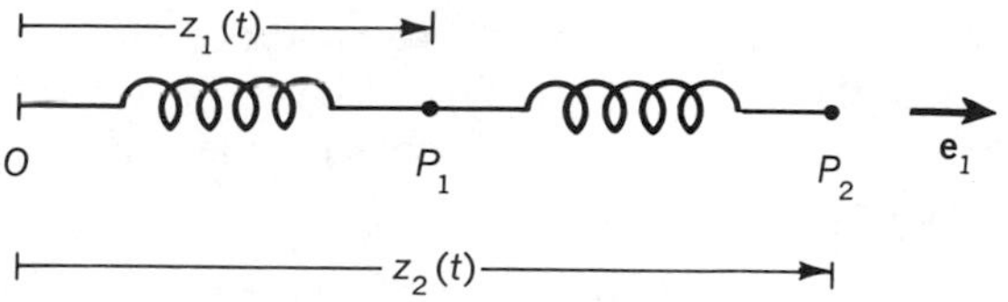

Figure 9.1

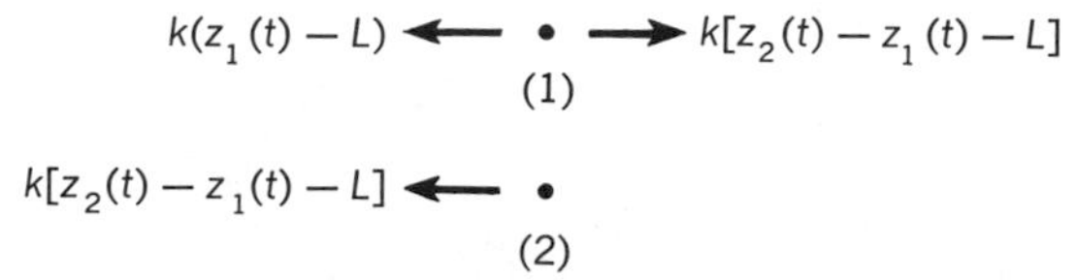

Figure 9.2

If one studies Figure 9.1 it will be seen that the particles are subject to forces as indicated in Figure 9.2 (k is the spring constant of each spring).

Now we write down Newton's laws for the two particles. If $\mathbf{e}_1$ is a unit vector as in Figure 9.1, then these equations become

$$m_1\ddot{z}_1(t)\mathbf{e}_1 = [-k(z_1(t) - L) + k(z_2(t) - z_1(t) - L)]\mathbf{e}_1$$
$$m_2\ddot{z}_2(t)\mathbf{e}_1 = -k[z_2(t) - z_1(t) - L]\mathbf{e}_1.$$

If we let $y_1 = z_1 - L$ and $y_2 = z_2 - 2L$, these equations become

$$\ddot{y}_1(t) = \frac{k}{m_1}[y_2(t) - 2y_1(t)]$$

$$\ddot{y}_2(t) = -\frac{k}{m_2}[y_2(t) - y_1(t)].$$

(b) COUPLED *LCR* CIRCUITS. Consider two *LCR* circuits which are coupled through a mutual inductance M (Figure 9.3). There are potential drops

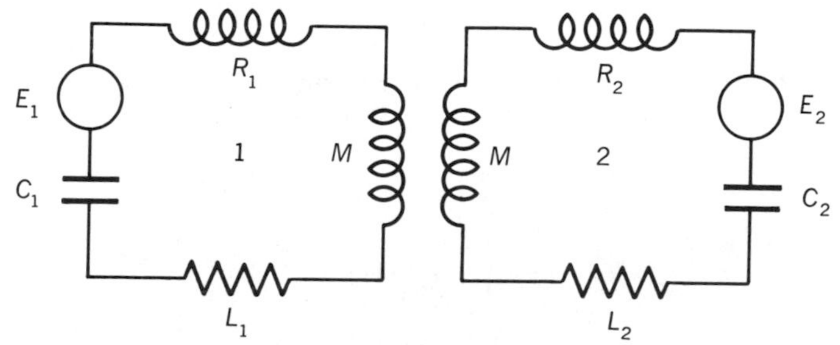

Figure 9.3

across the resistances, inductances, and capacitors exactly as in example (5.3.2b). In addition, there is a potential drop $M\ddot{y}_2(t)$ in circuit 1 and $M\ddot{y}_1(t)$ in circuit 2, where y_1 and y_2 are the charges on the capacitors. Hence the equations for the charges are

$$\begin{aligned} L_1\ddot{y}_1(t) + M\ddot{y}_2(t) + R_1\dot{y}_1(t) + (1/C_1)y_1(t) &= E_1(t) \\ L_2\ddot{y}_2(t) + M\ddot{y}_1(t) + R_2\dot{y}_2(t) + (1/C_2)y_2(t) &= E_2(t). \end{aligned} \tag{1.2}$$

Each of the pairs of equations in these examples has the following form:

$$\begin{aligned} a_{11}\ddot{y}_1(t) + a_{12}\ddot{y}_2(t) + b_{11}\dot{y}_1(t) + b_{12}\dot{y}_2(t) & \\ + c_{11}y_1(t) + c_{12}y_2(t) &= w_1(t) \\ a_{21}\ddot{y}_1(t) + a_{22}\ddot{y}_2(t) + b_{21}\dot{y}_1(t) + b_{22}\dot{y}_2(t) & \\ + c_{21}y_1(t) + c_{22}y_2(t) &= w_2(t). \end{aligned} \tag{1.3}$$

Each of the above examples could be extended to more general situations in which several masses are connected by springs or several circuits are coupled. These latter situations can also be described by systems of the form (1.3), but with more dependent variables. It becomes quite tedious to write out such systems, and so our first application of linear algebra will be to devise a compact notation.

Recall that we discussed vector-valued functions of t in Chapter 2. These are functions $\mathbf{y}$ which assume, for each t, a value $\mathbf{y}(t) \in \mathcal{V}$, where $\mathcal{V}$ denotes a given vector space. The case of interest here is that of functions with values in $\mathcal{R}^n$. That is,

$$\mathbf{y}(t) = \begin{pmatrix} y_1(t) \\ \vdots \\ y_n(t) \end{pmatrix}, \tag{1.4}$$

where the y_k's are scalar functions of t. We pointed out that such an $\mathcal{R}^n$-valued vector function is differentiable if and only if each y_k is differentiable, and that $\dot{\mathbf{y}}$ and $\ddot{\mathbf{y}}$ are then given by the following formulas:

$$\dot{\mathbf{y}}(t) = \begin{pmatrix} \dot{y}_1(t) \\ \vdots \\ \dot{y}_n(t) \end{pmatrix}, \quad \ddot{\mathbf{y}}(t) = \begin{pmatrix} \ddot{y}_1(t) \\ \vdots \\ \ddot{y}_n(t) \end{pmatrix}. \tag{1.5}$$

Now let us consider equations (1.3) carefully. Suppose we have a solution. This means we have a pair y_1, y_2 of twice-differentiable functions of t which satisfy (1.3). These functions serve to define an $\mathcal{R}^2$-valued function $\mathbf{y}$ of t by means of

$$\mathbf{y}(t) = \begin{pmatrix} y_1(t) \\ y_2(t) \end{pmatrix}, \tag{1.6}$$

and, as in (1.5),

$$\dot{\mathbf{y}}(t) = \begin{pmatrix} \dot{y}_1(t) \\ \dot{y}_2(t) \end{pmatrix}, \qquad \ddot{\mathbf{y}}(t) = \begin{pmatrix} \ddot{y}_1(t) \\ \ddot{y}_2(t) \end{pmatrix}. \tag{1.7}$$

Observe next that (1.3) is equivalent to the following equation involving vectors in $\mathcal{R}^2$:

$$\begin{pmatrix} a_{11}\ddot{y}_1(t) + a_{12}\ddot{y}_2(t) \\ a_{21}\ddot{y}_1(t) + a_{22}\ddot{y}_2(t) \end{pmatrix} + \begin{pmatrix} b_{11}\dot{y}_1(t) + b_{12}\dot{y}_2(t) \\ b_{21}\dot{y}_1(t) + b_{22}\dot{y}_2(t) \end{pmatrix} + \begin{pmatrix} c_{11}y_1(t) + c_{12}y_2(t) \\ c_{21}y_1(t) + c_{22}y_2(t) \end{pmatrix} = \begin{pmatrix} w_1(t) \\ w_2(t) \end{pmatrix}. \tag{1.8}$$

Now for each fixed value of t the first term in (1.8) is the result of applying a certain linear transformation A to the vector $\ddot{\mathbf{y}}(t)$:

$$\begin{pmatrix} a_{11}\ddot{y}_1(t) + a_{12}\ddot{y}_2(t) \\ a_{21}\ddot{y}_1(t) + a_{12}\ddot{y}_2(t) \end{pmatrix} = \begin{pmatrix} a_{11} & a_{12} \\ a_{21} & a_{22} \end{pmatrix} \begin{pmatrix} \ddot{y}_1(t) \\ \ddot{y}_2(t) \end{pmatrix} = A\ddot{\mathbf{y}}(t).$$

Likewise, we note that

$$\begin{pmatrix} b_{11}\dot{y}_1(t) + b_{12}\dot{y}_2(t) \\ b_{21}\dot{y}_1(t) + b_{22}\dot{y}_2(t) \end{pmatrix} = \begin{pmatrix} b_{11} & b_{12} \\ b_{21} & b_{22} \end{pmatrix} \begin{pmatrix} \dot{y}_1(t) \\ \dot{y}_2(t) \end{pmatrix} = B\dot{\mathbf{y}}(t),$$

$$\begin{pmatrix} c_{11}y_1(t) + c_{12}y_2(t) \\ c_{21}y_1(t) + c_{22}y_2(t) \end{pmatrix} = \begin{pmatrix} c_{11} & c_{12} \\ c_{21} & c_{22} \end{pmatrix} \begin{pmatrix} y_1(t) \\ y_2(t) \end{pmatrix} = C\mathbf{y}(t).$$

Therefore, we can write (1.3) in the abbreviated form

$$A\ddot{\mathbf{y}}(t) + B\dot{\mathbf{y}}(t) + C\mathbf{y}(t) = \mathbf{w}(t), \tag{1.9}$$

where A, B, C denote the transformations on $\mathcal{R}^2$ to $\mathcal{R}^2$ specified above and where

$$\mathbf{w}(t) = \begin{pmatrix} w_1(t) \\ w_2(t) \end{pmatrix}.$$

It is not hard to see that a similar abbreviation can be applied to describe *any* system of differential equations with constant coefficients, for instance, the system

(1.10)

$$\begin{aligned} a_{11}\ddot{y}_1(t) + \cdots + a_{1n}\ddot{y}_n(t) + b_{11}\dot{y}_1(t) + \cdots + b_{1n}\dot{y}_n(t) + c_{11}y_1(t) + \cdots + c_{nn}y_n(t) &= w_1(t) \\ \vdots \qquad\qquad\qquad\qquad\qquad \vdots \qquad\qquad\qquad \vdots \quad &\quad \vdots \\ a_{n1}\ddot{y}_1(t) + \cdots + a_{nn}\ddot{y}_n(t) + b_{n1}\dot{y}_1(t) + \cdots + b_{nn}\dot{y}_n(t) + c_{n1}y_1(t) + \cdots + c_{nn}y_n(t) &= w_n(t). \end{aligned}$$

In fact, equation (1.10) reduces to the form (1.9) if we define

$$\mathbf{y}(t) = \begin{pmatrix} y_1(t) \\ \vdots \\ y_n(t) \end{pmatrix}, \qquad A = \begin{pmatrix} a_{11} & \cdots & a_{1n} \\ \vdots & & \vdots \\ a_{n1} & \cdots & a_{nn} \end{pmatrix}, \qquad B = \begin{pmatrix} b_{11} & \cdots & b_{1n} \\ \vdots & & \vdots \\ b_{n1} & \cdots & b_{nn} \end{pmatrix},$$

$$C = \begin{pmatrix} c_{11} & \cdots & c_{1n} \\ \vdots & & \vdots \\ c_{n1} & \cdots & c_{nn} \end{pmatrix}, \qquad \mathbf{w}(t) = \begin{pmatrix} w_1(t) \\ \vdots \\ w_n(t) \end{pmatrix}.$$

On the other hand, a *first-order* system

$$\begin{aligned} b_{11}\dot{y}_1(t) + \cdots + b_{1n}\dot{y}_n(t) + c_{11}y_1(t) + \cdots + c_{1n}y_n(t) &= w_1(t) \\ \vdots \qquad\qquad\qquad \vdots \qquad\qquad\qquad \vdots \quad &\quad \vdots \\ b_{n1}\dot{y}_1(t) + \cdots + b_{nn}\dot{y}_n(t) + c_{n1}y_1(t) + \cdots + c_{nn}y_n(t) &= w_n(t) \end{aligned} \tag{1.11}$$

can be reduced to the form

$$B\dot{\mathbf{y}}(t) + C\mathbf{y}(t) = \mathbf{w}(t), \tag{1.12}$$

where

$$B = \begin{pmatrix} b_{11} & \cdots & b_{1n} \\ \vdots & & \vdots \\ b_{n1} & \cdots & b_{nn} \end{pmatrix}, \qquad C = \begin{pmatrix} c_{11} & \cdots & c_{1n} \\ \vdots & & \vdots \\ c_{n1} & \cdots & c_{nn} \end{pmatrix}, \qquad \mathbf{w}(t) = \begin{pmatrix} w_1(t) \\ \vdots \\ w_n(t) \end{pmatrix}.$$

(1.13) Examples. Systems of Differential Equations (Vector Form)

(a) Example (1.1a) has the form (1.9) provided that we set

$$A = \begin{pmatrix} 1 & 0 \\ 0 & 1 \end{pmatrix}, \quad B = \begin{pmatrix} 0 & 0 \\ 0 & 0 \end{pmatrix}, \quad C = \begin{pmatrix} 2k/m_1 & -k/m_1 \\ -k/m_2 & k/m_2 \end{pmatrix}, \quad \mathbf{w} = \begin{pmatrix} 0 \\ 0 \end{pmatrix}.$$

(b) Equation (1.2) has the form (1.9) provided that we set

$$A = \begin{pmatrix} L_1 & M \\ M & L_2 \end{pmatrix}, \qquad B = \begin{pmatrix} R_1 & 0 \\ 0 & R_2 \end{pmatrix}, \qquad C = \begin{pmatrix} 1/C_1 & 0 \\ 0 & 1/C_2 \end{pmatrix},$$

$$\mathbf{w}(t) = \begin{pmatrix} E_1(t) \\ E_2(t) \end{pmatrix}.$$

The ideas of linear analysis go much deeper than the mere giving of a compact notation for systems such as (1.10) and (1.11). As we shall see in subsequent sections, they also provide the means for obtaining, explicitly, solutions of these systems. In addition, they provide analogs of the splitting and superposition theorems for such systems.

In the present section we apply our *principle for initial conditions* [(4.9) of Chapter 4] to determine which initial conditions are required to select a unique solution of systems (1.10) and (1.11).

(1.14) Existence and Uniqueness Theorem for Second-Order Systems. *Suppose that* $\mathbf{w}$ *is a continuous* $\mathcal{R}^n$*-valued function defined for all* t. *Let* t_0 *be given and let*

$$\mathbf{y}^0 = \begin{pmatrix} y_1^0 \\ \cdot \\ \cdot \\ \cdot \\ y_n^0 \end{pmatrix}, \qquad \dot{\mathbf{y}}^0 = \begin{pmatrix} \dot{y}_1^0 \\ \cdot \\ \cdot \\ \cdot \\ \dot{y}_n^0 \end{pmatrix}$$

be any vectors in $\mathcal{R}^n$. *Then—assuming* $A\colon \mathcal{R}^n \to \mathcal{R}^n$ *is invertible*†*—there exists a unique solution* $\mathbf{y}$ *of the problem*

$$A\ddot{\mathbf{y}}(t) + B\dot{\mathbf{y}}(t) + C\mathbf{y}(t) = \mathbf{w}(t),$$

$$(*) \qquad \mathbf{y}(t_0) = \mathbf{y}^0, \qquad \dot{\mathbf{y}}(t_0) = \dot{\mathbf{y}}^0.$$

That is, there exists one and only one n-tuple of functions $y_1, \ldots, y_n$ *satisfying the given second-order system of differential equations together with the initial conditions*

$$\begin{array}{ll} y_1(t_0) = y_1^0, & \dot{y}_1(t_0) = \dot{y}_1^0 \\ \cdot \quad \cdot & \cdot \quad \cdot \\ \cdot \quad \cdot & \cdot \quad \cdot \\ y_n(t_0) = y_n^0, & \dot{y}_n(t_0) = \dot{y}_n^0. \end{array}$$

For first-order systems we have an analogous result.

---

†This excludes $A = 0$, for example, which is a case in which the "second-order" system is actually first order. (A invertible means A^{-1} exists.)

(1.15) Existence and Uniqueness Theorem for First-Order Systems. *Suppose that* $\mathbf{w}$ *is a continuous* $\mathbb{R}^n$*-valued function defined for all* t*. Let* t_0 *be given and let*

$$\mathbf{y}^0 = \begin{pmatrix} y_1^0 \\ \cdot \\ \cdot \\ \cdot \\ y_n^0 \end{pmatrix},$$

be any vector in $\mathbb{R}^n$*. Then—assuming* $B\colon \mathbb{R}^n \to \mathbb{R}^n$ *is invertible*†*—there exists a unique solution* $\mathbf{y}$ *of the problem*

$$B\dot{\mathbf{y}}(t) + C\mathbf{y}(t) = \mathbf{w}(t)$$
$$(**) \qquad \mathbf{y}(t_0) = \mathbf{y}^0.$$

That is, there exists one and only one n-tuple of functions $y_1, \ldots, y_n$ *satisfying the given first-order system of differential equations together with the initial conditions*

$$y_1(t_0) = y_1^0, \;\ldots,\; y_n(t_0) = y_n^0.$$

We shall not prove either of these theorems in full generality, although a proof could be obtained by the method of successive approximations discussed in Chapter 4. What we *shall* do is show how to construct the solution *explicitly* in most situations, which is, of course, an acceptable way to prove existence for those situations.

One useful point. It will be noted that both for second-order systems (1.9) and for first-order systems (1.12) our theorems presuppose that the transformation operating on the highest derivative of $\mathbf{y}$ is invertible. This being the case, we can always, by a purely algebraic manipulation, reduce the system to one in which the transformation acting on the highest derivative of $\mathbf{y}$ is I, the *identity transformation* on $\mathbb{R}^n$. We proceed to prove this fact

Recall that, by definition, when A is invertible the linear transformation A^{-1} satisfies

$$A^{-1}(A\boldsymbol{\alpha}) = \boldsymbol{\alpha} = I\boldsymbol{\alpha} \qquad \text{for all } \boldsymbol{\alpha} \in \mathbb{R}^n.$$

Let us apply A^{-1} to each term of equation (1.9). The first term becomes

$$\text{(i)} \qquad A^{-1}\big(A\ddot{\mathbf{y}}(t)\big) = \ddot{\mathbf{y}}(t)$$

†This excludes $B = 0$, for example, which is a case in which the "first-order" system is really not a system of differential equations at all.

Moreover, by problem 16 of Chapter 8, §4, we have

$$\text{(ii)} \qquad A^{-1}(B\dot{\mathbf{y}}(t)) = \hat{B}\dot{\mathbf{y}}(t)$$

$$\text{(iii)} \qquad A^{-1}(C\mathbf{y}(t)) = \hat{C}\mathbf{y}(t)$$

for certain linear transformations $\hat{B}$, $\hat{C}$: $\mathbb{R}^n \to \mathbb{R}^n$. (The transformations $\hat{B}$ and $\hat{C}$ are called *products* and are denoted by $\hat{B} = A^{-1}B$, $\hat{C} = A^{-1}C$. An efficient way to calculate their matrices is described in the problem referred to above.)

Finally, if we let

$$\text{(iv)} \qquad A^{-1}(\mathbf{w}(t)) = \hat{\mathbf{w}}(t)$$

then by (i)–(iv) we obtain from (1.9) the new equation

$$\ddot{\mathbf{y}}(t) + \hat{B}\dot{\mathbf{y}}(t) + \hat{C}\mathbf{y}(t) = \hat{\mathbf{w}}(t), \tag{1.16}$$

where $\hat{B}$, $\hat{C}$, and $\hat{\mathbf{w}}(t)$ are defined in (ii), (iii) and (iv).

In a similar manner, if we apply B^{-1} to both sides of (1.12) we get

$$\dot{\mathbf{y}}(t) + \hat{C}\mathbf{y}(t) = \hat{\mathbf{w}}(t), \tag{1.17}$$

where $\hat{C}\mathbf{y}(t)$ and $\hat{\mathbf{w}}(t)$ are defined by

$$\hat{C}\mathbf{y}(t) = B^{-1}(C\mathbf{y}(t)), \qquad \hat{\mathbf{w}}(t) = B^{-1}(\mathbf{w}(t)).$$

Now $\mathbf{y}$ is a solution of (1.16) if and only if it satisfies (1.9), likewise $\mathbf{y}$ is a solution of (1.17) if and only if it satisfies (1.12) (problem 8). Hence we shall usually reduce a second- or first-order system to the form (1.16) or (1.17) as a preliminary step in attempting to obtain its solutions explicitly.

The final point to be made in this section is of a rather deep theoretical nature. We shall find that our reformulation of systems of equations in vector language will enable us to obtain solutions. This fact, however, only begins to indicate the unifying effects of our methods.

The reader will recall that in Chapter 2 we were careful to point out that the concepts of continuity and differentiability could be extended to functions $\mathbf{y}$ with values in any vector space which has an inner product. Similarly, the concept of linear transformation was defined for any vector space (Chapter 8). Thus, while we have, up to now, considered equations (1.16) and (1.17) only for functions $\mathbf{y}$ with values in $\mathbb{R}^n$, there really is no reason that we *must* make this restriction. We could give a meaning to the equations (1.16) and (1.17) in *any* vector space with an inner product.

It turns out that if one is willing to take the step of studying (1.16) and (1.17) in arbitrary vector spaces, then not only can systems of differential equations with constant coefficients be handled, but the *same methods* serve to treat many other situations including most of the partial differential equation problems in Chapter 7. These methods, in fact, go far beyond Chapter 7 and apply to much more complicated problems in partial differential equations.

We cannot hope to develop here this general theory of equations (1.16) and (1.17) in arbitrary spaces. For this reason we have restricted ourselves mainly to the systems of equations (1.10) and (1.11). However, we have tried in §3 to indicate the flavor of the extensions by discussing, briefly, the heat equation. We hope that the reader will make an effort to reflect on this example and on the way in which the methods presented are parallel to the developments for the simpler systems (1.10) and (1.11).

PROBLEMS

1. Reduce each of the following systems of equations to the form (1.9) or (1.12) by calculating the matrices in question:

(a) $$\begin{aligned}\dot{y}_1(t) + y_2(t) &= 0\\ \dot{y}_2(t) + y_1(t) &= 0\end{aligned}$$

(b) $$\begin{aligned}\ddot{y}_1(t) + y_2(t) &= 0\\ \ddot{y}_2(t) + y_1(t) &= 0\end{aligned}$$

(c) $$\begin{aligned}2\ddot{y}_1(t) - \ddot{y}_2(t) + 3\dot{y}_1(t) + 2y_1(t) - y_2(t) &= -1\\ \ddot{y}_1(t) + \ddot{y}_2(t) - 4\dot{y}_2(t) + y_1(t) - y_2(t) &= 1\end{aligned}$$

(d) $$\begin{aligned}\dot{y}_2(t) - 2\dot{y}_1(t) &= 0\\ \dot{y}_2(t) + 2\dot{y}_1(t) &= 0\end{aligned}$$

(e) $$\begin{aligned}\ddot{y}_2(t) - \dot{y}_1(t) + \dot{y}_2(t) &= t\\ \ddot{y}_1(t) + \ddot{y}_2(t) - \dot{y}_1(t) &= 4\end{aligned}$$

(f) $$\begin{aligned}\ddot{y}_1(t) + 2\dot{y}_1(t) - y_2(t) &= 0\\ \ddot{y}_1(t) + \dot{y}_2(t) + y_1(t) &= 1\end{aligned}$$

2. Reduce each of the following systems of equations to the form (1.16) or (1.17) by calculating the matrices in question.

(a) $$\begin{aligned}\dot{y}_1(t) + 2\dot{y}_2(t) + y_1(t) &= 1\\ \dot{y}_1(t) - \dot{y}_2(t) + y_1(t) &= t\end{aligned}$$

(b) $$\begin{aligned}\dot{y}_1(t) + \dot{y}_2(t) + y_1(t) - y_2(t) &= 0\\ \dot{y}_1(t) - \dot{y}_2(t) - y_1(t) - y_2(t) &= 1\end{aligned}$$

(c) $$\begin{aligned}\ddot{y}_2(t) + y_1(t) &= 0\\ \ddot{y}_1(t) - y_2(t) &= 0\end{aligned}$$

(d) $$\begin{aligned}\ddot{y}_2(t) + \dot{y}_1(t) + y_2(t) &= 1\\ \ddot{y}_1(t) - \dot{y}_2(t) &= t\end{aligned}$$

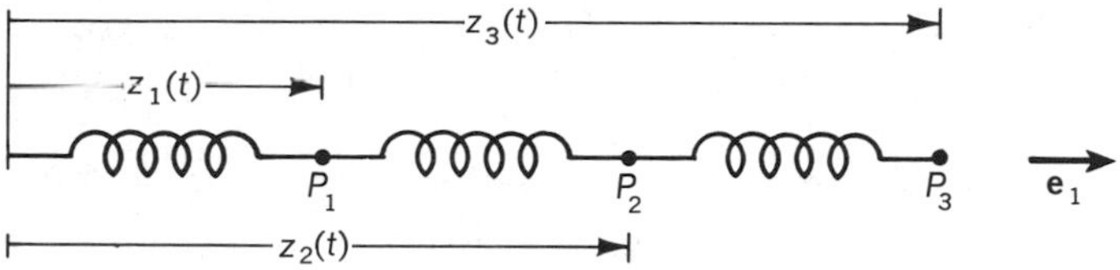

Figure 9.4

3. Transform the equations of example (1.1b) into the form (1.16).
4. Formulate the differential equations for a system of three masses connected by springs as shown in Figure 9.4. Assume the springs all have unstretched length L.
5. Use the methods of Chapter 4 to rewrite each of the sets of equations in example (1.1) as a *first-order* system.
6. A matrix T is called *diagonal* if its entries t_{ij} are zero for i not equal to j. Thus every 3×3 diagonal matrix has the form

$$\begin{pmatrix} t_{11} & 0 & 0 \\ 0 & t_{22} & 0 \\ 0 & 0 & t_{33} \end{pmatrix}.$$

   (a) If a transformation T from $\mathcal{R}^n$ to $\mathcal{R}^n$ has a diagonal matrix, show that T is invertible (T^{-1} exists) if and only if the diagonal elements $t_{11}, \ldots, t_{nn}$ of the matrix are all nonzero.

   (b) In theorem (1.15) suppose B and C have diagonal matrices and that B is invertible. Show how to obtain a solution satisfying (**).

7. Show how to obtain a solution of (1.9) when A, B, and C have diagonal matrices and A is invertible.

*8. (a) Prove that every solution of (1.9) is a solution of (1.16), and vice versa.

   (b) Give a proof of the same relation between (1.12) and (1.17).

2. First-Order Systems: Solution Procedure

We begin our discussion of systems of differential equations with constant coefficients by studying first-order systems. Such systems have the form (1.12) and, as was indicated in §1, can usually be converted into a form in which $B = I$, that is, to

$$\dot{\mathbf{y}}(t) + C\mathbf{y}(t) = \mathbf{w}(t). \tag{2.1}$$

Thus we shall concentrate our attention on (2.1) in this section.

We are going to show that under certain circumstances one can reduce the study of (2.1) to the study of *individual* first-order linear nonhomogeneous equations in *one* unknown (Chapter 4). To do this we must make the following assumption:

(2.2) Assumption. *The transformation* $C: \mathcal{R}^n \to \mathcal{R}^n$ *which appears in* (2.1) *has* n *eigenvectors* $\gamma_1, \ldots, \gamma_n$ *which form a basis for* $\mathcal{R}^n$.

We assume throughout this section that (2.2) is true. As we point out in example (2.14), it does not always hold. If it is not true, then the procedure we are going to describe simply does not work. However, in Chapter 10 we shall discuss methods which will enable us also to treat (2.1) in many cases in which (2.2) is violated.

Our goal is to solve (2.1), under assumption (2.2), for a solution $\mathbf{y}$ which is subject to the condition (**) of theorem (1.15); that is,

$$\mathbf{y}(t_0) = \mathbf{y}^0, \qquad \mathbf{y}^0 \text{ given.} \tag{2.3}$$

Suppose that we have such a solution. This means a differentiable function $\mathbf{y}$ of t with values in $\mathcal{R}^n$ such that (2.1) and (2.3) are satisfied. For a particular value of t the quantities $\mathbf{y}(t)$ and $\mathbf{w}(t)$ are simply vectors in $\mathcal{R}^n$. Since, by (2.2), the system $\mathbf{B}$: $\gamma_1, \ldots, \gamma_n$ forms a basis for $\mathcal{R}^n$, we can write

$$\begin{aligned} \mathbf{y}(t) &= u_1(t)\gamma_1 + \cdots + u_n(t)\gamma_n \\ \mathbf{w}(t) &= v_1(t)\gamma_1 + \cdots + v_n(t)\gamma_n, \end{aligned} \tag{2.4}$$

where the u_k's and v_k's are the B-coordinates of $\mathbf{y}(t)$ and $\mathbf{w}(t)$, respectively. These quantities are uniquely determined by $\mathbf{y}(t)$ and $\mathbf{w}(t)$, but of course they change with t since $\mathbf{y}(t)$ and $\mathbf{w}(t)$ do.

The vector $\dot{\mathbf{y}}(t)$ can also be represented as a unique linear combination of the γ_k's and, in fact, by theorem (2.1.14) we have

$$\dot{\mathbf{y}}(t) = \dot{u}_1(t)\gamma_1 + \cdots + \dot{u}_n(t)\gamma_n. \tag{2.5}$$

Now we substitute (2.4) and (2.5) into (2.1) and obtain, since C is a linear transformation,

$$\begin{aligned} &\dot{u}_1(t)\gamma_1 + \cdots + \dot{u}_n(t)\gamma_n + C\big(u_1(t)\gamma_1 + \cdots + u_n(t)\gamma_n\big) \\ &\quad = \dot{u}_1(t)\gamma_1 + \cdots + \dot{u}_n(t)\gamma_n + u_1(t)C\gamma_1 + \cdots + u_n(t)C\gamma_n \\ &\quad = v_1(t)\gamma_1 + \cdots + v_n(t)\gamma_n. \end{aligned} \tag{2.6}$$

But the γ_k's are eigenvectors of C, which means that

$$C\gamma_1 = a_1\gamma_1, \quad \ldots, \quad C\gamma_n = a_n\gamma_n, \tag{2.7}$$

where $a_1, \ldots, a_n$ are the eigenvalues corresponding to $\gamma_1, \ldots, \gamma_n$. Thus we can rewrite (2.6) in the form

$$(2.8) \qquad (\dot{u}_1(t) + a_1 u_1(t))\gamma_1 + \cdots + (\dot{u}_n(t) + a_n u_n(t))\gamma_n = v_1(t)\gamma_1 + \cdots + v_n(t)\gamma_n.$$

The two vectors on the left and right sides of (2.8) must be equal; hence their B coordinates, that is, the coefficients of $\gamma_1, \ldots, \gamma_n$ in their expansions, must be equal. Thus we can equate the coefficients of $\gamma_1, \ldots, \gamma_n$ on the two sides of (2.8) and obtain

$$(2.9) \qquad \begin{aligned} \dot{u}_1(t) + a_1 u_1(t) &= v_1(t) \\ &\vdots \\ \dot{u}_n(t) + a_n u_n(t) &= v_n(t). \end{aligned}$$

Observe that each of the equations in (2.9) is a single first-order equation *involving only one function*, and thus can be easily solved.

We have shown that *if* $\mathbf{y}$ is a solution of (2.1), then it can be expanded in the form (2.4), where the u_k's satisfy (2.9). Conversely, it is easy to work backward and show that if the u_k's satisfy (2.9), then the function $\mathbf{y}$ defined by (2.4) will satisfy (2.1).

We can treat the condition (2.3) in a similar fashion. Since $\mathbf{y}^0$ is in $\mathcal{R}^n$ we can write

$$(2.10) \qquad \mathbf{y}^0 = u_1^0\gamma_1 + \cdots + u_n^0\gamma_n,$$

where the u_k^0's are uniquely determined. Thus, if we substitute (2.10) and (2.4) into (2.3) we obtain

$$u_1(t_0)\gamma_1 + \cdots + u_n(t_0)\gamma_n = u_1^0\gamma_1 + \cdots + u_n^0\gamma_n$$

or

$$(2.11) \qquad u_1(t_0) = u_1^0, \; \ldots, \; u_n(t_0) = u_n^0.$$

The result of our computations is that each function u_k in (2.4) satisfies a problem of the type we studied in §1 of Chapter 4. Those problems are

$$(2.12) \qquad \dot{u}_k(t) + a_k u_k(t) = v_k(t), \qquad u_k(t_0) = u_k^0, \qquad k = 1, \ldots, n.$$

The solutions of these problems are obtained from Chapter 4, (1.12). The reader should check that these solutions are

$$(2.13) \qquad u_k(t) = u_k^0 e^{-a_k(t-t_0)} + e^{-a_k t}\int_{t_0}^t e^{a_k\tau} v_k(\tau)\, d\tau, \qquad k = 1, \ldots, n.$$

(2.14) Examples

(a) Find the solution of the problem

$$\text{(i)}\quad \begin{aligned} \dot{y}_1(t) + y_1(t) + 3y_2(t) &= 1, \qquad & y_1(0) &= 1 \\ \dot{y}_2(t) + 2y_1(t) + 2y_2(t) &= t, \qquad & y_2(0) &= 0. \end{aligned}$$

This problem has the form of (2.1) and (2.3) with

$$C = \begin{pmatrix} 1 & 3 \\ 2 & 2 \end{pmatrix}, \qquad \mathbf{w}(t) = \begin{pmatrix} 1 \\ t \end{pmatrix}, \qquad \mathbf{y}^0 = \begin{pmatrix} 1 \\ 0 \end{pmatrix}.$$

First, let us find the eigenvalues a of C. By the procedure of (4.14) of Chapter 8 we determine a by the condition that the determinant† of $C - aI$ is zero

$$\begin{vmatrix} 1 - a & 3 \\ 2 & 2 - a \end{vmatrix} = (1 - a)(2 - a) - 6$$
$$= a^2 - 3a - 4 = (a - 4)(a + 1) = 0;$$

thus $a = 4$ or -1. Set $a_1 = 4$ and $a_2 = -1$. Then, again by (4.14) of Chapter 8, one finds that eigenvectors γ_1 and γ_2 for a_1 and a_2, respectively, can be taken as

$$\gamma_1 = \begin{pmatrix} 1 \\ 1 \end{pmatrix}, \qquad \gamma_2 = \begin{pmatrix} 1 \\ -\frac{2}{3} \end{pmatrix}.$$

One checks easily that γ_1 and γ_2 form a basis for $\mathcal{R}^2$; hence assumption (2.2) is valid.

We have

$$\mathbf{w}(t) = \begin{pmatrix} 1 \\ t \end{pmatrix} = v_1(t)\begin{pmatrix} 1 \\ 1 \end{pmatrix} + v_2(t)\begin{pmatrix} 1 \\ -\frac{2}{3} \end{pmatrix},$$

from which it follows that

$$v_1(t) = \tfrac{2}{5} + \tfrac{3}{5}t, \qquad v_2(t) = \tfrac{3}{5} - \tfrac{3}{5}t.$$

Also, we have

$$y^0 = \begin{pmatrix} 1 \\ 0 \end{pmatrix} = u_1^0\begin{pmatrix} 1 \\ 1 \end{pmatrix} + u_2^0\begin{pmatrix} 1 \\ -\frac{2}{3} \end{pmatrix};$$

hence

$$u_1^0 = \tfrac{2}{5}, \qquad u_2^0 = \tfrac{3}{5}.$$

---

†For any matrix $T = \begin{pmatrix} \alpha & \beta \\ \gamma & \delta \end{pmatrix}$ the symbol $\begin{vmatrix} \alpha & \beta \\ \gamma & \delta \end{vmatrix}$ denotes the determinant of T, that is $\alpha\delta - \beta\gamma$.

Thus equations (2.12) become

$$\text{(ii)} \qquad \begin{aligned} \dot{u}_1(t) + 4u_1(t) &= \tfrac{2}{5} + \tfrac{3}{5}t, \qquad & u_1(0) &= \tfrac{2}{5} \\ \dot{u}_2(t) - u_2(t) &= \tfrac{3}{5} - \tfrac{3}{5}t, \qquad & u_2(0) &= \tfrac{3}{5}. \end{aligned}$$

The functions u_1 and u_2 can then be obtained from formula (2.13), or one can solve (ii) by the method of undetermined coefficients as in Chapter 4. Either way the solutions are readily found to be

$$\text{(iii)} \qquad \begin{aligned} u_1(t) &= \tfrac{27}{80}e^{-4t} + \tfrac{1}{16} + \tfrac{3}{20}t \\ u_2(t) &= \tfrac{3}{5}e^{t} + \tfrac{3}{5}t. \end{aligned}$$

To recover the solution $\mathbf{y}$ we must substitute (iii) into equation (2.4); that is,

$$\mathbf{y}(t) = \begin{pmatrix} y_1(t) \\ y_2(t) \end{pmatrix} = [\tfrac{27}{80}e^{-4t} + \tfrac{1}{16} + \tfrac{3}{30}t]\begin{pmatrix} 1 \\ 1 \end{pmatrix} + [\tfrac{3}{5}t + \tfrac{3}{5}e^{t}]\begin{pmatrix} 1 \\ -\frac{2}{3} \end{pmatrix}.$$

Thus the solution (y_1, y_2) of (i) is given by

$$y_1(t) = \tfrac{27}{80}e^{-4t} + \tfrac{3}{5}e^{t} + \tfrac{1}{16} + \tfrac{3}{4}t, \qquad y_2(t) = \tfrac{27}{80}e^{-4t} - \tfrac{2}{3}e^{t} + \tfrac{1}{16} - \tfrac{1}{4}t.$$

(b) Consider the system of equations

$$\begin{aligned} \dot{y}_1(t) - y_2(t) &= 2, \qquad & y_1(0) &= 1 \\ \dot{y}_2(t) + y_1(t) &= t, \qquad & y_2(0) &= 2. \end{aligned}$$

These have the form (2.1) with

$$C = \begin{pmatrix} 0 & -1 \\ 1 & 0 \end{pmatrix}, \qquad \mathbf{w}(t) = \begin{pmatrix} 2 \\ t \end{pmatrix}.$$

The eigenvalues a would have to satisfy

$$\begin{vmatrix} -a & -1 \\ 1 & -a \end{vmatrix} = a^2 + 1 = 0.$$

Hence there are no eigenvalues, and accordingly no eigenvectors, so our method fails.†

(c) Consider the system

$$\begin{aligned} \dot{y}_1(t) - y_1(t) + y_2(t) &= 0 \\ \dot{y}_2(t) - y_1(t) - 3y_2(t) &= 0. \end{aligned}$$

†This problem is solved in example (3.18a) of Chapter 10.

This time the matrix C is

$$C = \begin{pmatrix} -1 & 1 \\ -1 & -3 \end{pmatrix}.$$

Thus the eigenvalues are given by

$$\begin{vmatrix} -1 - a & 1 \\ -1 & -3 - a \end{vmatrix} = (a + 2)^2 = 0.$$

There is only one eigenvalue, $a = -2$, and moreover all eigenvectors have the form

$$\gamma = \begin{pmatrix} \beta \\ -\beta \end{pmatrix} = \beta \begin{pmatrix} 1 \\ -1 \end{pmatrix}.$$

Since all of these are multiples of one vector, there is *no* basis of eigenvectors for $\mathcal{R}^2$ and again our method fails.

We can learn a great deal about equation (2.1) from a careful study of formulas (2.13) and (2.4). Consider first the *homogeneous* system $\mathbf{w} \equiv \mathbf{0}$. Then equation (2.1) becomes

(2.15) $$\dot{\mathbf{y}}(t) + C\mathbf{y}(t) = \mathbf{0}.$$

The solution of (2.15) which satisfies (2.3) is given by (2.13), with $v_k = 0$, and (2.4). Thus this solution is

(2.16) $$\begin{aligned} \mathbf{y}(t) &= u_1(t)\gamma_1 + \cdots + u_n(t)\gamma_n \\ &= (e^{-a_1(t-t_0)}u_1^0)\gamma_1 + \cdots + (e^{-a_n(t-t_0)}u_n^0)\gamma_n \end{aligned}$$

Equation (2.16) gives us a rule for solving (2.15) subject to (2.3).

(2.17) Rule for Solution of Homogeneous Systems. *Suppose assumption* (2.2) *holds. Expand* $\mathbf{y}^0$ *in terms of the eigenvectors of* C. *Then to obtain the solution of* (2.15) *that satisfies* (2.3), *multiply each term* $u_k^0\gamma_k$ *in the expansion of* $\mathbf{y}_0$ *by* $e^{-a_k(t-t_0)}$, *where* a_k *is the eigenvalue for* γ_k. *The resulting expression is the expansion for* $\mathbf{y}(t)$.

Rule (2.17) is an extension of the procedure discussed in Chapter 4 for the single first-order equation (4.1.4) [in the special case where $p(t)$ is constant]. There exist several other analogies between (2.15) and the corresponding single equation (4.1.4). First we have a uniqueness and existence result.

(2.18) Theorem.† *If* (2.2) *is valid then there exists one and only one solution of* (2.15) *and* (2.3).

Proof. Formula (2.16) establishes existence by providing one solution. The proof of uniqueness is just like that of proposition (4.1.9) and is left as a problem. ▮

Note that (2.18) is theorem (1.15), stated for the system (2.15). A corollary of this theorem is the following analog of proposition (4.1.10), the proof of which is also left to the problems.

(2.19) Proposition. *Suppose* (2.2) *is satisfied. Then if a solution* $\mathbf{y}$ *of* (2.15) *is zero at one point it must be identically zero.*

Formula (2.16) illustrates an extremely important concept for systems of differential equations, the idea of stability.

(2.20) Definition. Equation (2.15) is called *stable* if every solution $\mathbf{y}$ satisfies

$$\text{(i)} \qquad \lim_{t\to\infty} \|\mathbf{y}(t)\| = 0.$$

The equation is called *unstable* if some solution satisfies

$$\text{(ii)} \qquad \lim_{t\to\infty} \|\mathbf{y}(t)\| = \infty.$$

The notion of stability is important in the study of systems of differential equations which describe physical phenomena. An unstable equation would usually be undesirable physically as it would lead to catastrophies. Thus, just as with lack of existence or uniqueness, the instability of a system of equations leads one to suspect the validity of the model being used (see problem 16). These remarks make the following result of interest.

(2.21) Proposition. *Suppose* (2.2) *is valid. If all the eigenvalues* a_k *of* C *are positive, then* (2.15) *is stable. If one or more of the eigenvalues is negative, then* (2.15) *is unstable.*‡

Proof. Let $\mathbf{y}$ be any solution, let t_0 be some number, and set $\mathbf{y}(t_0) = \mathbf{y}^0$. Then $\mathbf{y}$ satisfies (2.16). By repeated use of theorem (1.2.11)–(ii) we have

$$\text{(i)} \qquad \|\mathbf{y}(t)\| \le e^{-a_1(t-t_0)}|u_1^0|\,\|\gamma_1\| + \cdots + e^{-a_n(t-t_0)}|u_n^0|\,\|\gamma_n\|.$$

---

†Both theorem (2.18) and proposition (2.19) are true whether or not (2.2) is satisfied, but the argument we are using would not apply in other situations.

‡The remaining case where one or more eigenvalues is zero and the rest are positive is discussed in a problem.

If all the eigenvalues a_k are positive, then each term in (i) tends to zero as t tends to infinity; hence $\|\mathbf{y}(t)\|$ must tend to zero.

Suppose now that some eigenvalue a_k is negative. Choose $\mathbf{y}^0 = \gamma_k$. Then the solution of (2.15) such that $\mathbf{y}(t_0) = \mathbf{y}^0$ is, by (2.16), $\mathbf{y}(t) = e^{-a_k t}\gamma_k$. Hence $\|\mathbf{y}(t)\| = e^{-a_k t}\|\gamma_k\|$, which clearly tends to infinity as t tends to infinity. Hence the system is unstable. ▮

Let us turn now to the nonhomogeneous equation (2.1). If we substitute (2.13) into (2.4) we obtain, for the solution of (2.1) satisfying (2.3), the formula

$$\begin{aligned}(2.22)\qquad \mathbf{y}(t) = {} & u_1^0 e^{-a(t-t_0)}\gamma_1 + \cdots + u_n^0 e^{-a_n(t-t_0)}\gamma_n \\ & + \left(e^{-a_1 t}\int_{t_0}^{t} e^{a_1\tau}v_1(\tau)\,d\tau\right)\gamma_1 + \cdots \\ & + \left(e^{-a_n t}\int_{t_0}^{t} e^{a_n\tau}v_n(\tau)\,d\tau\right)\gamma_n.\end{aligned}$$

Formula (2.22) yields a solution for (2.1) and (2.3) and thus establishes *existence* for that problem. The uniqueness of solutions is to be established in the problems.

Observe that formula (2.22) can be written

$$(2.23)\qquad \mathbf{y}(t) = \eta(t) + \mathbf{y}^*(t),$$

where

$$\eta(t) = u_1^0 e^{-a_1(t-t_0)}\gamma_1 + \cdots + u_n^0 e^{-a_n(t-t_0)}\gamma_n,$$

$$\mathbf{y}^*(t) = \left(e^{-a_1 t}\int_{t_0}^{t} e^{a_1\tau}w_1(\tau)\,d\tau\right)\gamma_1 + \cdots + \left(e^{-a_n t}\int_{t_0}^{t} e^{a_n\tau}w_n(\tau)\,d\tau\right)\gamma_n.$$

Note that $\mathbf{y}^*$ is a particular solution of (2.1) which does not depend on the initial condition $\mathbf{y}^0$. On the other hand, η is a solution of the *homogeneous* equation (2.15). Thus we have a decomposition of solutions of (2.1) into the sums of particular solutions and solutions of the homogeneous equation. This is an analog of proposition (4.1.16) for a single equation and also looks very much like the splitting theorem of §1. In fact, as we shall see shortly, it *is* the splitting theorem when (2.1) is interpreted in an appropriate way.

PROBLEMS

Note: The calculation of eigenvalues and eigenvectors requires rather tedious work. Since such calculations do little to aid in the understanding of differential equation problems, we have used the same matrices several times in this chapter. Thus by recording his results the reader need compute the eigenvectors only once. In addition, we have tried to use the same initial conditions and right-hand sides.

Find the solutions of each of the following problems.

1. $\dot{y}_1(t) + y_2(t) = 0, \ y_1(0) = 1$
$\dot{y}_2(t) + y_1(t) = 0, \ y_2(0) = -1.$

2. $\dot{y}_1(t) + y_2(t) = 2e^{3t}, \ y_1(0) = 0$
$\dot{y}_2(t) + y_1(t) = e^{3t} - e^{-3t}, \ y_2(0) = 0.$

3. $\dot{y}_1(t) = 4y_1(t) - 2y_2(t), \ y_1(1) = 1$
$\dot{y}_2(t) = -y_1(t) + 3y_2(t), \ y_2(1) = 0.$

4. $\dot{y}_1(t) + 4y_1(t) - y_2(t) = t, \ y_1(0) = 0$
$\dot{y}_2(t) + 2y_1(t) + y_2(t) = 1, \ y_2(0) = 1.$

5. $\dot{y}_1(t) + 3y_1(t) + 2y_2(t) = 0, \ y_1(-1) = 1$
$\dot{y}_2(t) + 4y_1(t) + y_2(t) = 0, \ y_2(-1) = 0.$

6. $\dot{y}_1(t) + 3y_1(t) + 2y_2(t) = \sin t, \ y_1(0) = 0$
$\dot{y}_2(t) + 4y_1(t) + y_2(t) = 0, \ y_2(0) = 0.$

7. $\dot{y}_1(t) = y_3(t), \ y_1(0) = 1$
$\dot{y}_2(t) = 2y_2(t), \ y_2(0) = 0$
$\dot{y}_3(t) = y_1(t), \ y_3(0) = 0.$

8. $\dot{y}_1(t) + 2y_1(t) + 2y_2(t) = 2e^{3t}, \ y_1(0) = 0$
$\dot{y}_2(t) + y_3(t) = e^{3t}, \ y_2(0) = 0$
$\dot{y}_3(t) + y_2(t) = -e^{3t}, \ y_3(0) = 0.$

Problems 9–12 are designed to indicate alternative approaches to the study of (2.1). Note the analog of the method of undetermined coefficients. We assume that (2.2) holds throughout.

9. (a) Consider the homogeneous system (2.15). Show that a function $\mathbf{y}$ of the form

$$(*) \qquad \mathbf{y}(t) = \gamma e^{-at}$$

is a solution if and only if γ is an eigenvector of C with eigenvalue a.

(b) Find all solutions of the form (*) for the system in problem 7.

10. (a) Consider the system (2.1) when $\mathbf{w}$ has the form

$$\mathbf{w}(t) = \omega e^{-bt}.$$

Show that if b is *not* an eigenvalue of C, then it is possible to find a particular solution $\mathbf{y}^*$ of (2.1) of the form

$$\mathbf{y}^*(t) = \beta e^{-bt}.$$

(b) Apply part (a) to obtain a particular solution of the system in problem 8.

11. (a) Show that the method of problem 10 fails to give a particular solution of the system

$$\dot{y}_1(t) + y_2(t) = e^t$$
$$\dot{y}_2(t) + y_1(t) = 2e^t.$$

(b) Obtain a solution of these equations.

***12.** (a) Consider the system (2.1) when $\mathbf{w}$ has the form

$$\mathbf{w}(t) = \boldsymbol{\omega} \sin bt.$$

Show that one can always obtain a particular solution $\mathbf{y}^*$ of (2.1) having the form

$$\mathbf{y}^*(t) = \boldsymbol{\alpha} \sin bt + \boldsymbol{\beta} \cos bt.$$

(*Hint:* Show that the eigenvalues of C^2 are the squares of the eigenvalues of C, hence ≥ 0.)

(b) Apply the method of part (a) to obtain a particular solution of the system in problem 6.

13. (a) Prove the uniqueness part of theorem (2.8). [*Hint:* Let $\mathbf{w}$ and $\mathbf{z}$ be solutions and determine the problem which is solved by $\mathbf{y} = \mathbf{w} - \mathbf{z}$. Show that if $\mathbf{y}$ is expanded as in (2.4), then the u_k's satisfy problems to which proposition (4.1.10) applies.]

(b) Prove that there exists at most one solution of the problem (2.1) and (2.3).

14. Prove proposition (2.19).

15. If (2.2) is valid and one or more of the a's is zero but the rest of the a's are positive, show that (2.15) is neither stable nor unstable.

16. Consider the equations in example (1.1b) for the special case

$$E_1 = E_2 = C_1^{-1} = C_2^{-1} = 0.$$

If we set $z_1 = \dot{y}_1$ and $z_2 = \dot{y}_2$, then these equations become a homogeneous first-order system. Show that this system is stable if $L_1L_2 > M^2$ and unstable if $L_1L_2 < M^2$. (It is clear that we do not want the z_k's, which are the currents in the circuits, to become infinite as time becomes large. Hence physically one would expect the relation $L_1L_2 > M^2$ to hold. In fact, it always does hold.)

***17.** (a) Show how the theory of this chapter could be used to study systems of equations of the form

$$\dot{\mathbf{y}}(t) + p(t)C\mathbf{y}(t) = \mathbf{w}(t),$$

where $p(t)$ is a scalar function of t and C is a linear transformation from $\mathcal{R}^n$ to $\mathcal{R}^n$.

(b) Apply the result of part (a) to the problem

$$\dot{y}_1(t) + ty_2(t) = 1, \qquad y_1(0) = 0$$
$$\dot{y}_2(t) + ty_1(t) = t, \qquad y_2(0) = 0.$$

3. First-Order Systems: Further Considerations

In this section we are going to discuss systems of differential equations from a slightly different point of view. This new approach will make certain aspects of the equations more apparent. We are going to proceed along the lines of example (2.3b) of Chapter 8. It will be very helpful to the reader to keep that example in mind.

Our goal is to formulate (2.1) as a conditional equation. Such a formulation requires two ingredients: two vector spaces and a linear transformation on one of the vector spaces. In Chapter 8 we found that the single differential equation

$$\dot{y}(t) + cy(t) = w(t)$$

can be considered as a conditional equation from $\mathcal{C}^1(-\infty, \infty)$ to $\mathcal{C}(-\infty, \infty)$. The linear transformation T in question is then given by the formula

$$Ty = \dot{y} + cy.$$

To extend this idea to (2.1) we must first find a new vector space. The solutions of (2.1) consist of n functions of t, so what we do now is to make our vector space consist of *n-tuples* of continuous functions. Thus a vector $\mathbf{y}$ in our space will have the form

$$\text{(3.1)} \qquad \mathbf{y} = \begin{pmatrix} y_1 \\ \cdot \\ \cdot \\ \cdot \\ y_n \end{pmatrix} \quad \text{or} \quad \mathbf{y}(t) = \begin{pmatrix} y_1(t) \\ \cdot \\ \cdot \\ \cdot \\ y_n(t) \end{pmatrix},$$

where $y_1, \ldots, y_n$ all belong to $\mathcal{C}(-\infty, \infty)$. We make a vector space out of such quantities by giving rules for addition and multiplication by a scalar. These rules, and the corresponding zero vector and negatives, are the following:

$$\text{(3.2)} \qquad \begin{aligned} &\mathbf{y} = \begin{pmatrix} y_1 \\ \cdot \\ \cdot \\ \cdot \\ y_n \end{pmatrix}, \quad \mathbf{z} = \begin{pmatrix} z_1 \\ \cdot \\ \cdot \\ \cdot \\ z_n \end{pmatrix}, \quad \mathbf{y} + \mathbf{z} = \begin{pmatrix} y_1 + z_1 \\ \cdot \\ \cdot \\ \cdot \\ y_n + z_n \end{pmatrix} \\ &c\mathbf{y} = \begin{pmatrix} cy_1 \\ \cdot \\ \cdot \\ \cdot \\ cy_n \end{pmatrix}, \quad \mathbf{0} = \begin{pmatrix} 0 \\ \cdot \\ \cdot \\ \cdot \\ 0 \end{pmatrix}, \quad -\mathbf{y} = \begin{pmatrix} -y_1 \\ \cdot \\ \cdot \\ \cdot \\ -y_n \end{pmatrix}. \end{aligned}$$

In these formulas the y_k's and z_k's are in $\mathcal{C}(-\infty, \infty)$ and $y_k + z_k$ means addition in $\mathcal{C}(-\infty, \infty)$; that is,

$$(y_k + z_k)(t) = y_k(t) + z_k(t) \qquad \text{for all } t.$$

Similar remarks hold for multiplication by a scalar, for the zero vector and for negatives. The reader should check that elements of the form (3.1) with the rules (3.2) do indeed form a vector space. We call it $\mathcal{C}_n(-\infty, \infty)$. It is not difficult to see that the set of **y**'s of the form (3.1) for which each of the y_k's has a continuous derivative is a subspace of $\mathcal{C}_n(-\infty, \infty)$. We call this subspace $\mathcal{C}_n^{(1)}(-\infty, \infty)$.

Now we define a transformation T on $\mathcal{C}_n^{(1)}(-\infty, \infty)$ as follows. If $\mathbf{y} \in \mathcal{C}_n^{(1)}(-\infty, \infty)$, then $T\mathbf{y}$ is the vector in $\mathcal{C}_n(-\infty, \infty)$ given by the formula

$$(3.3) \qquad (T\mathbf{y})(t) = \begin{pmatrix} \dot{y}_1(t) \\ \cdot \\ \vdots \\ \dot{y}_n(t) \end{pmatrix} + C \begin{pmatrix} y_1(t) \\ \cdot \\ \vdots \\ y_n(t) \end{pmatrix} \qquad \text{for all } t,$$

where C is the transformation from $\mathcal{R}^n$ to $\mathcal{R}^n$ occurring in equation (2.1). The reader is asked to verify in the problems that T is indeed a linear transformation from $\mathcal{C}_n^{(1)}(-\infty, \infty)$ into $\mathcal{C}_n(-\infty, \infty)$. Consider now the conditional equation

$$(3.4) \qquad T\mathbf{y} = \mathbf{w},$$

where $\mathbf{w} \in \mathcal{C}_n(-\infty, \infty)$ is defined by

$$\mathbf{w}(t) = \begin{pmatrix} w_1(t) \\ \cdot \\ \vdots \\ w_n(t) \end{pmatrix}.$$

By (3.3) this conditional equation, when written out for a particular value of t, will yield precisely the equations (2.1). Thus we can now apply all our theory of Chapter 8 to equations (2.1).

Consider first the null space N_T of the transformation T. This consists simply of those **y**'s in $\mathcal{C}_n^{(1)}(-\infty, \infty)$ such that $T\mathbf{y} = 0$. But by (3.3) this simply means that

$$\mathbf{y} = \begin{pmatrix} y_1 \\ \cdot \\ \vdots \\ y_n \end{pmatrix}$$

is a solution of the *homogeneous* system (2.15). Now we can apply the splitting theorem to (3.4) as follows. Let

$$\mathbf{y}^* = \begin{pmatrix} y_1^* \\ \cdot \\ \vdots \\ y_n^* \end{pmatrix}$$

be one solution of (3.4), that is, of (2.1). Then any other solution $\mathbf{y}$ of (3.4) has the form

$$\mathbf{y} = \mathbf{y}^* + \boldsymbol{\eta},$$

where $\boldsymbol{\eta}$ is a solution of $T\boldsymbol{\eta} = 0$. We summarize this result in the following analog of proposition (4.1.16).

(3.5) Proposition. *Let*

$$\mathbf{y}^* = \begin{pmatrix} y_1^* \\ \cdot \\ \cdot \\ \cdot \\ y_n^* \end{pmatrix}$$

be some particular solution of (2.1). *Then every solution of* (2.1) *can be written in the form*

$$\mathbf{y} = \begin{pmatrix} y_1 \\ \cdot \\ \cdot \\ \cdot \\ y_n \end{pmatrix} = \mathbf{y}^* + \boldsymbol{\eta} = \begin{pmatrix} y_1^* \\ \cdot \\ \cdot \\ \cdot \\ y_n^* \end{pmatrix} + \begin{pmatrix} \eta_1 \\ \cdot \\ \cdot \\ \cdot \\ \eta_n \end{pmatrix},$$

where $\boldsymbol{\eta}$ *is a solution of* (2.15).

Our new point of view also allows us to reinterpret the solution (2.16) of the homogeneous system (2.15) in a way which is analogous to theorem (3.5) of Chapter 5.

(3.6) Theorem. *If assumption* (2.2) *is satisfied, then the set* N_T *of all solutions of* (2.15) *forms an n-dimensional subspace of* $\mathcal{C}_n^{(1)}(-\infty, \infty)$.†

Proof. That N_T is a subspace follows from theorem (8.1.7). Let $\mathbf{y} \in N_T$; that is, let

$$\mathbf{y} = \begin{pmatrix} y_1 \\ \cdot \\ \cdot \\ \cdot \\ y_n \end{pmatrix}$$

be a solution of (2.15). Let t_0 be some value of t and let

$$\mathbf{y}(t_0) = \mathbf{y}^0 = u_1^0\boldsymbol{\gamma}_1 + \cdots + u_n^0\boldsymbol{\gamma}_n.$$

†Once again, the theorem is valid even when (2.2) is not satisfied, but our present proof does not apply to such cases.

Then $\mathbf{y}$ must have the form (2.16). Now let $\mathbf{Y}_1, \ldots, \mathbf{Y}_n$ denote the vectors in $\mathcal{C}_n^{(1)}(-\infty, \infty)$ defined by

(i)

$$\mathbf{Y}_1(t) = e^{-a_1 t}\gamma_1 = \begin{pmatrix} \gamma_{11}e^{-a_1 t} \\ \cdot \\ \cdot \\ \cdot \\ \gamma_{1n}e^{-a_1 t} \end{pmatrix}, \ldots, \quad \mathbf{Y}_n(t) = e^{-a_n t}\gamma_n = \begin{pmatrix} \gamma_{n1}e^{-a_n t} \\ \cdot \\ \cdot \\ \cdot \\ \gamma_{nn}e^{-a_n t} \end{pmatrix},$$

where

$$\gamma_1 = \begin{pmatrix} \gamma_{11} \\ \cdot \\ \cdot \\ \cdot \\ \gamma_{1n} \end{pmatrix}, \ldots, \quad \gamma_n = \begin{pmatrix} \gamma_{n1} \\ \cdot \\ \cdot \\ \cdot \\ \gamma_{nn} \end{pmatrix}$$

are the eigenvectors of C. Then (2.16) shows that $\mathbf{y}$ can be written in the form

$$\text{(ii)} \qquad \mathbf{y} = (u_1^0 e^{a_1 t_0})\mathbf{Y}_1 + \cdots + (u_n^0 e^{a_n t_0})\mathbf{Y}_n.$$

Conversely *every* function which is a linear combination of the $\mathbf{Y}$'s is easily seen to satisfy equation (2.15).

The above implies that the vectors $\mathbf{Y}_1, \ldots, \mathbf{Y}_n$ span N_T. To show that these vectors form a basis we must show that the decomposition (ii) has a uniquely determined set of coefficients. As was pointed out in Chapter 5 one way to verify that a spanner such as $\mathbf{Y}_1, \ldots, \mathbf{Y}_n$ is a basis is to show that the relation

$$\text{(iii)} \qquad \alpha_1\mathbf{Y}_1 + \cdots + \alpha_n\mathbf{Y}_n = \mathbf{0}$$

implies that all the α's are zero. Note that in the present context (iii) means that the function on the left side is zero for *all* t. In particular, it is zero for $t = 0$, which by (i) yields,

$$\text{(iv)} \qquad \alpha_1\gamma_1 + \cdots + \alpha_n\gamma_n = \mathbf{0}.$$

But, since the γ_k's form a basis of $\mathcal{R}^n$, (iv) does indeed imply that the α_k's are all zero. Thus the functions $\mathbf{Y}$ form a basis, and the dimension of N_T is n. ▮

(3.7) Example. Basis for N_T. Consider the system of equations in example (2.14). We found the eigenvectors and eigenvalues of C to be

$$\gamma_1 = \begin{pmatrix} 1 \\ 1 \end{pmatrix}, \quad a_1 = 4; \qquad \gamma_2 = \begin{pmatrix} 1 \\ -\frac{2}{3} \end{pmatrix}, \quad a_2 = -1.$$

Thus (i) of theorem (3.6) states that a basis is given by

$$\mathbf{Y}_1(t) = e^{-4t}\begin{pmatrix}1\\1\end{pmatrix} = \begin{pmatrix}e^{-4t}\\e^{-4t}\end{pmatrix}; \qquad \mathbf{Y}_2(t) = e^t\begin{pmatrix}1\\-\frac{2}{3}\end{pmatrix} = \begin{pmatrix}e^t\\-\frac{2}{3}e^t\end{pmatrix}.$$

Let us make clear what this means. It states first that the pair of functions, $y_1^1(t) = e^{-4t}$, $y_2^1(t) = e^{-4t}$, as well as the pair of functions, $y_1^2(t) = e^t$, $y_2^2(t) = -\frac{2}{3}e^t$, constitute solutions of the system

$$\text{(i)}\qquad \begin{aligned} \dot{y}_1(t) + y_1(t) + 3y_2(t) &= 0\\ \dot{y}_2(t) + 2y_1(t) + 2y_2(t) &= 0. \end{aligned}$$

Further it states that *any* solution

$$\mathbf{y}(t) = \begin{pmatrix}y_1(t)\\y_2(t)\end{pmatrix}$$

of (i) can be written *uniquely* as

$$\mathbf{y}(t) = \alpha_1\mathbf{Y}_1(t) + \alpha_2\mathbf{Y}_2(t)$$

or

$$\begin{aligned} y_1(t) &= \alpha_1 y_1^1(t) + \alpha_2 y_1^2(t) = \alpha_1 e^{-4t} + \alpha_2 e^t\\ y_2(t) &= \alpha_1 y_2^1(t) + \alpha_2 y_2^2(t) = \alpha_1 e^{-4t} - \tfrac{2}{3}\alpha_2 e^t, \end{aligned}$$

for some constants α_1 and α_2.

We can also apply the superposition theorem to the system (2.1). It states the following.

(3.8) Proposition. *Let* $\mathbf{y}_1, \ldots, \mathbf{y}_k$ *be solutions of* (2.1) *for* $\mathbf{w}$ *equal to*

$$\mathbf{w}_1 = \begin{pmatrix}w_1^1\\ \cdot\\ \cdot\\ \cdot\\ w_n^1\end{pmatrix}, \ldots, \qquad \mathbf{w}_k = \begin{pmatrix}w_1^k\\ \cdot\\ \cdot\\ \cdot\\ w_n^k\end{pmatrix},$$

respectively. Then $\mathbf{y}^* = b_1\mathbf{y}_1 + \cdots + b_k\mathbf{y}_k$ *is a solution of* (2.1) *for*

$$\mathbf{w} = b_1\mathbf{w}_1 + \cdots + b_k\mathbf{w}_k.$$

We emphasize that (3.5) and (3.8) follow directly from general results of Chapter 8 and need not be proved again. Propositions (3.5) and (3.8) can sometimes be used to simplify the solutions of equations (2.1) by a method of undetermined coefficients similar to that used for single equations. This idea is developed in the problems.

We conclude this section by giving a brief discussion of the heat equation.† Our goal is to show that that *partial* differential equation can be treated by methods quite analogous to those we used in §2. Recall that the heat equation has the form (taking $K = 1$)

$$u_t(x, t) - u_{xx}(x, t) = 0. \tag{3.9}$$

We want to interpret this somehow as an equation similar to (2.1). The key idea, as indicated in §2, is to find a vector space on which to study it.

We are led to an appropriate vector space by the following considerations. We chose the space $\mathcal{R}^n$ to go with equations (2.1) because, for each value of t, the *value* of a solution of (2.1) at that t is simply a set of numbers $\big(y_1(t), \ldots, y_n(t)\big)$, that is, an element of $\mathcal{R}^n$. Now we ask — for each t what will the values of a solution of (3.9) be? The answer is that for each fixed t the solution will be a *function of* x. This function, if (3.9) is to make sense, must have a second derivative with respect to x. In addition, we requirc it to satisfy certain boundary conditions. For example, in one problem we require that u satisfy the conditions

$$u(0, t) = u(L, t) = 0. \tag{3.10}$$

Let us denote by $\hat{\mathcal{C}}_0^2[0, L]$ the set of functions X of x which are continuous on $0 \leq x \leq L$, have continuous second derivatives on $0 < x < L$, and satisfy

$$X(0) = X(L) = 0. \tag{3.11}$$

This will form a vector space (a subspace of $\mathcal{C}[0, L]$) if we define $X + Y$ and cX for scalars c by

$$(X + Y)(x) = X(x) + Y(x), \qquad (cX)(x) = cX(x).$$

On this space we can also define an inner product by

$$(X, Y) = \int_0^L X(x)Y(x)\,dx, \qquad \|X\| = \left(\int_0^L X(x)^2\,dx\right)^{1/2}. \tag{3.12}$$

Now we can discuss functions of t with values in the space $\mathcal{V} = \hat{\mathcal{C}}_0^2[0, L]$. In particular, if $\mathbf{U}$ is such a function we define $\dot{\mathbf{U}}$ by means of (1.6) of

†We reiterate that this material is relatively sophisticated and will not be needed in later chapters.

Chapter 2. That is, for each t we require $\mathbf{U}(t) \in \hat{\mathcal{C}}_0^2[0, L]$ to satisfy

$$\lim_{\Delta t \to 0} \left\| \frac{\mathbf{U}(t + \Delta t) - \mathbf{U}(t)}{\Delta t} - \dot{\mathbf{U}}(t) \right\| = 0. \tag{3.13}$$

To restate this in the present case we need to further clarify our notation. For each t, $\mathbf{U}$ is a function of x on $0 \leq x \leq L$; different values of t, of course, give different functions of x. We denote by $u(x, t)$ the value of the function $\mathbf{U}(t)$ *at* x. Note that u is then simply a function of the two variables x and t. Then (3.13) becomes, by (3.12),

$$\lim_{\Delta t \to 0} \left\{ \int_0^L \left(\frac{u(x, t + \Delta t) - u(x, t)}{\Delta t} - \dot{U}(t)(x) \right)^2 dx \right\}^{1/2} = 0. \tag{3.14}$$

Here $\dot{\mathbf{U}}(t)(x)$ denotes the value of $\dot{\mathbf{U}}(t)$ (a function of x) at x. It is a theorem of calculus that, under reasonable conditions, the *partial derivative* u_t is a function $\dot{\mathbf{U}}(t)$ of x satisfying (3.14). Thus one has the formula

$$\dot{\mathbf{U}}(t)(x) = u_t(x, t). \tag{3.15}$$

The reader should study formula (3.15) carefully. The understanding of its rather subtle meaning is the key to what follows.

Now let us introduce a transformation C on $\hat{\mathcal{C}}_0^2[0, L]$ to $\mathcal{C}[0, L]$ as follows. For a given X in $\hat{\mathcal{C}}_0^2(0, L)$ we define CX to be the function $-X''$, the negative of the second derivative of X. Note that $CX \in \mathcal{C}[0, L]$ is, in general, no longer in $\hat{\mathcal{C}}_0^2[0, L]$ since it need not have a continuous second derivative. Now if $\mathbf{U}$ is a function of t with values in $\hat{\mathcal{C}}_0^2[0, L]$, then for each *fixed* t we can apply the transformation C to $\mathbf{U}(t)$ to obtain the function $C\mathbf{U}(t)$ which is equal to minus the second derivative of the function $\mathbf{U}(t)$ *of* x. Since $\mathbf{U}(t)(x) = u(x, t)$ we thus have (t is fixed)

$$C\mathbf{U}(t)(x) = -u_{xx}(x, t). \tag{3.16}$$

From equations (3.15) and (3.16) we may write (3.9) as

$$\dot{\mathbf{U}}(t) + C\mathbf{U}(t) = \mathbf{0}, \tag{3.17}$$

where the $\mathbf{0}$ on the right side denotes that function of x which is 0 for all x on $0 \leq x \leq L$. Equation (3.17) looks the same as equation (2.1) or, more precisely, the same as the homogeneous equation (2.15). There is also an analog of the initial condition (2.3). In Chapter 7 we required that the solution of (3.9) satisfy the condition $u(x, 0) = f(x)$. In our present language this states that at $t = 0$, the quantity $\mathbf{U}(0) \in \hat{\mathcal{C}}_0^2[0, L]$ is the function f; that is,

$$\mathbf{U}(0) = f. \tag{3.18}$$

Suppose we try to solve (3.17) and (3.18) in the same way as we solved (2.15) and (2.3). First we look for eigenvectors of C. What kinds of things are these? They are functions X of x belonging to $\hat{\mathfrak{C}}_0^2[0, L]$, so that they have continuous second derivatives and satisfy (3.11). Further they are to satisfy $CX = aX$; that is,

$$\text{(3.19)} \qquad -X''(x) = aX(x), \qquad 0 < x < L.$$

Now the problem of finding solutions of (3.19) subject to (3.11) is one we have seen before. In fact, it is precisely that of (2.5) (with $K = 1$) and (2.11) of Chapter 7. Thus we know that one obtains solutions only if a has one of the values

$$\text{(3.20)} \qquad a_n = \frac{n^2\pi^2}{L^2}, \qquad n = 1, 2, \ldots.$$

The corresponding functions, or eigenvectors of C, are given by

$$\text{(3.21)} \qquad X_n(x) = \sin\frac{n\pi x}{L}, \qquad n = 1, 2, \ldots$$

or multiples of these. Thus the transformation C has infinitely many eigenvectors.

If we followed precisely the procedure used earlier for (2.16) and (2.8), we would now expand $\mathbf{U}$ and the initial function f in terms of the X_n's and then use rule (2.17). The difficulty here is that, since there are infinitely many X_n's, the formulas which would correspond to (2.4) and (2.10) would be unending expressions,

$$\text{(3.22)} \qquad \begin{aligned} \mathbf{U}(t) &= U_1(t)X_1 + U_2(t)X_2 + \cdots \\ f &= f_1X_1 + f_2X_2 + \cdots. \end{aligned}$$

Formulas (3.22) have no meaning unless we discuss convergence as in Chapter 7. It is possible to give such a discussion and to show that the rule (2.17) can be carried over to the present problem. This rule states that to obtain the solution $\mathbf{U}$ of (3.17) and (3.18) we expand f in the eigenvectors X_n, as in (3.22), and then multiply each term f_kX_k by e^{-a_kt}. This yields the unending expression

$$e^{-a_1t}f_1X_1 + e^{-a_2t}f_2X_2 + \cdots$$

or, by (3.20) and (3.21),

$$\text{(3.23)} \qquad e^{-\pi^2t/L}f_1\sin\frac{\pi x}{L} + e^{-4\pi^2t/L}f_2\sin\frac{2\pi x}{L} + \cdots.$$

We can give a meaning to the above formulas in terms of least-squares convergence. We assert that if in the second of formulas (3.22) we interpret the expression on the right as being the *Fourier series* for f in the system $X_1, X_2, \ldots$, then (3.23) is precisely the *Fourier series* for the solution of the problem (3.9) and (3.10) which satisfies $u(x, 0) = f(x)$. This is readily confirmed by comparing (3.23) with formula (1.12′) of Chapter 7.

PROBLEMS

1. Find a basis for the set of solutions of the following systems (see the problems in §2).

(a) $\dot{y}_1(t) + y_2(t) = 0$
$\dot{y}_2(t) + y_1(t) = 0$

(b) $\dot{y}_1(t) = 4y_1(t) - 2y_2(t)$
$\dot{y}_2(t) = -y_1(t) + 3y_2(t)$

(c) $\dot{y}_1(t) + 4y_1(t) - y_2(t) = 0$
$\dot{y}_2(t) + 2y_1(t) + y_2(t) = 0$

(d) $\dot{y}_1(t) + 3y_1(t) + 2y_2(t) = 0$
$\dot{y}_2(t) + 4y_1(t) + y_2(t) = 0$

(e) $\dot{y}_1(t) = y_3(t)$
$\dot{y}_2(t) = 2y_2(t)$
$\dot{y}_3(t) = y_1(t)$

2. Verify that the transformation T defined by (3.3) is a linear transformation from $\mathcal{C}_n^{(1)}(-\infty, \infty)$ into $\mathcal{C}_n(-\infty, \infty)$.

3. Find particular solutions of the following problems. Use the ideas given in problems 10–12 of §2 and in proposition (3.8).

(a) $\dot{y}_1(t) + y_2(t) = 2e^{2t} - e^{-2t}$
$\dot{y}_2(t) + y_1(t) = -e^{2t} + e^{-2t}$

(b) $\dot{y}_1(t) = 4y_1(t) - 2y_2(t) + t$
$\dot{y}_2(t) = -y_1(t) + 3y_2(t) + e^t$

(c) $\dot{y}_1(t) + 4y_1(t) - y_2(t) = \cos t$
$\dot{y}_2(t) + 2y_1(t) + y_2(t) = \sin t$

(d) $\dot{y}_1(t) = y_3(t) + 1$
$\dot{y}_2(t) = 2y_2(t) + t$
$\dot{y}_3(t) = y_1(t)$

4. Find the most general solutions of each of the equations in problem 3. Use problems 2 and 3 and proposition (3.5).

The following problem gives an analog of proposition (1.19) of Chapter 4.

*5. (a) Define a transformation S as follows. If $\mathbf{y}^0 \in \mathcal{R}^n$, let $S\mathbf{y}^0$ be the unique solution of (2.15) such that $\mathbf{y}(t_0) = \mathbf{y}^0$. Prove that S is a linear transformation from $\mathcal{R}^n$ into $\mathcal{C}_n^{(1)}(-\infty, \infty)$.

(b) Illustrate the result of part (a) by expressing the solution of the problem

$$(*) \qquad \begin{aligned} \dot{y}_1(t) &= 4y_1(t) - 2y_2(t), \qquad & y_1(0) &= -5 \\ \dot{y}_2(t) &= -y_1(t) + 3y_2(t), \qquad & y_2(0) &= 2 \end{aligned}$$

in terms of the functions

$$\mathbf{u}(t) = \begin{pmatrix} u_1(t) \\ u_2(t) \end{pmatrix} \qquad \mathbf{v}(t) = \begin{pmatrix} v_1(t) \\ v_2(t) \end{pmatrix},$$

where $\mathbf{u}$ and $\mathbf{v}$ satisfy the same differential equations as in (*), but

$$\mathbf{u}(0) = \begin{pmatrix} 1 \\ 0 \end{pmatrix}, \qquad \mathbf{v}(0) = \begin{pmatrix} 0 \\ 1 \end{pmatrix}.$$

*6. State and prove an analog of proposition (1.20) of Chapter 4 for the system (2.1).

4. Second-Order Systems

We have indicated in §1 that second-order systems can usually be reduced to the form

$$\ddot{\mathbf{y}}(t) + B\dot{\mathbf{y}}(t) + C\mathbf{y}(t) = \mathbf{w}(t). \tag{4.1}$$

These systems could in turn be reduced to first-order systems by the methods of Chapter 4 and then we would be able to study them as in §2. It turns out, however, that when $B: \mathcal{R}^n \to \mathcal{R}^n$ is the zero transformation (that is $B\boldsymbol{\alpha} = \mathbf{0}$ for all $\boldsymbol{\alpha}$), so that equation (4.1) reduces to

$$\ddot{\mathbf{y}}(t) + C\mathbf{y}(t) = \mathbf{w}(t), \tag{4.2}$$

it is more convenient to treat (4.2) directly. We discuss this situation in the present section.

According to theorem (1.15) the appropriate initial conditions for (4.2) are

$$\mathbf{y}(t_0) = \mathbf{y}^0, \qquad \dot{\mathbf{y}}(t_0) = \dot{\mathbf{y}}^0. \tag{4.3}$$

We can obtain an explicit solution of the problem (4.2) and (4.3) by a procedure which is quite analogous to the one in §2. Assume that (2.2) is valid;

that is, C has a set of eigenvectors $\gamma_1, \ldots, \gamma_n$ which form a basis for $\mathcal{R}^n$. Let $a_1, \ldots, a_n$ be the corresponding eigenvalues.

We expand the solution $\mathbf{y}$, as well as $\mathbf{w}$, $\mathbf{y}^0$, and $\dot{\mathbf{y}}^0$, all in terms of $\gamma_1, \ldots, \gamma_n$. Thus we write

$$\mathbf{y}(t) = u_1(t)\gamma_1 + \cdots + u_n(t)\gamma_n \tag{4.4}$$

$$\mathbf{w}(t) = v_1(t)\gamma_1 + \cdots + v_n(t)\gamma_n \tag{4.5}$$

$$\mathbf{y}^0 = u_1^0\gamma_1 + \cdots + u_n^0\gamma_n \tag{4.6}$$

$$\dot{\mathbf{y}}^0 = u_1^0\gamma_1 + \cdots + \dot{u}_n^0\gamma_n. \tag{4.7}$$

Now if we substitute (4.4) and (4.5) into (4.1) and use the fact that C is a linear transformation satisfying

$$C\gamma_k = a_k\gamma_k,$$

then we obtain, just as in §2,

$$\begin{aligned}
\ddot{\mathbf{y}}(t) + C\mathbf{y}(t) &= \ddot{u}_1(t)\gamma_1 + \cdots + \ddot{u}_n(t)\gamma_n + C\big(u_1(t)\gamma_1 + \cdots + u_n(t)\gamma_n\big) \\
&= \ddot{u}_1(t)\gamma_1 + \cdots + \ddot{u}_n(t)\gamma_n + u_1(t)C\gamma_1 + \cdots + u_n(t)C\gamma_n \\
&= \big(\ddot{u}_1(t) + a_1u_1(t)\big)\gamma_1 + \cdots + \big(\ddot{u}_n(t) + a_nu_n(t)\big)\gamma_n \\
&= v_1(t)\gamma_1 + \cdots + v_n(t)\gamma_n.
\end{aligned}$$

Hence we conclude that the u_k's satisfy the equations

$$\begin{aligned}
\ddot{u}_1(t) + a_1u_1(t) &= v_1(t) \\
&\;\vdots \\
\ddot{u}_n(t) + a_nu_n(t) &= v_n(t).
\end{aligned} \tag{4.8}$$

Substitution of (4.4) into (4.3) yields the initial conditions

$$\begin{aligned}
u_1(t_0) &= u_1^0, & u_1(t_0) &= \dot{u}_1^0 \\
&\;\vdots & &\;\vdots \\
u_n(t_0) &= u_n^0, & \dot{u}_n(t_0) &= \dot{u}_n^0.
\end{aligned} \tag{4.9}$$

In (4.8) each equation has the form of a single second-order nonhomogeneous equation of the type studied in §§3 and 4 of Chapter 5. If we apply the results given in those sections we can solve (4.8) and (4.9). Then substitution into (4.4) will yield the (unique) solution of (4.1) and (4.3). Let us give a simple example.

(4.10) Example. Solve the problem

$$\text{(i)}\quad \begin{aligned} \ddot{y}_1(t) + y_1(t) + 3y_2(t) &= 1, & y_1(0) &= 1, & \dot{y}_1(0) &= 0 \\ \ddot{y}_2(t) + 2y_2(t) + 2y_2(t) &= t, & y_2(0) &= 0, & \dot{y}_2(0) &= 1. \end{aligned}$$

These equations have the form of (4.2) with

$$C = \begin{pmatrix} 1 & 3 \\ 2 & 2 \end{pmatrix}, \quad \mathbf{w}(t) = \begin{pmatrix} 1 \\ t \end{pmatrix}, \quad \mathbf{y}^0 = \begin{pmatrix} 1 \\ 0 \end{pmatrix}, \quad \dot{\mathbf{y}}_0 = \begin{pmatrix} 0 \\ 1 \end{pmatrix}.$$

Thus (i) is just like example (2.14a) except that there are second derivatives rather than first and there are two initial conditions rather than one.

We make use of the results of example (2.14a). First, we saw that the eigenvectors were

$$\gamma_1 = \begin{pmatrix} 1 \\ 1 \end{pmatrix} \quad \text{and} \quad \gamma_2 = \begin{pmatrix} 1 \\ -\frac{2}{3} \end{pmatrix},$$

corresponding to the eigenvalues $a_1 = 4$ and $a_2 = -1$, respectively. Second, we saw that

$$\text{(ii)}\quad \mathbf{w}(t) = \begin{pmatrix} 1 \\ t \end{pmatrix} = v_1(t)\gamma_1 + v_2(t)\gamma_2$$

with

$$v_1(t) = \tfrac{2}{5} + \tfrac{3}{5}t, \qquad v_2(t) = \tfrac{3}{5} - \tfrac{3}{5}t.$$

Also, we found that

$$\text{(iii)}\quad \mathbf{y}^0 = \begin{pmatrix} 1 \\ 0 \end{pmatrix} = u_1^0 \begin{pmatrix} 1 \\ 1 \end{pmatrix} + u_2^0 \begin{pmatrix} 1 \\ -\frac{2}{3} \end{pmatrix}, \qquad u_1^0 = \tfrac{2}{5}, \qquad u_2^0 = \tfrac{3}{5}.$$

In a similar way one obtains

$$\text{(iv)}\quad \dot{\mathbf{y}}^0 = \begin{pmatrix} 0 \\ 1 \end{pmatrix} = \dot{u}_1^0 \begin{pmatrix} 1 \\ 1 \end{pmatrix} + \dot{u}_2^0 \begin{pmatrix} 1 \\ -\frac{2}{3} \end{pmatrix}, \qquad \dot{u}_1^0 = \tfrac{3}{5}, \qquad \dot{u}_2^0 = -\tfrac{3}{5}.$$

Thus equations (4.8) and (4.9) become

$$\text{(v)}\quad \begin{aligned} \ddot{u}_1(t) + 4u_1(t) &= \tfrac{2}{5} + \tfrac{3}{5}t, & u_1(0) &= \tfrac{2}{5}, & \dot{u}_1(0) &= \tfrac{3}{5} \\ \ddot{u}_2(t) - u_2(t) &= \tfrac{3}{5} - \tfrac{3}{5}t, & u_2(0) &= \tfrac{3}{5}, & \dot{u}_2(0) &= -\tfrac{3}{5}. \end{aligned}$$

Equations (v) are easily solved by the methods of Chapter 5; hence we simply write down the answers. We find

$$\text{(vi)}\quad \begin{aligned} u_1(t) &= \tfrac{3}{10}\cos 2t + \tfrac{9}{40}\sin 2t + \tfrac{1}{10} + \tfrac{3}{20}t \\ u_2(t) &= \tfrac{6}{5}e^{-t} - \tfrac{3}{5} + \tfrac{3}{5}t. \end{aligned}$$

We substitute (vi) into equation (4.4) to obtain the solution of (i) as

$$\mathbf{y}(t) = \begin{pmatrix} y_1(t) \\ y_2(t) \end{pmatrix} = [\tfrac{3}{10}\cos 2t + \tfrac{9}{40}\sin 2t + \tfrac{1}{10} + \tfrac{3}{20}t]\begin{pmatrix} 1 \\ 1 \end{pmatrix} + [\tfrac{6}{5}e^{-t} - \tfrac{3}{5} + \tfrac{3}{5}t]\begin{pmatrix} 1 \\ -\tfrac{2}{3} \end{pmatrix}$$

or

$$y_1(t) = \tfrac{3}{10}\cos 2t + \tfrac{9}{40}\sin 2t + \tfrac{6}{5}e^{-t} - \tfrac{1}{2} + \tfrac{3}{4}t$$
$$y_2(t) = \tfrac{3}{10}\cos 2t + \tfrac{9}{40}\sin 2t - \tfrac{4}{5}e^{-t} + \tfrac{1}{2} - \tfrac{1}{4}t.$$

It is possible to develop an analysis of equation (4.2) as a conditional equation in a way which parallels that in §3 for first-order systems. We shall not do this since the ideas are very similar and the computations more complicated. We have however included a problem in which the reader is asked to show that the space of all solutions of the *homogeneous* equation is $2n$-dimensional.

We do want to make some comments on the concept of stability as it applies to the homogeneous equation corresponding to (4.2),

$$\text{(4.11)} \qquad \ddot{\mathbf{y}}(t) + C\mathbf{y}(t) = \mathbf{0}.$$

A definition for stability was given in (2.20) and that definition can be applied to (4.11). One has the following result.

(4.12) Proposition. *If assumption* (2.2) *is satisfied and if any of the eigenvalues of C is negative or zero, then* (4.11) *is unstable.*

The reader is asked to give a proof of this proposition in the problems. The idea is simple enough. It amounts to the observation that if any a_k is negative, the corresponding equation for u_k in (4.8) (with $w_k = 0$) has solutions which are linear combinations of $e^{\sqrt{-a_k}t}$ and $e^{-\sqrt{-a_k}t}$, the first of which becomes large as t tends to infinity.

The result in the case of positive eigenvalues is different from what it was for first-order equations.

(4.13) Proposition. *If* (2.2) *is valid and all the eigenvalues of C are* positive, *then any solution* $\mathbf{y}$ *of* (4.11) *satisfies the condition*

(i) $\|\mathbf{y}(t)\|$ *remains bounded for all t.*

Condition (i) is not as strong a condition as (i) of definition (2.20), but at least it shows that catastrophies do not occur. The reader is asked to prove

(4.13) in the problems. This proof follows from the fact that if a_k is positive, then the corresponding u_k is a linear combination of $\cos \sqrt{a_k}\, t$ and $\sin \sqrt{a_k}\, t$.

(4.14) Example. Normal Modes. We present here an example which illustrates the last proposition and also describes an important physical concept. We consider again the problem in example (1.1a). This concerned two masses connected by springs and led to the system of differential equations

$$\ddot{y}_1(t) + \frac{k}{m_1}(2y_1(t) - y_2(t)) = 0$$

$$\ddot{y}_2(t) - \frac{k}{m_2}(y_1(t) - y_2(t)) = 0,$$

In matrix notation this reads

$$\text{(i)} \qquad \ddot{\mathbf{y}}(t) + C\mathbf{y}(t) = \mathbf{0},$$

where

$$C = \begin{pmatrix} \dfrac{2k}{m_1} & -\dfrac{k}{m_1} \\ -\dfrac{k}{m_2} & \dfrac{k}{m_2} \end{pmatrix}.$$

We set $k/m_1 = \alpha$ and $k/m_2 = \beta$. Then the eigenvalues of C are given by

$$\begin{vmatrix} 2\alpha - a & -\alpha \\ -\beta & \beta - a \end{vmatrix} = (2\alpha - a)(\beta - a) - \alpha\beta = \alpha\beta - a(2\alpha + \beta) + a^2 = 0$$

or

$$\text{(ii)} \qquad a = \frac{2\alpha + \beta \pm \sqrt{(2\alpha + \beta)^2 - 4\alpha\beta}}{2} = \frac{(2\alpha + \beta) \pm \sqrt{4\alpha^2 + \beta^2}}{2}.$$

The formulas in (ii) show that both eigenvalues are positive; hence proposition (4.13) applies and all solutions remain bounded for all time.

Let us proceed a little further in the computations. To simplify them a little we shall assume that $\alpha = 2$ and $\beta = 3$. Then the eigenvalues from (ii) are $a_1 = 6$ and $a_2 = 1$. The matrix C becomes

$$\begin{pmatrix} 4 & -2 \\ -3 & 3 \end{pmatrix}$$

and eigenvectors γ_1 and γ_2 corresponding to a_1 and a_2 are

$$\text{(iii)} \qquad \gamma_1 = \begin{pmatrix} 1 \\ -1 \end{pmatrix}, \qquad \gamma_2 = \begin{pmatrix} 1 \\ \frac{3}{2} \end{pmatrix}.$$

Equations (4.8) become

$$\text{(iv)} \qquad \begin{aligned} \ddot{u}_1(t) + 6u_1(t) &= 0 \\ \ddot{u}_2(t) + u_2(t) &= 0. \end{aligned}$$

The solutions of equations (iv) have the form

$$\text{(v)} \qquad \begin{aligned} u_1(t) &= A_1 \cos \sqrt{6}\, t + B_1 \sin \sqrt{6}\, t \\ u_2(t) &= A_2 \cos t + B_2 \sin t, \end{aligned}$$

where A_1, B_1, A_2, and B_2 are constants which must be adjusted to satisfy initial conditions. If we substitute (iii) and (v) into equation (4.4) we obtain for the solution of (4.2) the formula

$$\text{(vi)} \qquad \mathbf{y}(t) = \begin{pmatrix} y_1(t) \\ y_2(t) \end{pmatrix} = (A_1 \cos \sqrt{6}\, t + B_1 \sin \sqrt{6}\, t) \begin{pmatrix} 1 \\ -1 \end{pmatrix} + (A_2 \cos t + B_2 \sin t) \begin{pmatrix} 1 \\ \frac{3}{2} \end{pmatrix}.$$

The expression (vi) corresponds physically to what is called a decomposition into *normal modes*. We have indicated already that the constants A_i and B_i are determined by $\mathbf{y}(t_0)$ and $\dot{\mathbf{y}}(t_0)$. If these vectors are chosen carefully one can make A_2 and B_2 or A_1 and B_1 zero. (See the problems.) But by (vi) this would mean that both y_1 and y_2 would be periodic of the same period: $2\pi/\sqrt{6}$ if $A_2 = B_2 = 0$, 2π if $A_1 = B_1 = 0$. In each case *both* masses would oscillate with the same period. These are the only periods at which periodic motions occur, and they are called the *natural periods*. They play a role in the study of resonance phenomena which is completely analogous to that in example (4.9) of Chapter 5. Again this is discussed in the problems. Once more we emphasize that, in general, if the masses are set in motion, *both* terms in (vi) will be present and *neither* mass will move with a periodic motion.

We end this section with a remark concerning the more general second-order system (4.1). As we have said, this can be converted to a first-order system. What is true, however, is that in important physical cases the methods of §§2 and 3 do not apply to the resulting system. In particular this will be true of the system derived from example (1.1b) involving coupled *LCR* circuits. However, methods to be developed in Chapter 10 *can* be applied to the equations from (1.1b).

PROBLEMS

Find the solutions of each of the following problems.

1. $\ddot{y}_1(t) + y_2(t) = 0,\ y_1(0) = 1, \dot{y}_1(0) = 0$
$\ddot{y}_2(t) + y_1(t) = 0,\ y_2(0) = 0, \dot{y}_2(0) = 1.$

2. $\ddot{y}_1(t) + y_2(t) = 2e^{3t}, \qquad y_1(0) = 0, \dot{y}_1(0) = 0$
$\ddot{y}_2(t) + y_1(t) = e^{3t} - e^{-3t},\ y_2(0) = 0, \dot{y}_2(0) = 0.$

3. $\ddot{y}_1(t) = 4y_1(t) - 2y_2(t),\ y_1(1) = 1, \dot{y}_1(1) = 0$
$\ddot{y}_2(t) = -y_1(t) + 3y_2(t),\ y_2(1) = 0,\ \dot{y}_2(1) = 1.$

4. $\ddot{y}_1(t) + 4y_1(t) - y_2(t) = t,\ y_1(0) = 0,\ \dot{y}_1(0) = 1$
$\ddot{y}_2(t) + 2y_1(t) + y_2(t) = 1,\ y_2(0) = 1,\ \dot{y}_2(0) = 0.$

5. $\ddot{y}_1(t) + 3y_1(t) + 2y_2(t) = 0,\ y_1(-1) = 1,\ \dot{y}_1(-1) = 0$
$\ddot{y}_2(t) + 4y_1(t) + \ y_2(t) = 0,\ y_2(-1) = 0,\ \dot{y}_2(-1) = 0.$

6. $\ddot{y}_1(t) + 3y_1(t) + 2y_2(t) = \sin t,\ y_1(0) = 0,\ \dot{y}_1(0) = 0$
$\ddot{y}_2(t) + 4y_1(t) + \ y_2(t) = 0, \qquad y_2(0) = 0,\ \dot{y}_2(0) = 0.$

7. $\ddot{y}_1(t) = y_3(t),\ y_1(0) = 1,\ \dot{y}_1(0) = 0$
$\ddot{y}_2(t) = 2y_2(t),\ y_2(0) = 0,\ \dot{y}_2(0) = 0$
$\ddot{y}_3(t) = y_1(t),\ y_3(0) = 0,\ \dot{y}_3(0) = 1.$

8. $\ddot{y}_1(t) + y_1(t) + 2y_2(t) = 2e^{3t},\ y_1(0) = 0,\ \dot{y}_1(0) = 0$
$\ddot{y}_2(t) \qquad\qquad + \ y_3(t) = e^{3t},\ y_2(0) = 0,\ \dot{y}_2(0) = 0$
$\ddot{y}_3(t) + y_2(t) \qquad\qquad = -e^{3t},\ y_3(0) = 0,\ \dot{y}_3(0) = 0.$

Problems 9–12 are analogous to those in §2.

9. (a) Consider the homogeneous equation (4.11). Show that functions **y** of the form

$$(*) \qquad \mathbf{y}(t) = \boldsymbol{\gamma} e^{-at} \qquad \text{or} \qquad \boldsymbol{\gamma} e^{at}$$

are solutions if and only if $\boldsymbol{\gamma}$ is an eigenvector of C with eigenvalue $-a^2$.

(b) Show that functions of the form

$$(**) \qquad \mathbf{y}(t) = \boldsymbol{\gamma} \cos at \qquad \text{or} \qquad \boldsymbol{\gamma} \sin at$$

are solutions of (4.11) if and only if $\boldsymbol{\gamma}$ is an eigenvector of C with eigenvalue a^2.

10. (a) Consider the system (4.2) when **w** has the form

$$\mathbf{w}(t) = \boldsymbol{\omega} e^{-bt}.$$

Show that if $-b^2$ is not an eigenvalue of C, then (4.2) has a solution $\mathbf{y}^*$ of the form

$$\mathbf{y}^*(t) = \boldsymbol{\beta} e^{-bt}.$$

(b) Apply the result to obtain a particular solution of the equations in problem 8.

11. (a) Consider the system (4.2) when **w** has the form

$$\mathbf{w}(t) = \boldsymbol{\omega} \sin bt.$$

Show that if b^2 is not an eigenvalue of C, then (4.2) has a solution $\mathbf{y}^*$ of the form

$$\mathbf{y}^*(t) = \boldsymbol{\beta} \sin bt.$$

(b) Apply the result to the equations in problem 6.

12. (a) Show that the method of problem 11 fails for both of the systems

$$\text{(i)}\quad \begin{aligned} \ddot{u}_1(t) + 6u_1(t) &= \sin\sqrt{6}\,t \\ \ddot{u}_2(t) + u_2(t) &= 2\sin\sqrt{6}\,t. \end{aligned}$$

$$\text{(ii)}\quad \begin{aligned} \ddot{u}_1(t) + 6u_1(t) &= \sin t \\ \ddot{u}_2(t) + u_2(t) &= 2\sin t. \end{aligned}$$

(b) Find the set of all solutions of (i) and (ii) and show that for any solution both u_1 and u_2 will assume arbitrarily large values as t becomes large. This is *resonance* as mentioned in example (4.14). It can be shown that the following generalization holds. Consider a system of the form

$$\text{(iii)}\qquad \ddot{\mathbf{y}}(t) + C\mathbf{y}(t) = \boldsymbol{\alpha}\cos bt + \boldsymbol{\beta}\sin bt, \qquad \boldsymbol{\alpha}, \boldsymbol{\beta} \text{ not both } \mathbf{0}.$$

If b^2 is an eigenvalue of C, then *any* solution of (iii) will assume arbitrarily large values as t becomes large.

***13.** (a) Show how to define a space $\mathcal{C}_n^{(2)}(-\infty, \infty)$ and a transformation T on $\mathcal{C}_n^{(2)}(-\infty, \infty)$ so that (2.2) becomes the conditional equation $T\mathbf{y} = \mathbf{w}$.

(b) Show that if (2.2) is satisfied, the null space of the transformation T in (a) is a $2n$-dimensional subspace of $\mathcal{C}_n^{(2)}(-\infty, \infty)$. (*Hint:* Use problem 9.)

14. Prove proposition (4.12).

15. Prove proposition (4.13).

16. In Chapter 8 we said that a linear transformation C from a vector space $\mathcal{V}$ into a vector space $\mathcal{V}$ would be called *symmetric* if

$$C\boldsymbol{\alpha} \cdot \boldsymbol{\beta} = \boldsymbol{\alpha} \cdot C\boldsymbol{\beta}$$

for every pair $\boldsymbol{\alpha}$ and $\boldsymbol{\beta}$ in V. Let C be a symmetric linear transformation from $\mathcal{R}^n$ into $\mathcal{R}^n$.

(a) If $\mathbf{y}$ is a differentiable function of t with values in $\mathcal{R}^n$, show that

$$C\mathbf{y}(t) \cdot \dot{\mathbf{y}}(t) = \frac{1}{2}\frac{d}{dt}\big(C\mathbf{y}(t) \cdot \mathbf{y}(t)\big).$$

(b) If $\mathbf{y}$ is a solution of the equation

$$\text{(E)}\qquad \ddot{\mathbf{y}}(t) + C\mathbf{y}(t) = 0,$$

show that

$$\tfrac{1}{2}\|\dot{\mathbf{y}}(t)\|^2 + \tfrac{1}{2}\big(C\mathbf{y}(t) \cdot \mathbf{y}(t)\big) = w_0,$$

where w_0 is a constant. [*Hint:* Take the scalar product of (E) with $\dot{\mathbf{y}}(t)$.]

(c) If the symmetric transformation C satisfies the condition

$$(*)\qquad C\boldsymbol{\alpha} \cdot \boldsymbol{\alpha} > 0 \qquad \text{for } \boldsymbol{\alpha} \neq 0,$$

show that a solution of (E) such that $\mathbf{y}(t_0) = \mathbf{0}$, $\dot{\mathbf{y}}(t_0) = \mathbf{0}$ must be the function $\mathbf{y}(t) \equiv 0$.

(d) Use part (c) to show that there exists at most one solution of the problem

$$\ddot{\mathbf{y}}(t) + C\mathbf{y}(t) = \mathbf{w}(t), \qquad \mathbf{y}(t_0) = \mathbf{y}_0, \qquad \dot{\mathbf{y}}(t_0) = \dot{\mathbf{y}}_0$$

if C satisfies (*).

(e) Show that the matrix in problem 7 is symmetric and satisfies (*).

10

Complex Analysis

1. Complex Numbers

We saw in Chapter 9 that the methods given there often fail because the transformations in question do not have eigenvalues. This difficulty can usually be overcome by the introduction of what are called *complex* vector spaces. In order to discuss these spaces we must first talk a little about complex numbers.

Complex numbers can be thought of as a device which is introduced to enable one to "solve" certain equations. One introduces negative numbers in order to be able to solve an equation of the form $2 + x = 1$. Rational numbers (fractions) are introduced to solve equations such as $2x = 1$. Irrational numbers are introduced to solve equations such as $x^2 = 2$. None of these numbers, though, can be used to solve the equation $x^2 = -1$, and it is for such equations that we need complex numbers. One might ask why equations of the form $x^2 = -1$ need to be solved. The results of this chapter give one answer to this question.

We are going to give an abstract definition of complex numbers in much the same way as we defined vector spaces. Our motivation, as with vector spaces, is frankly that we know what we are going to need. The definition follows.

(1.1) Definition. The **complex number system** consists of the set $\mathcal{C}$ of all quantities $a + ib$, $c + id$, . . . , where $a, b, c, d, \ldots$ are real numbers and $+$ and i are simply symbols, together with two prescribed operations. The elements $a + ib, c + id, \ldots$ are called *complex numbers*, and the operations are called *addition* and *multiplication*. The operation of addition assigns to each pair of complex numbers $a + ib$, $c + id$ a third complex number which is called their sum and is given by the formula

$$\text{(A)} \qquad (a + ib) + (c + id) = (a + c) + i(b + d).$$

The operation of multiplication assigns to each pair of complex numbers $a + ib$, $c + id$ a third complex number which is called their *product* and is given by the formula

$$\text{(M)} \qquad (a + ib) \cdot (c + id) = (ac - bd) + i(ad + bc).$$

Formulas (A) and (M) imply (see the problems) that equations of the form

$$\text{(i)} \qquad (c + id) + z = a + ib,$$

$$\text{(ii)} \qquad (c + id) \cdot z = a + ib, \qquad c, d \text{ not both zero},$$

always possess unique solutions z, these solutions being complex numbers. Equation (i) is satisfied if and only if z is the complex number, called the *difference* of $a + ib$ and $c + id$, which is given by the formula

$$\text{(S)} \qquad z = (a + ib) - (c + id) = (a - c) + i(b - d).$$

Equation (ii) is satisfied if and only if z is the complex number, called the *quotient* of $a + ib$ and $c + id$, which is given by the formula

$$\text{(D)} \qquad z = \frac{a + ib}{c + id} = \left(\frac{ac + bd}{c^2 + d^2}\right) + i\left(\frac{bc - ad}{c^2 + d^2}\right).$$

The formal definition of $\mathcal{C}$ is now complete; however, it requires considerable comment. Observe first that both addition and multiplication are operations under which $\mathcal{C}$ is *closed*, in a terminology we used in the study of subspaces. This means that the result of adding or multiplying two elements of $\mathcal{C}$ is, by definition, again an element of $\mathcal{C}$.

The formula (A) requires very careful thought because in it the symbol + is used in *three* different ways. On the left side the + in $a + ib$ and $c + id$ is simply a symbol used in expressing† elements of $\mathcal{C}$. The plus between the parentheses on the left denotes the fact that we are adding the two elements $a + ib$ and $c + id$ in $\mathcal{C}$. The + in $a + c$ and $b + d$ on the right means

†See problem 9.

ordinary addition of real numbers. Finally, the + immediately before i on the right is once again simply a symbol for an element of $\mathcal{C}$. Formulas (M), (S), and (D) require similar careful attention. In (M), for example, the quantities $ac - bd$ and $bc + ad$ on the right have their usual meaning for real numbers. The dot on the left (which is often omitted) denotes the fact that we are multiplying elements in $\mathcal{C}$.

Let us look at some examples to clarify the operations and give some notion of their utility.

(1.2) Examples

(a) Let a and c be real numbers and consider the complex numbers $a + i0$, $c + i0$. By (A), (M), (S), and (D) we have

$$(a + i0) + (c + i0) = (a + c) + i(0 + 0) = (a + c) + i0$$
$$(a + i0) \cdot (c + i0) = (ac - 0 \cdot 0) + i(a \cdot 0 + c \cdot 0) = ac + i0$$
$$(a + i0) - (c + i0) = (a - c) + i(0 - 0) = (a - c) + i0$$
$$\frac{a + i0}{c + i0} = \left(\frac{ac + 0}{c^2 + 0}\right) + i\left(\frac{0 - 0}{c^2 + 0}\right) = \frac{a}{c} + i0 \quad \text{if } c \text{ is not zero.}$$

Complex numbers of the form $a + i0$ are called *real*. The above computations show that the sum, product, difference, or quotient of real numbers is once again real. It is customary with real complex numbers such as $a + i0$ to omit the $+i0$ and write them simply as a. With this understanding the above rules say that the addition, multiplication, subtraction, and division of real complex numbers is just ordinary addition, multiplication, subtraction, and division of real numbers. Furthermore, multiplication of a real complex number with any other complex number takes the simple form

$$a \cdot (c + id) = (ac) + i(ad).$$

(b) Consider the complex number $0 + i \cdot 1$. We have, by (M),

$$(0 + i \cdot 1) \cdot (0 + i \cdot 1) = (0 \cdot 0 - 1 \cdot 1) + i(0 \cdot 1 + 0 \cdot 1) = -1 + i0.$$

Again, it is customary to write i for the number $0 + i \cdot 1$ or more generally bi for $0 + ib$. Then with the understanding in (a) we may write the above result as $i \cdot i = -1$. Thus if we agree, for every complex number $a + ib$, to write $(a + ib)^2$ for $(a + ib) \cdot (a + ib)$, then we see that the complex number i *is* a solution of the equation $x^2 = -1$.

(c) Suppose a, b, and c are real numbers with $b^2 < 4ac$. Let z_1 and z_2 denote the complex numbers

$$z_1 = -\frac{b}{2a} + i\frac{\sqrt{4ac - b^2}}{2a}, \qquad z_2 = -\frac{b}{2a} - i\frac{\sqrt{4ac - b^2}}{2a}.$$

Then the reader should check that both z_1 and z_2 are solutions of the equation

$$\text{(E)} \qquad az^2 + bz + c = 0.$$

If a, b, and c are real numbers with $a \neq 0$ and $b^2 > 4ac$, then the *real* complex numbers

$$z_1 = \left(-\frac{b}{2a} + \frac{\sqrt{b^2 - 4ac}}{2a}\right) + i \cdot 0,$$

$$z_2 = \left(-\frac{b}{2a} - \frac{\sqrt{b^2 - 4ac}}{2a}\right) + i \cdot 0$$

are solutions of (E). If $b^2 = 4ac$, then there is only the one solution $-b/2a$ [that is, $-(b/2a) + i \cdot 0$)].

Example (c) is the key to the usefulness of complex numbers. It is a special case of a much more general theorem. If $z = a + ib$ is any complex number, then we can define z^n for any positive integer n as follows. As above, we set

$$z^2 = (a + ib) \cdot (a + ib).$$

This is a complex number; hence we can form its product with z. This we call z^3; that is,

$$z^3 = (a + ib) \cdot [(a + ib) \cdot (a + ib)].$$

The product of this complex number with z is called z^4, and so on. With this definition, the usual formula

$$\text{(1.3)} \qquad z^m \cdot z^n = z^{m+n}$$

holds. (The reader should verify that $i^4 = 1$ while $i^6 = -1$.)

With the above notion of powers of z together with the notions of addition and multiplication, it makes sense to ask for a solution of the equation

$$\text{(1.4)} \qquad a_0 z^n + a_1 z^{n-1} + \cdots + a_{n-1} z + a_n = 0.$$

Here $a_0, a_1, \ldots, a_n$ are given complex numbers and we are required to find a complex number z such that the expression on the left side equals the complex number 0, that is, $0 + i0$.

(1.5) Theorem (Fundamental Theorem of Algebra). *If $a_0 \neq 0$ and $n > 0$, there always exists a complex number z satisfying* (1.4). *If $z_1, z_2, \ldots, z_r$ $(r \leq n)$ are the distinct values of z satisfying* (1.4), *then there exist positive integers $\alpha_1, \alpha_2, \ldots, \alpha_r$ such that one can write*

$$(*) \qquad a_0 z^n + \cdots + a_n = a_0(z - z_1)^{\alpha_1} \cdots (z - z_r)^{\alpha_r}.$$

In this formula one has $\alpha_1 + \alpha_2 + \cdots + \alpha_r = n$.

The numbers $z_1, \ldots, z_r$ are called the *zeros* or *roots* of the polynomial on the left side of (1.4).

The proof of theorem (1.5) is quite a deep result, much beyond our grasp here, but example (1.2c) illustrates it quite well. The reader should check that the following formulas hold when a, b, and c are real:

$$(1.6)\ az^2 + bz + c$$
$$= \begin{cases} a\left[z + \left(\dfrac{b}{2a} + \dfrac{\sqrt{b^2 - 4ac}}{2a}\right)\right]\left[z + \left(\dfrac{b}{2a} - \dfrac{\sqrt{b^2 - 4ac}}{2a}\right)\right] & \text{if } b^2 > 4ac \\ a\left[z + \left(\dfrac{b}{2a} + i\dfrac{\sqrt{4ac - b^2}}{2a}\right)\right]\left[z + \left(\dfrac{b}{2a} - i\dfrac{\sqrt{4ac - b^2}}{2a}\right)\right] & \text{if } b^2 < 4ac \\ a\left(z + \dfrac{b}{2a}\right)^2 & \text{if } b^2 = 4ac. \end{cases}$$

In general, the determination of the roots of (1.4) is very difficult, so most of our examples are restricted to the case $n = 2$.

The two roots of $az^2 + bz + c = 0$, for a, b, c real and $b^2 < 4ac$, have a special relationship, and this again illustrates a general fact which is of importance to us. If the quantity $z = a + ib$ is a complex number, we call a and b the *real* and *imaginary* parts of z, respectively, and we write $a = \operatorname{Re} z$, $b = \operatorname{Im} z$. In addition, for $z = a + ib$ the complex number $a - ib$ $(a + i(-b))$ is called the *conjugate* of z and is written $\bar{z}$. Now, by (1.6), if the two roots of $az^2 + bz + c = 0$ $(a, b, c \text{ real})$ are *complex* (that is, nonreal), then they are always conjugates of each other. What is true in general is that if the coefficients $a_0, \ldots, a_n$ in (1.4) are *all* real, then the nonreal roots always occur in conjugate pairs; that is, if z_1 is a nonreal root, then so is $\bar{z}_1$ (see problem 10).

Once we have the notion of complex number we can talk about functions with values which are complex numbers.

(1.7) Definition. A **complex-valued function** of t is a rule which assigns to each real number t in some interval $\alpha < t < \beta$ a unique complex number $f(t)$.

Since each value $f(t)$ of the function is an element of $\mathcal{C}$, we can write it

$$f(t) = r(t) + is(t),$$

where $r(t)$ and $s(t)$ are real numbers. Hence the complex-valued function f can be thought of in terms of the two *real-valued* functions r and s.

We make still another definition.

(1.8) Definition. A complex-valued function f is **continuous** (or **differentiable**) if when one writes $f(t) = r(t) + is(t)$, the functions r and s so defined are continuous (or differentiable). If f is differentiable we write

$$\dot{f}(t) = \dot{r}(t) + i\dot{s}(t)$$

and call $\dot{f}$ the **derivative** of f. If f, defined by $f(t) = r(t) + is(t)$, is continuous, then we define the **integral** of f from a to b by

$$\int_a^b f(t)\,dt = \left(\int_a^b r(t)\,dt\right) + i\left(\int_a^b s(t)\,dt\right) \cdot$$

(1.9) Examples

(a) If $z = a + ib$, define $f(t) = tz$ by

$$f(t) = ta + itb.$$

Then $r(t) = at$ and $s(t) = bt$, so $\dot{f}(t) = a + ib = z$.

(b) If $z = a + ib$, define $f(t) = \sin tz$ and $g(t) = \cos tz$ by

$$\begin{aligned} f(t) &= \sin at \cosh bt + i \cos at \sinh bt \\ g(t) &= \cos at \cosh bt - i \sin at \sinh bt. \end{aligned}$$

The reader should check that $\dot{f}(t) = g(t)z$ while $\dot{g}(t) = -f(t)z$.

(c) If $z = a + ib$, define $f(t) = e^{tz}$ by

$$e^{tz} = e^{at} \cos bt + ie^{at} \sin bt.$$

Here $r(t) = e^{at} \cos bt$ and $s(t) = e^{at} \sin bt$. Thus we find

$$\begin{aligned}\dot{f}(t) &= \dot{r}(t) + i\dot{s}(t) = ae^{at} \cos bt - be^{at} \sin bt + i[ae^{at} \sin bt + be^{at} \cos bt] \\ &= (a + ib)[e^{at} \cos bt + ie^{at} \sin bt] = zf(t).\end{aligned}$$

Note that in each of the above examples, when b is zero and hence z is real, $f(t)$ reduces to a well-known real-valued function and $\dot{f}$ becomes simply the corresponding derivative of this function.

To motivate our work in the next sections, and to fix some of the ideas in this one, let us indicate how we can apply our results to the differential equation

$$\ddot{y}(t) + a\dot{y}(t) + by(t) = 0 \tag{1.10}$$

which we studied in Chapter 5. In particular we indicate the origin of the mnemonic device (3.15) of Chapter 5. Let us try to find solutions of (1.10) which are *complex-valued* functions y having the form

$$y(t) = e^{zt}. \tag{1.11}$$

By the result of example (1.9c) we have

$$\dot{y}(t) = zy(t) = ze^{zt}, \qquad \ddot{y}(t) = z\dot{y}(t) = z^2e^{zt}.$$

Hence (1.10) becomes

$$(z^2 + az + b)e^{zt} = 0.$$

This equation will be satisfied if we choose z as a root of the equation

$$z^2 + az + b = 0. \tag{1.12}$$

We discussed equations of the form (1.12) in example (1.2c). From that example we find that if $a^2 - 4b$ is nonzero, then there are always two roots of (1.12),

$$\begin{aligned} z_1, z_2 &= -\frac{a}{2} \pm \frac{1}{2}\sqrt{a^2 - 4b} \qquad \text{if } a^2 - 4b > 0 \\ z_1, z_2 &= -\frac{a}{2} \pm \frac{i}{2}\sqrt{4b - a^2} \qquad \text{if } a^2 - 4b < 0. \end{aligned} \tag{1.13}$$

Now we write down, formally, the two solutions of the form (1.11) corresponding to (1.10); that is,

$$y_1(t) = e^{z_1t}, \qquad y_2(t) = e^{z_2t}. \tag{1.14}$$

In the case $a^2 - 4b > 0$, one sees from (1.13) that the two solutions (1.14) are precisely the two solutions of (1.10) which we obtained in §5.

When $a^2 - 4b < 0$, the two functions in (1.14) become, by example (1.9c),

$$y_1(t) = e^{z_1 t} = e^{-(a/2)t}\,[\cos \sqrt{b - a^2/4}\, t + i \sin \sqrt{b - a^2/4}\, t]$$
$$y_2(t) = e^{z_2 t} = e^{-(a/2)t}\,[\cos \sqrt{b - a^2/4}\, t - i \sin \sqrt{b - a^2/4}\, t].$$

Each of these is a *complex* function of t. Note, however, that for each value of t, $y_2(t)$ is the complex conjugate of $y_1(t)$. It can be verified that the real and imaginary parts of either y_1 or y_2 are themselves *real* solutions of (1.10). In fact, the real and imaginary parts of y_1 are precisely the two solutions we gave in Case 2 of Chapter 5.

The above example illustrates a general principle which we shall develop further in §3. We make it precise there, but it says in a rough way the following: In order to find *real* solutions of differential equations with *real* constant coefficients, one can find *complex* solutions and then take real and imaginary parts.

PROBLEMS

1. Calculate the following [$(a - ib)$ means always $a + i(-b)$].

(a) $(1 + i) + (2 + 3i)$
(b) $(2 - i) + (3 + 4i)$
(c) $(1 - i)2$
(d) $(1 - i)(2 + i)$
(e) $(1 + i)(1 - i)$
(f) $(2 + 3i)\cdot(4 - 2i)$
(g) $(2 + i)/(1 + i)$
(h) $(1 + i)/(1 - i)$
(i) $(1 + i)^3$
(j) $(1 + i)^2/(1 - i)^2$

2. Find solutions of the following equations.

(a) $z^2 + z + 2 = 0$

(b) $2z^2 + z + 2 = 0$

(c) $z^2 = -2$

3. Prove that each of the equations

(i) $a + z = b, \qquad a = r + is,\ b = u + iv$

and

(ii) $az = b, \qquad a \neq 0$

has a unique solution: that given by formulas (S) and (D) following (1.1). [*Hint:* To derive (D), multiply both sides of (ii) by $\bar{a} = r - is$.]

4. (a) Let $w = a + ib$ be a complex number. Show that there is a unique angle θ, $0 \leq \theta < 2\pi$, such that $w = \sqrt{a^2 + b^2}\,(\cos\theta + i\sin\theta)$. [*Hint:* If the squares of two real numbers sum to 1, $c^2 + d^2 = 1$, then there is a unique angle θ, $0 \leq \theta < 2\pi$, such that $c = \cos\theta$, $d = \sin\theta$. But $a/\sqrt{a^2+b^2}$, $b/\sqrt{a^2+b^2}$ are numbers with this property.]

(b) If $w = a + ib$, show that the complex numbers z_1 and z_2 defined by

$$z_{1,2} = \pm(a^2 + b^2)^{1/4}\left(\cos\frac{\theta}{2} + i\sin\frac{\theta}{2}\right),$$

where θ is the angle in part (a), satisfy $z^2 = w$. The numbers z_1 and z_2 are accordingly called the *square roots* of w.

5. (a) Let $w = a + ib$. Show that the product $w\overline{w} = (a + ib)(a - ib)$ reduces to a real number. This number is called the *square of the absolute value of* w:

$$|w|^2 = w\overline{w} = (a + ib)(a - ib).$$

(b) Show that the formulas in problem 4 reduce to

$$\text{(i)} \qquad w = |w|(\cos\theta + i\sin\theta)$$

$$\text{(ii)} \qquad z_{1,2} = \pm\sqrt{|w|}\left(\cos\frac{\theta}{2} + i\sin\frac{\theta}{2}\right).$$

6. Use the result in problem 4 to solve the following equations.

(a) $z^2 = i$ (b) $z^4 = 1$

7. Show that the functions $\sin tz$ and $\cos tz$ are solutions of the differential equation

$$\ddot{y}(t) + z^2y(t) = 0.$$

8. Find the most general solutions of the following differential equations.

(a) $\ddot{y}(t) + \dot{y}(t) + 2y(t) = 0$ (b) $\ddot{y}(t) - 2\dot{y}(t) + 4y(t) = 0$

9. To avoid having to use the symbol $+$ in defining complex numbers, many people use the notation of ordered pairs (a, b), instead of $a + ib$, for complex numbers. Verify that in this notation, formula (A) for addition becomes the same as addition in $\mathcal{R}^2$.

10. (a) Verify the following facts concerning the conjugate $\bar{z}$ of a complex number:

(i) If z and w are complex numbers, then $(\overline{zw}) = \bar{z}\cdot\overline{w}$; that is, the conjugate of a product is the product of the conjugates.

(ii) If a is real and z is complex, then $(\overline{za}) = a\bar{z}$.

(iii) If z and w are complex numbers, then $(\overline{z + w}) = \bar{z} + \overline{w}$; that is, the conjugate of a sum is the sum of the conjugates.

(b) Use the results of part (a) to show that if z_1 is a root of a polynomial,

$$a_0z^n + a_1z^{n-1} + \cdots + a_n$$

with *real* coefficients $a_0, \ldots, a_n$, then $\bar{z}_1$ is also a root.

11. (a) Show that complex exponentials obey the "law of exponents." Given $z = a + ib$, $z' = a' + ib'$, show that the definition in (1.9c) implies

$$\text{(i)} \qquad e^{tz}\cdot e^{tz'} = e^{t(z+z')} \qquad \text{for all } t.$$

Hence, taking $t = 1$, prove that

$$\text{(ii)} \qquad e^z \cdot e^{z'} = e^{z+z'}.$$

(b) Show that the conjugate of e^{tz} is $e^{t\bar{z}}$:

$$\text{(i)} \qquad \overline{(e^{tz})} = e^{t\bar{z}}.$$

Hence, taking $t = 1$, prove that

$$\text{(ii)} \qquad \overline{(e^{z})} = e^{\bar{z}}.$$

12. Show that complex sinusoidal functions obey the usual "addition formulas." That is, verify, using the definitions in (1.9b), that

$$\text{(i)} \qquad \begin{aligned} \sin t(z + z') &= \sin tz \cdot \cos tz' + \cos tz \cdot \sin tz' &&\text{for all } t \\ \cos t(z + z') &= \cos tz \cdot \cos tz' - \sin tz \cdot \sin tz' &&\text{for all } t. \end{aligned}$$

Hence, taking $t = 1$, prove that

$$\text{(ii)} \qquad \begin{aligned} \sin(z + z') &= \sin z \cdot \cos z' + \cos z \cdot \sin z' \\ \cos(z + z') &= \cos z \cdot \cos z' - \sin z \cdot \sin z'. \end{aligned}$$

2. Complex Vector Spaces

In order to be able to exploit the ideas of complex numbers in the study of differential equations we need the idea of a **complex vector space.** The definition of such a space is almost like (1.1) of Chapter 1. The only change is that the scalars which occur in scalar multiplication are now allowed to be in $\mathcal{C}$. Thus, if $\mathcal{V}$ is a complex vector space, α being any vector in $\mathcal{V}$ and c any *complex* number, then there must be defined a vector $c\alpha$ which still belongs to $\mathcal{V}$. All the axioms of definition (1.1) of Chapter 1 remain in force, with the understanding that in (M_1) the number 1 is to be understood as the real complex number $1 + i \cdot 0$. Proposition (1.3) remains true in a complex vector space, where 0 and -1 are understood as $0 + i0$ and $-1 + i0$, respectively.

(2.1) Examples. Complex Vector Spaces

(a) $\mathcal{C}^n$. This is the analog of the space $\mathcal{R}^n$ of Chapter 1. The vectors α of $\mathcal{C}^n$ are ordered n-tuples of *complex* numbers, $\alpha = (c_1, c_2, \ldots, c_n)$. If $\alpha = (c_1, \ldots, c_n)$ and $\beta = (d_1, \ldots, d_n)$ and c is any complex number, then,

$$\text{(i)} \qquad \alpha + \beta = (c_1 + d_1, c_2 + d_2, \ldots, c_n + d_n)$$

$$\text{(ii)} \qquad c\alpha = (cc_1, cc_2, \ldots, cc_n).$$

In (i) $c_k + d_k$ means the sum of c_k and d_k *as complex numbers*, hence is itself a complex number. Similarly, cc_k means the product of c and c_k as complex numbers, and hence it too is a complex number. For **0** we have the n-tuple $(0, 0, \ldots, 0)$ and for $-(c_1, \ldots, c_n)$ we have $(-c_1, -c_2, \ldots, -c_n)$.

(b) $\mathcal{K}[a, b]$. This is the analog of $\mathcal{C}[a, b]$ of Chapter 1. It consists of complex-valued functions f of t which are continuous on $a \leq t \leq b$ (definition (1.8)). The rule for adding two such functions looks just the same as in $\mathcal{C}[a, b]$; that is,

$$(f + g)(t) = f(t) + g(t),$$

but we observe that the right side now denotes the sum of two *complex* numbers. Similarly, cf for c complex is defined by

$$(cf)(t) = cf(t),$$

where the right side is the product of *complex* numbers c and $f(t)$. The 0 element is simply that function which equals $0(= 0 + i0)$ for all t. The space $\mathcal{K}(-\infty, \infty)$ is defined in an analogous fashion.

For complex vector spaces, just as for real vector spaces, we have such notions as subspace, basis, and dimension. As is evidenced by the definitions below, these concepts are direct analogs of the ones encountered in Chapter 5. The notion of inner product, on the other hand, is somewhat less straightforward and will be examined only in the problems.

(2.2) Definition. A subset S of a vector space $\mathcal{V}$ is called a **subspace** if it is closed under addition and under multiplication by (complex) scalars. That is, S is a subspace if:

(i) For all $\boldsymbol{\alpha}, \boldsymbol{\beta} \in S$, $\boldsymbol{\alpha} + \boldsymbol{\beta}$ is in S.

(ii) For all $\boldsymbol{\alpha} \in S$ and $c \in \mathcal{C}$, $c\boldsymbol{\alpha}$ is in S.

The above properties imply that S, with the same operations $+$ and $\cdot$ as $\mathcal{V}$, by itself forms a complex vector space.

(2.3) Examples. Subspaces

(a) In $\mathcal{C}^2$ consider the set S of all ordered pairs (c_1, c_2) such that $c_1 = ic_2$. S is a subspace since if $\boldsymbol{\alpha} = (c_1, c_2)$ and $\boldsymbol{\beta} = (d_1, d_2)$ with $c_1 = ic_2$, $d_1 = id_2$, then

$$\begin{aligned} \boldsymbol{\alpha} + \boldsymbol{\beta} &= (c_1 + d_1, c_2 + d_2) = (ic_2 + id_2, c_2 + d_2) \\ &= \big(i(c_2 + d_2), c_2 + d_2\big); \end{aligned}$$

hence $\boldsymbol{\alpha} + \boldsymbol{\beta}$ is in S. Similarly, if $\boldsymbol{\alpha} = (c_1, c_2)$ with $c_1 = ic_2$, then $c\boldsymbol{\alpha} = (cc_1, cc_2) = (cic_2, cc_2) = \big(i(cc_2), cc_2\big)$; hence $c\boldsymbol{\alpha}$ is in S.

(b) In $\mathcal{K}(-\infty, \infty)$ consider the sets $\mathcal{K}^{(1)}(-\infty, \infty)$ and $\mathcal{K}^{(2)}(-\infty, \infty)$ in which the functions f are once and twice continuously differentiable, respectively. The reader should convince himself that these are both subspaces.

(2.4) Definition. Let S denote a subspace of a complex vector space $\mathcal{V}$ (possibly $\mathcal{V}$ itself). A system of vectors $\boldsymbol{\beta}_1, \ldots, \boldsymbol{\beta}_n \in S$ is called a **basis** for S if each vector $\boldsymbol{\gamma} \in S$ can be expressed as a linear combination of the $\boldsymbol{\beta}$'s,

$$\text{(a)} \qquad \boldsymbol{\gamma} = c_1\boldsymbol{\beta}_1 + \cdots + c_n\boldsymbol{\beta}_n, \qquad c_i \in \mathcal{C},$$

and if there is *only one* set of (complex) coefficients $c_1, \ldots, c_n$ such that (a) is satisfied. The number n of elements in a basis for S is called the **dimension** of S. (It is again a theorem that all bases for S will have the same number of vectors.)

(2.5) Examples. Bases and Dimension

(a) Consider the subspace S of example (2.3a), that is, elements $\boldsymbol{\alpha} = (c_1,c_2)$ of $\mathcal{C}^2$ such that $c_1 = ic_2$. Let $\boldsymbol{\beta}_1$ be the vector $(i, 1)$. Then if $\boldsymbol{\alpha}$ is any vector of S we have

$$\boldsymbol{\alpha} = (ic_2, c_2) = c_2(i, 1) = c_2\boldsymbol{\beta}_1.$$

Hence any $\boldsymbol{\alpha}$ in S is uniquely determined as a multiple of $\boldsymbol{\beta}_1$. It follows that $\boldsymbol{\beta}_1$ is a basis for S and S is one-dimensional.

(b) $\mathcal{C}^n$. Define vectors $\boldsymbol{\beta}_1, \boldsymbol{\beta}_2, \ldots, \boldsymbol{\beta}_n$ by

$$\boldsymbol{\beta}_1 = (1, 0, \ldots, 0), \qquad \boldsymbol{\beta}_2 = (0, 1, 0, \ldots, 0), \ldots,$$
$$\boldsymbol{\beta}_n = (0, 0, \ldots, 0, 1).$$

Then given any $\boldsymbol{\alpha} = (c_1, c_2, \ldots, c_n)$ we can write

$$\begin{aligned}\boldsymbol{\alpha} &= c_1(1, 0, \ldots, 0) + c_2(0, 1, 0, \ldots, 0) + \cdots + c_n(0, 0, \ldots, 0, 1)\\ &= c_1\boldsymbol{\beta}_1 + \cdots + c_n\boldsymbol{\beta}_n.\end{aligned}$$

Hence $\boldsymbol{\alpha}$ is expressed uniquely as a linear combination of $\boldsymbol{\beta}_1, \ldots, \boldsymbol{\beta}_n$ so that $\boldsymbol{\beta}_1, \ldots, \boldsymbol{\beta}_n$ is a basis and $\mathcal{C}^n$ is n-dimensional. Note that the basis $\boldsymbol{\beta}_1, \ldots, \boldsymbol{\beta}_n$ is the same as the standard basis for $\mathcal{R}^n$. The difference between $\mathcal{C}^n$ and $\mathcal{R}^n$ is that in order to get all of $\mathcal{C}^n$ we must take all linear combinations of $\boldsymbol{\beta}_1, \ldots, \boldsymbol{\beta}_n$ with *complex* coefficients.

Next we come to notions involving a linear transformation on a complex vector space. They also look quite familiar.

(2.6) Definition. A **linear transformation** of a complex vector space $\mathfrak{D}$ into a complex vector space $\mathcal{W}$ is a rule T which assigns to each single vector $\mathbf{y}$ in $\mathfrak{D}$ a single element $\mathbf{w} = T\mathbf{y}$ in W in such a way that the *linearity identity*,

$$\text{(L)} \qquad T(c_1\mathbf{y}_1 + c_2\mathbf{y}_2) = c_1T\mathbf{y}_1 + c_2T\mathbf{y}_2,$$

is maintained for all $\mathbf{y}_1, \mathbf{y}_2 \in \mathfrak{D}$ and all (complex) scalars c_1, c_2.

With the above definition, all the properties of linear transformations discussed in Chapter 8 have direct analogs. In particular, we can define eigenvalues and eigenvectors.

(2.7) Definition. Let T be a linear transformation from a complex vector space $\mathfrak{D}$ into itself. A nonzero vector $\mathbf{y} \in \mathfrak{D}$ whose T-image is a scalar multiple of itself,

$$T\mathbf{y} = \lambda\mathbf{y}, \qquad \lambda \in \mathcal{C},$$

is called an **eigenvector** of T, and the complex number λ giving the factor of proportionality between y and its T-image is called the associated *eigenvalue* of T.

Our final definition is that of the *matrix* for a transformation from $\mathcal{C}^n$ to $\mathcal{C}^n$. Just as in the real case, the purpose of this definition is to introduce a convenient notation for computations.† Its utility depends on the fact that the analog of theorem (4.1) of Chapter 8 is valid. That is, *every* linear transformation T: $\mathcal{C}^n \to \mathcal{C}^n$ has the form

$$\begin{aligned} &T(y_1, \ldots, y_n) \\ &\qquad = (t_{11}y_1 + t_{12}y_2 + \cdots + t_{1n}y_n, \ldots, t_{n1}y_1 + t_{n2}y_2 + \cdots + t_{nn}y_n) \\ &\qquad\qquad \text{for all } \mathbf{y} = (y_1, \ldots, y_n) \in \mathcal{C}^n, \end{aligned}$$

where $t_{11}, t_{12}, \ldots, t_{1n}; t_{21}, t_{22}, \ldots, t_{2n}; \ldots; t_{n1}, t_{n2}, \ldots, t_{nn}$ is some fixed system of complex scalars. Rewriting this in vertical form we have the formula

$$\text{(2.8)} \qquad T\begin{pmatrix} y_1 \\ \vdots \\ y_n \end{pmatrix} = \begin{pmatrix} t_{11}y_1 + t_{12}y_2 + \cdots + t_{1n}y_n \\ \vdots \\ t_{n1}y_1 + t_{n2}y_2 + \cdots + t_{nn}y_n \end{pmatrix}.$$

†The method of Gauss reduction also works for equations with complex coefficients and hence can be used to check for bases and to determine eigenvectors.

(2.9) Definition. For any linear transformation $T: \mathcal{C}^n \to \mathcal{C}^n$, the array

$$\begin{pmatrix} t_{11} & t_{12} & \cdots & t_{1n} \\ \vdots & & & \vdots \\ t_{n1} & t_{n2} & \cdots & t_{nn} \end{pmatrix}$$

consisting of the n^2 complex scalars t_{ij} which occur in computing $T\mathbf{y}$ from $\mathbf{y}$ is called the *standard matrix form* for T, or briefly the **matrix** for T.

It is clear from (2.8) that the rule for computing $\mathbf{w} = T\mathbf{y}$ from the n-tuple $\mathbf{y}$ and the matrix for T is just the same as in the real-vector-space case [see (5.6) of Chapter 8]. *Hereafter we shall adopt the procedure of writing vectors in $\mathcal{C}^n$ vertically, as was done with $\mathcal{R}^n$ earlier.*

We turn now to the question of existence of eigenvalues and eigenvectors for transformations on $\mathcal{C}^n$ to $\mathcal{C}^n$. Consider first the case in which A is a linear transformation on the vector space $\mathcal{C}^2$ to $\mathcal{C}^2$. Then

$$A\begin{pmatrix} y_1 \\ y_2 \end{pmatrix} = \begin{pmatrix} a_{11}y_1 + a_{12}y_2 \\ a_{21}y_1 + a_{22}y_2 \end{pmatrix}. \tag{2.10}$$

We restrict ourselves to the case which will be of interest to us; we assume that the a_{ij}'s are all real. In order for $\beta = \begin{pmatrix} b_1 \\ b_2 \end{pmatrix}$ to be an eigenvector and $\lambda = \sigma + i\tau$ to be the associated eigenvalue we must have $A\beta = \lambda\beta$, so that, by (2.10),

$$\begin{aligned} a_{11}b_1 + a_{12}b_2 &= \lambda b_1 \\ a_{21}b_1 + a_{22}b_2 &= \lambda b_2. \end{aligned} \tag{2.11}$$

Equations (2.11) look just like systems of algebraic equations of the kind solved before. Now, however, the number λ is in general complex and hence the solutions will be complex. Assuming $a_{11} - \lambda$ is not zero and rewriting we find

$$\begin{aligned} (a_{11} - \lambda)b_1 + a_{12}b_2 &= 0 \\ a_{21}b_1 + (a_{22} - \lambda)b_2 &= 0 \end{aligned} \quad \xrightarrow{(a_{11} - \lambda)^{-1}[1]} \quad \begin{aligned} b_1 + \frac{a_{12}}{a_{11} - \lambda}b_2 &= 0 \\ a_{21}b_1 + (a_{22} - \lambda)b_2 &= 0 \end{aligned}$$

$$\xrightarrow{[2] - a_{21}[1]} \quad \begin{aligned} b_1 + \frac{a_{12}}{a_{11} - \lambda}b_2 &= 0 \\ 0b_1 + ((a_{22} - \lambda) - a_{21} \cdot a_{12}/(a_{11} - \lambda))b_2 &= 0. \end{aligned}$$

For this system to have any nonzero solutions at all, it is clearly *necessary* that the coefficient of b_2 in the second equation be zero. For it it were not, then the second equation would imply that $b_2 = 0$ and the first would yield $b_1 = 0$ also. Hence we must have

$$\frac{(a_{11} - \lambda)(a_{22} - \lambda) - a_{12}a_{21}}{a_{11} - \lambda} = 0,$$

so that

$$(2.12) \qquad (a_{11} - \lambda)(a_{22} - \lambda) - a_{12}a_{21} \\ = \lambda^2 - (a_{11} + a_{22})\lambda + (a_{11}a_{22} - a_{12}a_{21}) = 0.$$

Observe that (2.12) is just the statement that the determinant of the system of equations (2.11) is zero.

In real vector spaces of dimension 2 we were sometimes stopped at this stage because the corresponding quadratic equation had no real solutions. Now, however, (2.12) *does* have solutions, although these may be complex numbers. [The corresponding general result is that *any* linear transformation *on* $\mathcal{C}^n$ *to* $\mathcal{C}^n$ must have eigenvalues. This is related to theorem (1.5), but the connection requires a discussion of $n \times n$ determinants which we do not wish to include.] In fact, by (1.2c), unless the quantity

$$(a_{11} + a_{22})^2 - 4(a_{11}a_{22} - a_{12}a_{22})$$

happens to be zero, there will be two *distinct* solutions λ_1 and λ_2 of (2.12). Then the following result applies.

(2.13) Proposition. *Let* λ_1 *and* λ_2 *be distinct roots of equation* (2.12). *Let* $\gamma_1 = \begin{pmatrix} -a_{12} \\ a_{11} - \lambda_1 \end{pmatrix}$, $\gamma_2 = \begin{pmatrix} -a_{12} \\ a_{11} - \lambda_2 \end{pmatrix}$. *Then* λ_1 *and* λ_2 *are eigenvalues of* A *with* γ_1 *and* γ_2 *as associated eigenvectors.*† *Moreover,* γ_1 *and* γ_2 *form a basis for* $\mathcal{C}^2$.

(2.14) Example. Eigenvalues and Eigenvectors. Suppose A is a linear transformation on $\mathcal{C}^2$ to $\mathcal{C}^2$ with matrix

$$\begin{pmatrix} 1 & 1 \\ -2 & 1 \end{pmatrix};$$

that is, $a_{11} = 1$, $a_{12} = 1$, $a_{21} = -2$, $a_{22} = 1$. Equation (2.12) then becomes

$$(1 - \lambda)(1 - \lambda) + 2 = \lambda^2 - 2\lambda + 3 = 0.$$

†If both $a_{11} - \lambda$ and a_{12} are zero, then in the formulas for γ_1, γ_2 replace these quantities by a_{21} and $a_{22} - \lambda$, respectively.

The roots are

$$\lambda_1 = 1 + i\sqrt{2}, \qquad \lambda_2 = 1 - i\sqrt{2}.$$

Thus the claim of the proposition is that

$$\gamma_1 = \begin{pmatrix} -1 \\ 1 - (1 + i\sqrt{2}) \end{pmatrix} = \begin{pmatrix} -1 \\ -i\sqrt{2} \end{pmatrix},$$

$$\gamma_2 = \begin{pmatrix} -1 \\ 1 - (1 - i\sqrt{2}) \end{pmatrix} = \begin{pmatrix} -1 \\ i\sqrt{2} \end{pmatrix} = \bar{\gamma}_1,$$

are eigenvectors of A and that they form a basis. The reader should verify that this is the case.

Example (2.14) illustrates an important point. We state the following result without proof.

(2.15) Proposition. *Let A be a linear transformation on $\mathcal{C}^n$ to $\mathcal{C}^n$. Suppose that its matrix has all entries a_{ij} real. Then if λ is a nonreal eigenvalue with eigenvector* $\gamma = \begin{pmatrix} c_1 \\ \cdot \\ \cdot \\ \cdot \\ c_n \end{pmatrix}$, *it follows that $\bar{\lambda}$ is also an eigenvalue with* $\bar{\gamma} = \begin{pmatrix} \bar{c}_1 \\ \cdot \\ \cdot \\ \cdot \\ \bar{c}_n \end{pmatrix}$ *as an eigenvector. Moreover, if λ is a* real *eigenvalue, then one can find an associated eigenvector* $\gamma = \begin{pmatrix} c_1 \\ \cdot \\ \cdot \\ \cdot \\ c_n \end{pmatrix}$ *with* all *the c's real.*

This result states that for transformations on $\mathcal{C}^n$ to $\mathcal{C}^n$ having real matrix entries, nonreal eigenvalues and corresponding eigenvectors always occur in conjugate pairs.

PROBLEMS

1. Which of the following are subspaces of $\mathcal{C}^2$? For those which are, find a basis and the dimension.

(a) S = set of vectors $\boldsymbol{\alpha} = (c_1, c_2)$ with $c_1 = 1$

(b) S = set of vectors $\boldsymbol{\alpha} = (c_1, c_2)$ with $c_1 = 0$

(c) S = set of vectors $\boldsymbol{\alpha} = (c_1, c_2)$ with $2c_1 - c_2 = 1$

2. Which of the following are subspaces of $\mathcal{C}^3$? For those which are, find a basis and the dimension.

(a) S = set of vectors $\alpha = (c_1, c_2, c_3)$ with $c_1 + c_2 + c_3 = 0$

(b) S = set of vectors $\alpha = (c_1, c_2, c_3)$ with $ic_1 - 2ic_2 = 0$

(c) S = set of vectors $\alpha = (c_1, c_2, c_3)$ with $c_1 + c_3 = 2$

3. A linear transformation A from $\mathcal{C}^2$ into $\mathcal{C}^2$ transforms the vectors $(1, i)$, $(0, 1)$ according to the formulas

$$A(1, i) = (1, 1)$$
$$A(0, 1) = (1, 0).$$

Find the matrix of A.

4. Calculate the eigenvalues and eigenvectors of the transformations A which have the following matrices. In each case verify the validity of propositions (2.13) and (2.15).

(a) $\begin{pmatrix} 1 & 1 \\ 0 & 1 \end{pmatrix}$

(b) $\begin{pmatrix} 1 & -1 \\ 2 & 1 \end{pmatrix}$

(c) $\begin{pmatrix} 0 & 2 \\ -1 & 3 \end{pmatrix}$

5. Prove proposition (2.13).

6. Show that if A is a linear transformation from $\mathcal{C}^2$ into $\mathcal{C}^2$ with a matrix of the form

$$\begin{pmatrix} a_{11} & b \\ b & a_{22} \end{pmatrix}, \qquad a_{11}, b, a_{22} \text{ real},$$

then the eigenvalues are *all* real.

7. Show that if A is a linear transformation from $\mathcal{C}^2$ into $\mathcal{C}^2$ with a matrix of the form

$$\begin{pmatrix} a_{11} & b \\ -b & a_{22} \end{pmatrix}, \qquad a_{11}, b, a_{22} \text{ real},$$

then the eigenvalues have the form $c_1 = 0 + ia$, $c_2 = 0 - ia$; that is, they are *both* imaginary (or zero).

8. Show that a transformation from $\mathcal{C}^3$ into $\mathcal{C}^3$ whose matrix has all real entries must have at least one *real* eigenvalue.

*9. (a) Show that there is a function J which assigns a *real* number $J(\alpha, \beta)$ to each pair of vectors

$$\alpha = (a_1, a_2) = (r_1 + is_1, r_2 + is_2),$$
$$\beta = (b_1, b_2) = (u_1 + iv_1, u_2 + iv_2),$$

in $\mathcal{C}^2$ and obeys the axioms for an inner product on a real vector space ((2.8)) in Chapter 1). [*Hint:* Try $J(\alpha, \beta) = r_1u_1 + s_1v_1 + r_2u_2 + s_2v_2$.]

(b) Real-valued functions on the complex vector space $\mathcal{C}^2$ which satisfy (2.8) of Chapter 1 are *not* referred to as "inner products." Instead one reserves the term inner product for a *complex-valued* function I which assigns a *complex* number $I(\boldsymbol{\alpha}, \boldsymbol{\beta})$ to each pair of vectors $\boldsymbol{\alpha} = (a_1, a_2) = (r_1 + is_1, r_2 + is_2)$, $\boldsymbol{\beta} = (b_1, b_2) = (u_1 + iv_1, u_2 + iv_2)$ in $\mathcal{C}^2$ and, in addition, obeys the following modification of (2.8) of Chapter 1.

(i) I is *sesquilinear:*

$$I(c_1\boldsymbol{\alpha}_1 + c_2\boldsymbol{\alpha}_2, \boldsymbol{\beta}) = c_1 I(\boldsymbol{\alpha}_1, \boldsymbol{\beta}) + c_2 I(\boldsymbol{\alpha}_2, \boldsymbol{\beta})$$
$$I(\boldsymbol{\alpha}, c_1\boldsymbol{\beta}_1 + c_2\boldsymbol{\beta}_2) = \bar{c}_1 I(\boldsymbol{\alpha}, \boldsymbol{\beta}_1) + \bar{c}_2 I(\boldsymbol{\alpha}, \boldsymbol{\beta}_2) \qquad (!)$$

(ii) I is *conjugate-symmetric:*

$$I(\boldsymbol{\beta}, \boldsymbol{\alpha}) = \bar{I}(\boldsymbol{\alpha}, \boldsymbol{\beta}).$$

(iii) I is *positive definite:*

$$I(\boldsymbol{\alpha}, \boldsymbol{\alpha}) \geq 0 \text{ and } I(\boldsymbol{\alpha}, \boldsymbol{\alpha}) = 0 \qquad \text{only if } \boldsymbol{\alpha} = \mathbf{0}.$$

Show that the function defined by

$$I(\boldsymbol{\alpha}, \boldsymbol{\beta}) = a_1\bar{b}_1 + a_2\bar{b}_2 = (r_1 + is_1)(u_1 - iv_1) + (r_2 + is_2)(u_2 - iv_2)$$

is an inner product on $\mathcal{C}^2$. Compare the formula given for $I(\boldsymbol{\alpha}, \boldsymbol{\alpha})$ by this inner product with the formula for $J(\boldsymbol{\alpha}, \boldsymbol{\alpha})$ in (a).

***10.** The conditions (i), (ii), and (iii) define the notion of inner product on *any* complex vector space. Show that on $\mathcal{K}[0, 2\pi]$, the vector space of continuous complex-valued functions on $0 \leq t \leq 2\pi$, the following formula defines an inner product

$$I(f, g) = \int_0^{2\pi} f(t)\overline{g(t)}\, dt.$$

The quantity

$$I(f, f) = \|f\|^2$$

is again called the *norm* of f.

***11.** (a) Show that in $\mathcal{K}[0, 2\pi]$ the system of functions E_e: $e_0, e_1, e_{-1}, e_2, e_{-2}, e_3, \ldots$ such that

$$e_n(t) = \frac{1}{\sqrt{2\pi}} e^{int}, \qquad n = 0, \pm 1, \pm 2, \ldots$$

is orthonormal — with the inner product as in problem 10. [*Hint:* Use problem 9 of §1.]

**(b) Show that for any function $f \in \mathcal{K}[0, 2\pi]$, the linear combination

$$c_0e_0 + c_1e_1 + c_{-1}e_{-1} + c_2e_2 + c_{-2}e_{-2} + \cdots + c_me_m + c_{-m}e_{-m}$$

which is *closest to* f is as follows:

$$(f \cdot e_0)e_0 + (f \cdot e_1)e_1 + (f \cdot e_{-1})e_{-1} + \cdots + (f \cdot e_m)e_m + (f \cdot e_{-m})e_{-m}$$
$$= \left(f \cdot \frac{1}{\sqrt{2\pi}}\right)\frac{1}{\sqrt{2\pi}} + \left(f \cdot \frac{1}{\sqrt{2\pi}} e^{it}\right)e^{it} + \left(f \cdot \frac{1}{\sqrt{2\pi}} e^{-it}\right)e^{-it} + \cdots$$
$$+ \left(f \cdot \frac{1}{\sqrt{2\pi}} e^{imt}\right)e^{imt} + \left(f \cdot \frac{1}{\sqrt{2\pi}} e^{-imt}\right)e^{-imt}.$$

[*Hint:* Examine the proofs of theorems (1.8) and (2.2) of Chapter 6. "Closest" here is to be interpreted in terms of the norm in problem 10.]

(c) Justify the practice of calling the expression

$$\left(f\cdot\frac{1}{\sqrt{2\pi}}\right)\frac{1}{\sqrt{2\pi}}+\left(f\cdot\frac{1}{\sqrt{2\pi}}e^{it}\right)\frac{1}{\sqrt{2\pi}}e^{it}+\cdots$$
$$+\left(f\cdot\frac{1}{\sqrt{2\pi}}e^{imt}\right)\frac{1}{\sqrt{2\pi}}e^{imt}+\cdots$$

the *Fourier E_e-expansion of f*, where f is a function in $\mathcal{K}[0, 2\pi]$.

The orthonormal system E_e is a *complete* orthonormal system in $\mathcal{K}[0, 2\pi]$. It is called the *complex-exponential orthonormal system.*

****12.** Given $f \in \mathcal{C}[0, 2\pi]$, we may regard f as being in $\mathcal{K}[0, 2\pi]$ by writing

$$f(t) = f(t) + i0.$$

Show that in such cases the expansion

$$f \sim c_0e_0 + c_1e_1 + c_{-1}e_{-1} + c_2e_2 + c_{-2}e_{-2} + \cdots$$

has the property

$$c_{-1} = \bar{c}_1, \qquad c_{-2} = \bar{c}_2, \qquad c_{-3} = \bar{c}_3, \ldots.$$

3. Systems of Differential Equations with Constant Coefficients

We are going to indicate in this section how the material we have developed on complex analysis can be used to extend our results on differential equations. We can treat both first- and second-order systems, but for purposes of brevity we restrict ourselves to the first-order case (see problem 8). Thus we want to consider the system

$$\dot{\mathbf{y}}(t) + C\mathbf{y}(t) = \mathbf{w}(t), \qquad \mathbf{y}(t_0) = \mathbf{y}^0 \in \mathcal{R}^n. \tag{3.1}$$

We know how to handle (3.1) in case $C\colon \mathcal{R}^n \to \mathcal{R}^n$ has a basis of (real) eigenvectors; hence we are primarily interested here in the case in which it does not have such a basis. It will be seen that when C does possess a basis of real eigenvectors, then the procedure of this section reduces to that of §2 of Chapter 9.

We indicated at the end of §2 what our basic trick will be. We first look for *complex* solutions of (3.1) and then take real and imaginary parts. First let us remark that looking for complex solutions is a meaningful operation. A *complex solution* of (3.1) is a function $\mathbf{y}$ of t whose values lie in the space $\mathcal{C}^n$ of n-tuples of complex numbers. Thus

$$\mathbf{y}(t) = \begin{pmatrix} y_1(t) \\ \vdots \\ y_n(t) \end{pmatrix} = \begin{pmatrix} r_1(t) + is_1(t) \\ \vdots \\ r_n(t) + is_n(t) \end{pmatrix}. \tag{3.2}$$

We can define the derivative $\dot{\mathbf{y}}$ of $\mathbf{y}$ by a formula analogous to that in formula (1.6) of Chapter 9 and definition (1.8):

$$\dot{\mathbf{y}}(t) = \begin{pmatrix} \dot{y}_1(t) \\ \vdots \\ \dot{y}_n(t) \end{pmatrix} = \begin{pmatrix} \dot{r}_1(t) + i\dot{s}_1(t) \\ \vdots \\ \dot{r}_n(t) + i\dot{s}_n(t) \end{pmatrix}. \tag{3.3}$$

Now we can interpret $C\mathbf{y}(t)$ in (3.1) by formula (2.8); that is

(3.4)

$$C\mathbf{y}(t) = \begin{pmatrix} c_{11} & \cdots & c_{1n} \\ \vdots & & \vdots \\ c_{n1} & \cdots & c_{nn} \end{pmatrix} \begin{pmatrix} y_1(t) \\ \vdots \\ y_n(t) \end{pmatrix} = \begin{pmatrix} c_{11}y_1(t) + \cdots + c_{1n}y_n(t) \\ \vdots \\ c_{n1}y_1(t) + \cdots + c_{nn}y_n(t) \end{pmatrix}.$$

Note the subtle, but important, point, that even though the matrix for C has real entries, we are considering it as a linear transformation *from* $\mathcal{C}^n$ *into* $\mathcal{C}^n$ in (3.4). With this interpretation in mind, we make the following assumption, which is analogous to (2.2).

(3.5) Assumption. *The transformation C, considered on $\mathcal{C}^n$, has n eigenvectors $\gamma_1, \ldots, \gamma_n$ which form a basis for $\mathcal{C}^n$.*

Let $a_1, \ldots, a_n$ be the eigenvalues associated with $\gamma_1, \ldots, \gamma_n$, respectively. In general these are complex, $a_k = \alpha_k + i\beta_k$, and the γ_k's themselves are complex n-tuples, that is, vectors in $\mathcal{C}^n$. It is important in what follows that we observe proposition (2.15) in our choice of eigenvectors. For this reason we state a precise rule for the choice of a set of eigenvectors [this will be illustrated in example (3.18)].

(3.6) Rule for Eigenvector Selection

CASE 1. *All eigenvalues of C are real.* Here we choose eigenvectors $\gamma_1, \ldots, \gamma_n$ such that

$$\gamma_k = \begin{pmatrix} c_{k1} \\ \vdots \\ c_{kn} \end{pmatrix}, \qquad k = 1, 2, \ldots, n$$

with *all* the c_{kj}'s real. This is possible by (2.15).

CASE 2. *Some eigenvalues of C are nonreal.* Here we select the eigenvectors $\gamma_1, \ldots, \gamma_n$ as follows. Let $a_1, \ldots, a_{2r}$ denote the *nonreal* eigenvalues and

$a_{2r+1}, \ldots, a_n$ denote the *real* eigenvalues of C. Arranging the nonreal eigenvalues in conjugate pairs we have

$$\text{(i)} \qquad a_2 = \bar{a}_1,\ a_4 = \bar{a}_3, \ldots, a_{2r} = \bar{a}_{2r-1}$$

$$\text{(ii)} \qquad a_{2r+1}, \ldots, a_n \text{ are real.}$$

Using (2.15) we shall now select the eigenvectors of C so as to satisfy

$$\text{(i}'\text{)} \qquad \gamma_2 = \bar{\gamma}_1,\ \gamma_4 = \bar{\gamma}_3, \ldots, \gamma_{2r} = \bar{\gamma}_{2r-1}$$

$$\text{(ii}'\text{)} \qquad \gamma_{2r+1}, \ldots, \gamma_n \text{ are real.}$$

That is,

$$\text{(iii)} \qquad \gamma_1 = \begin{pmatrix} c_{11} \\ \cdot \\ \cdot \\ \cdot \\ c_{1n} \end{pmatrix}, \quad \gamma_2 = \begin{pmatrix} \bar{c}_{11} \\ \cdot \\ \cdot \\ \cdot \\ \bar{c}_{1n} \end{pmatrix}, \quad \gamma_3 = \begin{pmatrix} c_{31} \\ \cdot \\ \cdot \\ \cdot \\ c_{3n} \end{pmatrix}, \quad \gamma_4 = \begin{pmatrix} \bar{c}_{31} \\ \cdot \\ \cdot \\ \cdot \\ \bar{c}_{3n} \end{pmatrix}, \ldots,$$

$$\gamma_{2r-1} = \begin{pmatrix} c_{2r-1,1} \\ \cdot \\ \cdot \\ \cdot \\ c_{2r-1,n} \end{pmatrix}, \quad \gamma_{2r} = \begin{pmatrix} \bar{c}_{2r-1,1} \\ \cdot \\ \cdot \\ \cdot \\ \bar{c}_{2r-1,n} \end{pmatrix},$$

$$\text{(iv)} \qquad \gamma_{2r+1} = \begin{pmatrix} c_{2r+1,1} \\ \cdot \\ \cdot \\ \cdot \\ c_{2r+1,n} \end{pmatrix}, \ldots, \quad \gamma_n = \begin{pmatrix} c_{n1} \\ \cdot \\ \cdot \\ \cdot \\ c_{nn} \end{pmatrix}$$

$c_{2r+1,1}, \ldots, c_{nn}$ all real.

[The number $2r$ in (i), (i′), and (iii) may be n, which means that *all* the eigenvalues and eigenvectors of C are "complex" (nonreal). On the other hand, this number may be less than n, which means that there are also real eigenvalues and eigenvectors as in (ii), (ii′), and (iv).]

Once we have taken the trouble to arrange the eigenvectors according to rule (3.6), the process we are going to describe becomes completely automatic and is *guaranteed* to yield *the real solution* $\mathbf{y}$ of (3.1). Also this process exactly parallels the one we used in §2 of Chapter 9. Let us describe the process.

First we write

$$\mathbf{y}(t) = u_1(t)\gamma_1 + \cdots + u_n(t)\gamma_n \tag{3.7}$$

$$\mathbf{w}(t) = v_1(t)\gamma_1 + \cdots + v_n(t)\gamma_n \tag{3.8}$$

$$\gamma^0 = u_1^0\gamma_1 + \cdots + u_n^0\gamma_n. \tag{3.9}$$

It is important to note that even though $\mathbf{w}(t)$ and $\mathbf{y}^0$ are n-tuples of real numbers, the quantities $v_1(t), \ldots, v_n(t)$ and $u_1^0, \ldots, u_n^0$ in (3.8) and (3.9) will, in general, be complex numbers since the $\gamma_1, \ldots, \gamma_n$ are complex [see example (3.18)]. However, we remark that $v_1(t), \ldots, v_n(t)$ and $u_1^0, \ldots, u_n^0$ will be related in the same way as the a_k's and γ_k's. That is, one has the following result concerning (3.8) and (3.9) when $\mathbf{w}(t)$ and $\mathbf{y}_0$ are real.

(3.10) Proposition. *Let the γ_k's be chosen according to rule* (3.6). *Then:*

(i) *If all the a_k's are real, all the v_k's and u_k^0's will be real.*

(ii) *If $a_1, \ldots, a_{2r}$ are complex, we have*

$$v_2(t) = \overline{v_1(t)}, \qquad v_4(t) = \overline{v_3(t)}, \ldots, \qquad v_{2r}(t) = \overline{v_{2r-1}}(t);$$
$$v_{2r+1}(t), \ldots, v_n(t) \quad \textit{real;}$$
$$u_2^0 = \bar{u}_1^0, \qquad u_4^0 = \bar{u}_3^0, \ldots, \qquad u_{2r}^0 = \bar{u}_{2r-1}^0; \qquad u_{2r+1}^0, \ldots, u_n^0 \quad \textit{real.}$$

The proof of this proposition is an exercise in complex vector spaces and we leave it as a problem. However, it will be illustrated in example (3.18).

We now proceed along the lines of §2 of Chapter 9. We have, from (3.7),

$$\dot{\mathbf{y}}(t) = \dot{u}_1(t)\gamma_1 + \cdots + \dot{u}_n(t)\gamma_n. \tag{3.11}$$

Also since the γ_k's and a_k's are related by

$$C\gamma_k = a_k\gamma_k, \qquad k = 1, 2, \ldots, n,$$

we have

$$\begin{aligned} C\mathbf{y}(t) &= C(u_1(t)\gamma_1 + \cdots + u_n(t)\gamma_n) \\ &= u_1(t)a_1\gamma_1 + \cdots + u_n(t)a_n\gamma_n. \end{aligned} \tag{3.12}$$

If we substitute (3.8), (3.11), and (3.12) into (3.1) and equate coefficients of γ_k, we obtain, just as in §2 of Chapter 9,

$$\begin{aligned} \dot{u}_1(t) + a_1u_1(t) &= v_1(t) \\ &\vdots \\ \dot{u}_n(t) + a_nu_n(t) &= v_n(t). \end{aligned} \tag{3.13}$$

Substitution of (3.9) into $\mathbf{y}(t_0) = \mathbf{y}^0$ yields, as in §2 of Chapter 9,

$$u_1(t_0) = u_1^0, \ldots, u_n(t_0) = u_n^0. \tag{3.14}$$

Problems (3.13) and (3.14) look exactly like the ones we studied in §2 of Chapter 9. The only difference is that some of the a_k's may be complex.

Recall that we wrote down the solutions when the a_k's were real. These solutions were given in (3.13) as

$$u_k(t) = u_k^0 e^{-a_k t} + e^{-a_k t} \int_{t_0}^{t} e^{a_k \tau} v_k(\tau)\, d\tau, \qquad k = 1, \ldots, n. \tag{3.15}$$

It turns out that we can use exactly the same formulas for (3.13) and (3.14). All we have to do is to interpret the functions $e^{-a_k t}$ and $e^{a_k t}$, when a_k is complex, by means of the formula in example (1.9c). Thus if $a_k = \alpha_k + i\beta_k$, then

$$\begin{aligned} e^{-a_k t} &= e^{-\alpha_k t}(\cos(-\beta_k)t + i \sin(-\beta_k)t) \\ &= e^{-\alpha_k t}(\cos \beta_k t - i \sin \beta_k t). \end{aligned} \tag{3.16}$$

Of course the products $u_k^0 e^{-a_k t}$ and so forth in (3.15) are products of complex numbers in general, and the integrals in (3.15) are integrals of complex functions of t, to be defined as in (1.8).

We now state our final result.

(3.17) Theorem. *Choose the* γ_k*'s according to rule* (3.6). *Define functions* $u_k(t)$ *by* (3.15) *and define* $\mathbf{y}(t)$ *by* (3.7). *Then* $\mathbf{y}(t)$ *will be a* real *n-tuple for each* t *and will be a solution of* (3.1).†

This rather remarkable result states that although there are various complex quantities involved in the formulas, they are always going to combine in exactly the right way so that the imaginary parts cancel out. Again we do not give a proof here, although some indications occur in the problems. Rather we study two examples.

(3.18) Examples

(a) We consider again the equations

$$\text{(i)} \qquad \begin{aligned} \dot{y}_1(t) - y_2(t) &= 2, \qquad & y_1(0) &= 1 \\ \dot{y}_2(t) + y_1(t) &= t, \qquad & y_2(0) &= 2, \end{aligned}$$

of example (2.14b). There we were stopped because the transformation C with matrix

$$C = \begin{pmatrix} 0 & -1 \\ 1 & 0 \end{pmatrix}$$

†Actually there is a uniqueness theorem for problem (3.1) so that the vector $\mathbf{y}$ in theorem (3.17) is *the* solution of (3.1).

had no eigenvalues. However, as we now know, it would have been more proper to say that it had no *real* eigenvalues. We found that the eigenvalues a would have to satisfy

$$\begin{vmatrix} -a & -1 \\ 1 & -a \end{vmatrix} = a^2 + 1 = 0,$$

and we see that there *are* complex eigenvalues, namely, $\pm i$. Let us find eigenvectors (*in* $\mathcal{C}^2$) corresponding to $\pm i$. If $\gamma = \begin{pmatrix} c_{11} \\ c_{12} \end{pmatrix}$ is an eigenvector for $+i$, then

$$\begin{pmatrix} 0 & -1 \\ 1 & 0 \end{pmatrix}\begin{pmatrix} c_{11} \\ c_{12} \end{pmatrix} = i\begin{pmatrix} c_{11} \\ c_{12} \end{pmatrix}$$

or $-c_{12} = ic_{11}$. Thus one eigenvector is $\gamma_1 = \begin{pmatrix} 1 \\ -i \end{pmatrix}$, corresponding to $a_1 = +i$. An eigenvector

$$\gamma = \begin{pmatrix} c_{21} \\ c_{22} \end{pmatrix} \qquad \text{for } a = -i$$

must satisfy

$$\begin{pmatrix} 0 & -1 \\ 1 & 0 \end{pmatrix}\begin{pmatrix} c_{21} \\ c_{22} \end{pmatrix} = -i\begin{pmatrix} c_{21} \\ c_{22} \end{pmatrix}$$

or $-c_{22} = -ic_{22}$. Thus one eigenvector is $\gamma_2 = \begin{pmatrix} 1 \\ i \end{pmatrix}$, this for $a_2 = -i$. Note that γ_1 and γ_2 have been chosen according to rule (3.6).

We have in this problem

$$\mathbf{w}(t) = \begin{pmatrix} 2 \\ t \end{pmatrix}.$$

Thus (3.8) becomes

$$\begin{pmatrix} 2 \\ t \end{pmatrix} = v_1(t)\begin{pmatrix} 1 \\ -i \end{pmatrix} + v_2(t)\begin{pmatrix} 1 \\ i \end{pmatrix} \qquad \text{or} \qquad \begin{aligned} v_1(t) + v_2(t) &= 2 \\ -iv_1(t) + iv_2(t) &= t. \end{aligned}$$

Hence we obtain

$$\text{(ii)} \qquad v_1(t) = 1 + \tfrac{1}{2}it, \qquad v_2(t) = 1 - \tfrac{1}{2}it.$$

We have, for (3.9),

$$\mathbf{y}^0 = \begin{pmatrix} 1 \\ 2 \end{pmatrix} = u_1^0\begin{pmatrix} 1 \\ -i \end{pmatrix} + u_2^0\begin{pmatrix} 1 \\ i \end{pmatrix} \qquad \text{or} \qquad \begin{aligned} u_1^0 + u_2^0 &= 1 \\ -iu_1^0 + iu_2^0 &= 2, \end{aligned}$$

and therefore

$$\text{(iii)} \qquad u_1^0 = \tfrac{1}{2}(1 + 2i), \qquad u_2^0 = \tfrac{1}{2}(1 - 2i).$$

[Note how (ii) and (iii) illustrate proposition (3.10).] Equations (3.13) and (3.14) become

$$\text{(iv)} \qquad \begin{aligned} \dot{u}_1(t) + iu_1(t) &= 1 + \tfrac{1}{2}it, & u_1^0 &= \tfrac{1}{2}(1 + 2i) \\ \dot{u}_2(t) - iu_2(t) &= 1 - \tfrac{1}{2}it, & u_2^0 &= \tfrac{1}{2}(1 - 2i). \end{aligned}$$

Equations (iv) can be solved using formulas (3.15). However, we take this opportunity to point out that we can also solve them by applying the ideas of the splitting theorem and of undetermined coefficients to equations with complex coefficients. Consider the first of equations (iv). We seek a particular solution of the form $u_1^*(t) = A + Bt$. We substitute into the equation and find

$$B + i(A + Bt) = 1 + \tfrac{1}{2}it.$$

Hence $iB = \frac{1}{2}i$ and $B + iA = 1$ or $B = \frac{1}{2}$, $\quad A = -\frac{1}{2}i$ and

$$u_1^*(t) = -\tfrac{1}{2}i + \tfrac{1}{2}t.$$

Now consider the homogeneous equation

$$\dot{u}_1(t) + iu_1(t) = 0.$$

By example (1.9c) any function of the form De^{-it}, where D is a complex constant, will be a solution. Thus if we proceed as with real equations we would write

$$u_1(t) = De^{-it} + u_1^*(t) = De^{-it} - \tfrac{1}{2}i + \tfrac{1}{2}t.$$

D is then adjusted so that this expression satisfies the initial condition; that is,

$$u_1(0) = De^{-i0} - \tfrac{1}{2}i + \tfrac{1}{2}\cdot 0 = D - \tfrac{1}{2}i = \tfrac{1}{2}(1 + 2i),$$

so $D = \frac{1}{2} + \frac{3}{2}i$. Hence

$$\text{(v)} \qquad u_1(t) = (\tfrac{1}{2} + \tfrac{3}{2}i)e^{-it} - \tfrac{1}{2}i + \tfrac{1}{2}t.$$

In a similar way one finds

$$\text{(vi)} \qquad u_2(t) = (\tfrac{1}{2} - \tfrac{3}{2}i)e^{it} + \tfrac{1}{2}i + \tfrac{1}{2}t.$$

Now we substitute (v) and (vi) into (3.7) and obtain

$$\text{(vii)}\qquad \mathbf{y}(t) = u_1(t)\gamma_1 + u_2(t)\gamma_2 = [(\tfrac{1}{2} + \tfrac{3}{2}i)e^{-it} - \tfrac{1}{2}i + \tfrac{1}{2}t]\begin{pmatrix}1\\ -i\end{pmatrix}$$
$$+ [(\tfrac{1}{2} - \tfrac{3}{2}i)e^{it} + \tfrac{1}{2}i + \tfrac{1}{2}t]\begin{pmatrix}1\\ i\end{pmatrix}$$
$$= \begin{pmatrix}\tfrac{1}{2}(e^{-it} + e^{it}) + \tfrac{3}{2}i(e^{-it} - e^{it}) + t\\ -\tfrac{1}{2}(e^{-it} - e^{it})i + \tfrac{3}{2}(e^{-it} + e^{it}) - 1\end{pmatrix}.$$

Observe that example (1.9c) yields

$$e^{-it} + e^{it} = (\cos t - i\sin t) + (\cos t + i\sin t) = 2\cos t$$
$$e^{-it} - e^{it} = (\cos - i\sin t) - (\cos t + i\sin t) = -2i\sin t.$$

Hence (vii) can be rewritten

$$\text{(viii)}\qquad \mathbf{y}(t) = \begin{pmatrix}y_1(t)\\ y_2(t)\end{pmatrix} \begin{matrix}=\\=\end{matrix} \begin{pmatrix}\cos t + 3\sin t + t\\ -\sin t + 3\cos t - 1\end{pmatrix}.$$

Observe that indeed everything has combined to yield real solutions (y_1, y_2). The reader should verify that (viii) does yield a solution of (i).

(b) Consider the system of equations

$$\begin{aligned}
\dot{y}_1(t) \qquad\qquad - y_2(t) \qquad\qquad\qquad &= 0\\
\dot{y}_2(t) + y_1(t) \qquad\qquad\qquad\qquad &= 0\\
\dot{y}_3(t) \qquad\qquad\qquad + \ y_3(t) + 3y_4(t) &= 0\\
\dot{y}_4(t) \qquad\qquad\qquad + 2y_3(t) + 2y_4(t) &= 0.
\end{aligned}$$

Here we must analyze a system of equations in which there are both complex and real eigenvalues. Eigenvalues and eigenvectors can be found without great difficulty by the Gauss reduction method of Chapter 5 but we shall simply write down the answers.† The matrix in question is

$$C = \begin{pmatrix}0 & -1 & 0 & 0\\ 1 & 0 & 0 & 0\\ 0 & 0 & 1 & 3\\ 0 & 0 & 2 & 2\end{pmatrix}.$$

†The reader may note that this is merely a combination of two earlier problems.

It can be checked that eigenvectors and eigenvalues can be chosen as follows:

$$\gamma_1 = \begin{pmatrix} 1 \\ -i \\ 0 \\ 0 \end{pmatrix}, \quad a_1 = i; \qquad \gamma_2 = \begin{pmatrix} 1 \\ i \\ 0 \\ 0 \end{pmatrix}, \quad a_2 = -i;$$

$$\gamma_3 = \begin{pmatrix} 0 \\ 0 \\ 1 \\ 1 \end{pmatrix}, \quad a_3 = 4; \qquad \gamma_4 = \begin{pmatrix} 0 \\ 0 \\ 1 \\ -\frac{2}{3} \end{pmatrix}, \quad a_4 = -1.$$

It should also be verified that $\gamma_1, \gamma_2, \gamma_3, \gamma_4$ form a basis for $\mathcal{C}^4$. Note that the eigenvectors are arranged according to rule (3.6). This system is analyzed further in the problems to illustrate some of our earlier statements.

By the methods of this section we have extended the procedure of §2 of Chapter 9 to cover all systems of first order in which the transformation C has a basis of eigenvectors in $\mathcal{C}^n$. It should be reasonably clear that the procedure in §3 of Chapter 9 can be similarly extended. However, the reader may recall that we gave one example, (2.14c) of Chapter 9, in which there was only one eigenvector for a transformation on $\mathcal{R}^2$, hence certainly not a basis. The introduction of complex spaces does not help here; the transformation has only one eigenvector, even on $\mathcal{C}^2$. Thus some equations still escape our methods. The general procedure for handling equations in which C does not have a basis of eigenvectors, even on $\mathcal{C}^n$, is quite complicated. We shall simply give a hint of it in the problems by studying a procedure for (2.14c) of Chapter 9.

We close this section with the remark that theorem (4.13) of Chapter 8, the eigenvalue criterion, remains true even in complex vector spaces. We restate this result here. Observe that, once again, it is of great importance for the success of the methods of this chapter.

(3.19) Theorem. *Let $T: \mathcal{C}^n \to \mathcal{C}^n$ be a linear transformation. If T has n distinct eigenvalues $a_1, \ldots, a_n$ and $\gamma_1, \ldots, \gamma_n$ form an associated set of eigenvectors, then $\gamma_1, \ldots, \gamma_n$ forms a basis for $\mathcal{C}^n$.*

PROBLEMS

1. Find solutions of the following problems.

(a) $\dot{y}_1(t) - y_2(t) = 0, \ \ y_1(0) = 0$
$\dot{y}_2(t) + y_1(t) = 0, \ \ y_2(0) = 1$

(b) $\dot{y}_1(t) - y_2(t) = e^t, \ \ y_1(0) = 0$
$\dot{y}_2(t) + y_1(t) = 0, \ \ y_2(0) = 0$

(c) $\dot{y}_1(t) + y_1(t) + y_2(t) = 0, \ y_1(1) = 0$
$\dot{y}_2(t) - 2y_1(t) + y_2(t) = 0, \ y_2(1) = 1$

(d) $\dot{y}_1(t) + y_1(t) + y_2(t) = t, \ y_1(0) = 1$
$\dot{y}_2(t) - 2y_1(t) + y_2(t) = 0, \ y_2(0) = 1$

(e) $\dot{y}_1(t) - 3y_1(t) - 4y_2(t) = 0, \ y_1(0) = 1$
$\dot{y}_1(t) + 2y_1(t) + y_1(t) = 0, \ y_2(0) = 1$

(f) $\dot{y}_1(t) - 3y_1(t) - 4y_2(t) = \sin t, \ y_1(0) = 0$
$\dot{y}_2(t) + 2y_1(t) + y_1(t) = \cos t, \ y_2(0) = 0$

(g) $\dot{y}_1(t) - y_2(t) = 1, \qquad y_1(0) = 1$
$\dot{y}_2(t) + y_1(t) = t, \qquad y_2(0) = 0$
$\dot{y}_3(t) + y_3(t) + 3y_4(t) = -1, \qquad y_3(0) = -1$
$\dot{y}_4(t) + 2y_3(t) + 2y_2(t) = 0, \qquad y_4(0) = 0$ [See example (3.18b).]

2. Prove proposition (3.10).

3. Prove theorem (3.17) in the special case where $\mathbf{w}(t) \equiv \mathbf{0}$. Write out the solution as given by (3.15) and (3.7) and verify that the imaginary parts are zero.

***4.** STABILITY. Consider definition (2.20) of Chapter 9, for stability of a system of equations of the form

$$(*) \qquad \dot{\mathbf{y}}(t) + C\mathbf{y}(t) = \mathbf{0}.$$

Prove that if assumption (3.5) is valid, then equation (*) is stable if and only if all the eigenvalues of C have *negative* real parts. Show that it is unstable if some eigenvalue has a positive real part.

***5.** Here we give a procedure for obtaining particular solutions of (3.1) when $\mathbf{w}(t)$ is a trigonometric function.

(a) Consider a system of differential equations of the form

$$\dot{\mathbf{y}}(t) + C\mathbf{y}(t) = \boldsymbol{\rho}(t) + i\boldsymbol{\sigma}(t),$$

where $\boldsymbol{\rho}$ and $\boldsymbol{\sigma}$ are functions of t with values in $\mathcal{R}^n$. Here C is a transformation from $\mathcal{R}^n$ into $\mathcal{R}^n$ so its matrix has real entries. Show that if $\mathbf{y}(t) = \mathbf{r}(t) + i\mathbf{s}(t)$ is a solution, then $\mathbf{r}$ and $\mathbf{s}$ satisfy

$$\dot{\mathbf{r}}(t) + C\mathbf{r}(t) = \boldsymbol{\rho}(t), \qquad \dot{\mathbf{s}}(t) + C\mathbf{s}(t) = \boldsymbol{\sigma}(t).$$

(b) Show that there exists a complex solution of the equation

$$\dot{\mathbf{y}}(t) + C\mathbf{y}(t) = \boldsymbol{\alpha}e^{i\omega t}, \qquad \omega \text{ real},$$

of the form

$$\mathbf{y}(t) = \boldsymbol{\beta}e^{i\omega t}, \qquad \boldsymbol{\beta} \text{ complex},$$

whenever $i\omega$ is not an eigenvalue of C.

(c) From parts (a) and (b) show how to obtain *real* solutions of the equations

$$\dot{\mathbf{y}}(t) + C\mathbf{y}(t) = \boldsymbol{\alpha}\cos\omega t, \qquad \dot{\mathbf{y}}(t) + C\mathbf{y}(t) = \boldsymbol{\alpha}\sin\omega t, \qquad \boldsymbol{\alpha} \in \mathcal{R}^n.$$

6. Consider the system in example (2.14c) of Chapter 9; that is,

$$\dot{y}_1(t) - y_1(t) + y_2(t) = 0$$
$$\dot{y}_2(t) - y_1(t) - 3y_2(t) = 0.$$

Show that γe^{2t} is a solution if γ is an eigenvector for

$$C = \begin{pmatrix} -1 & 1 \\ -1 & -3 \end{pmatrix}$$

Find a vector $\boldsymbol{\delta}$ such that

$$\gamma t e^{2t} + \boldsymbol{\delta} e^{2t}$$

is a second solution.

7. Use the results of example (3.18b) to find a solution of the problem

$$\begin{aligned}
&\dot{y}_1(t) - y_2(t) && = 1 && y_1(0) = 1 \\
&\dot{y}_2(t) + y_1(t) && = t && y_2(0) = 0 \\
&\dot{y}_3(t) \qquad + y_3(t) + y_4(t) && = 0 && y_3(0) = 1 \\
&\dot{y}_4(t) \qquad + 2y_3(t) + 2y_2(t) && = -1, && y_4(0) = 0
\end{aligned}$$

***8.** Show how the methods of this section can be extended to solve the system of *second-order* equations

$$\begin{aligned}
\ddot{y}_1(t) + y_2(t) &= 1, \qquad y_1(0) = 1, \qquad \dot{y}_1(0) = 0 \\
\ddot{y}_2(t) - y_1(t) &= t, \qquad y_2(0) = 0, \qquad \dot{y}_2(0) = 1.
\end{aligned}$$

[*Hint:* Show that the single equation

$$\ddot{y}(t) + zy(t) = 0, \qquad z \text{ complex}$$

has solutions $e^{\sqrt{z}t}$ and $e^{-\sqrt{z}t}$, where $\sqrt{z}$ is defined in problem 4 of §1 and the exponentials are defined as in example (1.9c).]

11

Scalar and Vector Fields

1. Coordinatization of Fields; α-Derivatives and Gradients of Scalar Fields

Consider some physical substance filling a region $\mathfrak{D}$ of space, for instance a volume of fluid occupying a cylindrical container (Figure 11.1). At a given instant of time $t = t_0$, a definite portion of the fluid is located at each point P in the region $\mathfrak{D}$. Thus one way to keep track of properties such as

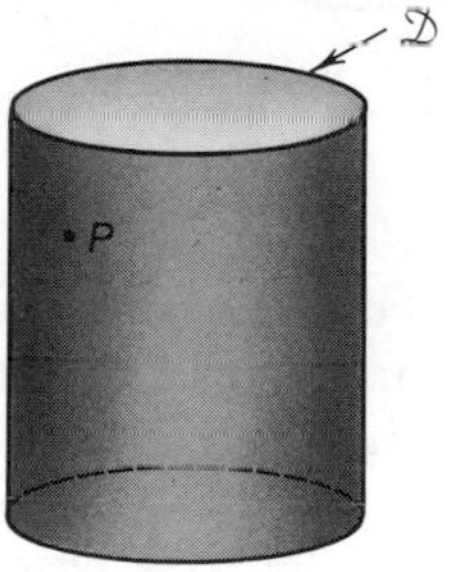

Figure 11.1

the temperature, density, and velocity of the various parts of the fluid at time t_0 is to record, for each point P in $\mathfrak{D}$, the temperature, density, and velocity of the portion of fluid which happens to be located at P. For instance, we can keep track of the distribution of temperature by simply recording for each point P in $\mathfrak{D}$ the temperature $T(P)$ of the particular mass of fluid which at time t_0 is located at P. That is, the *distribution* of temperature can be recorded by specifying the *function* which assigns the scalar $T(P)$ to each point P. Likewise the distributions of density and of velocity can be recorded by specifying appropriate functions. This leads us to make an important definition.

(1.1) Definition. Any transformation ("function") $f\colon \mathfrak{D} \to \mathcal{W}$ whose domain is a region $\mathfrak{D}$ in space and whose values are in a vector space $\mathcal{W}$, is called a **field.** If the transformation is scalar-valued, that is, $\mathcal{W} = (-\infty, \infty)$, then it is called a *scalar field*. If the transformation is arrow-valued, that is, $\mathcal{W} = \mathcal{A}$, the vector space of arrows, then it is called a *vector field.*

Note that in giving the above definition we have overstepped our standard meaning for the term "transformation" [(1.1) of Chapter 8], since the three-dimensional region $\mathfrak{D}$ is no longer a vector space.† We shall deal occasionally with transformations of this new type whose domain consists of a *two-dimensional* region $\mathfrak{D}$ (Figure 11.2). Such transformations are *also* called "fields." They are important mainly because there are idealized physical situations in which the properties of a fluid or other substance can be regarded as depending only on two dimensions.

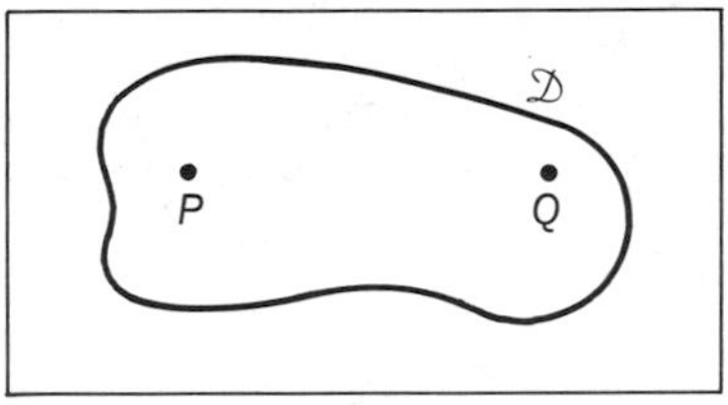

Figure 11.2

In Chapter 3 we discovered that there are many physical situations whose description is facilitated by introducing coordinates. The coordinate method which we developed there assigns coordinates to all points of space and to all vectors in $\mathcal{A}$. This method is as follows. Select a point O as origin and select three mutually perpendicular axes passing through O, calling these axes Ox^1, Ox^2, Ox^3 (Figure 11.3). Then assign to each *point* P the three numbers (x^1, x^2, x^3) obtained by projecting P on the axes Ox^1, Ox^2, Ox^3; assign to each *arrow* $\boldsymbol{\alpha}$ its coordinates $[\boldsymbol{\alpha}]_E$ relative to the basis E consisting of the unit vectors $\mathbf{e}_1$, $\mathbf{e}_2$, $\mathbf{e}_3$ along Ox^1, Ox^2, Ox^3.

†We continue to use the symbol $\mathfrak{D}$ in the present context because of an *analogy* to the situation of transformations on a vector space.

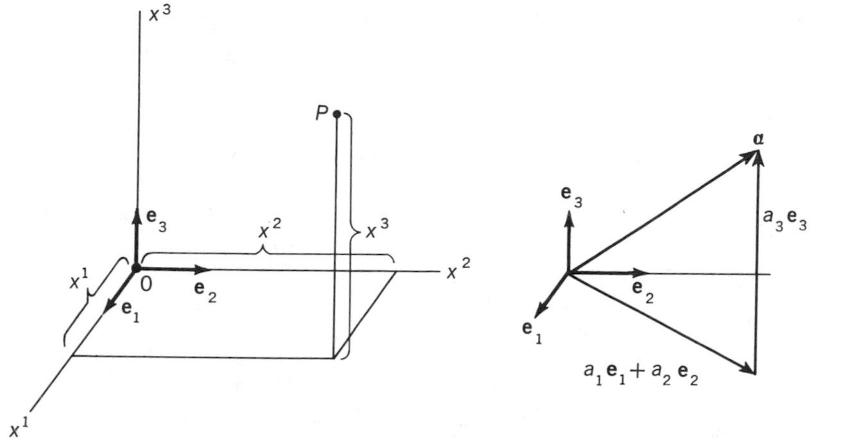

Figure 11.3

Using this scheme we can coordinatize scalar and vector fields. That is, we can reexpress them as functions of the coordinates (x^1, x^2, x^3) of points in $\mathfrak{D}$. [For convenience we shall hereafter abbreviate statements of the form "P is the point with coordinates (c_1, c_2, c_3)" by $P \sim (c_1, c_2, c_3)$.]

(1.2) Examples. Scalar and Vector Fields (Coordinatization)

(a) Let $\mathfrak{D}$ denote the sphere of radius R centered at a point P_0 and let the scalar field f: $\mathfrak{D} \to (-\infty, \infty)$ be defined as follows:

$$\text{(i)} \qquad f(P) = k\|\overrightarrow{P_0P}\|^2 \qquad k \text{ a constant,} \qquad \|\overrightarrow{P_0P}\| < R.$$

That is, the value of f at P is k times the square of the distance from P to P_0 (Figure 11.4).

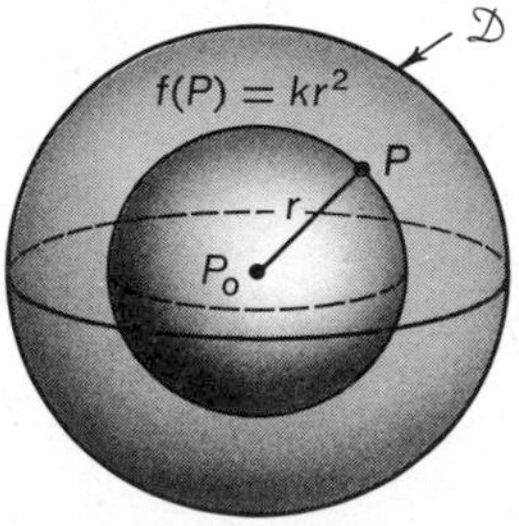

Figure 11.4

To express this field in terms of coordinates let us take the origin of our coordinate system to be $O = P_0$ and introduce three mutually perpendicular axes Ox^1, Ox^2, Ox^3 (Figure 11.5). If (x^1, x^2, x^3) denote the coordinates of P in this coordinate system, then

$$\|\overrightarrow{P_0P}\|^2 = (x^1)^2 + (x^2)^2 + (x^3)^2.$$

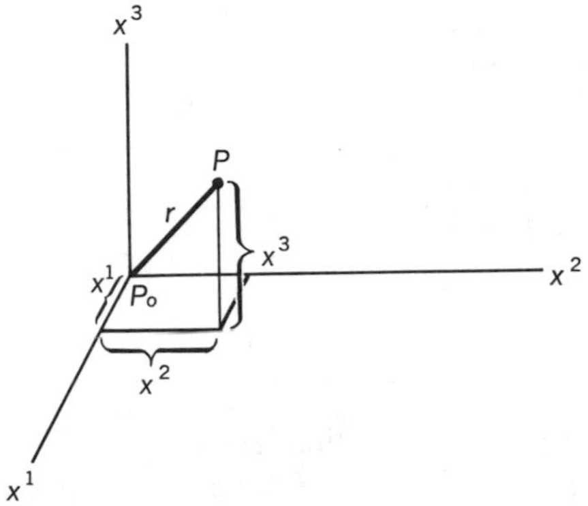

Figure 11.5

Thus the field f corresponds to the following function $\tilde{f}$ of the coordinates (x^1, x^2, x^3),

$$\text{(ii)} \qquad \tilde{f}(x^1, x^2, x^3) = k[(x^1)^2 + (x^2)^2 + (x^3)^2].$$

(b) Let P_0 be a given point and take $\mathfrak{D}$ to be all of space, excluding P_0. Then we can define a vector field $\mathbf{F}\colon \mathfrak{D} \to \mathfrak{A}$ as follows (see Figure 11.6):

$$\text{(i)} \qquad \mathbf{F}(P) = \frac{k}{\|\overrightarrow{P_0P}\|^2}(\overrightarrow{P_0P}), \qquad k \text{ a scalar.}$$

The reason for excluding P_0 from $\mathfrak{D}$ is clear: Formula (i) leaves $\mathbf{F}(P_0)$ undefined.

The vector field $\mathbf{F}$ can be expressed in terms of coordinates as follows. Let us take $O = P_0$ and Ox^1, Ox^2, Ox^3 as in (a). Then if (x^1, x^2, x^3) are the coordinates of P in this coordinate system it follows that (Figure 11.5)

$$\|\overrightarrow{P_0P}\|^2 = (x^1)^2 + (x^2)^2 + (x^3)^2, \qquad \overrightarrow{P_0P} = x^1\mathbf{e}_1 + x^2\mathbf{e}_2 + x^3\mathbf{e}_3.$$

Therefore, the field $\mathbf{F}$ corresponds to the following vector function $\tilde{\mathbf{F}}$ of the quantities (x^1, x^2, x^3):

$$\text{(ii)} \qquad \tilde{\mathbf{F}}(x^1, x^2, x^3) = \frac{k}{(x^1)^2 + (x^2)^2 + (x^3)^2}(x^1\mathbf{e}_1 + x^2\mathbf{e}_2 + x^3\mathbf{e}_3).$$

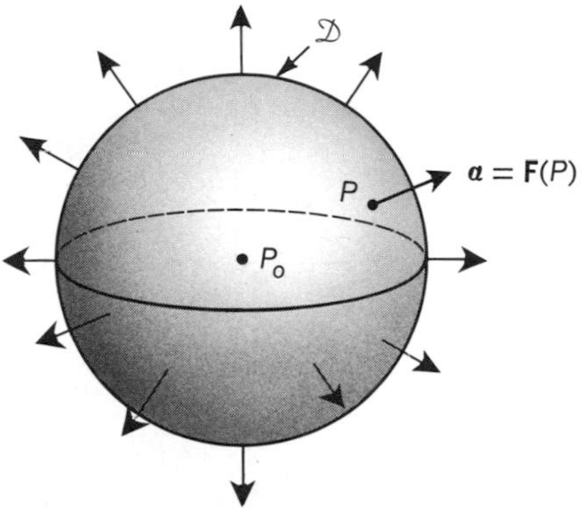

Figure 11.6

The above examples illustrate the fact that all scalar and vector fields can be described by means of one or more scalar-valued functions of several variables. Conversely, functions of several variables can be used to prescribe scalar and vector fields.

In order to study scalar and vector fields we want to use the methods of Calculus; that is, we want to integrate and differentiate. However, since fields are in essence functions of two or three variables rather than one variable, it requires a little thought even to decide what this means. For example, consider the two-dimensional scalar field f, with $\mathfrak{D}$ = the entire plane, such that (Figure 11.7)

$$f(P) = \|\overrightarrow{P_0P}\|^2. \tag{1.3}$$

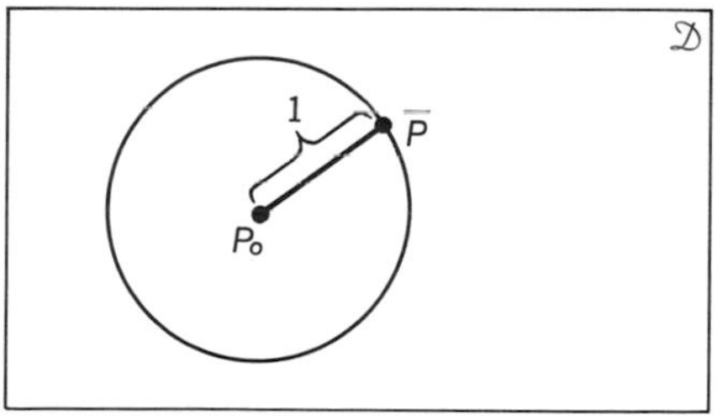

Figure 11.7

The corresponding function $\tilde{f}$ for the coordinate system in Figure 11.8 is then

$$\tilde{f}(x^1, x^2) = (x^1)^2 + (x^2)^2. \tag{1.4}$$

Clearly the *value* of f at point $\overline{P}$ indicated in Figure 11.7 is $f(\overline{P}) = 1$. However, what is to be meant by the "rate of change" of f at $\overline{P}$? Obviously f

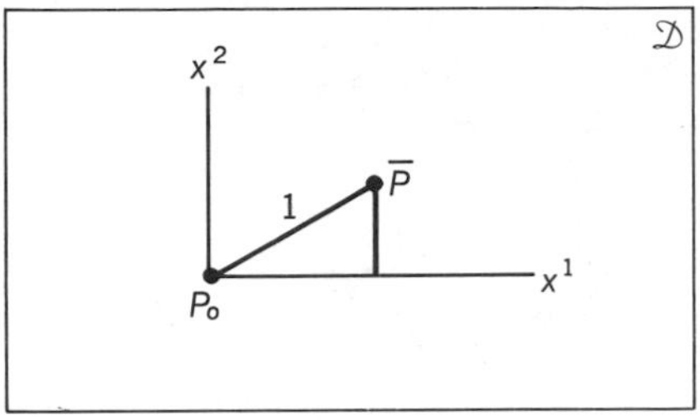

Figure 11.8

increases as one moves away from $\overline{P}$ in any direction which increases the distance from P_0 and *decreases* as one moves in any direction which decreases the distance from P_0, but its precise rate of increase or decrease varies with the choice of direction. Thus it appears that we must somehow keep track of as many derivatives for f as there are directions of departure from $\overline{P}$. This leads to the following definition. [For convenience we hereafter use the notation $Q = P + s\boldsymbol{\alpha}$ to denote the point Q which satisfies $\overrightarrow{PQ} = s\boldsymbol{\alpha}$.]

(1.5) Definition. Given a scalar field f with domain $\mathfrak{D}$ and a point $\overline{P} \in \mathfrak{D}$, we associate to every vector $\boldsymbol{\alpha} \in \mathfrak{A}$ a scalar $\delta f(\overline{P}; \boldsymbol{\alpha})$ called the **$\boldsymbol{\alpha}$-derivative** of f at $\overline{P}$. The quantity $\delta f(\overline{P}; \boldsymbol{\alpha})$ denotes the limit

$$\text{(a)} \qquad \delta f(\overline{P}; \boldsymbol{\alpha}) = \lim_{s \to 0} \frac{f(\overline{P} + s\boldsymbol{\alpha}) - f(\overline{P})}{s} = \frac{d}{ds} f(\overline{P} + s\boldsymbol{\alpha})\bigg|_{s=0}.$$

It therefore represents a rate of change of f as one departs from $\overline{P}$ in the direction of $\boldsymbol{\alpha}$ (Figure 11.9).

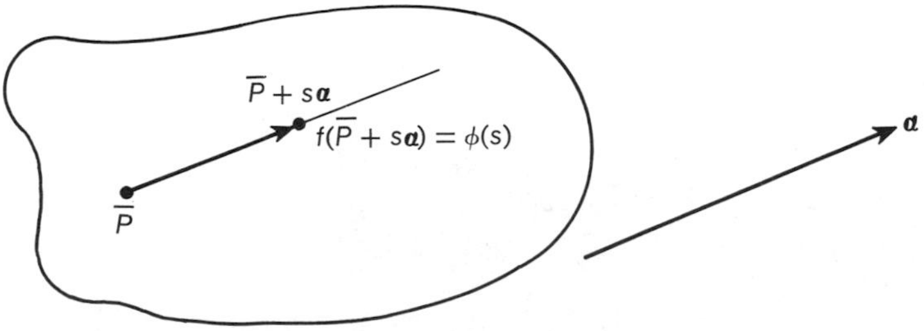

Figure 11.9

[The $\boldsymbol{\alpha}$-derivative of f can be computed by noting that for $\overline{P}$ and $\boldsymbol{\alpha}$ fixed the function

$$f(\overline{P} + s\boldsymbol{\alpha}) = \varphi(s)$$

reduces to a function of the one variable s. The limit in (1.5a) is then given by

$$\text{(b)} \qquad \delta f(\overline{P}; \boldsymbol{\alpha}) = \lim_{s\to 0} \frac{\varphi(s) - \varphi(0)}{s} = \dot{\varphi}(0).]$$

Note that when $\boldsymbol{\alpha}$ is a *unit vector*, then for $s > 0$ the denominator s in (1.5a) represents the distance from $\overline{P}$ to $\overline{P} + s\boldsymbol{\alpha}$, $s = \|\overrightarrow{\overline{P}(\overline{P} + s\boldsymbol{\alpha})}\|$, and hence

$$\begin{aligned} \delta f(\overline{P}; \boldsymbol{\alpha}) &= \lim_{s\to 0} \frac{f(\overline{P} + s\boldsymbol{\alpha}) - f(\overline{P})}{s} \\ &= \lim_{s\to 0} \frac{f(\overline{P} + s\boldsymbol{\alpha}) - f(\overline{P})}{\|\overrightarrow{\overline{P}(\overline{P} + s\boldsymbol{\alpha})}\|} \qquad \text{if } \|\boldsymbol{\alpha}\| = 1. \end{aligned} \tag{1.6}$$

In such cases $\delta f(\overline{P}; \boldsymbol{\alpha})$ denotes what is often called the *directional derivative* of f in the direction $\boldsymbol{\alpha}$. In general, however, $\delta f(\overline{P}; \boldsymbol{\alpha})$ represents $\|\boldsymbol{\alpha}\|$ times the directional derivative of f in the direction of $\boldsymbol{\alpha}$:

$$\text{(1.7)} \qquad \delta f(\overline{P}; \boldsymbol{\alpha}) = \|\boldsymbol{\alpha}\| \frac{df}{d\sigma} \qquad \text{where } \frac{df}{d\sigma} \text{ is the } \textit{directional derivative}.$$

(1.8) Examples. α-Derivatives

(a) Let us compute $\delta f(\overline{P}; \boldsymbol{\alpha})$ for the scalar field $f(P) = k\|\overrightarrow{P_0P}\|^2$ specified in (1.2a), where $\overline{P}$ is at unit distance from P_0. First take for $\boldsymbol{\alpha}$ a vector $\boldsymbol{\alpha}^*$ parallel to $\overrightarrow{P_0\overline{P}}$ (Figure 11.10). Now $\|\overrightarrow{P_0\overline{P}}\| = 1$. Thus it is evident that for the point $\overline{P} + s\boldsymbol{\alpha}^*$ ($s > 0$) one has

$$\begin{aligned} \|\overrightarrow{P_0(\overline{P} + s\boldsymbol{\alpha}^*)}\| &= \|\overrightarrow{P_0\overline{P}}\| + \|s\boldsymbol{\alpha}^*\| \\ &= 1 + s\|\boldsymbol{\alpha}^*\|. \end{aligned}$$

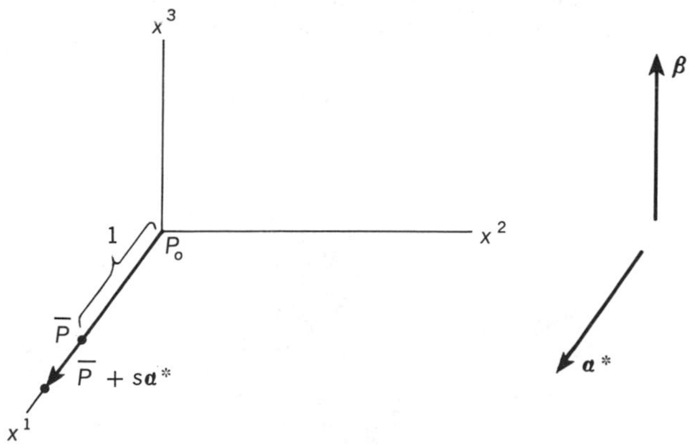

Figure 11.10

Hence

$$f(\overline{P} + s\boldsymbol{\alpha}^*) = k(1 + s\|\boldsymbol{\alpha}^*\|)^2 = \varphi(s).$$

Differentiating we obtain $\dot{\varphi}(s) = 2k(1 + s\|\boldsymbol{\alpha}^*\|)\|\boldsymbol{\alpha}^*\|$, so, by (1.5b),

$$\delta f(\overline{P}; \boldsymbol{\alpha}^*) = \dot{\varphi}(0) = 2k\|\boldsymbol{\alpha}^*\|.$$

Now let us compute $\delta f(\overline{P}; \boldsymbol{\alpha})$ with $\boldsymbol{\alpha}$ an arbitrarily selected arrow. Here we shall make use of the coordinate formula which we derived for f in (1.2a) (using the coordinate system indicated above):

$$\tilde{f}(x^1, x^2, x^3) = k[(x^1)^2 + (x^2)^2 + (x^3)^2].$$

Observe that the coordinates of $\overline{P}$ in this coordinate system are (1, 0, 0) (Figure 11.10). Hence if

$$\text{(i)} \qquad \boldsymbol{\alpha} = a_1\mathbf{e}_1 + a_2\mathbf{e}_2 + a_3\mathbf{e}_3,$$

then the coordinates of the point $P = \overline{P} + s\boldsymbol{\alpha}$ are given by

$$(x^1, x^2, x^3) = (1 + sa_1, sa_2, sa_3).$$

Therefore,

$$\begin{aligned}\varphi(s) &= f(\overline{P} + s\boldsymbol{\alpha}) = \tilde{f}(1 + sa_1, sa_2, sa_3) \\ &= k[(1 + sa_1)^2 + (sa_2)^2 + (sa_3)^2].\end{aligned}$$

Then, by (1.5b),

$$\text{(ii)} \qquad \delta f(\overline{P}; \boldsymbol{\alpha}) = \dot{\varphi}(0) = 2ka_1.$$

The above formula permits us to compute *all* $\boldsymbol{\alpha}$-derivatives of f at $\overline{P}$. For instance, take for $\boldsymbol{\alpha}$ a vector $\boldsymbol{\beta}$ which is vertical (Figure 11.10). Obviously

$$\boldsymbol{\beta} = 0\mathbf{e}_1 + 0\mathbf{e}_2 + b_3\mathbf{e}_3.$$

Hence we deduce from (ii) that for all such vectors,

$$\delta f(\overline{P}; \boldsymbol{\beta}) = 0.$$

(b) Let us compute $\delta f(\overline{P}; \boldsymbol{\alpha})$ for the field $f(P) = 2\|\overrightarrow{P_0P}\|^2 - \|\overrightarrow{P_1P}\|^2$ and the point $\overline{P}$ indicated in Figure 11.11. With the coordinate system shown we have

$$\begin{aligned}\|\overrightarrow{P_0P}\|^2 &= (x^1)^2 + (x^2)^2 + (x^3)^3 \\ \|\overrightarrow{P_1P}\|^2 &= (x^1 - 4)^2 + (x^2)^2 + (x^3)^2.\end{aligned}$$

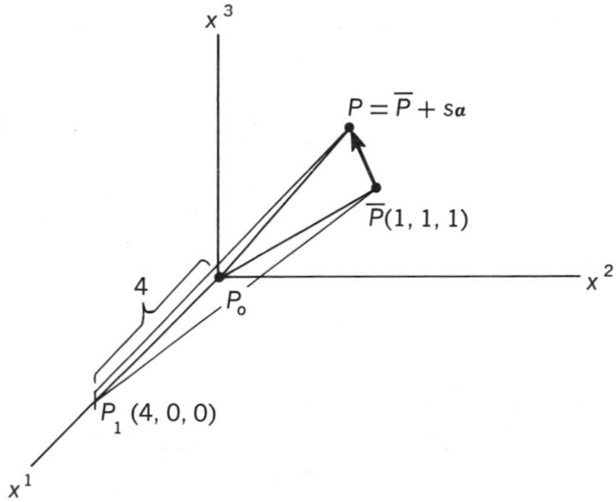

Figure 11.11

Hence the coordinatized form of f is the function

$$\text{(i)}\quad \tilde{f}(x^1, x^2, x^3) = 2[(x^1)^2 + (x^2)^2 + (x^3)^2] - (x^1 - 4)^2 - (x^2)^2 - (x^3)^2 = (x^1)^2 + (x^2)^2 + (x^3)^2 + 8x^1 - 16.$$

Moreover, $\overline{P}$ has the coordinates (1, 1, 1), so that for

$$\boldsymbol{\alpha} = a_1\mathbf{e}_1 + a_2\mathbf{e}_2 + a_3\mathbf{e}_3,$$

$\overline{P} + a\boldsymbol{\alpha}$ has the coordinates $(1 + sa_1, 1 + sa_2, 1 + sa_3)$. Thus $f(\overline{P} + s\boldsymbol{\alpha})$ is given by (i) as

$$f(\overline{P} + s\boldsymbol{\alpha}) = \tilde{f}(1 + sa_1, 1 + sa_2, 1 + sa_3) = (1 + sa_1)^2 + (1 + sa_2)^2 + (1 + sa_3)^2 + 8(1 + sa_1) - 16 = \varphi(s).$$

Applying (1.5b) we find

$$\text{(ii)}\quad \delta f(\overline{P}; \boldsymbol{\alpha}) = \dot{\varphi}(0) = [2(1 + sa_1)a_1 + 2(1 + sa_2)a_2 + 2(1 + sa_3)a_3 + 8a_1]|_{s=0} = 10a_1 + 2a_2 + 2a_3 \qquad \text{for all } \boldsymbol{\alpha} \in \mathcal{A}.$$

The preceding examples illustrate the fact that ordinarily the quantity $\delta f(\overline{P}; \boldsymbol{\alpha})$, with $\overline{P}$ fixed, is defined for *all* $\boldsymbol{\alpha} \in \mathcal{A}$. In such cases $\boldsymbol{\alpha}$-differentiation can be regarded as a *transformation* taking $\mathcal{D} = \mathcal{A}$ to $\mathcal{W} = (-\infty, \infty)$. Let us study closely the formulas for $\delta f(\overline{P}; \boldsymbol{\alpha})$ obtained in our examples. In (1.8a) we found, for $f(P) = k\|\overrightarrow{P - P_0}\|^2$ and $\overline{P} \sim (1, 0, 0)$, that

$$(1.9) \qquad \delta f(\overline{P}; \boldsymbol{\alpha}) = 2ka_1 \qquad \text{for } \boldsymbol{\alpha} = a_1\mathbf{e}_1 + a_2\mathbf{e}_2 + a_3\mathbf{e}_3.$$

Likewise in (1.8b) we found, for $f(P) = 2\|\overrightarrow{P_0P}\|^2 - \|\overrightarrow{P_1P}\|^2$ and $\overline{P} \sim (1, 1, 1)$, that

$$(1.10) \qquad \delta f(\overline{P}; \boldsymbol{\alpha}) = 10a_1 + 2a_2 + 2a_3 \qquad \text{for } \boldsymbol{\alpha} = a_1\mathbf{e}_1 + a_2\mathbf{e}_2 + a_3\mathbf{e}_3.$$

Now these formulas both have the following feature. They can be expressed by means of the inner product of $\boldsymbol{\alpha}$ with a fixed vector:

$$(1.9') \qquad \delta f(\overline{P}; \boldsymbol{\alpha}) = 2ka_1 = \boldsymbol{\gamma} \cdot \boldsymbol{\alpha} \qquad \text{where } \boldsymbol{\gamma} = 2k\mathbf{e}_1 + 0\mathbf{e}_2 + 0\mathbf{e}_3$$

and

(1.10′)

$$\delta f(\overline{P}; \boldsymbol{\alpha}) = 10a_1 + 2a_2 + 2a_3 = \boldsymbol{\gamma} \cdot \boldsymbol{\alpha} \qquad \text{where } \boldsymbol{\gamma} = 10\mathbf{e}_1 + 2\mathbf{e}_2 + 2\mathbf{e}_3.$$

This is a general phenomenon. In fact, we can state the following result.

(1.11) Theorem. *For every scalar field $f\colon \mathfrak{D} \to (-\infty, \infty)$ whose coordinate form $\tilde{f}$ has continuous first partial derivatives, the $\boldsymbol{\alpha}$-derivative $\delta f(P; \boldsymbol{\alpha})$ exists for each P in $\mathfrak{D}$ and each $\boldsymbol{\alpha} \in \mathcal{A}$. Moreover, for P fixed the quantity $\delta f(P; \boldsymbol{\alpha})$ can be expressed by means of the inner product of $\boldsymbol{\alpha}$ with a fixed arrow:*

$$\text{(a)} \qquad \delta f(P; \boldsymbol{\alpha}) = \boldsymbol{\gamma}_P \cdot \boldsymbol{\alpha} \qquad \textit{for } \boldsymbol{\alpha} \in \mathcal{A}.$$

We shall omit the proof of this theorem.† Note, however, that it has the following consequence. With P fixed, $\boldsymbol{\alpha}$-differentiation defines a *linear transformation* taking $\mathcal{A}$ to $(-\infty, \infty)$. That is, the transformation l_P which is determined by

$$\text{(b)} \qquad l_P(\boldsymbol{\alpha}) = \delta f(P; \boldsymbol{\alpha}) = \boldsymbol{\gamma}_P \cdot \boldsymbol{\alpha} \qquad \text{for } \boldsymbol{\alpha} \in \mathcal{A},$$

satisfies the linearity identity

$$\text{(L)} \qquad l_P(c\boldsymbol{\alpha} + d\boldsymbol{\beta}) = c\, l_P(\boldsymbol{\alpha}) + d\, l_P(\boldsymbol{\beta}).$$

---

†See G. B. Thomas, *Calculus and Analytic Geometry*, 3rd ed., Addison-Wesley, Reading, Mass., 1962.

This idea will reoccur in §2.

The arrow γ_P occurring in (1.11a) is rather important in the analysis of a scalar field f. Hence it is given a name.

(1.12) Definition. If the scalar field f: $\mathfrak{D} \to (-\infty, \infty)$ satisfies the conditions of theorem (1.11) then for each $P \in \mathfrak{D}$ the vector γ_P, which is uniquely determined by (1.11a), is called the **gradient** of f at P. It is denoted by

$$\text{(a)} \qquad \gamma_P = \nabla f(P) \qquad [\text{or } \gamma_P = \text{grad } f(P)].$$

[Thus (1.11a) can be written in the form

$$\text{(b)} \qquad \delta f(P; \boldsymbol{\alpha}) = \nabla f(P) \cdot \boldsymbol{\alpha} \qquad \text{for } \boldsymbol{\alpha} \in \mathfrak{A},\ P \in \mathfrak{D}.]$$

Since the gradient of a scalar field is at each point P in $\mathfrak{D}$ an arrow $\nabla f(P) \in \mathfrak{A}$, the gradient provides a transformation $\mathbf{F}$ from $\mathfrak{D}$ to $\mathfrak{A}$: $\mathbf{F}(P) = \nabla f(P)$. That is, the gradient of a *scalar* field f yields a *vector* field $\mathbf{F}$. This vector field is simply called the **gradient of** f and is denoted by

$$\text{(c)} \qquad \mathbf{F} = \nabla f \qquad (\text{or } \mathbf{F} = \text{grad } f).$$

(1.13) Examples. Gradient

(a) Let us compute $\boldsymbol{\alpha}$-derivatives for the scalar field $f(P) = k\|\overrightarrow{P_0P}\|^2$ of example (1.8a), this time at *all* points $P \in \mathfrak{D}$. With the coordinate system used earlier, we found that f has the coordinate form

$$\text{(i)} \qquad \bar{f}(x^1, x^2, x^3) = k[(x^1)^2 + (x^2)^2 + (x^3)^2].$$

Taking first the special case $P \sim (1, 1, 1)$, we obtain

$$\begin{aligned} f(P + s\boldsymbol{\alpha}) &= \bar{f}(1 + sa_1, 1 + sa_2, 1 + sa_3) \\ &= k[(1 + sa_1)^2 + (1 + sa_2)^2 + (1 + sa_3)^2] = \varphi(s). \end{aligned}$$

Hence we deduce by (1.5b) that

$$\begin{aligned} \delta f(P; \boldsymbol{\alpha}) = \dot{\varphi}(0) = 2ka_1 + 2ka_2 + 2ka_3 &= (2k\mathbf{e}_1 + 2k\mathbf{e}_2 + 2k\mathbf{e}_3) \cdot \boldsymbol{\alpha} \\ \text{for } \boldsymbol{\alpha} = a_1\mathbf{e}_1 + a_2\mathbf{e}_2 + a_3\mathbf{e}_3, &\qquad P \sim (1, 1, 1). \end{aligned}$$

In general, taking $P \sim (x^1, x^2, x^3)$ we obtain

$$\begin{aligned} f(P + s\boldsymbol{\alpha}) &= k[(x^1 + sa_1)^2 + (x^2 + sa_2)^2 + (x^3 + sa_3)^2] \\ &= \varphi(s), \end{aligned}$$

and therefore, by (1.5b),

$$\text{(ii)} \qquad \begin{aligned} \delta f(P; \alpha) = \dot{\varphi}(0) &= 2kx^1a_1 + 2kx^2a_2 + 2kx^3a_3 \\ &= (2kx^1\mathbf{e}_1 + 2kx^2\mathbf{e}_2 + 2kx^3\mathbf{e}_3) \cdot \boldsymbol{\alpha} \\ &\text{for } \boldsymbol{\alpha} = a_1\mathbf{e}_1 + a_2\mathbf{e}_2 + a_3\mathbf{e}_3, \qquad P \sim (x^1, x^2, x^3). \end{aligned}$$

Since (ii) can be written in the form

$$\text{(iii)} \qquad \delta f(P; \boldsymbol{\alpha}) = \boldsymbol{\gamma}_P \cdot \boldsymbol{\alpha} \qquad \boldsymbol{\alpha} \in \mathcal{A}, \qquad P \sim (x^1, x^2, x^3)$$

(with $\boldsymbol{\gamma}_P = (2kx^1)\mathbf{e}_1 + (2kx^2)\mathbf{e}_2 + (2kx^3)\mathbf{e}_3$), it follows that

$$\text{(iv)} \qquad \nabla f(P) = \boldsymbol{\gamma}_P = (2kx^1)\mathbf{e}_1 + (2kx^2)\mathbf{e}_2 + (2kx^3)\mathbf{e}_3 \qquad \text{for } P \sim (x^1, x^2, x^3).$$

(b) Let us compute the gradient of the scalar field g whose coordinate form is

$$\tilde{g}(x^1, x^2, x^3) = x^1x^2 + x^1x^2x^3.$$

Taking $P \sim (x^1, x^2, x^3)$ we have

$$\begin{aligned} g(P + s\boldsymbol{\alpha}) &= \tilde{g}(x^1 + sa_1, x^2 + sa_2, x^3 + sa_3) \\ &= (x^1 + sa_1)(x^2 + sa_2) + (x^1 + sa_1)(x^2 + sa_2)(x^3 + sa_3) \\ &= \varphi(s). \end{aligned}$$

Therefore,

$$\text{(i)} \qquad \begin{aligned} \delta g(P; \boldsymbol{\alpha}) = \dot{\varphi}(0) &= (x^2 + x^2x^3)a_1 + (x^1 + x^1x^3)a_2 + (x^1x^2)a_3 \\ &= [(x^2 + x^2x^3)\mathbf{e}_1 + (x^1 + x^1x^3)\mathbf{e}_2 + (x^1x^2)\mathbf{e}_3] \cdot \boldsymbol{\alpha} \\ &\text{for } \boldsymbol{\alpha} = a_1\mathbf{e}_1 + a_2\mathbf{e}_2 + a_3\mathbf{e}_3. \end{aligned}$$

Equation (i) shows that

$$\text{(ii)} \qquad \delta g(P; \boldsymbol{\alpha}) = \nabla g(P) \cdot \boldsymbol{\alpha} \qquad \boldsymbol{\alpha} \in \mathcal{A}, \qquad P \sim (x^1, x^2, x^3),$$

with

$$\text{(iii)} \qquad \nabla g(P) = (x^2 + x^2x^3)\mathbf{e}_1 + (x^1 + x^1x^3)\mathbf{e}_2 + (x^1x^2)\mathbf{e}_3.$$

What we wish to do next is develop a more efficient method for calculating the gradient of a prescribed scalar field f. To accomplish this we must examine the relationship between **α**-derivatives of a scalar field f and partial derivatives of its coordinate form $\tilde{f}$. This relationship is given in the following formula:

$$\text{(1.14)}\quad \begin{aligned} &\delta f(P; \mathbf{e}_1) = \tilde{f}_{x^1}(x^1, x^2, x^3), \qquad \delta f(P; \mathbf{e}_2) = \tilde{f}_{x^3}(x^1, x^2, x^3), \\ &\delta f(P; \mathbf{e}_3) = \tilde{f}_{x^3}(x^1, x^2, x^3) \qquad\qquad \text{for } P \sim (x^1, x^2, x^3). \end{aligned}$$

To see why (1.14) is correct, note that, by (1.5),

$$\text{(i)}\qquad \delta f(P; \mathbf{e}_1) = \frac{d}{ds} f(P + s\mathbf{e}_1) = \dot{\varphi}(0),$$

where

$$\varphi(s) = f(P + s\mathbf{e}_1) = \tilde{f}(x^1 + s, x^2, x^3).$$

It follows from the form of φ that differentiation of φ with respect to s is equivalent to calculation of the derivative of $\tilde{f}$ with respect to x^1, considering x^2 and x^3 as constant. Hence by §1 of the Review of Calculus we have

$$\text{(ii)}\qquad \dot{\varphi}(0) = \tilde{f}_{x^1}(x^1, x^2, x^3).$$

Equations (i) and (ii) give the first formula in (1.14), and precisely similar arguments establish the remaining formulas.

Equation (1.14) leads us to the desired method for calculating $\nabla f(P)$.

(1.15) Coordinate Formula for Gradient. *Let* $f\colon \mathfrak{D} \to (-\infty, \infty)$ *be a scalar field with coordinate form* $\tilde{f}$ *relative to some rectangular coordinate system. If* f *satisfies the conditions of theorem* (1.11) *then for every point* $P \sim (x^1, x^2, x^3)$ *in* $\mathfrak{D}$ *the following formula holds:*

$$\text{(a)}\qquad \nabla f(P) = \tilde{f}_{x^1}(x^1, x^2, x^3)\mathbf{e}_1 + \tilde{f}_{x^2}(x^1, x^2, x^3)\mathbf{e}_2 + \tilde{f}_{x^3}(x^1, x^2, x^3)\mathbf{e}_3.$$

Proof. By (1.12b) we have, in particular,

$$\text{(i)}\qquad \begin{aligned} \nabla f(P) \cdot \mathbf{e}_1 &= \delta f(P; \mathbf{e}_1) \\ \nabla f(P) \cdot \mathbf{e}_2 &= \delta f(P; \mathbf{e}_2) \\ \nabla f(P) \cdot \mathbf{e}_3 &= \delta f(P; \mathbf{e}_3), \end{aligned}$$

where $\mathbf{e}_1$, $\mathbf{e}_2$, $\mathbf{e}_3$ are the orthonormal vectors associated with the given rectangular coordinate system. Writing $\nabla f(P)$ in the form

$$\text{(ii)}\qquad \nabla f(P) = b_1\mathbf{e}_1 + b_2\mathbf{e}_2 + b_3\mathbf{e}_3$$

and inserting into (i), we deduce, by orthonormality of the **e**'s, that

$$\text{(iii)} \qquad b_1 = \delta f(P; \mathbf{e}_1), \qquad b_2 = \delta f(P; \mathbf{e}_2), \qquad b_3 = \delta f(P; \mathbf{e}_3).$$

Thus formula (1.14) yields

$$\begin{aligned}\text{(iv)} \qquad \nabla f(P) &= b_1\mathbf{e}_1 + b_2\mathbf{e}_2 + b_3\mathbf{e}_3 \\ &= \tilde{f}_{x^1}(x^1, x^2, x^3)\mathbf{e}_1 + \tilde{f}_{x^2}(x^1, x^2, x^3)\mathbf{e}_2 + \tilde{f}_{x^3}(x^1, x^2, x^3)\mathbf{e}_3.\end{aligned}$$

This, however, is simply equation (a). ▮

We will often abbreviate equation (1.15a) as

$$\text{(1.15b)} \qquad \nabla f = \tilde{f}_{x^1}\mathbf{e}_1 + \tilde{f}_{x^2}\mathbf{e}_2 + \tilde{f}_{x^3}\mathbf{e}_3.$$

(1.16) Examples. Gradient (Continued)

(a) Let us compute the gradient of the scalar field

$$f(P) = 2\|\overrightarrow{P_0P}\|^2 - \|\overrightarrow{P_1P}\|^2$$

occurring in example (1.8b). With the coordinate system taken as in Figure 11.11 we found

$$\tilde{f}(x^1, x^2, x^3) = (x^1)^2 + (x^2)^2 + (x^3)^2 + 8x^1 - 16.$$

This time we will bypass the computation of $\boldsymbol{\alpha}$-derivatives and will instead utilize formula (1.15b). Now it is easily seen that

$$\text{(i)} \qquad \begin{aligned}\tilde{f}_{x^1}(x^1, x^2, x^3) &= 2x^1 + 8 \\ \tilde{f}_{x^2}(x^1, x^2, x^3) &= 2x^2 \\ \tilde{f}_{x^3}(x^1, x^2, x^3) &= 2x^3.\end{aligned}$$

Hence, by (1.15b),

$$\text{(ii)} \qquad \nabla f(P) = (2x^1 + 8)\mathbf{e}_1 + (2x^2)\mathbf{e}_2 + (2x^3)\mathbf{e}_3 \qquad \text{for } P \sim (x^1, x^2, x^3),$$

and our task is completed.

The above example shows that (1.15b) does indeed simplify the calculation of ∇f. A different, so-called "coordinate-free," method for calculating ∇f is sometimes even simpler to apply than (1.15b). This latter method will be discussed in the problems.

There is an interesting point concerning definition (1.5) for $\boldsymbol{\alpha}$-derivatives of a scalar field f. The quantity

$$\delta f(P; \boldsymbol{\alpha}) = \frac{d}{ds} f(P + s\boldsymbol{\alpha})\bigg|_{s=0},$$

as specified in that definition, measures the rate of change of f as one departs from P along a *straight line* (Figure 11.12). This leaves open the question of measuring the rate of change of f as one departs from P along a *curve* (Figure 11.13). Fortunately, such "curve derivatives" introduce nothing new. In fact, we have the following result.

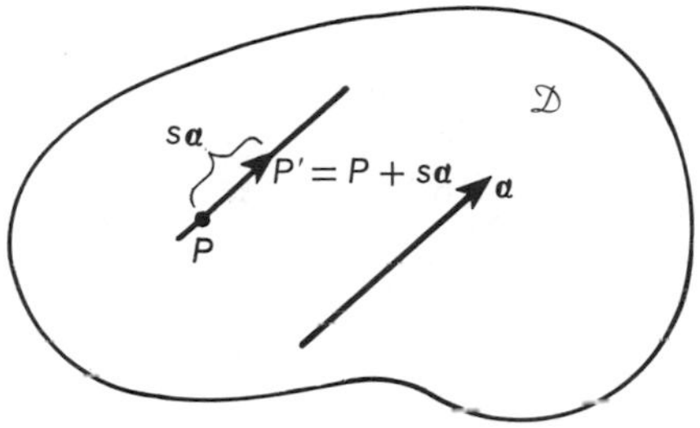

Figure 11.12

(1.17) Theorem (Chain Rule). *Let f: $\mathfrak{D} \to (-\infty, \infty)$ be a scalar field with coordinate form $\tilde{f}$ relative to a prescribed rectangular coordinate system, and let C: $\overrightarrow{OP(t)} = \mathbf{r}(t)$, $t_1 \leq t \leq t_2$, be a curve in $\mathfrak{D}$. If f satisfies the hypotheses of theorem* (11.11) *and if* $\mathbf{r}$ *is a continuously differentiable function of t, then the function φ whose values are obtained by evaluating f on C:*

$$\varphi(t) = f(P(t)) = \tilde{f}(x^1(t), x^2(t), x^3(t)), \qquad t_1 \leq t \leq t_2,$$

is differentiable. In fact, for each t, $\dot{\varphi}(t)$ is given by an $\boldsymbol{\alpha}$-derivative of f at $P(t)$:

$$\text{(a)} \qquad \dot{\varphi}(t) = \frac{d}{dt} f(P(t)) = \delta f(P(t); \dot{\mathbf{r}}(t))$$
$$= \nabla f(P(t)) \cdot \dot{\mathbf{r}}(t), \qquad t_1 < t < t_2.$$

In coordinate form,

$$\text{(b)} \qquad \dot{\varphi}(t) = \frac{d}{dt} \tilde{f}(x^1(t), x^2(t), x^3(t))$$
$$= \tilde{f}_{x^1}(x^1(t), x^2(t), x^3(t))\dot{x}^1(t)$$
$$+ \tilde{f}_{x^2}(x^1(t), x^2(t), x^3(t))\dot{x}^2(t)$$
$$+ \tilde{f}_{x^3}(x^1(t)\ x^2(t), x^3(t))\dot{x}^3(t), \qquad t_1 < t < t_2.$$

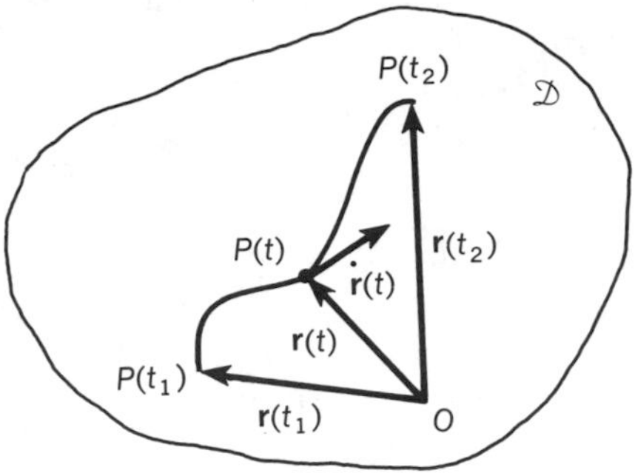

Figure 11.13

The reader is probably already familiar with (1.17b), the coordinate form of this chain rule. We shall omit the *proof* of (1.17a), but we can easily show how this equation leads to (1.17b). According to (1.15),

$$\text{(i)}\qquad \nabla f(P(t)) = \tilde{f}_{x^1}(x^1(t), x^2(t), x^3(t))\mathbf{e}_1 + \tilde{f}_{x^2}(x^1(t), x^2(t), x^3(t))\mathbf{e}_2 + \tilde{f}_{x^3}(x^1(t), x^2(t), x^3(t))\mathbf{e}_3.$$

On the other hand, $\mathbf{r}(t)$ has the form

$$\text{(ii)}\qquad \mathbf{r}(t) = x^1(t)\mathbf{e}_1 + x^2(t)\mathbf{e}_2 + x^3(t)\mathbf{e}_3,$$

which implies by (1.14) of Chapter 2 that

$$\text{(iii)}\qquad \dot{\mathbf{r}}(t) = \dot{x}^1(t)\mathbf{e}_1 + \dot{x}^2(t)\mathbf{e}_2 + \dot{x}^3(t)\mathbf{e}_3.$$

Since the $\mathbf{e}$'s are orthonormal, the inner product $\nabla f(P(t)) \cdot \dot{\mathbf{r}}(t)$ gives precisely the expression on the right side of (1.17b).

PROBLEMS

1. For each of the following scalar fields sketch the locus of points at which $f(P) = \pm 1$. Do the same for $f(P) = \pm 2$, $f(P) = 0$, and $f(P) = -1$.

Three dimensions:

(i) $f(P) = \dfrac{k}{\|\overrightarrow{P_0P}\|^2}$, k a constant, P_0 a prescribed point

(ii) $f(P) = (\overrightarrow{P_0P}) \cdot \gamma$, γ a prescribed arrow, P_0 a prescribed point

(iii) $f(P) = e^{\|\overrightarrow{P_0P}\|^2}$, P_0 a prescribed point.

Two dimensions:

(iv) $f(P) = (\overrightarrow{P_0P}) \cdot (\overrightarrow{P_1P})$, P_0, P_1 prescribed points.

2. Express each of the scalar fields of problem 1 in coordinate form, using a coordinate system with $O = P_0$.

3. Express each of the scalar fields of problem 1 in coordinate form, using a coordinate system whose origin O has the following relation to P_0: $\overrightarrow{OP_0} = \boldsymbol{\beta}$ with $\boldsymbol{\beta}$ a prescribed arrow. [*Hint:* $\|\overrightarrow{P_0P}\|^2 = (\overrightarrow{OP} - \boldsymbol{\beta}) \cdot (\overrightarrow{OP} - \boldsymbol{\beta})$.]

4. Express each of the following vector fields in coordinate form, using a coordinate system with origin at $O = P_0$. Also give a sketch of each field.

Three dimensions:

(i) $\mathbf{F}(P) = \dfrac{k}{\|\overrightarrow{P_0P}\|^2} (\overrightarrow{P_0P})$, k a constant

(ii) $\mathbf{F}(P) = [(\overrightarrow{P_0P}) \cdot \boldsymbol{\gamma}]\boldsymbol{\delta}$, $\boldsymbol{\gamma}$, $\boldsymbol{\delta}$ prescribed arrows.

Two dimensions:

(iii) $\mathbf{F}(P) = [(\overrightarrow{PP}) \cdot \boldsymbol{\gamma}]\boldsymbol{\delta}$, $\boldsymbol{\gamma}$, $\boldsymbol{\delta}$ prescribed arrows

(iv) $\mathbf{F}(P) = [(\overrightarrow{P_0P}) \cdot (\overrightarrow{P_1P})](\overrightarrow{P_0P} + \overrightarrow{P_1P})$, P_0, P_1 prescribed points.

5. Express each of the vector fields of problem 4 in coordinate form, using the coordinate system of problem 3.

6. (a) For each of the scalar fields in problem 1, express $f(P + s\boldsymbol{\alpha}) = \varphi(s)$ as a function of s.

(b) Use part (a) to compute $\delta f(P; \boldsymbol{\alpha})$ for each of these fields.

7. (a) Show that at any point P at which $\boldsymbol{\nabla} f(P)$ exists, the corresponding function l_P is a *linear* function: $l_P(\boldsymbol{\alpha} + \boldsymbol{\beta}) = l_P(\boldsymbol{\alpha}) + l_P(\boldsymbol{\beta})$, $l_P(c\boldsymbol{\alpha}) = c l_P(\boldsymbol{\alpha})$.

(b) Show that for any point P at which the transformation l_P defined by $l_P(\boldsymbol{\alpha}) = \delta f(P; \boldsymbol{\alpha})$ is a *linear* function, $\boldsymbol{\nabla} f(P)$ exists. [*Hint:* Let $l_P(\mathbf{e}_1) = c_1$, $l_P(\mathbf{e}_2) = c_2$, $l_P(\mathbf{e}_3) = c_3$. Then by linearity,

$$l_P(a_1\mathbf{e}_1 + a_2\mathbf{e}_2 + a_3\mathbf{e}_3) = a_1c_1 + a_2c_2 + a_3c_3.$$

Write this as an inner product.]

8. If f and g are scalar fields possessing gradients $\boldsymbol{\nabla} f(P)$, $\boldsymbol{\nabla} g(P)$ at all points P, show that the scalar field h defined by $h(P) = f(P) + g(P)$ also possesses a gradient and that $\boldsymbol{\nabla} h(P) = \boldsymbol{\nabla} f(P) + \boldsymbol{\nabla} g(P)$ for all P. [*Hint:* Compute $\delta h(P; \boldsymbol{\alpha})$.]

9. Calculate the gradient of the field in example (1.8a) directly from definition (1.12) as follows. The field in question is defined by

$$f(P) = k\|\overrightarrow{P_0P}\|^2,$$

where P_0 is a given point. We have then

$$\begin{aligned} f(P + s\boldsymbol{\alpha}) &= k\|\overrightarrow{P_0P} + s\boldsymbol{\alpha}\|^2 = k(\overrightarrow{P_0P} + s\boldsymbol{\alpha}) \cdot (\overrightarrow{P_0P} + s\boldsymbol{\alpha}) \\ &= k\{\|\overrightarrow{P_0P}\|^2 + 2s\boldsymbol{\alpha} \cdot (\overrightarrow{P_0P}) + s^2\|\boldsymbol{\alpha}\|^2\}. \end{aligned}$$

Now calculate the limit in equation (1.5b). Show that this limit can be written as the inner product of some vector $\boldsymbol{\gamma}_P$ with $\boldsymbol{\alpha}$. The vector $\boldsymbol{\gamma}_P$ is then the gradient $\boldsymbol{\nabla} f(P)$.

10. Use the same procedure as in problem 9 to calculate the gradient of the scalar field in example (1.8b).

***11.** If f is a differentiable real-valued function defined on $(-\infty, \infty)$ and g is a scalar field, defined on all of space, which is such that $\nabla g(P)$ exists for all P, show that the scalar field h defined by $h(P) = f(g(p))$ also has a gradient and

$$\nabla h(P) = f'(g(P))\,\nabla g(P), \qquad \text{for all } P.$$

12. Show that the two-dimensional scalar field whose coordinate form relative to a rectangular coordinate system is $\bar{f}(x^1, x^2) = x^1x^2$ does not have a relative maximum at any point P. [*Hint:* Evaluate $\delta f(P;\alpha)$ for $P \neq O \sim (0, 0)$; examine behavior at $P = O$ directly.]

Gradients and Normal Vectors

13. (a) Show that the gradient of a scalar field $f\colon \mathfrak{D} \to (-\infty, \infty)$ has the following property (see Figure 11.14). *The arrow* $\nabla f(P)$ *is orthogonal at* P *to all*

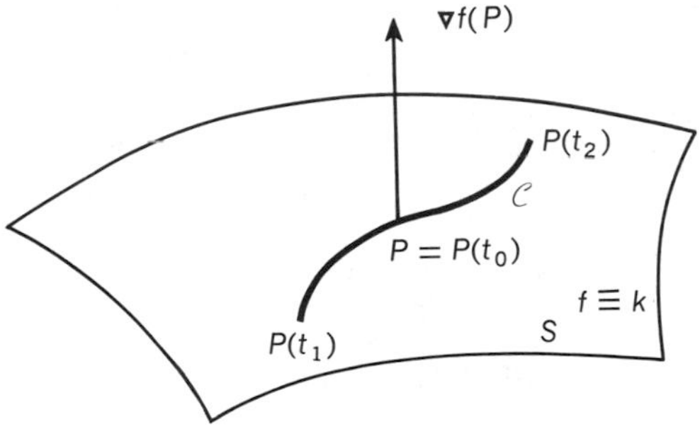

Figure 11.14

smooth curves C *on the level surface* $S\colon f(x^1, x^2, x^3) = k$ *passing through* P. [*Hint:* If $C\colon x^1(t) = c_1(t),\ x^2(t) = c_2(t),\ x^3(t) = c_3(t),\ t_1 \leq t \leq t_2$ is a curve on S with $P(t_0) = P$, then $\varphi(t) = f(c_1(t), c_2(t), c_3(t)) \equiv$ const. Hence $\dot{\varphi}(t) \equiv 0$ and thus $\dot{\varphi}(t_0) = 0$. Now apply (1.17a).]

(b) Show that for any surface of the form

$$S\colon x^3 = \psi(x^1, x^2)$$

the arrow

$$\mathbf{N}(P) = -\psi_{x^1}(x^1, x^2)\mathbf{e}_1 - \psi_{x^2}(x^1, x^2)\mathbf{e}_2 + \mathbf{e}_3 \qquad \text{for } P \sim (x^1, x^2, x^3)$$

is orthogonal to S for each point P in S. [*Hint:* By writing the equation of S in the form $S\colon x^3 - \psi(x^1, x^2) = 0$, we see that S is a level surface of the scalar field

$$f(x^1, x^2, x^3) = x^3 - \psi(x^1, x^2).]$$

2. α-Derivatives and Gradients of Vector Fields

The same method which we have applied to the differentiation of scalar fields carries over equally well to the differentiation of vector fields. The first step is to define $\boldsymbol{\alpha}$-derivatives.

(2.1) Definition. Given a vector field $\mathbf{F}\colon \mathfrak{D} \to \mathfrak{A}$ and a point P in $\mathfrak{D}$, we assign to each vector $\boldsymbol{\alpha} \in \mathfrak{A}$ an arrow $\delta\mathbf{F}(P; \boldsymbol{\alpha})$ called the **$\boldsymbol{\alpha}$-derivative** of **F** at P. The quantity $\delta\mathbf{F}(P; \boldsymbol{\alpha})$ denotes the following limit (Figure 11.15):

$$\text{(a)} \qquad \delta\mathbf{F}(P; \boldsymbol{\alpha}) = \lim_{s\to 0} \frac{\mathbf{F}(P + s\boldsymbol{\alpha}) - \mathbf{F}(P)}{s} = \frac{d}{ds}\mathbf{F}(P + s\boldsymbol{\alpha})\Big|_{s=0}$$

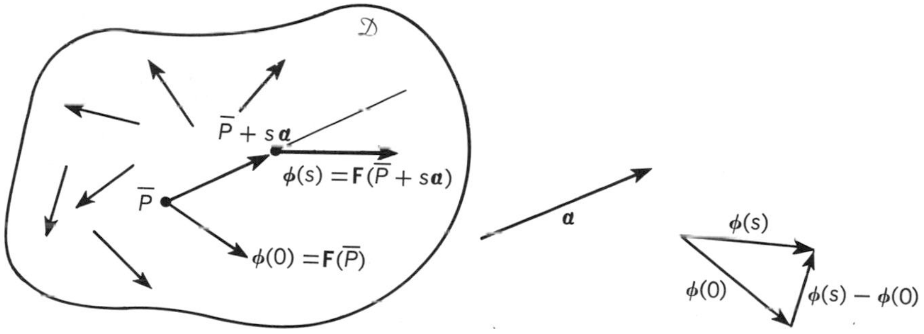

Figure 11.15

[Note that the quotient appearing in (2.1a) is the scalar $1/s$ multiplying a difference of two arrows and therefore makes sense. Moreover, since for fixed P and $\boldsymbol{\alpha}$, $\mathbf{F}(P + s\boldsymbol{\alpha})$ is a vector-valued function of the scalar s, the differentiation on the right side of (2.1a) also makes sense; see (1.6) of Chapter 2.]

The $\boldsymbol{\alpha}$-derivative of **F** can thus be computed by observing that for fixed P and $\boldsymbol{\alpha}$,

$$\mathbf{F}(P + s\boldsymbol{\alpha}) = \varphi(s)$$

reduces to a vector function of one variable. The limit in (2.1a) is then given by

$$\text{(b)} \qquad \delta\mathbf{F}(P; \boldsymbol{\alpha}) = \lim_{s\to 0} \frac{\varphi(s) - \varphi(0)}{s} = \dot{\varphi}(0).$$

(2.2) Examples. α-Derivatives

(a) Let us compute $\delta\mathbf{F}(P; \boldsymbol{\alpha})$ for a vector field $\mathbf{F}$ defined on all of space and having the following coordinate form (relative to a prescribed rectangular coordinate system):

$$\text{(i)} \qquad \tilde{\mathbf{F}}(x^1, x^2, x^3) = (x^1 + x^2 + x^3)\mathbf{e}_1 + (x^1x^2x^3)\mathbf{e}_2 + \big((x^1)^2 + (x^2)^2 + (x^3)^2\big)\mathbf{e}_3.$$

Take $P \sim (1, 1, 2)$. Then with $\boldsymbol{\alpha} = a_1\mathbf{e}_1 + a_2\mathbf{e}_2 + a_3\mathbf{e}_3$ we obtain

$$\begin{aligned}\mathbf{F}(P + s\alpha) &= \tilde{\mathbf{F}}(1 + sa_1, 1 + sa_2, 2 + sa_3)\\ &= [(1 + sa_1) + (1 + sa_2) + (2 + sa_3)]\mathbf{e}_1\\ &\quad + [(1 + sa_1)(1 + sa_2)(2 + sa_3)]\mathbf{e}_2\\ &\quad + [(1 + sa_1)^2 + (1 + sa_2)^2 + (2 + sa_3)^2]\mathbf{e}_3 = \varphi(s).\end{aligned}$$

Now by (2.1.14) differentiation of the vector function φ of s involves the differentiation of its coordinates relative to the vectors $\mathbf{e}_1$, $\mathbf{e}_2$, $\mathbf{e}_3$. Hence we obtain

$$\begin{aligned}\dot{\varphi}(s) = [a_1 + a_2 + a_3]\mathbf{e}_1 &+ [a_1(1 + sa_2)(2 + sa_3)\\ &+ (1 + sa_1)a_2(2 + sa_3) + (1 + sa_1)(1 + sa_2)a_3]\mathbf{e}_2\\ &+ [2a_1(1 + sa_1) + 2a_2(1 + sa_2) + 2a_3(2 + sa_3)]\mathbf{e}_3.\end{aligned}$$

Hence, by (2.1a),

$$\begin{aligned}\text{(ii)} \qquad \delta\mathbf{F}(P; \boldsymbol{\alpha}) = \dot{\varphi}(0) &= (a_1 + a_2 + a_3)\mathbf{e}_1 + (2a_1 + 2a_2 + a_3)\mathbf{e}_2\\ &\quad + (2a_1 + 2a_2 + 4a_3)\mathbf{e}_3\\ &\qquad \text{for } \boldsymbol{\alpha} = a_1\mathbf{e}_1 + a_2\mathbf{e}_2 + a_3\mathbf{e}_3.\end{aligned}$$

(b) Let us compute $\boldsymbol{\alpha}$-derivatives of the field defined by

$$\mathbf{F}(P) = \frac{k}{\|\overrightarrow{P_0P}\|^2}(\overrightarrow{P_0P}), \qquad \mathfrak{D} = \text{all of space except } P_0.$$

This has the coordinate form (Figure 11.16)

$$\text{(i)} \qquad \tilde{\mathbf{F}}(x^1, x^2, x^3) = \frac{k}{(x^1)^2 + (x^2)^2 + (x^3)^2}(x^1\mathbf{e}_1 + x^2\mathbf{e}_2 + x^3\mathbf{e}_3).$$

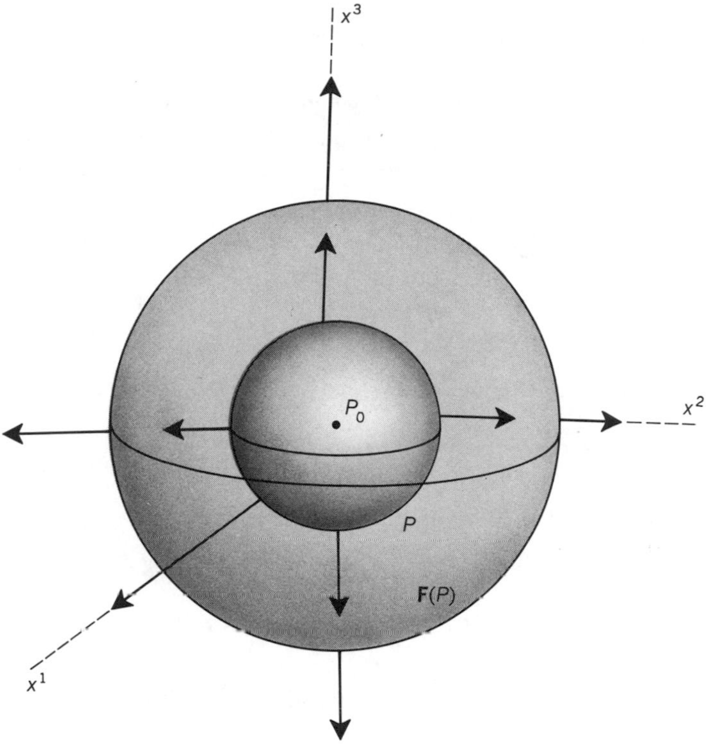

Figure 11.16

Thus if, for example, we take $P \sim (1, 2, -1)$ and $\boldsymbol{\alpha} = a_1\mathbf{e}_1 + a_2\mathbf{e}_2 + a_3\mathbf{e}_3$ we obtain

$$\begin{aligned}\mathbf{F}(P + s\boldsymbol{\alpha}) &= \tilde{\mathbf{F}}(1 + sa_1, 2 + sa_2, -1 + sa_3)\\ &= \frac{k}{(1 + sa_1)^2 + (2 + sa_2)^2 + (-1 + sa_3)^2}\\ &\qquad \times [(1 + sa_1)\mathbf{e}_1 + (2 + sa_2)\mathbf{e}_2 + (-1 + sa_3)\mathbf{e}_3]\\ &= \varphi(s).\end{aligned}$$

By (2.1.14), to differentiate φ we merely differentiate its coordinates. That is,

$$\begin{aligned}\dot{\varphi}(s) = k\,\frac{d}{ds}&\left(\frac{1 + sa_1}{(1 + sa_1)^2 + (2 + sa_2)^2 + (-1 + sa_3)^2}\right)\mathbf{e}_1\\ + k\,\frac{d}{ds}&\left(\frac{2 + sa_2}{(1 + sa_1)^2 + (2 + sa_2)^2 + (-1 + sa_3)^2}\right)\mathbf{e}_2\\ + k\,\frac{d}{ds}&\left(\frac{-1 + sa_3}{(1 + sa_1)^2 + (2 + sa_2)^2 + (-1 + sa_3)^2}\right)\mathbf{e}_3.\end{aligned}$$

Therefore by (2.1b) (the reader should check this),

$$\text{(ii)} \qquad \delta\mathbf{F}(P;\boldsymbol{\alpha}) = \dot{\varphi}(0) = (k/18)[(2a_1 - 2a_2 + a_3)\mathbf{e}_1 - (2a_1 + a_2 - 2a_3)\mathbf{e}_2 + (a_1 + 2a_2 + 2a_3)\mathbf{e}_3] \quad \text{for } \boldsymbol{\alpha} = a_1\mathbf{e}_1 + a_2\mathbf{e}_2 + a_3\mathbf{e}_3.$$

Let us study closely the formulas for $\delta\mathbf{F}(P;\boldsymbol{\alpha})$ obtained in the above examples. In (2.2a) we found, for

$$\tilde{\mathbf{F}}(x^1, x^2, x^3) = (x^1 + x^2 + x^3)\mathbf{e}_1 + (x^1x^2x^3)\mathbf{e}_2 + \big((x^1)^2 + (x^2)^2 + (x^3)^2\big)\mathbf{e}_3$$

and $P \sim (1, 1, 2)$, that

$$\text{(2.3)} \qquad \delta\mathbf{F}(P;\boldsymbol{\alpha}) = (a_1 + a_2 + a_3)\mathbf{e}_1 + (2a_1 + 2a_2 + a_3)\mathbf{e}_2 + (2a_1 + 2a_2 + 4a_3)\mathbf{e}_3, \quad \text{for } \boldsymbol{\alpha} = a_1\mathbf{e}_1 + a_2\mathbf{e}_2 + a_3\mathbf{e}_3.$$

In (2.2b) we found, for $\mathbf{F}(P) = (k/\|\overrightarrow{P_0P}\|^2)(\overrightarrow{P_0P})$ and $P \sim (1, 2, -1)$, that

$$\text{(2.4)} \qquad \delta\mathbf{F}(P;\boldsymbol{\alpha}) = \frac{k}{18}[(2a_1 - 2a_2 + a_3)\mathbf{e}_1 - (2a_1 + a_2 - 2a_3)\mathbf{e}_2 + (a_1 + 2a_2 + 2a_3)\mathbf{e}_3], \quad \text{for } \boldsymbol{\alpha} = a_1\mathbf{e}_1 + a_2\mathbf{e}_2 + a_3\mathbf{e}_3.$$

In both these cases the quantity $\delta\mathbf{F}(P;\boldsymbol{\alpha})$ with P fixed is defined for *all* $\boldsymbol{\alpha} \in \mathfrak{A}$, and hence $\boldsymbol{\alpha}$-differentiation can be regarded as a *transformation* from $\mathfrak{A}$ to $\mathfrak{A}$. Moreover, in each of the above formulas this is a *linear* transformation on $\mathfrak{A}$ to $\mathfrak{A}$. That is, the transformation L_P determined by

$$L_P\boldsymbol{\alpha} = \delta\mathbf{F}(P;\boldsymbol{\alpha}) \qquad \text{for } \boldsymbol{\alpha} \in \mathfrak{A}$$

satisfies the linearity identity

$$\text{(L)} \qquad L_P(c\boldsymbol{\alpha} + d\boldsymbol{\beta}) = c(L_P\boldsymbol{\alpha}) + d(L_P\boldsymbol{\beta}).$$

This is easily verified by reference to (2.3) and (2.4).

Just as with scalar fields, this is a general phenomenon. In fact, we can state the following result.

(2.5) Theorem. *For every vector field $\mathbf{F}\colon \mathfrak{D} \to \mathfrak{A}$ whose coordinate form $\tilde{\mathbf{F}} = \tilde{f}^1\mathbf{e}_1 + \tilde{f}^2\mathbf{e}_2 + \tilde{f}^3\mathbf{e}_3$ contains functions $\tilde{f}^i$ having continuous first partial derivatives, the $\boldsymbol{\alpha}$-derivative $\delta\mathbf{F}(P;\boldsymbol{\alpha})$ exists for each P in $\mathfrak{D}$ and each $\boldsymbol{\alpha} \in \mathfrak{A}$.*

Moreover, for P fixed, $\boldsymbol{\alpha}$-differentiation defines a linear *transformation L_P taking $\mathfrak{A}$ to $\mathfrak{A}$:*

$$\text{(a)} \qquad L_P\boldsymbol{\alpha} = \delta\mathbf{F}(P; \boldsymbol{\alpha}) \qquad \text{for } \boldsymbol{\alpha} \in \mathfrak{A}.$$

We omit the proof of this theorem.

The linear transformation L_P occurring in (2.5a) is as important in the analysis of a vector field as the arrow $\nabla f(P)$ is in the analysis of a scalar field. Hence L_P is given a name.

(2.6) Definition. If the vector field $\mathbf{F}\colon \mathfrak{D} \to \mathfrak{A}$ satisfies the conditions of theorem (2.5), then for each $P \in \mathfrak{D}$ the transformation $L_P\colon \mathfrak{A} \to \mathfrak{A}$, which is uniquely determined by (2.5a), is called the **gradient** of **F** at P. It is denoted by

$$\text{(a)} \qquad L_P = \text{grad}\, \mathbf{F}(P) \qquad [\text{or } L_P = \nabla\mathbf{F}(P)].$$

[Thus (2.5a) can be written in the form

$$\text{(b)} \qquad \delta\mathbf{F}(P; \boldsymbol{\alpha}) = [\text{grad}\, \mathbf{F}(P)]\boldsymbol{\alpha} \qquad \text{for } \boldsymbol{\alpha} \in \mathfrak{A},\ P \in \mathfrak{D}.]$$

(2.7) Example. Gradient. Let us compute $\boldsymbol{\alpha}$-derivatives for the vector field discussed in (2.2a) whose coordinate form (relative to a given rectangular coordinate system) is

$$\text{(i)} \qquad \tilde{\mathbf{F}}(x^1, x^2, x^3) = (x^1 + x^2 + x^3)\mathbf{e}_1 + (x^1x^2x^3)\mathbf{e}_2 + \big((x^1)^2 + (x^2)^2 + (x^3)^2\big)\mathbf{e}_3.$$

Let $\boldsymbol{\alpha} = a_1\mathbf{e}_1 + a_2\mathbf{e}_2 + a_3\mathbf{e}_3$ and consider the special case $P \sim (2, 2, 2)$. We obtain

$$\begin{aligned} \mathbf{F}(P + s\boldsymbol{\alpha}) &= \tilde{\mathbf{F}}(2 + sa_1, 2 + sa_2, 2 + sa_3) \\ &= [(2 + sa_1) + (2 + sa_2) + (2 + sa_3)]\mathbf{e}_1 \\ &\quad + [(2 + sa_1)(2 + sa_2)(2 + sa_3)]\mathbf{e}_2 \\ &\quad + [(2 + sa_1)^2 + (2 + sa_2)^2 + (2 + sa_3)^2]\mathbf{e}_3 \\ &= \varphi(s). \end{aligned}$$

Hence by (2.1b) we find that for $P \sim (2, 2, 2)$,

$$\begin{aligned} \delta\mathbf{F}(P; \boldsymbol{\alpha}) = \dot{\varphi}(0) &= (a_1 + a_2 + a_3)\mathbf{e}_1 + (4a_1 + 4a_2 + 4a_3)\mathbf{e}_2 \\ &\quad + (4a_1 + 4a_2 + 4a_3)\mathbf{e}_3 \end{aligned}$$

In general, taking $P \sim (x^1, x^2, x^3)$ we obtain

$$\begin{aligned}\mathbf{F}(P + s\boldsymbol{\alpha}) = {} & [(x^1 + sa_1) + (x^2 + sa_2) + (x^3 + sa_3)]\mathbf{e}_1 \\ & + [(x^1 + sa_1)(x^2 + sa_2)(x^3 + sa_3)]\mathbf{e}_2 \\ & + [(x^1 + sa_1)^2 + (x^2 + sa_2)^2 + (x^3 + sa_3)^2]\mathbf{e}_3 = \varphi(s),\end{aligned}$$

and therefore, by (2.1b),

$$\text{(ii)} \qquad \begin{aligned}\delta\mathbf{F}(P; \boldsymbol{\alpha}) = \dot{\varphi}(0) = {} & [a_1 + a_2 + a_3]\mathbf{e}_1 \\ & + [(x^2x^3)a_1 + (x^1x^3)a_2 + (x^1x^2)a_3]\mathbf{e}_2 \\ & + [(2x^1)a_1 + (2x^2)a_2 + (2x^3)a_3]\mathbf{e}_3 \\ \text{for } \boldsymbol{\alpha} = a_1\mathbf{e}_1 + a_2\mathbf{e}_2 + a_3\mathbf{e}_3, & \qquad P \sim (x^1, x^2, x^3).\end{aligned}$$

According to equation (ii) the transformation $L_P = \operatorname{grad} \mathbf{F}(P)$ has the form

$$\text{(iii)} \qquad \begin{aligned}[\operatorname{grad} \mathbf{F}(P)]\boldsymbol{\alpha} = {} & [a_1 + a_2 + a_3]\mathbf{e}_1 \\ & + [(x^2x^3)a_1 + (x^1x^3)a_2 + (x^1x^2)a_3]\mathbf{e}_2 \\ & + [(2x^1)a_1 + (2x^2)a_2 + (2x^3)a_3]\mathbf{e}_3 \\ \text{for } \boldsymbol{\alpha} = a_1\mathbf{e}_1 + a_2\mathbf{e}_2 + a_3\mathbf{e}_3, & \qquad P \sim (x^1, x^2, x^3).\end{aligned}$$

Our final task with vector fields, just as with scalar fields, is to develop an *efficient* method of computing $\operatorname{grad} \mathbf{F}(P)$. Once again this method depends on a study of the relationship between $\boldsymbol{\alpha}$-derivatives of $\mathbf{F}$ and partial derivatives of its coordinate form $\tilde{\mathbf{F}}$.

This time the equation analogous to equation (1.14) for scalar fields is

(2.8)

$$\begin{aligned}[\operatorname{grad} \mathbf{F}(P)]\mathbf{e}_1 &= \tilde{\mathbf{F}}_{x^1}(x^1, x^2, x^3) \\ &= \tilde{f}^1_{x^1}(x^1, x^2, x^3)\mathbf{e}_1 + \tilde{f}^2_{x^1}(x^1, x^2, x^3)\mathbf{e}_2 + \tilde{f}^3_{x^1}(x^1, x^2, x^3)\mathbf{e}_3 \\ [\operatorname{grad} \mathbf{F}(P)]\mathbf{e}_2 &= \tilde{\mathbf{F}}_{x^2}(x^1, x^2, x^3) \\ &= \tilde{f}^1_{x^2}(x^1, x^2, x^3)\mathbf{e}_1 + \tilde{f}^2_{x^2}(x^1, x^2, x^3)\mathbf{e}_2 + \tilde{f}^3_{x^2}(x^1, x^2, x^3)\mathbf{e}_3 \\ [\operatorname{grad} \mathbf{F}(P)]\mathbf{e}_3 &= \tilde{\mathbf{F}}_{x^3}(x^1, x^2, x^3) \\ &= \tilde{f}^1_{x^3}(x^1, x^2, x^3)\mathbf{e}_1 + \tilde{f}^2_{x^3}(x^1, x^2, x^3)\mathbf{e}_2 + \tilde{f}^3_{x^3}(x^1, x^2, x^3)\mathbf{e}_3 \\ & \qquad \text{for } P \sim (x^1, x^2, x^3).\end{aligned}$$

The justification of this equation is similar to that of (1.14) and is discussed in the problems.

Equation (2.8) leads us to the following simple method for calculating grad $\mathbf{F}(P)$.

(2.9) Coordinate Formula for Gradient. *Let* $\mathbf{F}: \mathfrak{D} \to \mathfrak{A}$ *be a vector field satisfying the hypotheses of theorem* (2.5) *and let* $\tilde{\mathbf{F}} = \tilde{f}^1\mathbf{e}_1 + \tilde{f}^2\mathbf{e}_2 + \tilde{f}^3\mathbf{e}_3$ *denote its coordinate form relative to some rectangular coordinate system. Then for every point* $P \sim (x^1, x^2, x^3)$ *in* $\mathfrak{D}$ *the following formula holds:*

$$\begin{aligned}
&[\text{grad}\,\mathbf{F}(P)]\boldsymbol{\alpha} \\
&= [\tilde{f}^1_{x^1}(x^1, x^2, x^3)a_1 + \tilde{f}^1_{x^2}(x^1, x^2, x^3)a_2 + \tilde{f}^1_{x^3}(x^1, x^2, x^3)a_3]\mathbf{e}_1 \\
\text{(a)}\quad &\quad + [\tilde{f}^2_{x^1}(x^1, x^2, x^3)a_1 + \tilde{f}^2_{x^2}(x^1, x^2, x^3)a_2 + \tilde{f}^2_{x^3}(x^1, x^2, x^3)a_3]\mathbf{e}_2 \\
&\quad + [\tilde{f}^3_{x^1}(x^1, x^2, x^3)a_1 + \tilde{f}^3_{x^2}(x^1, x^2, x^3)a_2 + \tilde{f}^3_{x^3}(x^1, x^2, x^3)a_3]\mathbf{e}_3 \\
&\qquad \text{for } \boldsymbol{\alpha} = a_1\mathbf{e}_1 + a_2\mathbf{e}_2 + a_3\mathbf{e}_3 \text{ and } P \sim (x^1, x^2, x^3).
\end{aligned}$$

The proof of this formula is left to the problems.

Since grad $\mathbf{F}(P) = L_P$ is a linear transformation from $\mathfrak{A}$ to $\mathfrak{A}$, it can be related in a fairly obvious way to a linear transformation from $\mathfrak{R}^3$ to $\mathfrak{R}^3$. We merely examine the linear transformation $L'_P: \mathfrak{R}^3 \to \mathfrak{R}^3$ which for every $\boldsymbol{\alpha} = a_1\mathbf{e}_1 + a_2\mathbf{e}_2 + a_3\mathbf{e}_3$ takes the triple in $\mathfrak{R}^3$ denoting the E-coordinates of $\boldsymbol{\alpha}$ to the triple denoting the E-coordinates of $L_P\boldsymbol{\alpha} = [\text{grad}\,\mathbf{F}(P)]\boldsymbol{\alpha}$

$$\text{(i)}\quad L'_P\begin{pmatrix} a_1 \\ a_2 \\ a_3 \end{pmatrix} = \begin{pmatrix} \tilde{f}^1_{x^1}(x^1, x^2, x^3)a_1 + \tilde{f}^1_{x^2}(x^1, x^2, x^3)a_2 + \tilde{f}^1_{x^3}(x^1, x^2, x^3)a_3 \\ \tilde{f}^2_{x^1}(x^1, x^2, x^3)a_1 + \tilde{f}^2_{x^2}(x^1, x^2, x^3)a_2 + \tilde{f}^2_{x^3}(x^1, x^2, x^3)a_3 \\ \tilde{f}^3_{x^1}(x^1, x^2, x^3)a_1 + \tilde{f}^3_{x^2}(x^1, x^2, x^3)a_2 + \tilde{f}^3_{x^3}(x^1, x^2, x^3)a_3 \end{pmatrix} \in \mathfrak{R}^3.$$

It follows from (i) that the matrix of L'_P has the following form:

(2.9b)

$$\text{grad}\,\mathbf{F}(P) \sim L'_P = \begin{pmatrix} \tilde{f}^1_{x^1}(x^1, x^2, x^3) & \tilde{f}^1_{x^2}(x^1, x^2, x^3) & \tilde{f}^1_{x^3}(x^1, x^2, x^3) \\ \tilde{f}^2_{x^1}(x^1, x^2, x^3) & \tilde{f}^2_{x^2}(x^1, x^2, x^3) & \tilde{f}^2_{x^3}(x^1, x^2, x^3) \\ \tilde{f}^3_{x^1}(x^1, x^2, x^3) & \tilde{f}^3_{x^2}(x^1, x^2, x^3) & \tilde{f}^3_{x^3}(x^1, x^2, x^3) \end{pmatrix}$$

(2.10) Example. Gradient (Continued). Let us compute the gradient of the vector field $\mathbf{F}$ such that

$$\text{(i)}\qquad \mathbf{F}(P) = \|\overrightarrow{P_0P}\|^2(\overrightarrow{P_0P}).$$

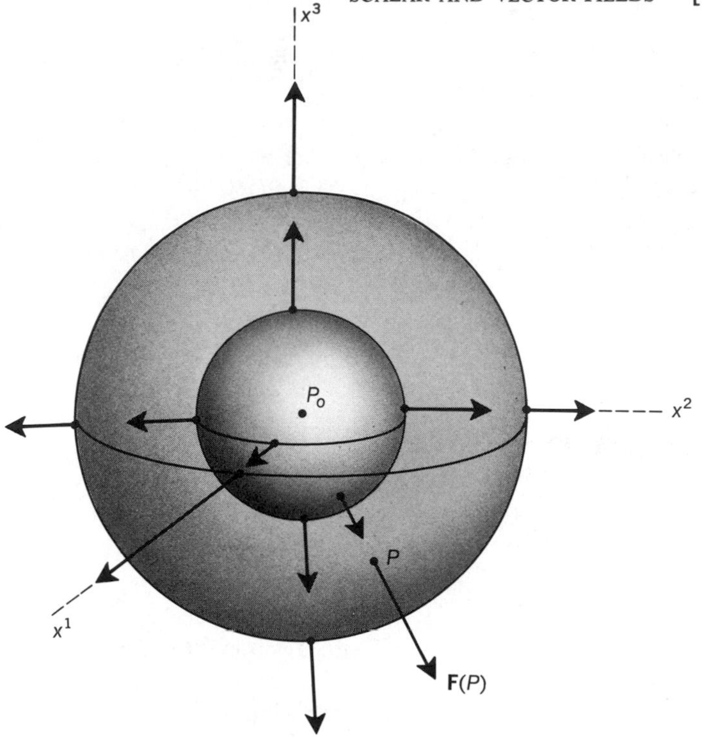

Figure 11.17

Using the coordinate system of Figure 11.17 we see that this field has the coordinate form

$$\text{(ii)} \qquad \begin{aligned} \tilde{\mathbf{F}}(x^1, x^2, x^3) &= [(x^1)^2 + (x^2)^2 + (x^3)^2](x^1\mathbf{e}_1 + x^2\mathbf{e}_2 + x^3\mathbf{e}_3) \\ &= [x^1((x^1)^2 + (x^2)^2 + (x^3)^2)]\mathbf{e}_1 \\ &\quad + [x^2((x^1)^2 + (x^2)^2 + (x^3)^2)]\mathbf{e}_2 \\ &\quad + [x^3((x^1)^2 + (x^2)^2 + (x^3)^2)]\mathbf{e}_3. \end{aligned}$$

To find grad $\mathbf{F}(P)$ we shall utilize formulas (2.9a) and (2.9b). Now it is easily seen that

$$\begin{aligned} \tilde{f}^1_{x^1}(x^1, x^2, x^3) &= 3(x^1)^2 + (x^2)^2 + (x^3)^2 \\ \tilde{f}^1_{x^2}(x^1, x^2, x^3) &= 2x^1x^2 \\ \tilde{f}^1_{x^3}(x^1, x^2, x^3) &= 2x^1x^3 \\ \tilde{f}^2_{x^1}(x^1, x^2, x^3) &= 2x^1x^2 \\ \tilde{f}^2_{x^2}(x^1, x^2, x^3) &= (x^1)^2 + 3(x^2)^2 + (x^3)^2 \\ \tilde{f}^2_{x^3}(x^1, x^2, x^3) &= 2x^2x^3 \end{aligned}$$

$$\tilde{f}^3_{x^1}(x^1, x^2, x^3) = 2x^1x^3$$
$$\tilde{f}^3_{x^2}(x^1, x^2, x^3) = 2x^2x^3$$
$$\tilde{f}^3_{x^3}(x^1, x^2, x^3) = (x^1)^2 + (x^2)^2 + 3(x^3)^2.$$

Hence, by (2.9a),

(iii) $[\text{grad } \mathbf{F}(P)]\boldsymbol{\alpha}$

$$\begin{aligned} &= [(3(x^1)^2 + (x^2)^2 + (x^3)^2)a_1 + (2x^1x^2)a_2 + (2x^1x^3)a_3]\mathbf{e}_1 \\ &\quad + [(2x^1x^2)a_1 + ((x^1)^2 + 3(x^2)^2 + (x^3)^2)a_2 + (2x^2x^3)a_3]\mathbf{e}_2 \\ &\quad + [(2x^1x^3)a_1 + (2x^2x^3)a_2 + ((x^1)^2 + (x^2)^2 + 3(x^3)^2)a_3]\mathbf{e}_3 \\ &\qquad \text{for } \boldsymbol{\alpha} = a_1\mathbf{e}_1 + a_2\mathbf{e}_2 + a_3\mathbf{e}_3, \qquad P \sim (x^1, x^2, x^3). \end{aligned}$$

Equivalently, by (2.9b), grad $\mathbf{F}(P) \sim L'_P$, where

(iv)

$$L'_P = \begin{pmatrix} 3(x^1)^2 + (x^2)^2 + (x^3)^2 & 2x^1x^2 & 2x^1x^3 \\ 2x^1x^2 & (x^1)^2 + 3(x^2)^2 + (x^3)^2 & 2x^2x^3 \\ 2x^1x^3 & 2x^2x^3 & (x^1)^2 + (x^2)^2 + 3(x^3)^2 \end{pmatrix}$$

As a final comment, let us observe that by the very definition of grad $\mathbf{F}$, knowledge of the transformation grad $\mathbf{F}(P)$ gives full information on the rate of change of the vector field $\mathbf{F}$ in the vicinity of the point P. However, there are many interesting situations in which one has only *partial* knowledge of grad $\mathbf{F}(P)$ at points P in $\mathfrak{D}$. In such cases it is still possible to obtain a good deal of information about the field $\mathbf{F}$.

One of the most frequently encountered incomplete pieces of information concerning the transformation L_P = grad $\mathbf{F}(P)$ is knowledge of its "trace." This is a scalar defined at each point at which grad $\mathbf{F}(P)$ exists, in other words, a scalar field.

(2.11) Definition. Given a vector field $\mathbf{F}: \mathfrak{D} \to \mathcal{A}$ satisfying the conditions of theorem (2.5), the **divergence** of $\mathbf{F}$ is the *scalar* field $f = \text{div } \mathbf{F}$ defined by the formula†

$$\text{(a)} \qquad \text{div } \mathbf{F}(P) = l_{11} + l_{22} + l_{33},$$

where

$$\text{grad } \mathbf{F}(P) \sim \begin{pmatrix} l_{11} & l_{12} & l_{13} \\ l_{21} & l_{22} & l_{23} \\ l_{31} & l_{32} & l_{33} \end{pmatrix}.$$

†Note that div $\mathbf{F}(P)$ is the sum of the diagonal elements of the matrix of grad $\mathbf{F}(P)$. The sum of the diagonal elements of any matrix is called the *trace* of that matrix.

That is, by (2.9b),

$$\text{(b)} \qquad \operatorname{div} \mathbf{F}(P) = \tilde{f}^1_{x^1}(x^1, x^2, x^3) + \tilde{f}^2_{x^2}(x^1, x^2, x^3) + \tilde{f}^3_{x^3}(x^1, x^2, x^3) \quad \text{for } P \sim (x^1, x^2, x^3),$$

where $\tilde{f}^1, \tilde{f}^2, \tilde{f}^3$ are the functions appearing in the coordinate form of **F**:

$$\tilde{\mathbf{F}}(x^1, x^2, x^3) = \tilde{f}^1(x^1, x^2, x^3)\mathbf{e}_1 + \tilde{f}^2(x^1, x^2, x^3)\mathbf{e}_2 + \tilde{f}^3(x^1, x^2, x^3)\mathbf{e}_3.$$

A second frequently encountered incomplete piece of information concerning the transformation $L_P = \operatorname{grad} \mathbf{F}(P)$ is knowledge of its "polar vector." This is an *arrow* defined at each point P at which grad **F**(P) exists, in other words, a vector field.

(2.12) Definition. Given a vector field $\mathbf{F}: \mathfrak{D} \to \mathfrak{A}$ satisfying the conditions of theorem (2.5), the **curl** of **F** is the *vector* field **G** = curl **F** defined by the formula†

$$\text{(a)} \qquad \operatorname{curl} \mathbf{F}(P) = (l_{32} - l_{23})\mathbf{e}_1 + (l_{13} - l_{31})\mathbf{e}_2 + (l_{21} - l_{12})\mathbf{e}_3,$$

where

$$\operatorname{grad} \mathbf{F}(P) \sim \begin{pmatrix} l_{11} & l_{12} & l_{13} \\ l_{21} & l_{22} & l_{23} \\ l_{31} & l_{32} & l_{33} \end{pmatrix}.$$

That is, by (2.9b),

$$\text{(b)} \qquad \begin{aligned} \operatorname{curl} \mathbf{F}(P) = {} & [\tilde{f}^3_{x^2}(x^1, x^2, x^3) - \tilde{f}^2_{x^3}(x^1, x^2, x^3)]\mathbf{e}_1 \\ & + [\tilde{f}^1_{x^3}(x^1, x^2, x^3) - \tilde{f}^3_{x^1}(x^1, x^2, x^3)]\mathbf{e}_2 \\ & + [\tilde{f}^2_{x^1}(x^1, x^2, x^3) - \tilde{f}^1_{x^2}(x^1, x^2, x^3)]\mathbf{e}_3 \\ & \text{for } P \sim (x^1, x^2, x^3), \end{aligned}$$

where $\tilde{f}^1, \tilde{f}^2, \tilde{f}^3$are the functions appearing in the coordinate form of **F**.

Both div **F** and curl **F** will occur later in this chapter. One final comment on notation. We have been careful to distinguish notationally between a *field* (f or **F**) and a *coordinate form* for that field relative to a given coordinate system ($\tilde{f}$ or $\tilde{\mathbf{F}}$). However, it is general practice *not* to make this dis-

†Note that curl **F**(P) is constructed from the off-diagonal elements of the matrix of grad **F**(P). The vector constructed in this way from the off-diagonal elements of any 3×3 matrix is called the *polar vector* of that matrix.

tinction notationally, but instead to use f and $\mathbf{F}$ both for fields *and* for coordinate forms of those fields, relying on the reader to deduce from context what a given symbol denotes. We shall adopt this latter procedure from time to time in what follows.

PROBLEMS

1. (a) For each of the following vector fields $\mathbf{F}$, given in their coordinate form $\tilde{\mathbf{F}}$, determine an appropriate domain $\mathfrak{D}$ and express $\mathbf{F}(P + s\boldsymbol{\alpha})$ as a function of s for $P \sim (x^1, x^2, x^3)$ and $\boldsymbol{\alpha}$ fixed.

(i) $$\tilde{\mathbf{F}}(x^1, x^2, x^3) = [x^1 + x^2 + x^3]\mathbf{e}_1 + [(x^1)^2 + (x^2)^2 + (x^3)^2]\mathbf{e}_2 + [x^1x^2x^3]\mathbf{e}_3$$

(ii) $$\tilde{\mathbf{F}}(x^1, x^2, x^3) = (x^2x^3)\mathbf{e}_1 + (x^1x^3)\mathbf{e}_2 + (x^1x^2)\mathbf{e}_3$$

(iii) $$\tilde{\mathbf{F}}(x^1, x^2, x^3) = (1 + (x^1)^2)\mathbf{e}_1 + (2 + (x^2)^2)\mathbf{e}_2 + (1 - (x^3)^2)\mathbf{e}_3$$

(iv) $$\tilde{\mathbf{F}}(x^1, x^2) = \frac{x_1}{\sqrt{x_1^2 + x_2^2}}\,\mathbf{e}_1 - \frac{x_2}{\sqrt{x_1^2 + x_2^2}}\,\mathbf{e}_2$$

(v) $$\tilde{\mathbf{F}}(x^1, x^2) = \frac{x_1}{x_1^2 + x_2^2}\,\mathbf{e}_1 + \frac{x_2}{x_1^2 + x_2^2}\,\mathbf{e}_2.$$

(b) Use part (a) to compute $\delta\mathbf{F}(P; \boldsymbol{\alpha})$, $P \sim (x^1, x^2, x^3)$, for each of these fields.

2. (a) For each of the following vector fields express $\mathbf{F}(P + s\boldsymbol{\alpha})$ as a function of s for P and $\boldsymbol{\alpha}$ fixed.

(i) $\mathbf{F}(P) = [(\overrightarrow{P_0P}) \cdot \boldsymbol{\gamma}]\boldsymbol{\delta}$, $\quad \boldsymbol{\gamma}$ and $\boldsymbol{\delta}$ fixed

(ii) $\mathbf{F}(P) = \|\overrightarrow{P_0P}\|^2(\overrightarrow{P_0P} + \boldsymbol{\beta})$, $\quad \boldsymbol{\beta}$ fixed

(iii) $$\mathbf{F}(P) = \frac{1}{\|\overrightarrow{P_0P}\|^2}\,(\overrightarrow{P_0P})$$

(iv) $\mathbf{F}(P) = [(\overrightarrow{P_0P}) \cdot (\overrightarrow{P_1P})](\overrightarrow{P_0P} + \overrightarrow{P_1P})$, $\quad P_0, P_1$ prescribed points.

(b) Use part (a) to compute $\delta\mathbf{F}(P; \boldsymbol{\alpha})$ for each of these fields.

3. Give the matrix corresponding to grad $\mathbf{F}(P)$, $P \sim (x^1, x^2, x^3)$, for each of the fields in problem 1. (For the two-dimensional fields, this should be a 2×2 matrix.)

4. Give the matrix corresponding to grad $\mathbf{F}(P)$ for each of the fields in problem 2.

5. If f is a scalar field possessing a gradient at all points P, and if the corresponding vector field $\mathbf{F} = \boldsymbol{\nabla} f$ possesses a gradient at all points,

$$L_P = \text{grad}\,(\boldsymbol{\nabla} f)(P),$$

then this latter transformation is called the *second gradient* of f. Find the matrix for L_P in terms of partial derivatives of $\tilde{f}$. [*Hint:* Combine (1.15a) with (2.9b).]

6. Show that for a scalar field f the *divergence* of the vector field $\mathbf{F}(P) = \nabla f(P)$—a quantity called the **Laplacian** of f and denoted by Δf—is given by

$$\Delta f(P) = \operatorname{div} \nabla f(P) = f_{x^1x^1}(x^1, x^2, x^3) + f_{x^2x^2}(x^1, x^2, x^3) + f_{x^3x^3}(x^1, x^2, x^3) \qquad \text{for } P \sim (x^1, x^2, x^3).$$

[*Hint:* Combine (1.15a) with (2.11b).]

7. If $\mathbf{F}$ and $\mathbf{G}$ are vector fields possessing gradients grad $\mathbf{F}(P)$, grad $\mathbf{G}(P)$ at all points P, then the vector field $\mathbf{H}$ defined by

$$\mathbf{H}(P) = c\mathbf{F}(P) + d\mathbf{G}(P), \qquad c, d \text{ scalars},$$

also possesses a gradient and

$$\operatorname{grad} \mathbf{H}(P) = c \operatorname{grad} \mathbf{F}(P) + d \operatorname{grad} \mathbf{G}(P).$$

Prove this. [*Hint:* Compute $\delta\mathbf{H}(P; \boldsymbol{\alpha})$ and use the definition of linear combinations of linear transformation in Chapter 8, §1, problem 16.]

8. Calculate the gradient of the vector field in example (2.10a) directly from definition (2.6) as follows. The field in question is defined by

$$\mathbf{F}(P) = \|\overrightarrow{P_0P}\|^2(\overrightarrow{P_0P}),$$

where P_0 is a given point. We have then

$$\begin{aligned}\mathbf{F}(P + s\boldsymbol{\alpha}) &= \|\overrightarrow{P_0P} + s\boldsymbol{\alpha}\|^2(\overrightarrow{P_0P} + s\boldsymbol{\alpha})\\ &= [(\overrightarrow{P_0P} + s\boldsymbol{\alpha}) \cdot (\overrightarrow{P_0P} + s\boldsymbol{\alpha})](\overrightarrow{P_0P} + s\boldsymbol{\alpha})\\ &= [\|\overrightarrow{P_0P}\|^2 + 2s\boldsymbol{\alpha} \cdot (\overrightarrow{P_0P}) + s^2\|\boldsymbol{\alpha}\|^2](\overrightarrow{P_0P} + s\boldsymbol{\alpha}).\end{aligned}$$

Now calculate the limit in (2.16). Show that this limit is the image of $\boldsymbol{\alpha}$ under some *linear* transformation L_P. The transformation L_P is then the gradient, grad $\mathbf{F}(P)$.

9. Compute div $\mathbf{F}(P)$ and curl $\mathbf{F}(P)$ for the vector fields in problem 1, (i), (ii), and (iii).

10. For each of the vector fields in problem 1 determine all points P at which $L_P = \operatorname{grad} \mathbf{F}(P)$ is a *one-to-one* linear transformation. [*Hint:* Compute $N_{L'_P}$.]

11. Prove that equation (2.8) is valid. [*Hint:* Examine the proof of (1.14).]

12. Prove (2.9), the coordinate formula for gradient. [*Hint:* Compute the arrows

$$\boldsymbol{\gamma}_1 = [\operatorname{grad} \mathbf{F}(P)]\mathbf{e}_1, \qquad \boldsymbol{\gamma}_2 = [\operatorname{grad} \mathbf{F}(P)]\mathbf{e}_2, \qquad \boldsymbol{\gamma}_3 = [\operatorname{grad} \mathbf{F}(P)]\mathbf{e}_3$$

and use the linearity of $L_P = \operatorname{grad} \mathbf{F}(P)$.]

Differentiation Identities

13. Prove that any scalar field $f: \mathfrak{D} \to (-\infty, \infty)$ for which the vector field $\mathbf{F} = \nabla f$ satisfies the conditions in theorem (2.5) satisfies the identity

$$\operatorname{curl} (\nabla f) \equiv \mathbf{0}.$$

[*Hint:* See theorem (1.2) of the Review of Calculus.]

14. Prove that any vector field $\mathbf{F}: \mathfrak{D} \to \mathfrak{A}$ for which the field $\mathbf{G} = \operatorname{curl} \mathbf{F}$ satisfies the conditions in theorem (2.5) satisfies the identity

$$\operatorname{div} (\operatorname{curl} \mathbf{F}) \equiv 0.$$

***15.** Prove that for any vector fields $\mathbf{F}: \mathfrak{D} \to \mathfrak{A}$, $\mathbf{F}': \mathfrak{D} \to \mathfrak{A}$ for which the fields $\mathbf{G} = \text{curl}\, \mathbf{F}$, $\mathbf{G}' = \text{curl}\, \mathbf{F}'$ satisfy the conditions in theorem (2.5), one has

$$\text{div}\,(\mathbf{F} \times \mathbf{F}') = \mathbf{F}' \cdot \text{curl}\, \mathbf{F} - \mathbf{F} \cdot \text{curl}\, \mathbf{F}'.$$

16. Prove that any scalar fields $f: \mathfrak{D} \to (-\infty, \infty)$, $g: \mathfrak{D} \to (-\infty, \infty)$, which satisfy the conditions in theorem (1.11) and whose gradients satisfy the conditions in theorem (2.5), satisfy the identity

$$\text{div}\,\big(f(P)\nabla g(P)\big) = f(P)\,\Delta g(P) + \nabla f(P) \cdot \nabla g(P) \qquad \text{for } P \in \mathfrak{D}.$$

3. Line Integrals; Conservative Fields

In §§1 and 2 we learned how to differentiate fields. In the next two sections we shall concentrate on the integration of fields. There is a *new* element which enters here. In contrast to integration of functions of one variable, there is not just one integral but *three* entirely different kinds of integrals applicable to fields. They are referred to as line integrals, surface integrals, and volume integrals, respectively.

Throughout our discussion of integration we shall assume that the fields involved are *continuous*. This means that their coordinate forms involve continuous functions of x^1, x^2, x^3.

In this section we shall study line integrals. These are patterned on the computation of *work* in particle dynamics [(4.4) of Chapter 3].

Consider a single particle moving under the action of a time-varying force $\mathbf{f}$ (Figure 11.18). If $\overrightarrow{OP}(t) = \mathbf{r}(t)$ denotes the position vector of the particle at time t relative to a fixed origin O, then, by definition (3.4.4), the *work* done by the time-varying force $\mathbf{f}$ on the particle over the time interval $t_1 \leq t \leq t_2$ is the quantity

$$\text{(i)} \qquad W_{12} = \int_{t_1}^{t_2} \mathbf{f}(t) \cdot \dot{\mathbf{r}}(t)\, dt.$$

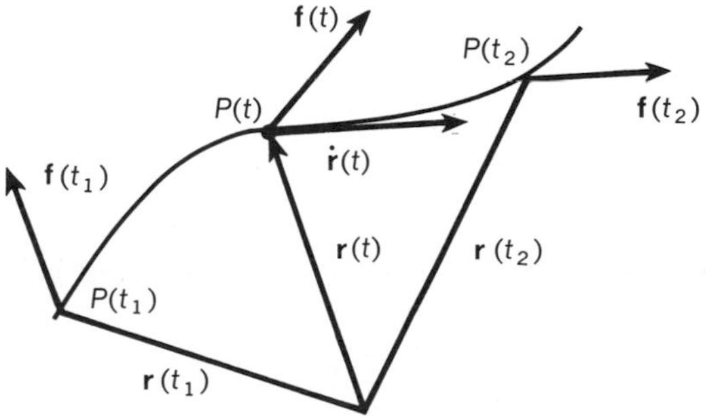

Figure 11.18

Of course, to evaluate W_{12} one must know the time-varying vector function **f**. Now in numerous situations the way in which **f** varies with time is determined—*if* we know the *position* of the particle—by the fact that **f** comes from a prescribed (time-independent) vector field **F** (Figure 11.19). In all such cases we have the formula

$$\mathbf{f}(t) = \mathbf{F}(P(t)), \qquad t_1 \leq t \leq t_2,$$

where $P(t)$ denotes the point where the particle is situated at time t. Hence equation (i) becomes

$$\text{(ii)} \qquad W_{12} = \int_{t_1}^{t_2} \mathbf{F}(P(t)) \cdot \dot{\mathbf{r}}(t)\, dt.$$

The above example is a prototype for the general notion of line integral. To state this notion we first introduce some terminology for describing curves.

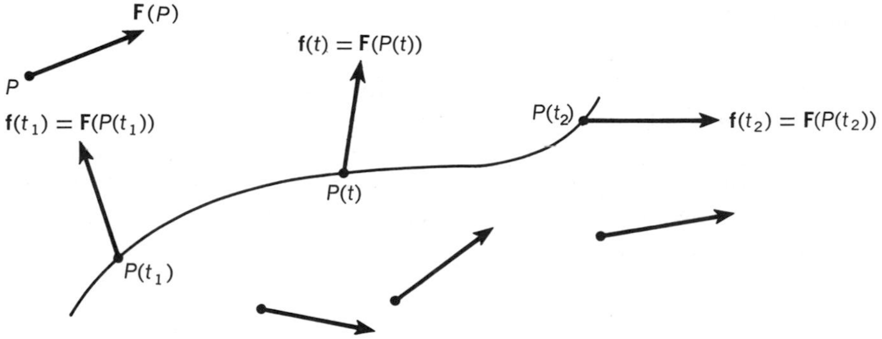

Figure 11.19

(3.1) Definition. Let O be a prescribed origin. A **smooth curve** is a curve of the form (Figure 11.20a)

$$C\colon \overrightarrow{OP}(t) = \mathbf{r}(t), \qquad t_1 \leq t \leq t_2,$$

for which the function **r** of t is continuously differentiable. In coordinate form this is

$$C\colon \mathbf{r}(t) = x^1(t)\mathbf{e}_1 + x^2(t)\mathbf{e}_2 + x^3(t)\mathbf{e}_3, \qquad t_1 \leq t \leq t_2,$$

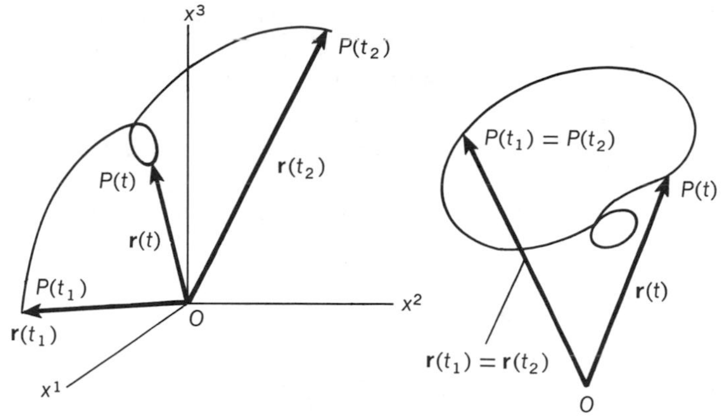

(a) C a smooth curve (b) C a closed curve

Figure 11.20

where x^1, x^2, x^3 are certain continuously differentiable functions of t. The curve C can be regarded as the path of $P(t)$ as t changes. In Figures 11.20 and 11.21 the direction of motion of $P(t)$ along the curve, as t increases, is indicated by arrows. Note that, in general, C can cross itself.

If $P(t_1) = P(t_2)$, then C is called a *closed curve* (Figure 11.20b). If C is closed and in addition $P(t)$ moves from $P(t_1)$ to $P(t_2) = P(t_1)$ without retracing any points other than $P(t_1)$, then C is called a *simple closed curve* (Figure 11.21).

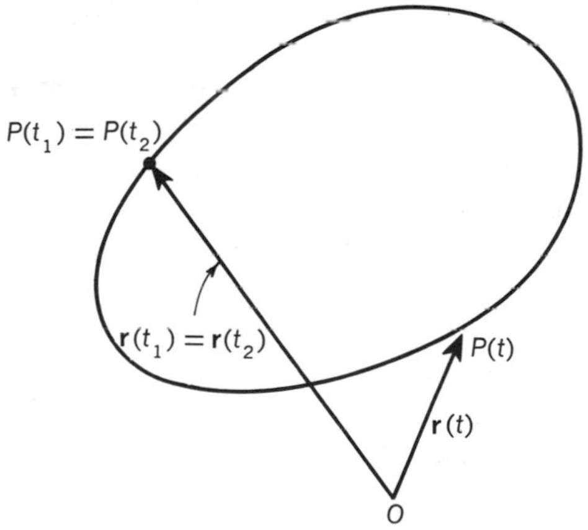

C a simple closed curve

Figure 11.21

We can now give the desired definition for line integral.

(3.2) Definition. Let $\mathbf{F}\colon \mathfrak{D} \to \mathfrak{A}$ be a continuous vector field with coordinate form $\tilde{\mathbf{F}} = \tilde{f}^1\mathbf{e}_1 + \tilde{f}^2\mathbf{e}_2 + \tilde{f}^3\mathbf{e}_3$ and let $C\colon \overrightarrow{OP}(t) = \mathbf{r}(t)$, $t_1 \le t \le t_2$, be a smooth curve in $\mathfrak{D}$ with coordinate form

$$C\colon \mathbf{r}(t) = x^1(t)\mathbf{e}_1 + x^2(t)\mathbf{e}_2 + x^3(t)\mathbf{e}_3, \qquad t_1 \le t \le t_2.$$

Then we associate to **F** and C a quantity called the (*tangential*) **line integral** of **F** along C and denoted by

$$\text{(a)} \qquad \int_C \mathbf{F}(P)\cdot d\mathbf{r} \qquad \text{or}$$

$$\int_C \tilde{f}^1(x^1, x^2, x^3)\,dx^1 + \tilde{f}^2(x^1, x^2, x^3)\,dx^2 + \tilde{f}^3(x^1, x^2, x^3)\,dx^3.$$

By definition this quantity denotes the ordinary definite integral

$$\text{(b)} \qquad \int_{t_1}^{t_2} \mathbf{F}(P(t))\cdot\dot{\mathbf{r}}(t)\,dt = \int_{t_1}^{t_2} [\tilde{f}^1(x^1(t), x^2(t), x^3(t))\dot{x}^1(t)$$
$$+ \tilde{f}^2(x^1(t), x^2(t), x^3(t))\dot{x}^2(t) + \tilde{f}^3(x^1(t), x^2(t), x^3(t))\dot{x}^3(t)]\,dt.$$

The reader can easily remember the formulas in (b) by observing that the appropriate definite integrals are constructed from the formulas in (a) by making the following transitions:

$$\text{(3.3)} \qquad d\mathbf{r} \to \dot{\mathbf{r}}(t)\,dt; \quad dx^1 \to \dot{x}^1(t)\,dt, \quad dx^2 \to \dot{x}^2(t)\,dt, \quad dx^3 \to \dot{x}^3(t)\,dt.$$

There will be many situations in which the curve C instead of being smooth will consist of several portions $C_1, C_2, \ldots, C_k$ each of which is itself a smooth curve. This is the case, for example, when C denotes two line segments meeting at right angles at their endpoints. In such situations the curve C is said to be **piecewise smooth**, and, by definition, any line integral along C is the sum of the individual line integrals along $C_1, C_2, \ldots, C_k$.

(3.4) Examples. Two-Dimensional Line Integrals

(a) Compute the line integral

$$\int_C x\,dx + y\,dy,$$

where C is the section of the parabola $y = x^2$ between $P_1 \sim (0, 0)$ and $P_2 \sim (1, 1)$ (Figure 11.22). (We are, as is usual in two-dimensional problems, replacing x^1, x^2 by x, y for convenience.)

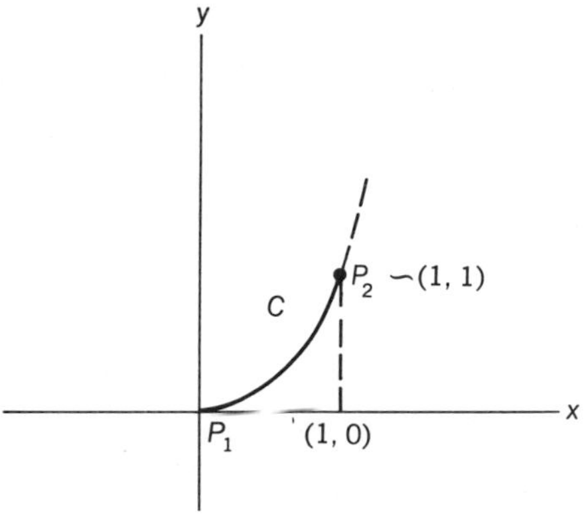

Figure 11.22

For the coordinate form of C we can use "x as parameter":

$$\text{(i)} \qquad C\colon x(t) = t, \qquad y(t) = t^2, \qquad 0 \le t \le 1.$$

Thus definition (3.2) gives

$$\int_C x\,dx + y\,dy = \int_0^1 [t \cdot 1 + t^2 \cdot 2t]\,dt = \tfrac{1}{2} + \tfrac{1}{2} = 1.$$

Let us compare the above result with what we get when using a different parametrization for C, for example,

$$\text{(ii)} \qquad C\colon x(t) = \sqrt{t}, \qquad y(t) = t, \qquad 0 \le t \le 1.$$

Then definition (3.2) gives

$$\int_C x\,dx + y\,dy = \int_0^1 \left[\sqrt{t} \cdot \frac{1}{2\sqrt{t}} + t \cdot 1\right] dt = \tfrac{1}{2} + \tfrac{1}{2} = 1.$$

This illustrates the general fact that *the value of a line integral is unaffected by which parametrization is taken for the curve.*

(b) Compute

$$\int_C x\,dy = \int_C 0\,dx + x\,dy$$

both for the curve C of part (a) and the curve C consisting of the segment of the line $y = x$ between $P_1 \sim (0, 0)$ and $P_2 \sim (1, 1)$.

For the parabolic arc let us use the coordinate form

$$\text{(i)} \qquad C\colon x(t) = t, \qquad y(t) = t^2, \qquad 0 \le t \le 1.$$

Thus for this curve

$$\int_C x\,dy = \int_0^1 t \cdot 2t\,dt = \tfrac{2}{3}.$$

For the linear segment we use the coordinatization

$$\text{(ii)} \qquad C\colon x(t) = t, \qquad y(t) = t, \qquad 0 \le t \le 1.$$

Thus for this curve we get

$$\int_C x\,dy = \int_0^1 t\,dt = \tfrac{1}{2}.$$

(c) Evaluate

$$\int_C y\,dx - x\,dy,$$

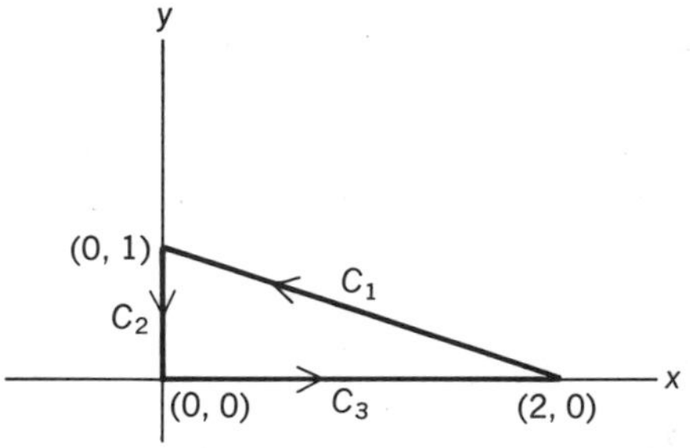

Figure 11.23

where C is the triangle in Figure 11.23. Here, where C is a closed curve, there is no need to specify the initial and terminal points for C, but the *direction* in which C is traversed must be indicated. In the present situation C is a simple closed curve, so one only needs to specify whether the direction is *clockwise* or *counterclockwise*. The notations for these two line integrals are as follows:

$$\text{(i)} \qquad \oint_C y\,dx - x\,dy \qquad \text{(counterclockwise case)}$$

$$\text{(ii)} \qquad \oint_C y\,dx - x\,dy \qquad \text{(clockwise case).}$$

Let us evaluate the counterclockwise integral (i). This requires us to compute three integrals. The first will be the integral along the hypotenuse C_1 from $P_1 \sim (2, 0)$ to $P_2 \sim (0, 1)$; the second will be along the segment C_2 from $P_2 \sim (0, 1)$ to $P_3 \sim (0, 0)$; the third will be along the segment C_3 from $P_3 \sim (0, 0)$ to $P_1 \sim (2, 0)$. Now C_1 lies on the line $x + 2y = 2$. Hence we can take

$$\text{(iii)} \qquad C_1\colon x(t) = 2 - 2t, \qquad y(t) = t, \qquad 0 \le t \le 1.$$

For C_2 and C_3 we can take

$$\text{(iv)} \qquad C_2\colon x(t) \equiv 0,\ y(t) = t, \qquad t_1 = 1,\ t_2 = 0$$

$$\text{(v)} \qquad C_3\colon x(t) = t,\ y(t) \equiv 0, \qquad 0 \le t \le 2.$$

Therefore, by (3.2),

$$\begin{aligned}\oint_C y\,dx - x\,dy &= \int_{C_1} y\,dx - x\,dy + \int_{C_2} y\,dx - x\,dy + \int_{C_3} y\,dx - x\,dy \\ &= \int_0^1 (t(-2) - (2 - 2t)\cdot 1)\,dt + \int_1^0 (t\cdot 0 - 0\cdot 1)\,dt \\ &\quad + \int_0^2 (0\cdot 1 - t\cdot 0)\,dt = -2.\end{aligned}$$

There is an interesting comment we can deduce from example (3.4b). There we evaluated two line integrals with the *same integrand*, $x\,dy$, along two different curves C going from the point $P_1 \sim (0, 0)$ to $P_2 \sim (1, 1)$. We obtained two *different* results. This illustrates a general feature of line integrals in two and three dimensions. That is, the value of a line integral along a curve joining two points P_1 and P_2,

$$\int_{\substack{C\\P_1}}^{P_2} \mathbf{F}(P)\cdot d\mathbf{r} = \int_{\substack{C\\P_1}}^{P_2} f^1(x^1, x^2, x^3)\,dx^1 + f^2(x^1, x^2, x^3)\,dx^2 + f^3(x^1, x^2, x^3)\,dx^3,$$

will generally be *path-dependent: Even if* f^1, f^2, f^3, P_1, *and* P_2 *are fixed, the value of the integral will vary with the choice of* C.

There is, however, an important class of situations where path dependence does *not* occur, so that the value

$$\int_{\substack{C\\P_1}}^{P_2} \mathbf{F}(P)\cdot d\mathbf{r} = \int_{\substack{C\\P_1}}^{P_2} f^1(x^1, x^2, x^3)\,dx^1 + f^2(x^1, x^2, x^3)\,dx^2 + f^3(x^1, x^2, x^3)\,dx^3$$

is the same for all curves C joining any given pair of points P_1 and P_2. In these situations we say that the integral is **path independent.** They are described in the following theorem.

(3.5) Path-Independence Theorem. *For any scalar field* $f\colon \mathfrak{D} \to (-\infty, \infty)$ *satisfying the conditions of theorem* (1.11), *the line integral of* ∇f,

$$\int \nabla f(P) \cdot d\mathbf{r} = \int \tilde{f}_{x^1}(x^1, x^2, x^3)\, dx^1 + \tilde{f}_{x^2}(x^1, x^2, x^3)\, dx^2 + \tilde{f}_{x^3}(x^1, x^2, x^3)\, dx^3,$$

is path-independent.† *In fact, for any pair of points* $P_1, P_2 \in \mathfrak{D}$ *and any piecewise smooth curve* C *joining* P_1 *to* P_2 *in* $\mathfrak{D}$,

$$\text{(a)} \quad \int_{C\,P_1}^{P_2} \nabla f(P) \cdot d\mathbf{r} = \int_{C\,P_1}^{P_2} \tilde{f}_{x^1}(x^1, x^2, x^3)\, dx^1 + \tilde{f}_{x^2}(x^1, x^2, x^3)\, dx^2 + \tilde{f}_{x^3}(x^1, x^2, x^3)\, dx^3 = f(P_2) - f(P_1).$$

Conversely, if $\mathbf{F}\colon \mathfrak{D} \to \mathfrak{A}$ *is a continuous vector field with the property that the line integral*

$$\int \mathbf{F}(P) \cdot d\mathbf{r} = \int \tilde{f}^1(x^1, x^2, x^3)\, dx^1 + \tilde{f}^2(x^1, x^2, x^3)\, dx^2 + \tilde{f}^3(x^1, x^2, x^3)\, dx^3$$

is path-independent, then there exists a scalar field $f\colon \mathfrak{D} \to (-\infty, \infty)$ *such that* f *satisfies the conditions of theorem* (1.11) *and*

$$\text{(b)} \quad \mathbf{F} = \nabla f$$

$$\text{(equivalently, } \tilde{f}^1\mathbf{e}_1 + \tilde{f}^2\mathbf{e}_2 + \tilde{f}^3\mathbf{e}_3 = \tilde{f}_{x^1}\mathbf{e}_1 + \tilde{f}_{x^2}\mathbf{e}_2 + \tilde{f}_{x^3}\mathbf{e}_3).$$

Proof. It suffices to consider smooth curves since integrals over piecewise smooth curves are sums of integrals over smooth curves. Let $C\colon \overrightarrow{OP}(t) = \mathbf{r}(t)$, $t_1 \le t \le t_2$, denote a smooth curve joining P_1 to P_2. Then by definition

$$\text{(i)} \quad \int_{C\,P_1}^{P_2} \nabla f(P) \cdot d\mathbf{r} = \int_{P(t_1)}^{P(t_2)} \nabla f(P(t)) \cdot \dot{\mathbf{r}}(t)\, dt.$$

†We omit the subscript C on the integral sign since we are discussing what happens for *different choices* of the curve.

However by (1.17a) the integrand in the definite integral on the right side is given by

$$\text{(ii)} \qquad \nabla f(P(t)) \cdot \dot{\mathbf{r}}(t) = \dot{\varphi}(t), \qquad \text{where } \varphi(t) = f(P(t)).$$

Hence

$$\text{(iii)} \qquad \int_{P_1}^{P_2} \nabla f(P) \cdot d\mathbf{r} = \int_{t_1}^{t_2} \dot{\varphi}(t)\,dt = \varphi(t_2) - \varphi(t_1),$$

which by the definition of φ is the formula in (3.5a).

For the converse we must exhibit a field $f\colon \mathfrak{D} \to (-\infty, \infty)$ whose gradient is the given vector field **F**. Select a point P_1 in $\mathfrak{D}$. By path independence one can define a scalar field f by setting

$$\text{(iv)} \qquad f(P) = \int_{\substack{C\\P_1}}^{P} \mathbf{F}(P) \cdot d\mathbf{r} \qquad \text{for } P \sim (x^1, x^2, x^3) \in \mathfrak{D},$$

where C denotes *any* path in $\mathfrak{D}$ joining P_1 to P. It will now be seen that this formula defines a scalar field $f\colon \mathfrak{D} \to (-\infty, \infty)$ whose gradient is **F**. That is,

$$\text{(v)} \qquad \tilde{f}_{x^1}\mathbf{e}_1 + \tilde{f}_{x^2}\mathbf{e}_2 + \tilde{f}_{x^3}\mathbf{e}_3 = \tilde{f}^1\mathbf{e}_1 + \tilde{f}^2\mathbf{e}_2 + \tilde{f}^3\mathbf{e}_3 = \mathbf{F}(P).$$

We will show only that

$$\tilde{f}_{x^1}(x^1, x^2, x^3) = \tilde{f}^1(x^1, x^2, x^3),$$

since the other equalities are proved in the same way. Now select the curve C joining P_1 to P to be piecewise smooth and consist of two pieces, a piece C_1 joining P_1 to some point $P_2 \sim (k, x^2, x^3)$ and a segment C_2 parallel to the x^1-axis, joining P_2 to P (Figure 11.24). Parametrizing C_2 by means of x^1

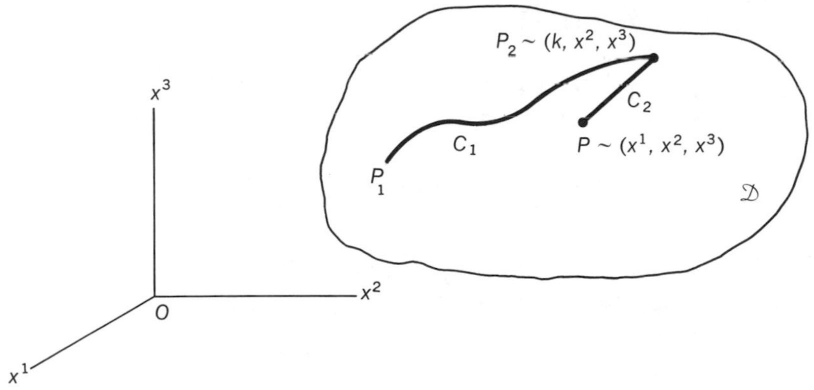

Figure 11.24

as

(vi) $\quad C_2\colon x^1(t) = t, \qquad x^2(t) \equiv x^2, \qquad x^3(t) \equiv x^3, \qquad k \le t \le x^1,$

we have

(vii) $\quad \bar{f}(x^1, x^2, x^3)$

$$= \int_{\substack{C_1\\P_1}}^{P_2} \bar{f}^1(x^1, x^2, x^3)\,dx^1 + \bar{f}^2(x^1, x^2, x^3)\,dx^2 + \bar{f}^3(x^1, x^2, x^3)\,dx^3$$
$$+ \int_{\substack{C_2\\P_2}}^{P} \bar{f}^1(x^1, x^2, x^3)\,dx^1 + \bar{f}^2(x^1, x^2, x^3)\,dx^2 + \bar{f}^3(x^1, x^2, x^3)\,dx^3$$

$$= \int_{\substack{C_1\\P_1}}^{P_2} \bar{f}^1(x^1, x^2, x^3)\,dx^1 + \bar{f}^2(x^1, x^2, x^3)\,dx^2 + \bar{f}^3(x^1, x^2, x^3)\,dx^3$$
$$+ \int_k^{x^1} [\bar{f}^1(t, x^2, x^3)\cdot 1 + \bar{f}^2(t, x^2, x^3)\cdot 0 + \bar{f}^3(t, x^2, x^3)\cdot 0]\,dt.$$

Now as x^1 is varied, with x^2, x^3 fixed, the first integral on the right is *constant* $(P_2 \sim (k, x^2, x^3))$ while the second integral is differentiable with respect to its upper limit x^1. Therefore, $\bar{f}$ has a partial derivative with respect to x^1, and, in fact,

(viii) $$\bar{f}_{x^1}(x^1, x^2, x^3) = 0 + \frac{d}{dx^1}\int_k^{x^1} \bar{f}^1(t, x^2, x^3)\,dt = \bar{f}^1(x^1, x^2, x^3),$$

which is what we set out to prove. ∎

For convenience we restate theorem (3.5) for two-dimensional fields (using x, y for x^1, x^2) as follows.

(3.6) Path Independence (Two-Dimensional Form). *If $f\colon \mathfrak{D} \to (-\infty, \infty)$ is a two-dimensional field with coordinate form $\bar{f}$, then the line integral*

$$\int \nabla f(P)\cdot dr = \int \bar{f}_x(x, y)\,dx + \bar{f}_y(x, y)\,dy$$

is path-independent. In fact, for any pair of points P_1, P_2 in the two-dimensional domain $\mathfrak{D}$ and any piecewise smooth curve C joining P_1 to P_2 in $\mathfrak{D}$,

(a) $$\int_{\substack{C\\P_1}}^{P_2} \nabla f(P)\cdot d\mathbf{r} = \int_{\substack{C\\P_1}}^{P_2} \bar{f}_x(x, y)\,dx + \bar{f}_y(x, y)\,dy = f(P_2) - f(P_1).$$

Conversely, if $\mathbf{F}: \mathfrak{D} \to \mathcal{A}$ *is a continuous two-dimensional vector field, with coordinate form* $\tilde{\mathbf{F}} = \tilde{f}^1\mathbf{e}_1 + \tilde{f}^2\mathbf{e}_2$, *having the property that the line integral*

$$\int \mathbf{F}(P) \cdot d\mathbf{r} = \int \tilde{f}^1(x, y)\, dx + \tilde{f}^2(x, y)\, dy$$

is path-independent, then there exists a scalar field $f: \mathfrak{D} \to (-\infty, \infty)$ *such that*

$$\text{(b)} \qquad \mathbf{F} = \nabla f \qquad (\text{equivalently, } \tilde{f}^1\mathbf{e}_1 + \tilde{f}^2\mathbf{e}_2 = \tilde{f}_x\mathbf{e}_1 + \tilde{f}_y\mathbf{e}_2).$$

(3.7) Examples. Path Independence

(a) Evaluate the line integral

$$\int_C e^{x^1}\, dx^1 + x^3 e^{x^2}\, dx^2 + e^{x^2}\, dx^3,$$

where C is the following path joining $P_1 \sim (0, 0, 0)$ to $P_2 \sim (1, 1, 1)$:

$$C\colon x^1(t) = t^2, \qquad x^2(t) = t^3, \qquad x^3(t) = t^4, \qquad 0 \le t \le 1.$$

A straightforward substitution gives the formidable definite integral

$$\int_C e^{x^1}\, dx^1 + x^3 e^{x^2}\, dx^2 + e^{x^2}\, dx^3 = \int_0^1 (2te^{t^2} + 3t^6 e^{t^3} + 4t^3 e^{t^3})\, dt.$$

Note, however, that the vector field $\mathbf{F}$ with coordinate form

$$\tilde{\mathbf{F}}(x^1, x^2, x^3) = e^{x_1}\mathbf{e}_1 + x^3 e^{x^2}\mathbf{e}_2 + e^{x^2}\mathbf{e}_3$$

is the gradient of the scalar field f with coordinate form

$$\tilde{f}(x^1, x^2, x^3) = e^{x^1} + x^3 e^{x^2}.$$

Hence our line integral is path independent and we can evaluate it by use of (2.5a),

$$\int_C e^{x^1}\, dx^1 + x^3 e^{x^2}\, dx^2 + e^{x^2}\, dx^3 = \int_{(0,0,0)}^{(1,1,1)} \nabla f(P) \cdot d\mathbf{r}$$
$$= [e^{x^1} + x^3 e^{x^2}]\Big|_{(0,0,0)}^{(1,1,1)} = 2e - 1.$$

(b) Evaluate the line integral

$$\text{(i)} \qquad \int_C e^x\, dx + ye^x\, dy,$$

where C is the following path joining $P_1 \sim (0, 0)$ to $P_2 \sim (1, 1)$:

$$\text{(ii)} \qquad C\colon x(t) = t, \qquad y(t) = t^2, \qquad 0 \le t \le 1.$$

If $\int e^x\,dx + y\,dy$ is path-independent, there must be some scalar field f such that

$$\text{(iii)} \qquad \nabla f(P) = \tilde{f}_x(x, y)\mathbf{e}_1 + \tilde{f}_y(x, y)\mathbf{e}_2 = e^x\mathbf{e}_1 + ye^x\mathbf{e}_2.$$

Now the relationship

$$\text{(iv)} \qquad \tilde{f}_x(x, y) = e^x$$

requires that f be of the form

$$\text{(v)} \qquad \tilde{f}(x, y) = e^x + a(y),$$

where a is some function of y [the reader should convince himself that differentiation with respect to x, with y held constant, will yield e^x only for functions of the form (v)]. Note, however, that for all *such* functions

$$\text{(vi)} \qquad \tilde{f}_y(x, y) = a'(y) \neq ye^x.$$

This demonstrates that the vector field

$$\tilde{\mathbf{F}}(x, y) = e^x\mathbf{e}_1 + ye^x\mathbf{e}_2$$

is *not* a gradient, and hence that the line integral in (i) is *not* path-independent. Thus we must compute (i) in the usual way by evaluating the definite integral

$$\int_0^1 (e^t \cdot 1 + t^2e^t \cdot 2t)\,dt.$$

The result can be shown to be

$$\int_{\mathcal{C}} e^x\,dx + ye^x\,dy = 11 - 3e.$$

(c) Evaluate the line integral

$$\text{(i)} \qquad \oint_C e^x\,dx + 2ye^{y^2}\,dy,$$

where C is the unit circle (Figure 11.25). One way to compute this line integral is to select an initial point P_1, say $P_1 \sim (1, 0)$, and the terminal

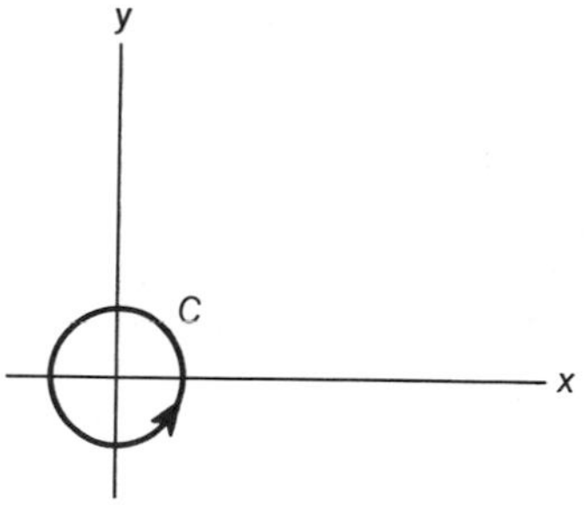

Figure 11.25

point $P_2 = P_1$, and to parametrize C accordingly. It can be seen that

$$C\colon x(t) = \cos t, \qquad y(t) = \sin t, \qquad 0 \leq t \leq 2\pi$$

is a parametrization for which $P(t)$ moves counterclockwise (once) around the circle, as required. Using this we could evaluate the relevant definite integral. However, note that with $\tilde{f}(x, y) = e^x + e^{y^2}$ we have,

$$\nabla f(P) = e^x\mathbf{e}_1 + 2ye^{y^2}\mathbf{e}_2 = \tilde{\mathbf{F}}(x, y) \qquad \text{for } P \sim (x, y).$$

Therefore (i) is path-independent, and hence

$$\oint_C e^x\,dx + 2ye^{y^2}\,dy = [e^x + e^{y^2}]\Big|_{(1,0)}^{(1,0)} = (e + 1) - (e + 1) = 0.$$

Example (3.7b) above illustrates the need for some *efficient* criterion to determine whether or not a prescribed line integral

$$\int \mathbf{F}(P)\cdot d\mathbf{r} = \int \tilde{f}^1(x^1, x^2, x^3)\,dx^1 + \tilde{f}^2(x^1, x^2, x^3)\,dx^2 + \tilde{f}^3(x^1, x^2, x^3)\,dx^3$$

$$\left(\text{or} \quad \int \mathbf{F}(P)\cdot d\mathbf{r} = \int \tilde{f}^1(x, y)\,dx + \tilde{f}^2(x, y)\,dy\right)$$

is path-independent. The identity discussed in §2, problem 13,

(3.8) $$\operatorname{curl}(\nabla f) \equiv 0,$$

is very helpful in this respect.

(3.9) Theorem. *In order for the line integral*

$$\int \mathbf{F}(P)\cdot d\mathbf{r} = \int \tilde{f}^1(x^1, x^2, x^3)\,dx^1 + \tilde{f}^2(x^1, x^2, x^3)\,dx^2 + \tilde{f}^3(x^1, x^2, x^3)\,dx^3$$

to be path-independent, it is necessary† that the vector field $\mathbf{F}: \mathfrak{D} \to \mathfrak{A}$ *have zero curl:*

(a)   curl $\mathbf{F}(P) = \big(\tilde{f}_{x^2}^3(x^1, x^2, x^3) - \tilde{f}_{x^3}^2(x^1, x^2, x^3)\big)\mathbf{e}_1$
$\qquad\qquad + \big(\tilde{f}_{x^3}^1(x^1, x^2, x^3) - \tilde{f}_{x^1}^3(x^1, x^2, x^3)\big)\mathbf{e}_2$
$\qquad\qquad + \big(\tilde{f}_{x^1}^2(x^1, x^2, x^3) - \tilde{f}_{x^2}^1(x^1, x^2, x^3)\big)\mathbf{e}_3 \equiv \mathbf{0}$
$\qquad\qquad\qquad\qquad$ for all $P \sim (x^1, x^2, x^3)$ in $\mathfrak{D}$.

Equivalently, the equations

(b) $\tilde{f}_{x^2}^3 = \tilde{f}_{x^3}^2, \qquad \tilde{f}_{x^3}^1 = \tilde{f}_{x^1}^3, \qquad \tilde{f}_{x^1}^2 = \tilde{f}_{x^2}^1$

must hold.

Proof. By theorem (3.5) path independence requires that

$\qquad \mathbf{F} = \nabla f \qquad$ or $\qquad \tilde{f}^1\mathbf{e}_1 + \tilde{f}^2\mathbf{e}_2 + \tilde{f}^3\mathbf{e}_3 = \tilde{f}_{x^1}\mathbf{e}_1 + \tilde{f}_{x^2}\mathbf{e}_2 + \tilde{f}_{x^3}\mathbf{e}_3.$

However, by (3.8) this implies that

$$\text{curl } \mathbf{F} = \text{curl } (\nabla f) \equiv \mathbf{0},$$

which is what we wanted to show.   ▮

We remark that in the two-dimensional case,‡ condition (3.9a) reduces to

(c)   curl $\mathbf{F}(P) = \big(\tilde{f}_x^2(x, y) - \tilde{f}_y^1(x, y)\big)\mathbf{e}_3 = \mathbf{0} \qquad$ for all $P \sim (x, y)$ in $\mathfrak{D}$.

Equivalently, (3.9b) reduces to

(d) $\tilde{f}_x^2(x, y) = \tilde{f}_y^1(x, y) \qquad$ for all $P \sim (x, y)$ in $\mathfrak{D}$.

(3.10) Examples. Path Independence (Continued)

(a) Let us check whether or not the line integral

$$\int x^1 \, dx^1 + x^1 x^2 \, dx^2 + x^1 x^2 x^3 \, dx^3$$

---

†The vanishing of the curl of $\mathbf{F}$ in a region *is not* a sufficient condition for independence of path unless restrictions are placed on the region (see problem 7).

‡By definition, in the two-dimensional case $\tilde{f}^3$ is identically zero while $\tilde{f}^1$ and $\tilde{f}^2$ are functions only of $x^1 = x$ and $x^2 = y$.

is path-independent. According to (3.9a), path independence requires that

$$\begin{aligned}\operatorname{curl}\mathbf{F}(P) &= \big(\tilde{f}^3_{x^2}(x^1,x^2,x^3) - \tilde{f}^2_{x^3}(x^1,x^2,x^3)\big)\mathbf{e}_1\\ &\quad + \big(\tilde{f}^1_{x^3}(x^1,x^2,x^3) - \tilde{f}^3_{x^1}(x^1,x^2,x^3)\big)\mathbf{e}_2\\ &\quad + \big(\tilde{f}^2_{x^1}(x^1,x^2,x^3) - \tilde{f}^1_{x^2}(x^1,x^2,x^3)\big)\mathbf{e}_3\\ &= (x^1x^3)\mathbf{e}_1 + (x^2x^3)\mathbf{e}_2 + (x^2)\mathbf{e}_3 \equiv \mathbf{0},\end{aligned}$$

which is clearly false. Thus the given line integral is guaranteed *not* to be path-independent.

(b) Let us check whether or not the line integral

$$\text{(i)} \qquad \int x\,dy - y\,dx$$

is path-independent. According to (3.9b), path independence requires that

$$\operatorname{curl}\mathbf{F}(P) = \big(f^2_x(x,y) - f^1_y(x,y)\big)\mathbf{e}_3 = (0-0)\mathbf{e}_3 \equiv \mathbf{0}.$$

The fact that this condition is met makes it *likely*, but not certain, that the field

$$\mathbf{F}(x,y) = x\mathbf{e}_1 - y\mathbf{e}_2$$

is the gradient of some scalar field and hence that path independence holds for (i). However, in the present case it is easy to see that for the scalar field f given by

$$\tilde{f}(x,y) = \tfrac{1}{2}x^2 - \tfrac{1}{2}y^2,$$

one has

$$\text{(ii)} \qquad \nabla f(P) = \tilde{f}_x(x,y)\mathbf{e}_1 + \tilde{f}_y(x,y)\mathbf{e}_2 = x\mathbf{e}_1 - y\mathbf{e}_2 = \tilde{\mathbf{F}}(x,y), \qquad P \sim (x,y).$$

Thus $\mathbf{F}$ *is* the gradient of some scalar field and hence (i) *is* path independent.

In example (3.7c) we evaluated the line integral

$$\text{(i)} \qquad \oint_C e^x\,dx + 2ye^{y^2}\,dy,$$

where C is the unit circle. Using the fact that the line integral

$$\text{(ii)} \qquad \int e^x\,dx + 2ye^{y^2}\,dy$$

is path independent, we were able to deduce that the integral in (i) has the value zero. The analysis depended only on the fact that the curve C is closed and that (ii) is path-independent. Hence it illustrates a general property of path-independent line integrals. What is much less obvious is that this property can *never* hold for path-*dependent* line integrals.

(3.11) Theorem. *If the continuous vector field* $\mathbf{F}: \mathfrak{D} \to \mathfrak{A}$ *has the property that*

$$\text{(a)} \qquad \int \mathbf{F}(P) \cdot d\mathbf{r} = \int f^1(x^1, x^2, x^3)\, dx^1 + f^2(x^1, x^2, x^3)\, dx^2 + f^3(x^1, x^2, x^3)\, dx^3$$

is path-independent, then

$$\text{(b)} \qquad \oint_{\mathcal{C}} \mathbf{F}(P) \cdot d\mathbf{r} = \oint_{\mathcal{C}} f^1(x^1, x^2, x^3)\, dx^1 + f^2(x^1, x^2, x^3)\, dx^2 + f^3(x^1, x^2, x^3)\, dx^3 = 0$$

for every piecewise smooth closed curve C in $\mathfrak{D}$. Conversely, if *F has the property that* (b) *holds for all piecewise smooth closed curves C, then the line integral in* (a) *is path-independent.*

Proof. If the line integral is path-independent, so that $\mathbf{F} = \nabla f$ for some $f: \mathfrak{D} \to (-\infty, \infty)$ then, selecting a point P_1 on the given closed curve C, we have

$$\oint \mathbf{F}(P) \cdot d\mathbf{r} = \int_{\substack{C \\ P_1}}^{P_1} \mathbf{F}(P) \cdot d\mathbf{r} = f(P)\Big|_{P_1}^{P_1} = 0.$$

Thus (b) holds.

For the converse, suppose that (b) holds but that the line integral in (a) is path-*dependent*. Then there exist points $P_1, P_2 \in \mathfrak{D}$ for which there are paths C_1, C_2 joining P_1 to P_2 such that the line integral evaluated along C_1 is *not* equal to the line integral evaluated along C_2 (Figure 11.26). Let C_1 and C_2 have the following parametrizations:

(i)

$$C_1: x^1(t) = c_1(t), \quad x^2(t) = c_2(t), \quad x^3(t) = c_3(t), \quad t_0 \le t \le t_1$$
$$C_2: x^1(t) = d_1(t), \quad x^2(t) = d_2(t), \quad x^3(t) = d_3(t), \quad t_2 \le t \le t_3.$$

Consider the curve C_2' (see Figure 11.26) in which the parametrization in the reverse of that of C_2:

$$\text{(ii)} \qquad C_2': x^1(t) = d_1(t), \quad x^2(t) = d_2(t), \quad x^3(t) = d_3(t),$$

t varying *from* $t = t_3$ *to* $t = t_2$.

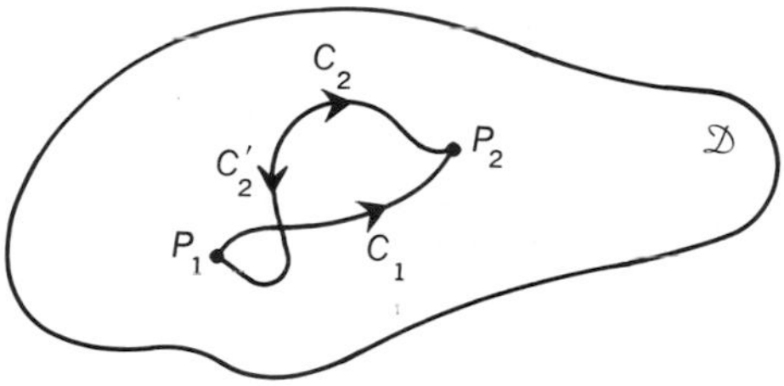

Figure 11.26

By comparing the relevant definite integrals it can be seen that

$$\text{(iii)} \qquad \int_{\substack{P_2\\C_2'}}^{P_1} \mathbf{F}(P) \cdot d\mathbf{r} = -\int_{\substack{P_1\\C_2}}^{P_2} \mathbf{F}(P) \cdot d\mathbf{r}.$$

Now consider the piecewise smooth curve C made up of C_1 and C_2'. C is a *closed* curve (!). Thus by (b) we have

$$\text{(iv)} \qquad \int_C \mathbf{F}(P) \cdot d\mathbf{r} = \int_{\substack{P_1\\C_1}}^{P_2} \mathbf{F}(P) \cdot d\mathbf{r} + \int_{\substack{P_2\\C_2'}}^{P_1} \mathbf{F}(P) \cdot d\mathbf{r} = 0.$$

That is, using (iii),

$$\text{(v)} \qquad \int_{\substack{P_1\\C_1}}^{P_2} \mathbf{F}(P) \cdot d\mathbf{r} = -\int_{\substack{P_2\\C_2'}}^{P_1} \mathbf{F}(P) \cdot d\mathbf{r} = \int_{\substack{P_1\\C_2}}^{P_2} \mathbf{F}(P) \cdot d\mathbf{r}.$$

However, this contradicts the assumption that the line integrals along C_1 and C_2 are *unequal*. Hence path dependence is impossible. ∎

We wish to point out that the converse in the theorem can be further strengthened to state that $\int \mathbf{F}(P) \cdot d\mathbf{r}$ is path-independent if (3.11b) holds just for *simple* closed curves C, but we shall not go into this matter further.

As a final comment in this section we point out that the notion of path independence, also called *conservativeness*, is very important in physical problems. Suppose there is a particle moving in a force field $\mathbf{F}$ in the domain $\mathfrak{D}$, $\mathbf{F}: \mathfrak{D} \to \mathfrak{A}$. To compute the work W_{12} done by the force field $\mathbf{F}$ as the particle moves from P_1 to P_2 we must, *generally speaking*, take careful note of the precise path C which the particle traverses from P_1 to P_2 (Figure 11.27), since W_{12} is given by the line integral

$$W_{12} = \int_{\substack{P_1\\C}}^{P_2} \mathbf{F}(P) \cdot d\mathbf{r} = \int_{t_1}^{t_2} \mathbf{F}(P(t)) \cdot \dot{\mathbf{r}}(t)\, dt.$$

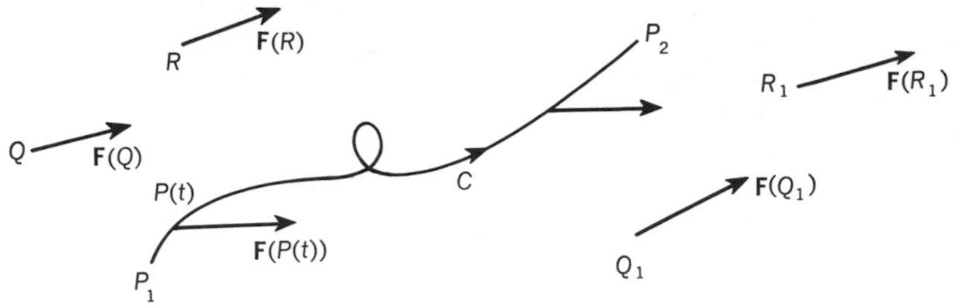

Figure 11.27

However, *if* the force field happens to be a *gradient* of some scalar field f (in such cases the field $V = -f$ is ordinarily called a *potential-energy field*),

$$\mathbf{F} = \nabla f = -\nabla(-f) = -\nabla V,$$

then the line integral is path-independent. Therefore, to compute W_{12} for such cases it is merely necessary to identify the initial point P_1 and terminal point P_2 of the particle; then theorem (3.5) gives

$$(3.12) \qquad W_{12} = \int_{C\,P_1}^{P_2} \mathbf{F}(P) \cdot d\mathbf{r} = f(P)\Big|_{P_1}^{P_2} = f(P_2) - f(P_1)$$
$$= -V(P_2) + V(P_1).$$

This is described in physics as follows: *Every conservative force field possesses a potential energy, and the work done by the force on a particle as it moves from P_1 to P_2 equals the change in potential energy of the particle as it moves from P_1 to P_2.* Note, in particular, that when the force field is conservative, then the work done in moving around any *closed* path is zero.

PROBLEMS

1. Evaluate the following line integrals, making a sketch of the curve C in every case.

(a) *Three-dimensional fields:*

(i) $\displaystyle\int_C \mathbf{F}(P) \cdot d\mathbf{r},$

with $\mathbf{F}(P) = \overrightarrow{OP}$ and C the parabolic arc $x^3 = (x^1)^2$, $x^1 = x^2$ joining $P_1 \sim (0, 0, 0)$ to $P_2 \sim (1, 1, 1)$.

(ii) $\int_C \mathbf{F}(P) \cdot d\mathbf{r}$,

with $\mathbf{F}(P) = \overrightarrow{OP}$ and C the line segment $x^1 = x^2 = x^3$ joining $P_1 \sim (0, 0, 0)$ to $P_2 \sim (1, 1, 1)$.

(iii) $\int_C \mathbf{F}(P) \cdot d\mathbf{r}$,

with $\mathbf{F}$ as above and C the "elbow" path joining $P_1 \sim (0, 0, 0)$ to $P_2 \sim (1, 1, 1)$ which consists of the segments successively joining P_1 to $P_3 \sim (1, 0, 0)$, P_3 to $P_4 \sim (1, 1, 0)$, and P_4 to P_2.

(iv) $\int_{(0,0,0)}^{(2,4,6)} (x^1x^2)\,dx^1 + (x^1x^3)\,dx^2 + (x^2x^3)\,dx^3$,

with C the "elbow" path similar to that in (iii), joining $P_1 \sim (0, 0, 0)$ to $P_2 \sim (2, 4, 6)$.

(v) $\int_{(0,0,0)}^{(1,1,1)} x^2\,dx^3 \quad \left(= \int_C 0\,dx^1 + 0\,dx^2 + x^2\,dx^3\right)$,

with C thc parabolic arc in (i).

(vi) $\int_{(1,1,1)}^{(x^1,x^2,x^3)} dx^1$,

with C the line segment joining $P_1 \sim (1, 1, 1)$ to $P_2 \sim (x^1, x^2, x^3)$.

(b) *Two-dimensional fields:*

(i) $\int_{(1,1)}^{(3,3)} x\,dx + y\,dy$,

with C the line segment joining the end points.

(ii) $\int_{(1,3)}^{(3,2)} y\,dx - x\,dy$,

with C the line segment joining the end points.

(iii) $\int_{(1,0)}^{(0,1)} \frac{y\,dx - x\,dy}{x^2 + y^2}$,

with C the (shorter) arc of the unit circle joining the end points.

(iv) $\int_{(1,0)}^{(0,1)} \frac{y\,dx - x\,dy}{x^2 + y^2}$,

with C the (longer) arc of the unit circle joining the end points.

(v) $\int_{(1,1)}^{(2,4)} x^2y\,dx - y^2x\,dy$,

with C the arc of the parabola $y = x^2$ joining the end points.

(vi) $\displaystyle\int_{(2,4)}^{(1,1)} x^2y\,dx - y^2x\,dy,$

with C the arc of the parabola $y = x^2$ joining the end points. (*Caution:* what are the *initial* and *final* t values in this case?)

(vii) $\displaystyle\int_C x\,dy - y\,dx,$

with C the path joining $P_1 \sim (0, 0)$ to itself which consists of the segments successively joining P_1 to $P_2 \sim (1, 0)$, P_2 to $P_3 \sim (1, 1)$, and P_3 to P_1.

2. Evaluate the following line integrals, making a sketch of the closed curve C in every case.

(a) *Two-dimensional fields:*

(i) $\displaystyle\oint_C (1 - y^2)\,dx - x\,dy,$

with C the unit circle.

(ii) $\displaystyle\oint_C (1 - y^2)\,dx - x\,dy,$

with C the unit circle.

(iii) $\displaystyle\oint_C x\,dy - y\,dx,$

with C consisting of the arc of the $y = x^2$ joining $(-1, -1)$ to $(1, 1)$ together with the segment joining these same points.

(iv) $\displaystyle\oint_C x\,dx,$

with C the unit circle centered at $P_0 \sim (1, 1)$.

(v) $\displaystyle\oint_C \mathbf{F}(P)\cdot d\mathbf{r},$

with $\mathbf{F}(P) = (\sin \|\overrightarrow{OP}\|^2)\overrightarrow{OP}$ and C the unit circle centered at $O \sim (0, 0)$.

(vi) $\displaystyle\oint_C \mathbf{F}(P)\cdot d\mathbf{r},$

with $\mathbf{F}(P) = (\|\overrightarrow{OP}\|^3)\overrightarrow{OP}$ and C the triangle consisting of the segments successively joining $O \sim (0, 0)$ to $P_1 \sim (1, 0)$, P_1 to $P_2 \sim (0, 1)$, and P_2 to O.

(b) *Three-dimensional fields:*

(i) $\displaystyle\oint_C x^1\,dx^1 + x^2\,dx^2 + x^3\,dx^3,$

with C consisting of the arc of the helix $x^1 = (x^2)^2 = (x^3)^3$ joining $O \sim (0, 0, 0)$ to $P_1 \sim (1, 1, 1)$, together with the line segment joining these points, the curve being traversed *upward* along the helix and *downward* along the segment.

(Note that in three dimensions a designation of a motion as *clockwise* or *counterclockwise* depends on the location from which the motion is being observed. Hence one cannot describe the direction as simply as in two dimensions.)

(ii) $\displaystyle\oint_C x^1\, dx^3,$

with C consisting of the elbow path joining $P_1 \sim (0, 0, 0)$ to $P_2 \sim (2, 4, 6)$ together with the line segment joining these points, the direction being *downward* along the line segment and *upward* along the elbow path.

(iii) $\displaystyle\oint_C \frac{x^2\, dx^1 - x^1\, dx^2}{(x^1)^2 + (x^2)^2 + (x^3)^2},$

with C consisting of the equator of the unit sphere traversed *twice* counterclockwise (looked at from above).

3. Determine by inspection a scalar field f such that $\mathbf{F} = \nabla f$, and use this to evaluate the given integrals.

(a) $\displaystyle\int_{(1,1)}^{(3,3)} x\, dx + y\, dy$

(b) $\displaystyle\int_{(-5,5)}^{(5,-5)} x \sin y\, dx + \tfrac{1}{2}x^2 \cos y\, dy$

(c) $\displaystyle\int_{(1,1)}^{(-1,-1)} (x\sqrt{x^2 + y^2})\, dx + (y\sqrt{x^2 + y^2})\, dy$

(d) $\displaystyle\int_{(1,1)}^{(x,y)} y \sin (xy)\, dx + x \sin (xy)\, dy.$

(e) $\displaystyle\int_{(1,1,1)}^{(-1,-1,-1)} e^{x^2}\, dx^1 + (x^1 e^{x^2} + e^{x^3})\, dx^2 + (x^2 e^{x^3})\, dx^3$

4. Determine which of the following line integrals are path-independent and which are not. For those about which the evidence is inconclusive, either produce explicitly a scalar field f such that $\mathbf{F} = \nabla f$ or show that the values of

$$\int_{(1,0)}^{(0,1)} \mathbf{F}(P) \cdot d\mathbf{r}$$

along the two arcs of the unit circle joining the end points are unequal.

(a) $\displaystyle\int (\sin y - y \sin x)\, dx + (x \cos y - \sin x)\, dy$

(b) $\int (\sin y + y \sin x)\, dx + (x \cos y + \sin x)\, dy$

(c) $\int xe^y\, dx + ye^x\, dy$

(d) $\int \mathbf{F}(P) \cdot d\mathbf{r}$, where $\mathbf{F}(P) = \|\overrightarrow{P_0P}\|^2 \overrightarrow{P_0P}$, P_0 fixed

(e) $\int \mathbf{F}(P) \cdot d\mathbf{r}$, where $\mathbf{F}(P) = \overrightarrow{P_0P} + \overrightarrow{P_1P}$, P_0, P_1 fixed

(f) $\int x^1\, dx^1 + x^2\, dx^2 + x^3\, dx^3$

5. It can be shown that for any simple closed curve C, the line integral

$$\oint_C x\, dy = -\oint_C y\, dx = \tfrac{1}{2}\oint_C x\, dy - y\, dx$$

gives the *area* enclosed by C.

Verify this explicitly in the following cases:

(a) $C =$ the unit circle

(b) $C =$ the triangle with vertices (1, 1), (1, 2), (0, 1)

(c) $C =$ the equilateral triangle with the segment $y = 0$, $0 \leq x \leq 1$, as its base

6. Show that if $\mathbf{F} = \nabla f$, then the following is an efficient scheme for reconstructing f (up to an additive constant) given $\mathbf{F}$. Define f by

$$f(x^1, x^2, x^3) = \int_{(0,0,0)}^{(x^1,x^2,x^3)} f^1_{x^1}(x^1, x^2, x^3)\, dx^1 + f^2_{x^2}(x^1, x^2, x^3)\, dx^2 + f^3_{x^3}(x^1, x^2, x^3)\, dx^3,$$

and evaluate along the elbow path joining $O \sim (0, 0, 0)$ to $P \sim (x^1, x^2, x^3)$ [see problem (1a-iii)].

Use this method to construct the scalar field f such that $\mathbf{F} = \nabla f$, for all those fields (both two- and three-dimensional) in problem 3 which are gradients.

***7.** *Path Independence and Simple Connectivity*. Show that the two-dimensional field $\mathbf{F}$ whose coordinate form is

$$\mathbf{F}(x, y) = \frac{y}{x^2 + y^2}\, \mathbf{e}_1 - \frac{x}{x^2 + y^2}\, \mathbf{e}_2$$

has zero curl, but that the line integral

$$\int \mathbf{F}(P) \cdot d\mathbf{r} = \int \frac{y\, dx - x\, dy}{x^2 + y^2}$$

is *not* path-independent if the region $\mathfrak{D}$ is taken as the x, y plane (excluding $O \sim (0, 0)$ since $\mathbf{F}$ is not defined at O). [*Hint:* Evaluate the integral $\int_{(1,0)}^{(0,1)} \mathbf{F} \cdot d\mathbf{r}$ along the two arcs of the unit circle joining the end points.]

In general line integrals along curves which join P_1 and P_2 on opposite sides of O are unequal. However,

$$\int \frac{y\,dx - x\,dy}{x^2 + y^2}$$

is path-independent if we restrict ourselves to paths in the region $\mathfrak{D}$ which consists of the right half-plane (Figure 11.28b).

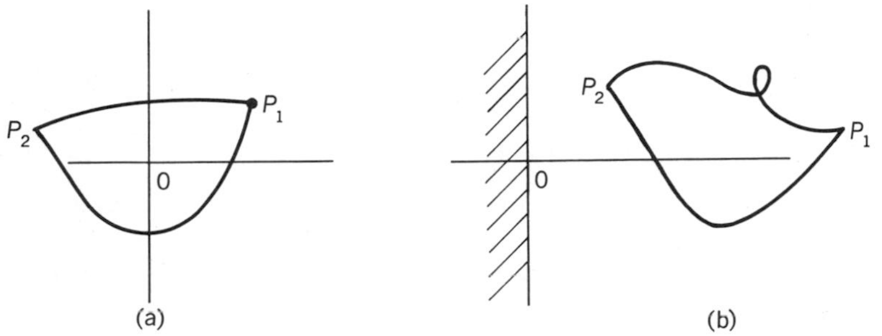

Figure 11.28

This is a general phenomenon. *If* **F** *is a vector field with curl zero, then* $\int_C \mathbf{F}(P) \cdot d\mathbf{r}$ *is path-independent* provided *that we restrict C to lie in a region* $\mathfrak{D}$ *which does not surround any points at which* **F** *is undefined or has nonzero curl.*

The technical name for regions $\mathfrak{D}$ such as that in (11.29b) which do *not* "surround" an excluded set of points as $\mathfrak{D}$ does in Figure 11.29a is *simply connected region*. Hence we can abbreviate the above statement to the following: *The line integral* $\int_C \mathbf{F}(P) \cdot d\mathbf{r}$ *is path-independent provided that paths C are restricted to lie in a simply connected region in which* curl $\mathbf{F} \equiv \mathbf{0}$.

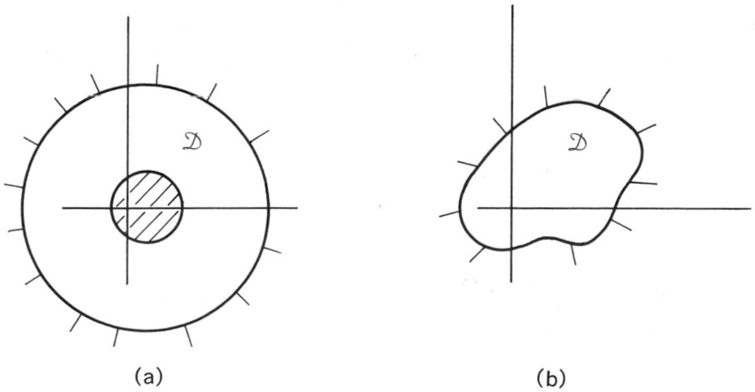

Figure 11.29

8. For each of the following force fields **F**, compute the work done on a particle which moves on the given path. For those fields **F** which are gradients of the negative of a potential energy field V, find V and compute the line integral by using this scalar field.

(a) $\mathbf{F}(P) = \dfrac{1}{\|\overrightarrow{P_0P}\|^3}(\overrightarrow{P_0P})$,
$C =$ the line segment joining $P_1 \sim (1, 1, 1)$ to $P_2 \sim (2, 2, 2)$

(b) $\mathbf{F}(P) = \dfrac{1}{\|\overrightarrow{P_0P}\|}(\overrightarrow{P_0P})$, C as above

(c) $\mathbf{F}(P) = \boldsymbol{\alpha} \times (\overrightarrow{P_0P})$,
$\boldsymbol{\alpha}$ fixed, C the equator of the unit sphere traversed in a counterclockwise direction (seen from above)

(d) $\mathbf{F}(P) = [\boldsymbol{\alpha} \cdot \overrightarrow{P_0P}]\boldsymbol{\alpha}$, $\boldsymbol{\alpha}$ fixed

(e) $\tilde{\mathbf{F}}(x^1, x^2, x^3) = x^1 \sin x^2\mathbf{e}_1 + x^2 \cos x^1\mathbf{e}_2 + \sin x^3\mathbf{e}_3$, C as in (c)

(f) $\tilde{\mathbf{F}}(x, y) = \dfrac{x}{x^2 + y^2}\mathbf{e}_1 + \dfrac{y}{x^2 + y^2}\mathbf{e}_2$, C as in (c)

(g) $\tilde{\mathbf{F}}(x, y) = (x^2 + y^2)\mathbf{e}_1 + (x^2 + y^2)\mathbf{e}_2$,
C the segment joining $P_1 \sim (1, 1)$ to $P_2 \sim (-5, -3)$

Line Integrals for Scalar Fields

9. It is possible to give a notion of line integral for *scalar* fields as well as vector fields: If $f\colon \mathfrak{D} \to (-\infty, \infty)$ is a scalar field and $C\colon \overrightarrow{OP}(t) = \mathbf{r}(t)$, $t_1 \le t \le t_2$, is a piecewise smooth curve in $\mathfrak{D}$,

$$C\colon \mathbf{r}(t) = x^1(t)\mathbf{e}_1 + x^2(t)\mathbf{e}_2 + x^3(t)\mathbf{e}_3, \qquad t_1 \le t \le t_2,$$

then we associate to f and C a quantity called the (arc-length) *line integral of f along C*, and denoted by

$$\text{(i)} \qquad \int_C f(P)\,ds \qquad \left[\text{or} \int_C \tilde{f}(x^1, x^2, x^3)\,ds\right]$$

(Figure 11.30). By definition, this quantity denotes the ordinary definite integral

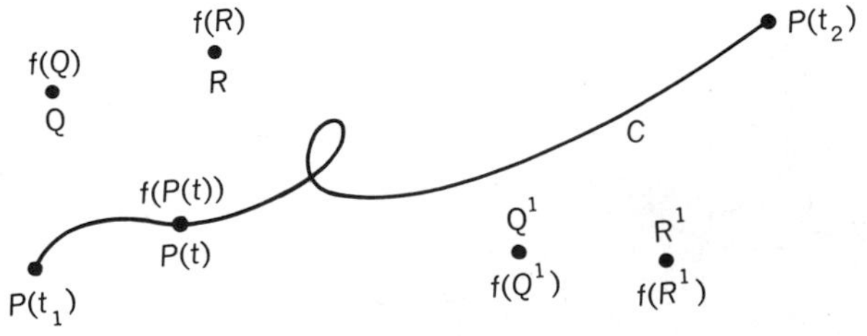

Figure 11.30

(ii) $$\int_{t_1}^{t_2} f(P(t))\dot{s}(t)\,dt$$
$$= \int_{t_1}^{t_2} \tilde{f}(x^1(t), x^2(t), x^3(t))\sqrt{(\dot{x}^1(t))^2 + (\dot{x}^2(t))^2 + (\dot{x}^3(t))^2}\,dt.$$

That is,

$$ds \to \dot{s}(t)\,dt = \sqrt{(\dot{c}_1(t))^2 + (\dot{c}_2(t))^2 + (\dot{c}_3(t))^2}\,dt.$$

Evaluate the following arc-length line integrals.

(a) $\displaystyle\int_{(0,0)}^{(1,1)} f(P)\,ds,$
with C the line segment joining $P_1 \sim (0, 0)$ and $P_2 \sim (1, 1)$ and $f(P) = \|\overrightarrow{OP}\|^2$

(b) $\displaystyle\int_{(0,1)}^{(1,0)} (xe^y + ye^x)\,ds,$
with C the shorter arc of the unit circle joining the end points

(c) $\displaystyle\oint_C x\sqrt{x^2 + y^2}\,ds,$
with C the unit circle

(d) $\displaystyle\int_{(0,0,0)}^{(1,1,1)} f(P)\,ds,$
with $f(P) = \|\overrightarrow{QP}\|^2$, $Q \sim (1, -1, -1)$ and C the line segment joining $(0, 0, 0)$ to $(1, 1, 1)$

(e) $\displaystyle\int_{(1,2,3)}^{(-3,3,-3)} (x^1x^2 + x^2x^3)\,ds,$
with C the line segment joining the end points

***10.** Show that the line integral

$$\int_C \mathbf{F}(P) \cdot d\mathbf{r}$$

can be interpreted as an arc-length line integral of a scalar field f such that on C

$$f(P) = (\mathbf{F}(P))_{\tan} = \mathbf{F}(P) \cdot \mathbf{T}(P), \qquad P \text{ on } C,$$

where $\mathbf{T}(P)$ denotes the *unit* tangent vector to C at P (in the direction of traverse). [*Hint:* $\mathbf{F}(P(t)) \cdot \dot{\mathbf{r}}(t) = \mathbf{F}(P(t)) \cdot (\dot{s}(t)\mathbf{T}(P(t)))$.]

4. Surface and Volume Integrals; Divergence Theorem; Stokes' Theorem

In this section we discuss surface and volume integrals of fields. We shall rely throughout on the fact that the reader knows how to compute an ordinary double integral, that is, the integral of a continuous function of two variables over a planar region (see §2 of the Review of Calculus). To simplify terminology, a scalar field f satisfying the conditions of theorem (1.11), or a vector field $\mathbf{F}$ satisfying the conditions of theorem (2.5), will hereafter be referred to as a *smooth scalar field* or a *smooth vector field*, respectively.

Given a region $\mathfrak{D}$ in space and a continuous scalar field $f\colon \mathfrak{D} \to (-\infty, \infty)$ or a continuous vector field $\mathbf{F}\colon \mathfrak{D} \to \mathcal{A}$, our aim is to discuss quantities

$$a = \iiint\limits_{\mathfrak{D}} f(P)\, dV, \qquad \alpha = \iiint\limits_{\mathfrak{D}} \mathbf{F}(P)\, dV$$

which represent the results obtained by:

(1) Evaluating f or $\mathbf{F}$ at points in various parts of $\mathfrak{D}$ (Figure 11.31)
(2) Multiplying these values by the volumes of the parts
(3) Adding the products together
(4) Taking the limit of these sums as the number of parts becomes large and their volumes become small.

Similarly, given a surface S we wish to discuss quantities denoted by

$$b = \iint\limits_{S} f(P)\, dA, \qquad \beta = \iint\limits_{S} \mathbf{F}(P)\, dA,$$

which represent the results obtained by:

(1) Evaluating f or $\mathbf{F}$ at points in various parts of S (Figure 11.32)
(2) Multiplying these values by the areas of the parts
(3) Adding the products together
(4) Taking the limit of these sums as the number of parts becomes large and their areas become small.

To keep matters as simple as possible we shall restrict ourselves to *capped domains* $\mathfrak{D}$ and to surfaces S which are on the boundaries of such domains. However, integrals over more complicated regions and surfaces can also be handled by these methods. We proceed to describe capped domains.

Let $\mathfrak{D}$ denote a region in space whose boundary is a smooth surface S. Suppose that relative to one of the axes of a prescribed rectangular coordinate system, S consists of two pieces which can be described by simple coordinate formulas, a "top" S_2 and a "bottom" S_1. For instance, suppose that relative to Ox^3 S has a top S_2 and a bottom S_1 which can be expressed in the form

$$S_2\colon x^3 = \psi^2(x^1, x^2), \qquad (x^1, x^2) \in \mathfrak{D}_{(3)}, \qquad \psi^2\colon \mathfrak{D}_{(3)} \to (-\infty, \infty) \text{ a smooth scalar field}$$

(4.1)

$$S_1\colon x^3 = \psi^1(x^1, x^2), \qquad (x^1, x^2) \in \mathfrak{D}_{(3)}, \qquad \psi^1\colon \mathfrak{D}_{(3)} \to (-\infty, \infty) \text{ a smooth scalar field,}$$

where $(x^1, x^2) \in \mathfrak{D}_{(3)}$ means that (x^1, x^2) are the coordinates of a point in the two-dimensional region obtained by projection of $\mathfrak{D}$ (Figure 11.33). Then we call $\mathfrak{D}$ a **capped domain** (relative to Ox^3).

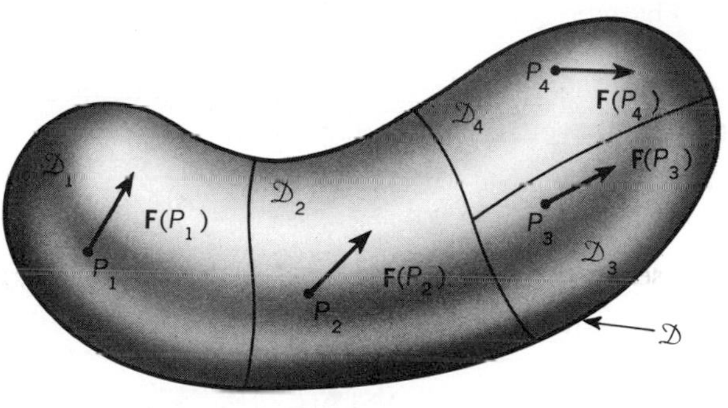

Figure 11.31

We are now able to define volume and surface integrals in accordance with the intuitive ideas expressed earlier.

(4.2) Definitions

1. Let $f\colon \mathfrak{D} \to (-\infty, \infty)$ denote a continuous scalar field defined on a capped domain $\mathfrak{D}$. Then we assign to f and $\mathfrak{D}$ a scalar called the **volume integral** of f over $\mathfrak{D}$ and denoted by

$$\text{(a)} \qquad \iiint_{\mathfrak{D}} f(P)\, dV.$$

By definition, if $\mathfrak{D}$ is capped relative to Ox^3, this quantity denotes the ordinary double integral [see (4.1)]:

$$\text{(b)} \qquad \iiint_{\mathfrak{D}} f(P)\, dV = \iint_{\mathfrak{D}_{(3)}} \left(\int_{\psi^1(x^1,x^2)}^{\psi^2(x^1,x^2)} f(x^1, x^2, s)\, ds \right) dx^1\, dx^2.$$

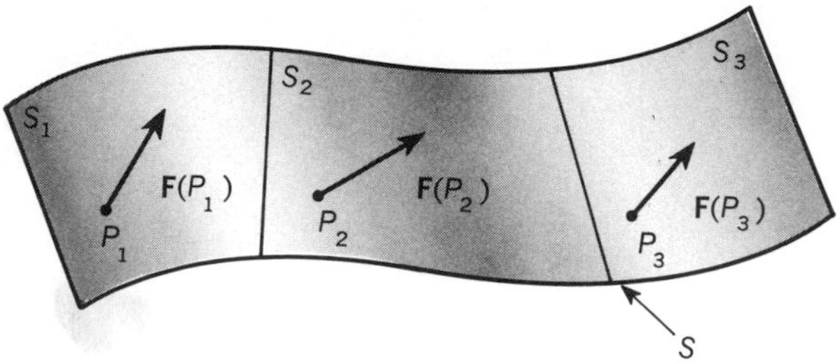

Figure 11.32

In other cases, when $\mathfrak{D}$ is capped relative to Ox^2 or Ox^1, the volume integral is equal to an ordinary double integral which is obtained from that in (b) by merely relabeling variables.†

2. Let $\mathbf{F}: \mathfrak{D} \to \mathfrak{A}$ denote a continuous vector field defined on the capped domain $\mathfrak{D}$ and having the coordinate form

$$\mathbf{F}(x^1, x^2, x^3) = f^1(x^1, x^2, x^3)\mathbf{e}_1 + f^2(x^1, x^2, x^3)\mathbf{e}_2 + f^3(x^1, x^2, x^3)\mathbf{e}_3.$$

Then we assign to $\mathbf{F}$ and $\mathfrak{D}$ an arrow called the **volume integral** of $\mathbf{F}$ over $\mathfrak{D}$ and denoted by

$$\text{(c)} \qquad \iiint\limits_{\mathfrak{D}} \mathbf{F}(P)\, dV.$$

By definition, if $\mathfrak{D}$ is capped relative to Ox^3, this quantity denotes the arrow

$$\text{(d)} \qquad \iiint \mathbf{F}(P)\, dV = \Big[\iint\limits_{\mathfrak{D}_{(3)}} \Big(\int_{\psi^1(x^1,x^2)}^{\psi^2(x^1,x^2)} f^1(x^1, x^2, s)\, ds\Big)\, dx^1\, dx^2\Big]\mathbf{e}_1$$
$$+ \Big[\iint\limits_{\mathfrak{D}_{(3)}} \Big(\int_{\psi^1(x^1,x^2)}^{\psi^2(x^1,x^2)} f^2(x^1, x^2, s)\, ds\Big)\, dx^1\, dx^2\Big]\mathbf{e}_2$$
$$+ \Big[\iint\limits_{\mathfrak{D}_{(3)}} \Big(\int_{\psi^1(x^1,x^2)}^{\psi^2(x^1,x^2)} f^3(x^1, x^2, s)\, ds\Big)\, dx^1\, dx^2\Big]\mathbf{e}_3.$$

In other cases, when $\mathfrak{D}$ is capped relative to Ox^2 or Ox^1, the ordinary double integrals in (d) are replaced by others obtained from them by merely relabeling variables.†

†It is a theorem that when $\mathfrak{D}$ is capped relative to two or more axes, then the double integrals in (b) or (d) corresponding to these various axes all turn out to be equal.

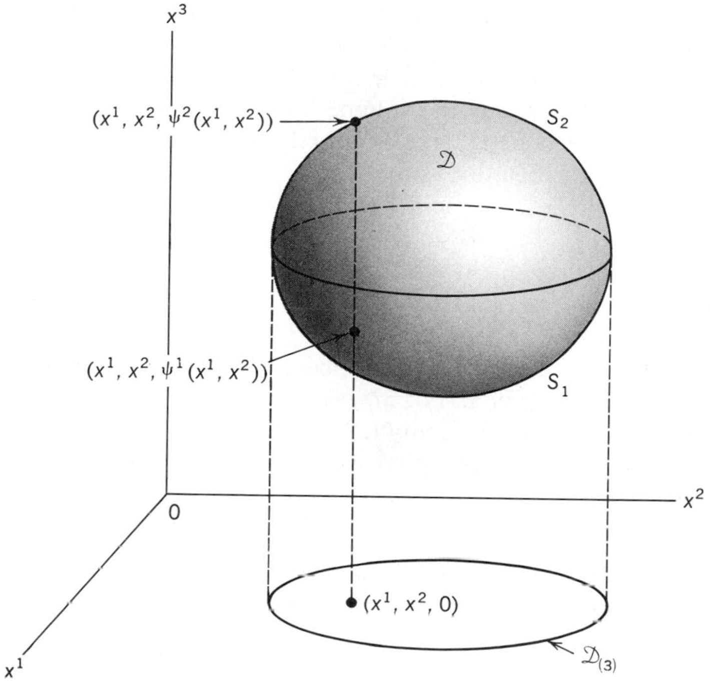

Figure 11.33

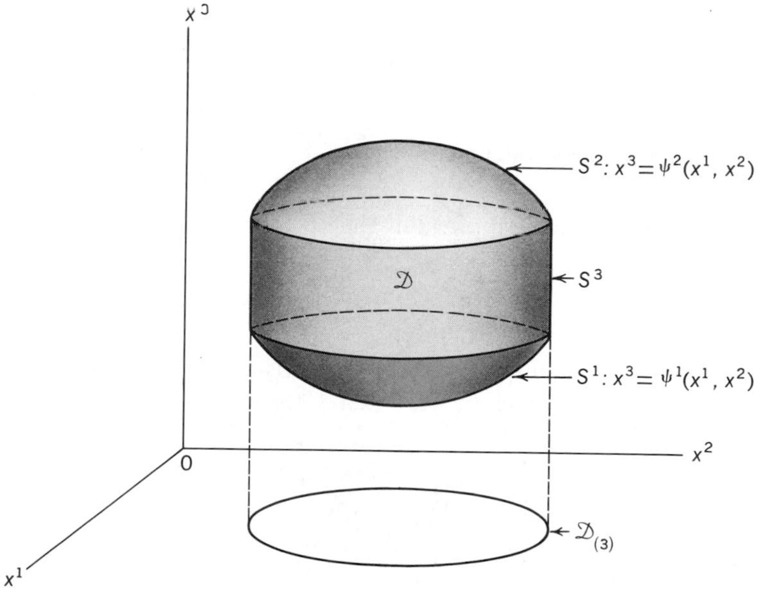

Figure 11.34

It should be noted that the formulas in the above definition make sense not only for capped domains but also for domains $\mathfrak{D}$ that have in addition to a top S_1 and a bottom S_2 a cylindrical *side* S_3 relative to some coordinate axis (Figure 11.34). Actually the volume integrals discussed above are also defined for such domains $\mathfrak{D}$, and by exactly the same formulas. We shall utilize this fact in examples and problems.

There is an important point regarding definition (4.2). Although $\iiint_{\mathfrak{D}} f(P)\,dV$ and $\iiint_{\mathfrak{D}} \mathbf{F}(P)\,dV$ as given by this definition actually *are* limits of sums over parts, as discussed earlier, this fact is by no means obvious. (A similar comment will be true of surface integrals.) Nevertheless results which are suggested by this intuitive viewpoint are usually valid. For instance, if $\mathfrak{D}$ is a simple domain, say a sphere or a cube, then, with $f(P) \equiv 1$, (4.2b) yields the volume of $\mathfrak{D}$. For more complicated domains the volume is *defined* as the value obtained from (4.2b) with $f(P) \equiv 1$.

Another result which one would expect is the following theorem, the proof of which we omit.

(4.3) Theorem. *If $f\colon \mathfrak{D} \to (-\infty, \infty)$ is a continuous scalar field defined on a capped domain $\mathfrak{D}$ and if f is everywhere nonnegative:*

$$f(P) \geq 0 \qquad \text{for } P \in \mathfrak{D},$$

then the volume integral of f over $\mathfrak{D}$ is nonnegative:

$$\iiint_{\mathfrak{D}} f(P)\,dV \geq 0.$$

(4.4) Examples. Volume Integrals

(a) Evaluate the volume integral of the scalar field

$$f(P) = \overrightarrow{OP} \cdot \boldsymbol{\gamma} \qquad \boldsymbol{\gamma} \text{ fixed},$$

over the unit sphere $\mathfrak{D}$ centered at O. Here $\mathfrak{D}$ is capped relative to all three axes. In particular, relative to Ox^3 it has the following top and bottom (see Figure 11.35):

$$\text{(i)}\quad \begin{aligned} S_2\colon x^3 &= \sqrt{1-(x^1)^2-(x^2)^2}, \qquad &(x^1)^2+(x^2)^2 \leq 1,\\ S_1\colon x^3 &= -\sqrt{1-(x^1)^2-(x^2)^2}, \qquad &(x^1)^2+(x^2)^2 \leq 1. \end{aligned}$$

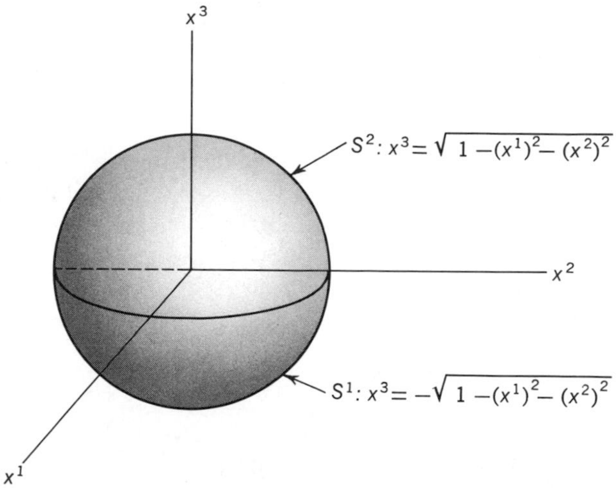

Figure 11.35

In this case $\mathfrak{D}_{(3)}$ is the region $(x^1)^2 + (x^2)^3 \leq 1$. Moreover, f has the following coordinate form:

(ii) $$f(P) = f(x^1, x^2, x^3) = c_1x^1 + c_2x^2 + c_3x^3, \qquad \text{where } \gamma = c_1\mathbf{e}_1 + c_2\mathbf{e}_2 + c_3\mathbf{e}_3.$$

Hence, by (4.2b),

(iii) $$\iiint\limits_{\mathfrak{D}} f(P)\, dV$$
$$= \iint\limits_{(x^1)^2+(x^2)^2\leq 1} \left(\int_{-\sqrt{1-(x^1)^2-(x^2)^2}}^{\sqrt{1-(x^1)^2-(x^2)^2}} (c_1x^1 + c_2x^2 + c_3s)\, ds\right) dx^1\, dx^2$$
$$= \iint\limits_{(x^1)^2+(x^2)^2\leq 1} (c_1x^1s + c_2x^2s + \tfrac{1}{2}c_3s^2)\Big|_{-\sqrt{1-(x^1)^2-(x^2)^2}}^{\sqrt{1-(x^1)^2-(x^2)^2}} dx^1\, dx^2$$
$$= \iint\limits_{(x^1)^2+(x^2)^2\leq 1} (2c_1x^1 + 2c_2x^2)\sqrt{1-(x^1)^2-(x^2)^2}\, dx^1\, dx^2.$$

It is not hard to show that the final double integral is zero (see the problems). Hence the answer is

(iv) $$\iiint\limits_{\mathfrak{D}} f(P)\, dV = 0.$$

(b) Evaluate the volume integral of the vector field

$$\mathbf{F}(P) = \|\overrightarrow{OP}\|^2(\overrightarrow{OP})$$

over the unit cube centered at O (Figure 11.36). Again $\mathfrak{D}$ is capped (with sides) relative to all three axes. In order to illustrate how (4.2) is to be modified let us this time exploit the fact that $\mathfrak{D}$ is capped relative to Ox^2. In particular, relative to Ox^2 it has the following top and bottom:

$$\text{(i)} \quad \begin{aligned} &S_2\colon x^2 \equiv \tfrac{1}{2}, \qquad |x^1| \le \tfrac{1}{2},\ |x^3| \le \tfrac{1}{2}, \\ &S_1\colon x^2 \equiv -\tfrac{1}{2}, \qquad |x^1| \le \tfrac{1}{2},\ |x^3| \le \tfrac{1}{2}. \end{aligned}$$

Moreover, $\mathbf{F}$ has the following coordinate form:

$$\text{(ii)} \quad \begin{aligned} \mathbf{F}(x^1, x^2, x^3) = {} & [x^1((x^1)^2 + (x^2)^2 + (x^3)^2)]\mathbf{e}_1 \\ & + [x^2((x^1)^2 + (x^2)^2 + (x^3)^2)]\mathbf{e}_2 \\ & + (x^3[(x^1)^2 + (x^2)^2 + (x^3)^2)]\mathbf{e}_3. \end{aligned}$$

Corresponding to (4.2d) we have,

$$\text{(iii)} \quad \iiint_{\mathfrak{D}} \mathbf{F}(P)\, dV$$

$$= \Big[\iint_{|x^1|,|x^3| \le 1/2} \Big(\int_{-1/2}^{1/2} x^1((x^1)^2 + s^2 + (x^3)^2)\, ds \Big)\, dx^1\, dx^3 \Big] \mathbf{e}_1$$

$$+ \Big[\iint_{|x^1|,|x^3| \le 1/2} \Big(\int_{-1/2}^{1/2} s((x^1)^2 + s^2 + (x^3)^2)\, ds \Big)\, dx^1\, dx^3 \Big] \mathbf{e}_2$$

$$+ \Big[\iint_{|x^1|,|x^3| \le 1/2} \Big(\int_{-1/2}^{1/2} x^3((x^1)^2 + s^2 + (x^3)^2)\, ds \Big)\, dx^1\, dx^3 \Big] \mathbf{e}_3.$$

It is not hard to show in this example that *all three* double integrals on the right are zero. Hence the answer is

$$\text{(iv)} \quad \iiint_{\mathfrak{D}} \mathbf{F}(P)\, dV = \mathbf{0}.$$

Next we define surface integrals.

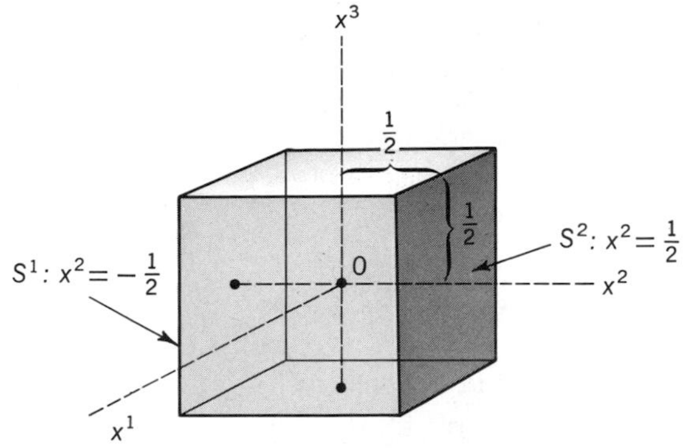

Figure 11.36

(4.5) Definitions

1. Let f: $\mathfrak{D} \to (-\infty, \infty)$ denote a continuous scalar field and let S denote a surface in $\mathfrak{D}$ which is part of the top (or bottom) of a capped domain $\mathfrak{D}'$ in $\mathfrak{D}$. For instance, suppose that relative to Ox^3, S can be expressed in the form (Figure 11.33)

(a) S: $x^3 = \psi(x^1, x^2)$, $(x^1, x^2) \in \mathfrak{D}_{(3)}$, ψ: $\mathfrak{D}_{(3)} \to (-\infty, \infty)$ a smooth scalar field.

Then we assign to f and S a scalar called the **surface integral** of f over S and denoted by

$$\text{(b)} \qquad \iint_S f(P)\, dA.$$

By definition, for S as in (a), this quantity denotes the ordinary double integral† [see (a)]:

$$\text{(c)} \qquad \iint_S f(P)\, dA$$

$$= \iint_{\mathfrak{D}_{(3)}} f(x^1, x^2, \psi(x^1, x^2))\sqrt{1 + (\psi_{x^1}(x^1, x^2))^2 + (\psi_{x^2}(x^1, x^2))^2}\, dx^1\, dx^2.$$

In other cases, when S is part of a cap relative to Ox^1 or Ox^2, the surface integral is equal to an ordinary double integral which is obtained from

†This integral, with $f(P) \equiv 1$, is used to *define* surface area.

that in (c) by relabeling variables†. [The factor $\sqrt{1 + (\psi_{x^1})^2 + (\psi_{x^2})^2}$ occurring in the double integral represents $|\sec \gamma|$, where γ is the angle between the normal to S and the arrow $\mathbf{e}_3$ (see the problems).]

2. Let $\mathbf{F}\colon \mathfrak{D} \to \mathfrak{A}$ denote a continuous vector field having coordinate form

$$\mathbf{F}(x^1, x^2, x^3) = f^1(x^1, x^2, x^3)\mathbf{e}_1 + f^2(x^1, x^2, x^3)\mathbf{e}_2 + f^3(x^1, x^2, x^3)\mathbf{e}_3$$

and let S be a surface in $\mathfrak{D}$ which is part of a cap relative to some axis. Then we assign to $\mathbf{F}$ and S a scalar called the (*upward*) **normal surface integral** of F over S and denoted by

$$\text{(d)} \qquad \iint_S \mathbf{F}(P) \cdot \mathbf{n}(P)\, dA.$$

By definition, for S as in (a), this quantity denotes the double integral

$$\text{(e)} \quad \iint_S \mathbf{F}(P) \cdot \mathbf{n}(P)\, dA = \iint_{\mathfrak{D}(3)} [-f^1(x^1, x^2, \psi(x^1, x^2))\psi_{x^1}(x^1, x^2) - f^2(x^1, x^2, \psi(x^1, x^2))\psi_{x^2}(x^1, x^2) + f^3(x^1, x^2, \psi(x^1, x^2))]\, dx^1\, dx^2.$$

In other cases, when S is part of a cap relative to Ox^1 or Ox^2, the surface integral is equal to an ordinary double integral which is obtained from that in (e) by relabeling variables.†

[There is another quantity, called the (*downward*) *normal surface integral* of $\mathbf{F}$ over S, which is likewise denoted by $\iint_S \mathbf{F}(P) \cdot \mathbf{n}(P)\, dA$ but which corresponds to the following ordinary double integral:

$$\text{(e}'\text{)} \quad \iint_{\mathfrak{D}(3)} [f^1(x^1, x^2, \psi(x^1, x^2))\psi_{x^1}(x^1, x^2) + f^2(x^1, x^2, \psi(x^1, x^2))\psi_{x^2}(x^1, x^2) - f^3(x^1, x^2, \psi(x^1, x^2))]\, dx^1\, dx^2$$

and hence is equal *except for sign* to the quantity in (e) (see Figure 11.37).]

†As with (4.2), it can be proved that when S is part of a cap relative to two or more axes, then the double integrals in (c) or (e) corresponding to these various axes all turn out to be equal.

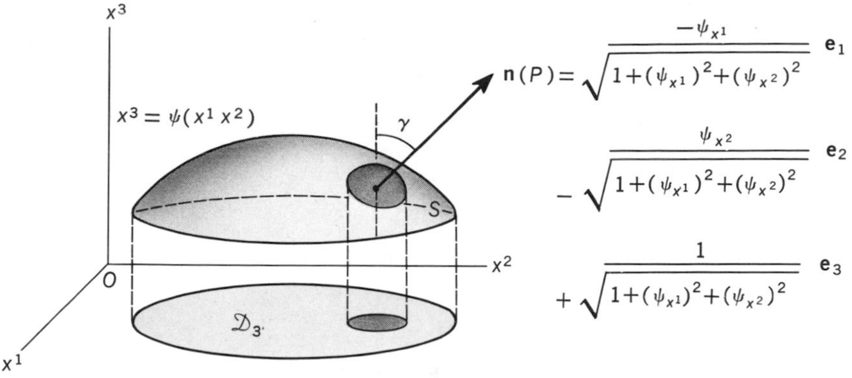

Figure 11.37

The reason for the factors multiplying f^1, f^2, f^3 in (4.5e) and (4.5e′) is that the upward unit normal at points of S has the following coordinate form (see the problems):

$$\mathbf{n}(P) = \frac{-\psi_{x^1}(x^1, x^2)}{\sqrt{1 + (\psi_{x^1})^2 + (\psi_{x^2})^2}}\,\mathbf{e}_1 - \frac{\psi_{x^2}(x^1, x^2)}{\sqrt{1 + (\psi_{x^1})^2 + (\psi_{x^2})^2}}\,\mathbf{e}_2$$
$$+ \frac{1}{\sqrt{1 + (\psi_{x^1})^2 + (\psi_{x^2})^2}}\,\mathbf{e}_3,$$

(and correspondingly for the downward unit normal) while according to (4.5c) dA is to be replaced by

$$\sqrt{1 + (\psi_{x^1})^2 + (\psi_{x^2})^2}\, dx^1\, dx^2.$$

(4.6) Examples. Surface Integrals

(a) Evaluate the surface integral of the scalar field

$$f(P) = \overrightarrow{OP} \cdot \gamma \qquad \gamma \text{ fixed},$$

over the "northern" hemisphere of the unit sphere centered at O. Here (see Figure 11.35) $S = S_2$ has the form

(i) $\quad S\colon x^3 = \sqrt{1 - (x^1)^2 - (x^2)^2}, \qquad (x^1)^2 + (x^2)^2 \leq 1,$

and f has the coordinate form

$$\text{(ii)} \quad f(x^1, x^2, x^3) = c_1x^1 + c_2x^2 + c_3x^3,$$
$$\text{where } \gamma = c_1\mathbf{e}_1 + c_2\mathbf{e}_2 + c_3\mathbf{e}_3.$$

Hence, by (4.4c), with $\mathfrak{D}_{(3)}$ the region

$$(x^1)^2 + (x^2)^2 \leq 1,$$

we have

$$\text{(iii)} \quad \iint_S f(P)\,dA = \iint_{\mathfrak{D}_{(3)}} \left(c_1x^1 + c_2x^2 + c_3\sqrt{1 - (x^1)^2 - (x^2)^2}\right) \times \frac{dx^1\,dx^2}{\sqrt{1 - (x^1)^2 - (x^2)^2}}.$$

It is not hard to show that only the term in the integrand involving c_3 makes a nonzero contribution and hence that

$$\text{(iv)} \quad \iint_S f(P)\,dA = c_3\left(\iint_{(x^1)^2+(x^2)^2\leq 1} 1\,dx^1\,dx^2\right) = c_3\pi.$$

(b) Evaluate the *outward* normal surface integral of the vector field

$$\mathbf{F}(P) = \|\overrightarrow{OP}\|^2(\overrightarrow{OP})$$

over the entire surface of the unit sphere. That is, take the *upward* normal surface integral over the northern hemisphere and the *downward* normal surface integral over the southern hemisphere (Figure 11.38). Here [see (4.3a)] the hemispheres have the coordinate form

$$\text{(i)} \quad \begin{aligned} S_2&: x^3 = \sqrt{1 - (x^1)^2 - (x^2)^2}, \qquad (x^1)^2 + (x^2)^2 \leq 1 \\ S_1&: x^3 = -\sqrt{1 - (x^1)^2 - (x^2)^2}, \qquad (x^1)^2 + (x^2)^2 \leq 1, \end{aligned}$$

and $\mathbf{F}$ has the coordinate form

$$\text{(ii)} \quad \begin{aligned} \mathbf{F}(x^1, x^2, x^3) = {} & x^1((x^1)^2 + (x^2)^2 + (x^3)^2)\mathbf{e}_1 \\ & + x^2((x^1)^2 + (x^2)^2 + (x^3)^2)\mathbf{e}_2 \\ & + x^3((x^1)^2 + (x^2)^2 + (x^3)^2)\mathbf{e}_3. \end{aligned}$$

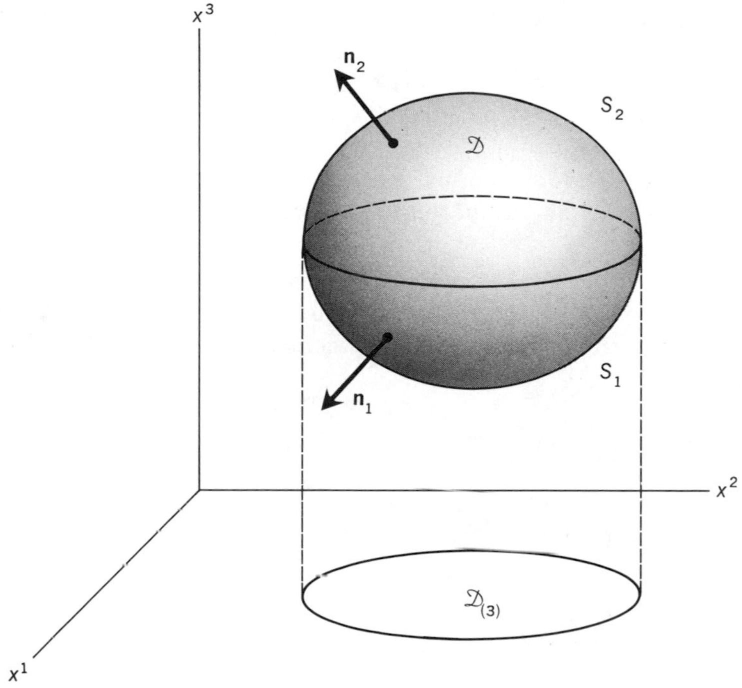

Figure 11.38

Hence by (4.4e), and (4.4e′), taking the integrals over S_1 and S_2 separately, we obtain

$$\text{(iii)} \qquad \iint_S \mathbf{F}(P)\cdot\mathbf{n}(P)\,dA$$

$$= \iint_{S_2} \mathbf{F}(P)\cdot\mathbf{n}_2(P)\,dA + \iint_{S_1} \mathbf{F}(P)\cdot\mathbf{n}_1(P)\,dA$$

$$= 2\iint_{(x^1)^2+(x^2)^2\le 1}\left[\frac{(x^1)^2}{\sqrt{1-(x^1)^2-(x^2)^2}} + \frac{(x^2)^2}{\sqrt{1-(x^1)^2-(x^2)^2}} + \sqrt{1-(x^1)^2-(x^2)^2}\right]dx^1\,dx^2$$

$$= 2\iint_{(x^1)^2+(x^2)^2\le 1}\left[\frac{1}{\sqrt{1-(x^1)^2-(x^2)^2}}\right]dx^1\,dx^2.$$

The final integral can readily be evaluated (see the problems) and we obtain

$$\text{(iv)} \qquad \iint_S \mathbf{F}(P) \cdot \mathbf{n}(P)\, dA = 4\pi.$$

The notion of *outward* normal surface integral as discussed in example (4.6b) is sufficiently important to be stated explicitly.

(4.7) Definition. Let $\mathbf{F}\colon \mathfrak{D} \to \mathfrak{A}$ denote a continuous vector field defined in a capped domain $\mathfrak{D}$ and let S denote the boundary of $\mathfrak{D}$. Then we assign to $\mathbf{F}$ and S a quantity called the **outward normal surface integral of F over** S and denoted by

$$\iint_S \mathbf{F}(P) \cdot \mathbf{n}(P)\, dA \qquad \left[\text{or } \oiint_S \mathbf{F}(P) \cdot \mathbf{n}(P)\, dA\right]\cdot$$

By definition this quantity denotes the sum of the *upward* normal surface integral of $\mathbf{F}$ over S_2 and the *downward* normal surface integral of $\mathbf{F}$ over S_1,

$$\text{(a)} \qquad \iint_S \mathbf{F}(P) \cdot \mathbf{n}(P)\, dA = \iint_{S_2} \mathbf{F}(P) \cdot \mathbf{n}(P)\, dA + \iint_{S_1} \mathbf{F}(P) \cdot \mathbf{n}(P)\, dA.$$

Here S_2 and S_1 denote the top and bottom of S relative to some coordinate axis, and the first integral on the right is an upward normal surface integral while the second is a downward normal surface integral.

There are several important theorems relating the various kinds of surface and volume integrals to one another. These results all bear an analogy to the formula

$$\text{(4.8a)} \qquad \int_a^b h'(x)\, dx = h(b) - h(a),$$

which expresses the integral of the derivative of h as a difference of h values at the end points of the interval, as well as to the formula

$$\text{(4.8b)} \qquad \int_{P_2}^{P_1} \nabla f(P) \cdot d\mathbf{r} = f(P_2) - f(P_1),$$

which expresses the line integral of ∇f as a difference of f values at the end points of the curve. Knowing that (4.8a) is the foundation stone of integration for functions of *one* variable and that (4.8b) plays a vital role for line integrals, the reader will not be overly surprised to learn that the corresponding theorems for surface and volume integrals are exceedingly important. The first such theorem is stated below.

(4.9) Divergence Theorem. *Let $\mathfrak{D}$ be a capped domain with boundary surface S. Let* $\mathbf{F}\colon \mathfrak{D} \to \mathcal{A}$ *be a smooth vector field defined over $\mathfrak{D}$. Then the* volume *integral over $\mathfrak{D}$ of the divergence of* $\mathbf{F}$ *equals the outward normal* surface *integral over S of* $\mathbf{F}$: *that is,*

$$\text{(a)} \qquad \iiint_{\mathfrak{D}} \operatorname{div} \mathbf{F}(P)\, dV = \iint_S \mathbf{F}(P) \cdot \mathbf{n}(P)\, dA.$$

[Note that both sides of equation (4.9a) are scalars, so the stated equality at least makes sense.]

Proof. In our proof we shall supply the argument only for domains $\mathfrak{D}$ which are capped relative to all the axes of a prescribed coordinate system. From this case it is possible to deduce the result for more general domains $\mathfrak{D}$ by splitting $\mathfrak{D}$ into capped pieces (with sides), but we shall not discuss that part of the process.

The key idea used in the argument is to regard the vector field $\mathbf{F}$, with coordinate form

$$\text{(i)} \quad \mathbf{F}(x^1, x^2, x^3) = f^1(x^1, x^2, x^3)\mathbf{e}_1 + f^2(x^1, x^2, x^3)\mathbf{e}_2 + f^3(x^1, x^2, x^3)\mathbf{e}_3,$$

as the sum of three other vector fields $\mathbf{G}^1$, $\mathbf{G}^2$, $\mathbf{G}^3$, each of which has two components equal to zero. That is,

$$\text{(ii)} \qquad \mathbf{F}(x^1, x^2, x^3) = \mathbf{G}^1(x^1, x^2, x^3) + \mathbf{G}^2(x^1, x^2, x^3) + \mathbf{G}^3(x^1, x^2, x^3),$$

where

$$\text{(iii)} \qquad \begin{aligned} \mathbf{G}^1(x^1, x^2, x^3) &= f^1(x^1, x^2, x^3)\mathbf{e}_1 + 0\mathbf{e}_2 + 0\mathbf{e}_3 \\ \mathbf{G}^2(x^1, x^2, x^3) &= 0\mathbf{e}_1 + f^2(x^1, x^2, x^3)\mathbf{e}_2 + 0\mathbf{e}_3 \\ \mathbf{G}^3(x^1, x^2, x^3) &= 0\mathbf{e}_1 + 0\mathbf{e}_2 + f^3(x^1, x^2, x^3)\mathbf{e}_3. \end{aligned}$$

Now it is easily verified by inspection of (2.11b) that

$$\text{(iv)} \qquad \operatorname{div} \mathbf{F} = \operatorname{div} \mathbf{G}^1 + \operatorname{div} \mathbf{G}^2 + \operatorname{div} \mathbf{G}^3.$$

It is also clear from (4.4e) that

$$\text{(v)} \quad \iint_S \mathbf{F}(P) \cdot \mathbf{n}(P)\, dA = \iint_S \mathbf{G}^1(P) \cdot \mathbf{n}(P)\, dA + \iint_S \mathbf{G}^2(P) \cdot \mathbf{n}(P)\, dA + \iint_S \mathbf{G}^3(P) \cdot \mathbf{n}(P)\, dA.$$

Hence in order to prove (4.9a), it suffices that we prove each of the following:

$$\text{(vi)} \qquad \iiint_{\mathfrak{D}} \operatorname{div} \mathbf{G}^i(P)\, dV = \iint_S \mathbf{G}^i(P) \cdot \mathbf{n}(P)\, dA, \qquad i = 1, 2, 3.$$

For, by adding together the three equations in (vi) and using (iv), we obtain (4.9a) itself.

We shall prove (vi) for $i = 3$, leaving the other two cases to the reader. That is, we will prove

$$\text{(vii)} \qquad \iiint_{\mathfrak{D}} \operatorname{div} \mathbf{G}^3(P)\, dV = \iint_S \mathbf{G}^3(P) \cdot \mathbf{n}(P)\, dA.$$

Now according to (4.2b) and (2.11b) the volume integral in (vii) is given by

$$\text{(viii)} \qquad \iiint_{\mathfrak{D}} \operatorname{div} \mathbf{G}^3(P)\, dV = \iint_{\mathfrak{D}(3)} \left(\int_{\psi^1(x^1,x^2)}^{\psi^2(x^1,x^2)} (0 + 0 + f^3_{x^3}(x^1, x^2, s))\, ds \right) dx^1\, dx^2.$$

However, we can evaluate the integral in parentheses by use of the result (4.8a) for functions of one variable, hence (viii) reduces to

$$\text{(ix)} \qquad \iiint_{\mathfrak{D}} \operatorname{div} \mathbf{G}^3(P)\, dV = \iint_{\mathfrak{D}(3)} [f^3(x^1, x^2, \psi^2(x^1, x^2)) - f^3(x^1, x^2, \psi^1(x^1, x^2))]\, dx^1\, dx^2.$$

On the other hand, according to (4.5e) and (4.5e′), the surface integral in (vii) is given by [using the decomposition (4.1) of S into a top and a bottom]:

$$\text{(x)} \qquad \iint_S \mathbf{G}^3(P) \cdot \mathbf{n}(P)\, dA = \iint_{\mathfrak{D}(3)} [0 + 0 + f^3(x^1, x^2, \psi^2(x^1, x^2))]\, dx^1\, dx^2 + \iint_{\mathfrak{D}(3)} [0 + 0 - f^3(x^1, x^2, \psi^1(x^1, x^2))]\, dx^1\, dx^2.$$

A comparison of (ix) and (x) yields (vii). This completes the proof, aside from the need for the reader to verify the analogs of (vii) for $\mathbf{G}^2$ and $\mathbf{G}^1$. ▌

Note that in proving the analogs of (vii) for $\mathbf{G}^2$ and $\mathbf{G}^1$ it will be necessary to express both the surface integral and volume integral as double integrals

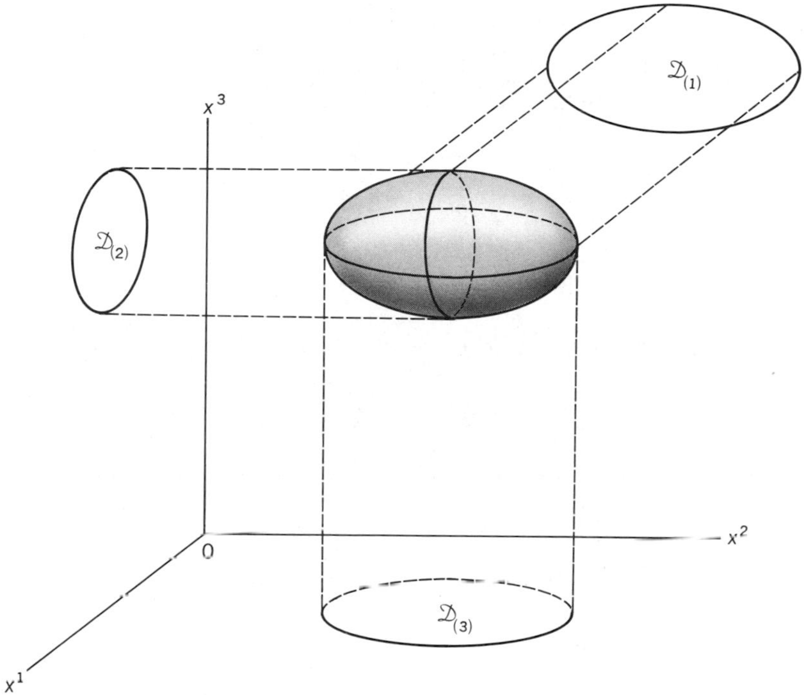

Figure 11.39

over $\mathfrak{D}_{(2)}$ in the case of $\mathbf{G}^2$, and as double integrals over $\mathfrak{D}_{(1)}$ in the case of $\mathbf{G}^1$ (see Figure 11.39).

The second of our integration theorems relates surface integrals to line integrals.

(4.10) Stokes' Theorem. *Let* $\mathbf{F}: \mathfrak{D} \to \mathfrak{A}$ *be a smooth vector field and let S be a surface in $\mathfrak{D}$ whose edge forms a piecewise smooth closed curve C (Figure* 11.40). *Then the upward normal surface integral of* curl **F** *over S is equal to the tangential line integral of* **F** *along C, the direction in which C is traversed being that which always maintains S on the left (when looked at from above). That is*

$$\text{(a)} \qquad \iint_S \operatorname{curl} \mathbf{F}(P) \cdot \mathbf{n}(P)\, dA = \oint_C \mathbf{F}(P) \cdot d\mathbf{r}.$$

We omit the proof of this result.

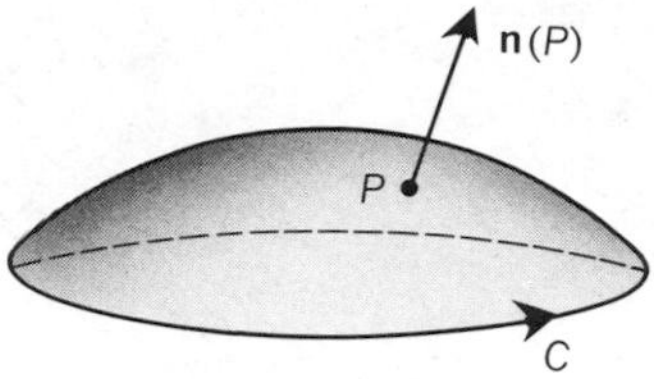

Figure 11.40

(4.11) Examples. Divergence Theorem

(a) Evaluate the outward normal surface integral of the vector field

$$\mathbf{F}(P) = \overrightarrow{OP}$$

over the unit sphere $\mathfrak{D}$. Here we can avoid the explicit evaluation of double integrals. Since $\mathbf{F}$ has the coordinate form

$$\text{(i)} \qquad \mathbf{F}(x^1, x^2, x^3) = x^1\mathbf{e}_1 + x^2\mathbf{e}_2 + x^3\mathbf{e}_3,$$

it follows by (2.11b) that

$$\text{(ii)} \qquad \operatorname{div} \mathbf{F}(P) = 3 \qquad \text{for all } P \in \mathfrak{D}.$$

Hence by (4.9) we deduce that

$$\text{(iii)} \qquad \iint_S \mathbf{F}(P) \cdot \mathbf{n}(P)\, dA = \iiint_{\mathfrak{D}} \operatorname{div} \mathbf{F}(P)\, dV$$

$$= 3 \iiint_{\mathfrak{D}} dV = 3 \operatorname{vol} \mathfrak{D}.$$

Since the volume of the unit sphere is $4\pi/3$, we deduce that

$$\text{(iv)} \qquad \iint_S \mathbf{F}(P) \cdot \mathbf{n}(P)\, dA = 4\pi.$$

(b) Evaluate the outward normal surface integral of the vector field

$$\text{(i)} \qquad F(P) = (\overrightarrow{OP}) \times \gamma, \qquad \gamma \text{ fixed},$$

over the surface of the unit cube. Here $\mathbf{F}$ has the coordinate form [see (2.9) of Chapter 2]

(ii) $\mathbf{F}(x^1, x^2, x^3) = (c_3x^2 - c_2x^3)\mathbf{e}_1 + (c_1x^3 - c_3x^1)\mathbf{e}_2 + (c_2x^1 - c_1x^2)\mathbf{e}_3,$

where $\gamma = c_1\mathbf{e}_1 + c_2\mathbf{e}_2 + c_3\mathbf{e}_3$.

It follows by (2.11b) that

(iii) $\operatorname{div} \mathbf{F}(P) = 0 \quad \text{for all } P.$

Hence by the divergence theorem

(iv) $$\iint_S \mathbf{F}(P) \cdot \mathbf{n}(P)\, dA = \iiint_{\mathfrak{D}} \operatorname{div} \mathbf{F}(P)\, dV = 0.$$

As a final comment in this section we point out that problems in surface and volume integrals are often facilitated by introducing polar coordinates. This device frequently simplifies the evaluation of the necessary double integrals. For example, suppose we want to integrate a function f of two variables x^1, x^2 over a region R in the (x^1, x^2) plane. We introduce polar coordinates r and θ defined by

(i) $x^1 = r\cos\theta, \qquad x^2 = r\sin\theta, \qquad 0 \le \theta < 2\pi.$

It often happens that the boundaries of R are easily described in terms of r and θ. For example, the region $a^2 < (x^1)^2 + (x^2)^2 < b^2$ in Figure 11.41a is a ring. In polar coordinates it is described by $a < r < b$, $0 \le \theta \le 2\pi$, so that its boundaries are $r = a$, $r = b$, $\theta = 0$, and $\theta = 2\pi$. The half-ring in Figure 11.41b is described by $a < r < b$, $0 \le \theta \le \pi$, so that here the boundaries are $r = a$, $r = b$, $\theta = 0$, and $\theta = \pi$.

Suppose we wished to integrate the function $f(x^1, x^2) = (x^1)^2(x^2)^2$ over either of the regions in Figure 11.41 It would be rather complicated to set up

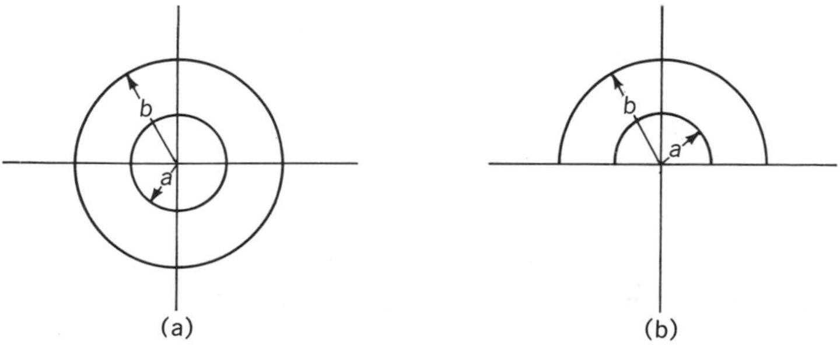

Figure 11.41

the integral in the usual way because of the fact that the boundaries depend in a complicated way on x^1 and x^2. Instead we can use polar coordinates and the following general principle: *When a function f of x^1, x^2 is to be integrated over a region R which can be described by*

$$r_1 < r < r_2, \qquad \theta_1 < \theta < \theta_2,$$

then the integral of f over R is equal to the quantity

$$\int_{\theta_1}^{\theta_2} \int_{r_1}^{r_2} f(r\cos\theta, r\sin\theta) r\, dr\, d\theta. \tag{4.12}$$

[Note the extra r in the integrand of (4.12).]

Let us apply this result to the integration of the function $f(x^1, x^2) = (x^1)^2(x^2)^2$ over the regions in Figure 11.41. For the region in Figure 11.41a formula (4.12) yields

$$\begin{aligned}\int_0^{2\pi} \int_a^b (r^2\cos^2\theta)(r^2\sin^2\theta) r\, dr\, d\theta &= \left[\frac{r^6}{6}\right]_a^b \int_0^{2\pi} \cos^2\theta \sin^2\theta\, d\theta \\ &= \left(\frac{b^6}{6} - \frac{a^6}{6}\right)\frac{1}{4}\int_0^{2\pi} \sin^2 2\theta\, d\theta \\ &= \frac{\pi}{4}\left(\frac{b^6}{6} - \frac{a^6}{6}\right).\end{aligned}$$

For the region in Figure 11.41b, the computation is the same except that θ now runs only from 0 to π. Thus we obtain, from (4.12),

$$\int_0^{\pi} \int_a^b r^2\cos^2\theta\; r^2\sin^2\theta\; r\, dr\, d\theta.$$

This is seen to yield

$$\frac{\pi}{8}\left(\frac{b^6}{6} - \frac{a^6}{6}\right).$$

Polar coordinates will often be of assistance in working the problems which follow.

PROBLEMS

In each of the problems below $\mathfrak{D}$ is the capped domain with $S_2: x^3 = \psi^2(x^1, x^2)$ as top and $S_1: x^3 = \psi^1(x^1, x^2)$ as bottom, where (x^1, x^2) ranges over the circle $(x^1)^2 + (x^2)^2 \leq 1$. For the given vector field F calculate separately the integrals

$$\iiint_{\mathfrak{D}} \operatorname{div} \mathbf{F}(P)\, dV, \qquad \iint_{S} \mathbf{F}(P) \cdot \mathbf{n}(P)\, dA,$$

taking the *outward* normal in the latter integral.

1. $\mathbf{F}(x^1, x^2, x^3) = x_1\mathbf{e}_1 + x_2\mathbf{e}_2 + x_3\mathbf{e}_3$

$$\psi^1(x^1, x^2) = 1 - \sqrt{(x^1)^2 + (x^2)^2}, \psi^2(x^1, x^2) = -1 + \sqrt{(x^1)^2 + (x^2)^2}.$$

2. $\mathbf{F}(x^1, x^2, x^3) = x^2\mathbf{e}_1 - x^1\mathbf{e}_2 + x^3\mathbf{e}_3$

$$\psi^1(x^1, x^2) = 1 - (x^1)^2 - (x^2)^2,\ \psi^2(x^1, x^2) = -1 + (x^1)^2 + (x^2)^2.$$

3. $\mathbf{F}(x^1, x^2, x^3) = x^1\mathbf{e}_1 + x^2\mathbf{e}_2 + x^3\mathbf{e}_3$

$$\psi^1(x^1, x^2) = 1 - \sqrt{(x^1)^2 + (x^2)^2},\ \psi^2(x^1, x^2) = -1 + \sqrt{(x^1)^2 + (x^2)^2}.$$

4. $\mathbf{F} = (x^1, x^2, x^3) = x^1x^2\mathbf{e}_1$

$$\psi^1(x^1, x^2) = 1 - (x^1)^2 - (x^2)^2,\ \psi^2(x^1, x^2) = -1 + (x^1)^2 + (x^2)^2.$$

5. $F(x^1, x^2, x^3) = x^1\mathbf{e}_1 + x^2\mathbf{e}_2 + x^3\mathbf{e}_3$

$$\psi^1(x^1, x^2) = \sqrt{1 - (x^1)^2 - (x^2)^2},\ \psi^2 = -\sqrt{1 - (x^1)^2 - (x^2)^2}.$$

6. Compute $\iiint_{\mathfrak{D}} f(P)\, dV$, where

$$f(x^1, x^2, x^3) = x^1 + x^2 + x^3$$

and $\mathfrak{D}$ is the right circular cylinder of height 2 whose base is the unit circle $(x^1)^2 + (x^2)^2 \leq 1$.

7. Show that if R denotes a region in the x-y plane which is symmetric about both axes, then

$$\iint_R f(x, y)\, dx\, dy = 0$$

in each of the following cases:

(i)	$f(-x, y) \equiv -f(x, y)$	f *is odd in* x
(ii)	$f(x, -y) \equiv -f(x, y)$	f *is odd in* y
(iii)	$f(-x, -y) \equiv -f(x, y)$	f *is odd in* x, y.

8. Given a rectangle R, located as in Figure 11.42, in a plane whose normal makes an angle γ with the normal to the x-y plane, show directly that the area of R has the following relation to the area of its projection R' on the x-y plane:

$$\text{area } R = (\text{area } R') \sec \gamma$$

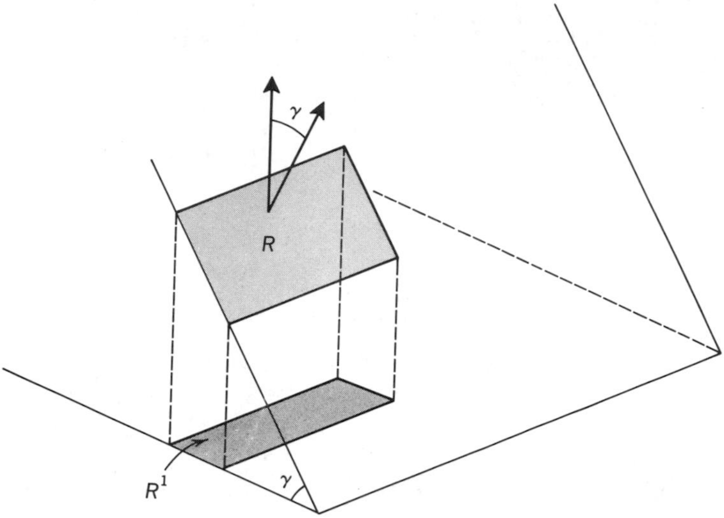

Figure 11.42

***9.** (a) Prove that, for a surface S of the form

$$S: x^3 = \psi(x^1, x^2) \qquad (x^1, x^2) \in \mathfrak{D}_{(3)},$$

the upward unit normal to S has the form

$$\mathbf{n}(P) = \frac{-\psi_{x^1}(x^1, x^2)}{\sqrt{1 + (\psi_{x^1}(x^1, x^2))^2 + (\psi_{x^2}(x^1, x^2))^2}}\,\mathbf{e}_1 - \frac{\psi_{x^2}(x^1, x^2)}{\sqrt{1 + (\psi_{x^1}(x^1, x^2))^2 + (\psi_{x^2}(x^1, x^2))^2}}\,\mathbf{e}_2 + \frac{1}{\sqrt{1 + (\psi_{x^1}(x^1, x^2))^2 + (\psi_{x^2}(x^1, x^2))^2}}\,\mathbf{e}_3 \qquad \text{for } P \sim (x^1, x^2).$$

(*Hint:* See §1, problem 13.)

(b) Show that with γ the angle between $\mathbf{n}(P)$ and $\mathbf{e}_3$ the following formula holds:

$$\sec \gamma(P) = \sqrt{1 + (\psi_{x^1}(x^1, x^2))^2 + (\psi_{x^2}(x^1, x^2))^2} \qquad \text{for } P \sim (x^1, x^2),$$

so that the transition

$$dA \to \sqrt{1 + (\psi_{x^1})^2 + (\psi_{x^2})^2}\, dx^1\, dx^2$$

is consistent with problem 7.

Linearity of Surface and Volume Integration

10. (a) Show that if $f: \mathfrak{D} \to (-\infty, \infty)$, $g: \mathfrak{D} \to (-\infty, \infty)$ are continuous scalar fields on the domain $\mathfrak{D}$, then

$$\iiint_{\mathfrak{D}} (cf(P) + dg(P))\, dV = c \iiint_{\mathfrak{D}} f(P)\, dV + d \iiint_{\mathfrak{D}} g(P)\, dV \qquad \text{for all } c, d.$$

That is, *for fixed* $\mathfrak{D}$ *the volume integration of scalar fields is linear with respect to the integrand.*

(b) Show that if $\mathbf{F}: \mathfrak{D} \to \mathfrak{A}$, $\mathbf{G}: \mathfrak{D} \to \mathfrak{A}$ are continuous vector fields on the domain $\mathfrak{D}$, then

$$\iiint_{\mathfrak{D}} (c\mathbf{F}(P) + d\mathbf{G}(P))\, dV = c \iiint_{\mathfrak{D}} \mathbf{F}(P)\, dV + d \iiint_{\mathfrak{D}} \mathbf{G}(P)\, dV \qquad \text{for all } c, d.$$

That is, *for fixed* $\mathfrak{D}$ *the volume integration of vector fields is linear with respect to the integrand.* (*Hint:* Examine the ordinary double integrals to which the volume integrals reduce.)

11. (a) Show that if $f: \mathfrak{D} \to (-\infty, \infty)$, $g: \mathfrak{D} \to (-\infty, \infty)$ are continuous scalar fields on the domain $\mathfrak{D}$ and S is a fixed surface lying on the top (or bottom) of a capped region $\mathfrak{D}'$ in $\mathfrak{D}$, then

$$\iint_{S} (cf(P) + dg(P))\, dA = c \iint_{S} f(P)\, dA + d \iint_{S} g(P)\, dA \qquad \text{for all } c, d.$$

That is, *for fixed* S *the surface integration of scalar fields is linear with respect to the integrand.*

(b) Show that if $\mathbf{F}: \mathfrak{D} \to \mathfrak{A}$, $\mathbf{G}: \mathfrak{D} \to \mathfrak{A}$ are continuous vector fields on the domain $\mathfrak{D}$ and S is a fixed surface lying on the top (or bottom) of a capped region $\mathfrak{D}'$ in $\mathfrak{D}$, then

$$\iint_{S} (c\mathbf{F}(P) + d\mathbf{G}(P)) \cdot \mathbf{n}(P)\, dA = c \iint_{S} \mathbf{F}(P) \cdot \mathbf{n}(P)\, dA + d \iint_{S} \mathbf{G}(P) \cdot \mathbf{n}(P)\, dA \qquad \text{for all } c, d.$$

That is, *for fixed* S *the* (*upward, downward, or outer*) *normal surface integration of vector fields is linear with respect to the integrand.*

12. Define $\boldsymbol{\beta} = \iint \mathbf{F}(P)\, dA$, the *surface integral of* $\mathbf{F}$ *over* S, by giving an appropriate formula for this arrow. (Here $\mathbf{F}: \mathfrak{D} \to \mathfrak{A}$ is a smooth vector field and S denotes a surface which is part of a cap, relative to Ox^3 say.) (*Hint:* Find the integral over S of each component of $\mathbf{F} = f^1\mathbf{e}_1 + f^2\mathbf{e}_2 + f^3\mathbf{e}_3$.)

13. Given a smooth vector field $\mathbf{F}: \mathfrak{D} \to \mathfrak{A}$, the surface integral $\iint \mathbf{F}(P) \cdot \mathbf{n}(P)\, dA$ is said to be *surface-independent* provided that for any two surfaces S, S' in $\mathfrak{D}$ *whose edges are the same curve* the condition

$$\iint_{S} \mathbf{F}(P) \cdot \mathbf{n}(P)\, dA = \iint_{S'} \mathbf{F}(P) \cdot \mathbf{n}(P)\, dA$$

is satisfied [here $\mathbf{n}(P)$ is to be the *upper* normal surface integral for both surfaces (Figure 11.43)]. Prove that for every field $\mathbf{F}$ with zero divergence the integral

$$\iint_S \mathbf{F}(P) \cdot \mathbf{n}(P)\, dA$$

is surface-independent. (*Hint:* Examine the case in which S and S' meet at C and are caps for a domain $\mathfrak{D}$. Apply the divergence theorem.)

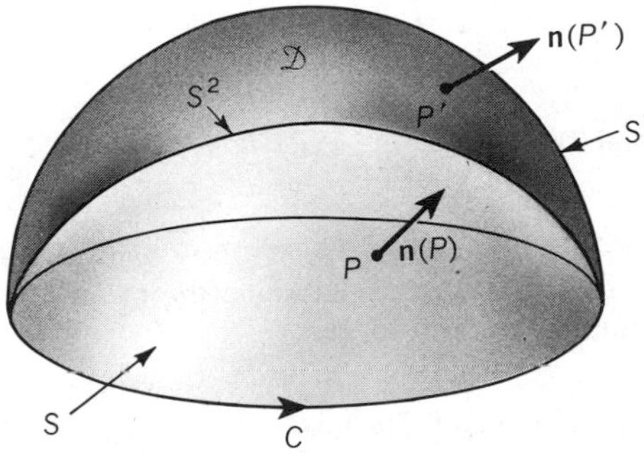

Figure 11.43

14. GREEN'S THEOREM FOR THE PLANE. Let $\mathbf{F}\colon \mathfrak{D} \to \mathfrak{A}$ be a smooth two-dimensional vector field with coordinate form

$$\mathbf{F}(x, y) = f^1(x, y)\mathbf{e}_1 + f^2(x, y)\mathbf{e}_2.$$

For any closed curve C lying in $\mathfrak{D}$ *all* of whose interior $\mathfrak{D}_C$ is also in $\mathfrak{D}$, the following relation holds:

$$\oint_C f^1(x, y)\, dx + f^2(x, y)\, dy = \iint_{\mathfrak{D}_C} (f_y^2(x, y) - f_x^1(x, y))\, dx\, dy.$$

Prove this. (*Hint:* The planar domain $\mathfrak{D}$ is a surface to which Stokes' theorem is applicable.)

15. If $\mathfrak{D}$ is a capped domain with boundary surface S and $f\colon \mathfrak{D} \to (-\infty, \infty)$ and $g\colon \mathfrak{D} \to (-\infty, \infty)$ are smooth scalar fields defined in $\mathfrak{D}$—∇f and ∇g also being smooth—show that

$$\iiint_{\mathfrak{D}} [f(P)\,\Delta g(P) + \nabla f(P) \cdot \nabla g(P)]\, dV = \iint_S (f(P)\nabla g(P)) \cdot \mathbf{n}(P)\, dA.$$

(*Hint:* Use problem 16, §2.)

16. Suppose $f\colon \mathfrak{D} \to (-\infty, \infty)$ is a smooth scalar field in the capped domain $\mathfrak{D}$ bounded by S, and that $\nabla f\colon \mathfrak{D} \to \mathfrak{A}$ is a smooth vector field. Suppose further that $\Delta f \equiv 0$ in $\mathfrak{D}$ and $f \equiv 0$ on S. Show that $f \equiv 0$ in $\mathfrak{D}$. (*Hint:* Use the formula in problem 15 with $g = f$ to show that $f \equiv 0$ in $\mathfrak{D}$.)

12

Partial Differential Equations–II

1. Conservation Laws

The divergence theorem, which we discussed in Chapter 11, is of very great importance in much of the study of physics. It plays two major roles. The first, to be discussed in this section, is in the derivation of differential equations from physical principles. The second, to be discussed in §2, is in the analysis of these differential equations once they are derived.

Many of the differential equations of physics describe what one calls *conservation laws*. The two dynamical principles discussed in §4 of Chapter 3 are of this form. For example, the principle of work and energy states, as a special case, that if no work is done on the particles, then the kinetic energy remains the same; that is, it is *conserved*. More generally it states that the change in kinetic energy is measured by the work done.

Let us now describe a situation in which the divergence theorem enters into the formulation of a conservation law. Imagine that we have a fluid, say water, filling a certain region $\mathfrak{D}$ of space (Figure 12.1). We fix our attention on a particular point P in $\mathfrak{D}$. At any instant of time t there will be a particle of fluid at P. In general this particle will be moving along some path; hence it will have a velocity. This velocity we denote by $\mathbf{v}(P, t)$. If we consider some other point P', at the same time, there will be a different particle at P' with, in general, a different velocity $\mathbf{v}(P', t)$.

If we consider all the different points in $\mathfrak{D}$ at the same time t, each one will be occupied by a specific particle which has a certain velocity. But this is

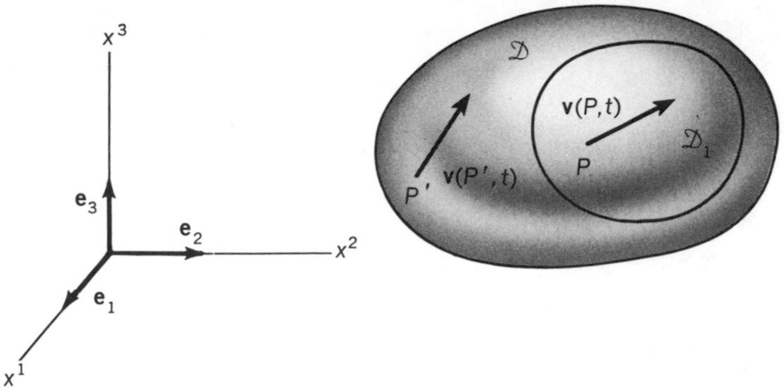

Figure 12.1

precisely the idea of a vector field on $\mathfrak{D}$: that is, we associate with *each* point P the velocity $\mathbf{v}(P, t)$ of the particle at *that* point at time t. This is a slightly more complicated situation than we have studied before because the vector field changes with time. That is, if we look at the same point P at a different time t', there will, in general, be a new particle there with a new velocity $\mathbf{v}(P, t')$. The time-varying vector field $\mathbf{v}$ is called the *fluid velocity*.

There is also a scalar field which plays a role in the study of the fluid. This is the *density*. It can be defined as follows. Again fix attention on the point P and imagine a sphere of radius δ with P as center (Figure 12.2). At time t the fluid inside this sphere will have a certain mass m which depends on δ. Now calculate the ratio of m to the volume $\frac{4}{3}\pi\delta^3$ of the sphere. This ratio is a function of δ which will have a limit as δ tends to zero. This limit, in general, will depend on P and also on the time t. We call it the *density* at point P at time t and denote it by $\rho(P, t)$. Thus at a particular time t we have a scalar $\rho(P, t)$ associated with each point P of $\mathfrak{D}$; that is, we have a scalar field at each time t.

The role of the density is to enable one to calculate the mass of fluid inside subregions of $\mathfrak{D}$. Let $\mathfrak{D}_1$ be such a subregion. Then it can be proved, that the mass of the fluid inside $\mathfrak{D}_1$ at time t, is given by,

$$M_1(t) = \iiint_{\mathfrak{D}_1} \rho(P, t)\, dV. \tag{1.1}$$

[Note that the right side of (1.1) does indeed vary with t since ρ does, hence the notation $M_1(t)$. We put the subscript 1 on M to indicate that this is the mass of fluid in region $\mathfrak{D}_1$.]

The two examples above indicate that an important idea in physics is that of fields which vary with time. To be able to formulate physical principles we need the concept of a time derivative for such fields. We pause to discuss

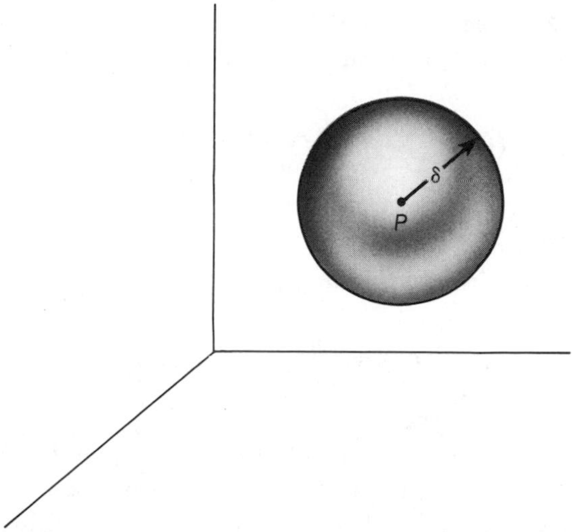

Figure 12.2

this idea now. Suppose we have a scalar field f which varies with time. We write $f(P, t)$ for its value at the point P at time t. Then we make the following definition.

(1.2) Definition. Suppose that for the scalar field $f: \mathfrak{D} \to (-\infty, \infty)$, the limit

$$(*) \qquad f_t(P, t) = \lim_{\Delta t \to 0} \frac{f(P, t + \Delta t) - f(P, t)}{\Delta t}$$

exists for each P in $\mathfrak{D}$ and each t. Then we say that f is **differentiable with respect to** t and that f_t is its t *derivative*. (Note that f_t is itself a time-varying scalar field in $\mathfrak{D}$.)

Equation (*) is seldom a useful formula for computation. A more useful formula is obtained if one introduces a set of coordinates x^1, x^2, x^3. Then at each t the field can be described by a function $\tilde{f}$ of x^1, x^2, x^3. Since f is varying with t, $\tilde{f}$ must also be a function of t. One then has the formula

$$(1.3) \qquad f_t(P, t) = \tilde{f}_t(x^1, x^2, x^3, t) \qquad \text{if } P \sim (x^1, x^2, x^3).$$

We could similarly define the concept of the time derivative of a *vector* field, but we shall not need this concept here and hence we omit it. There is, however, an important theorem concerning time derivatives which we do need.

(1.4) Theorem. *Let f be a scalar field defined in $\mathfrak{D}$ and varying with time t. Then for any subregion $\mathfrak{D}_1$ of $\mathfrak{D}$ one has*†

$$\text{(D)} \qquad \frac{d}{dt}\iiint_{\mathfrak{D}_1} f\,dV = \iiint_{\mathfrak{D}_1} f_t\,dV.$$

The proof of formula (D) is difficult and we do not attempt to give it. However, let us examine the meaning of (D). For each *fixed* t we can form the integral

$$I(t) = \iiint_{\mathfrak{D}_1} f(P, t)\,dV.$$

Since f changes with t the integral will also, hence the notation $I(t)$. In fact, I is just a function of the one variable t and one can ask what its derivative is. On the other hand, for each fixed t, f_t is itself a scalar field; hence we can form its integral

$$\iiint_{\mathfrak{D}_1} f_t(P, t)\,dV.$$

This integral will likewise vary with t, and (D) states that for each t it is equal to the derivative of I at that t.

We return to the specific situation of the fluid. We want to formulate what is called the *principle of conservation of mass*. This begins with the rather vague statement that mass can neither be created nor destroyed. In a little more precise way it states that for *any* region $\mathfrak{D}_1$ in $\mathfrak{D}$ the mass of fluid inside $\mathfrak{D}_1$ can change *only* by having mass flow out across the bounding surface S_1 of $\mathfrak{D}_1$. More precisely still, if we consider an interval of time from t to $t + \Delta t$ then the increase in mass *inside* $\mathfrak{D}_1$, that is, $M_1(t + \Delta t) - M_1(t)$, must equal the negative of the (net) amount of fluid which *flowed out* across S_1. If we divide $M_1(t + \Delta t) - M_1(t)$ by Δt we obtain the average rate at which the mass is increasing and this must equal the negative of the average rate at which fluid flows out across S_1. Finally, if we take the limit as Δt tends to zero we obtain the derivative of $M_1(t)$. Thus we have the equation

$$\text{(1.5)} \qquad \dot{M}_1(t) = \lim_{\Delta t \to 0} -\,[\text{average rate at which fluid flows out across } S_1].$$

Equation (1.5) is not a very good formula since the right side is not expressed in a usable form. There is however a formula for the right side,

†There are some technical hypotheses on fields in order that this theorem be true, but we shall not discuss these.

namely

$$(1.6)\qquad -\iint_{S_1} \rho\mathbf{v}(P, t)\cdot \mathbf{n}(P)\, dA.$$

That the right side of (1.5) actually equals (1.6) is true, but a proof is rather difficult and we shall not attempt to give it.

One obtains a precise analytical statement of the law of conservation of mass by replacing the right side of (1.5) by (1.6). This yields the equation

$$(1.7)\qquad \dot{M}_1(t) = \frac{d}{dt}\iiint_{\mathfrak{D}_1} \rho(P, t)\, dV = -\iint_{S_1} \rho\mathbf{v}(P, t)\cdot \mathbf{n}(P)\, dA.$$

We emphasize that this must hold for *all* regions $\mathfrak{D}_1$ in $\mathfrak{D}$.

Equation (1.7) is correct but is still not very usable. We propose to obtain a different kind of result from it by means of the divergence theorem. We note that the product of ρ and $\mathbf{v}$ is itself a vector field; call it $\mathbf{F}(P, t)$. If we apply the divergence theorem we obtain

$$\iint_{S_1} \rho\mathbf{v}\cdot\mathbf{n}\, dA = \iint_{S_1} \mathbf{F}\cdot\mathbf{n}\, dA = \iiint_{\mathfrak{D}_1} \operatorname{div}\mathbf{F}\, dV = \iiint_{\mathfrak{D}_1} \operatorname{div}(\rho\mathbf{v})\, dV.$$

Hence (1.7) becomes

$$(1.8)\qquad \frac{d}{dt}\iiint_{\mathfrak{D}_1} \rho\, dV + \iiint_{\mathfrak{D}_1} \operatorname{div}(\rho\mathbf{v})\, dV = 0.$$

Finally, we can transform the left side by means of theorem (1.4). This theorem yields

$$\frac{d}{dt}\iiint_{\mathfrak{D}_1} \rho\, dV = \iiint_{\mathfrak{D}_1} \rho_t\, dV.$$

Thus the law of conservation of mass is reduced to the formula

$$(1.9)\qquad \iiint_{\mathfrak{D}_1} \big(\rho_t + \operatorname{div}(\rho\mathbf{v})\big)\, dV = 0 \qquad \text{for } all\ \mathfrak{D}_1.$$

We need finally another theorem which we are unable to prove in this text, but which is fundamental to the ideas of this chapter.

(1.10) Theorem. *Let f be a continuous scalar field defined in a region $\mathfrak{D}$. If*

$$\iiint\limits_{\mathfrak{D}_1} f(P)\,dV = 0$$

for every *subregion $\mathfrak{D}_1$ of $\mathfrak{D}$, then $f(P)$ must be identically zero. The same result is true for a continuous vector field* $\mathbf{v}$.

If we apply this theorem to equation (1.9) we deduce that the equation

$$\rho_t + \operatorname{div}(\rho\mathbf{v}) = 0 \tag{1.11}$$

must hold at all points of $\mathfrak{D}$. Equation (1.11) is called the *equation of continuity*.

We have shown that if the principle of conservation of mass, as stated in (1.5), is valid, then (1.11) must hold. Conversely, if (1.11) holds, then (1.9) holds and so does (1.8), and hence by using the divergence theorem in the other direction we see that (1.5) holds; that is, conservation of mass is valid. We say then that equations (1.5) and (1.11) are *mathematically equivalent* in the sense that either both are true or both are false.

Our discussion illustrates an important sequence of ideas in physics. Equation (1.5) is a direct statement of a physical law. If one set out to do experiments to test the validity of conservation of mass one would design them to check that equation. On the other hand, if one wishes to do *computations* designed to obtain information about fluid flow, then it is equation (1.11) which would be used. Thus the knowledge that (1.5) and (1.11) are equivalent is very important.

Equation (1.11) is an example of a *partial differential equation*. If we introduce the coordinates x^1, x^2, x^3 of Figure 12.1 as well as unit vectors $\mathbf{e}_1$, $\mathbf{e}_2$, $\mathbf{e}_3$ as shown in that figure, then we can express ρ and $\mathbf{v}$ in coordinate form as

$$\rho(x^1, x^2, x^3, t)$$

and

$$v^1(x^1, x^2, x^3, t)\mathbf{e}_1 + v^2(x^1, x^2, x^3, t)\mathbf{e}_2 + v^3(x^1, x^2, x^3, t)\mathbf{e}_3,$$

respectively. By formula (11.2.11b) we can then write equation (1.11) as

$$\begin{aligned} \rho_t(x^1, x^2, x^3, t) &+ \big(\rho(x^1, x^2, x^3, t)v^1(x^1, x^2, x^3, t)\big)_{x^1} \\ &+ \big(\rho(x^1, x^2, x^3, t)v^2(x^1, x^2, x^3, t)\big)_{x^2} \\ &+ \big(\rho(x^1, x^2, x^3, t)v^3(x^1, x^2, x^3, t)\big)_{x^3} = 0. \end{aligned} \tag{1.12}$$

Thus we have one equation connecting certain partial derivatives of the four functions ρ, v^1, v^2, and v^3. This equation serves as a restriction on the types of fluid motion which are possible if conservation of mass is required to hold.

(1.13) Example. Fluid Flows

(a) ONE-DIMENSIONAL FLOWS. Suppose the fluid always moves parallel to a fixed direction. We choose the x^1 axis in this direction (Figure 12.3). Then the functions v^2 and v^3 must be identically zero and also equation (1.12) reduces to

$$\text{(i)} \qquad \rho_t + (\rho v^1)_{x^1} = 0.$$

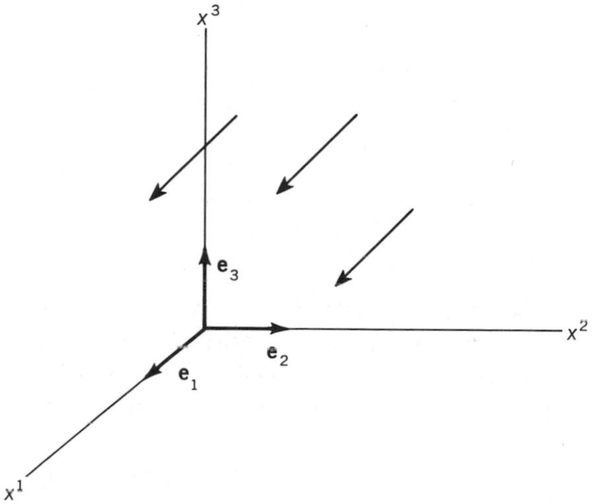

Figure 12.3

A common situation involves a fluid which is what is called *incompressible.* This means that its density is a constant ρ_0. Then (i) simplifies further to

$$\text{(ii)} \qquad \rho_0 v^1_{x^1} = 0.$$

Therefore in an *incompressible* one-dimensional flow the velocity cannot vary in the direction of the motion.

(b) TWO-DIMENSIONAL INCOMPRESSIBLE FLOWS. Here we assume again that ρ is a constant. We also assume that there is no motion of the fluid in the direction of $\mathbf{e}_3$ in Figure 12.4, that is, we assume that v^3 is zero, but we no longer assume that v^2 is zero. Finally, we assume that the motion is the same in all planes parallel to the (x^1, x^2) plane, that is, the v^1 and v^2 are functions only of x^1 and x^2 and are independent of x^3. Thus we can write v^1 and v^2 as $v^1(x^1, x^2, t)$, $v^2(x^1, x^2, t)$, and (1.12) reduces to

$$\text{(i)} \qquad v^1_{x^1}(x^1, x^2, t) + v^2_{x^2}(x^1, x^2, t) = 0.$$

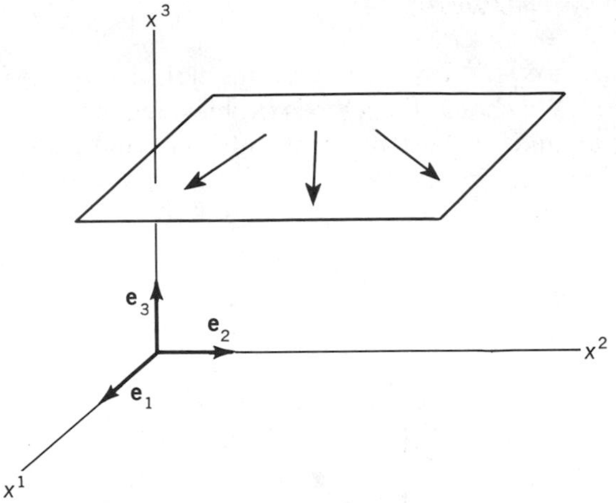

Figure 12.4

Equation (i) considerably restricts those two-dimensional, incompressible flows for which conservation of mass is satisfied. For instance, let us try to find all such flows in which v^1 and v^2 can be expressed as *linear* functions of x^1 and x^2. That is, let us seek solutions of (ii) having the form

$$\text{(ii)}\qquad \begin{aligned} v^1(x^1, x^2, t) &= a_1(t)x^1 + a_2(t)x^2 + a_0(t) \\ v^2(x^1, x^2, t) &= b_1(t)x^1 + b_2(t)x^2 + b_0(t). \end{aligned}$$

Then (i) requires that

$$\text{(iii)}\qquad a_1(t) + b_2(t) = 0 \qquad \text{for all } t.$$

(See problem 6 for a further discussion.)

There are many other situations in physics which lead from conservation laws in integral form, such as (1.5), to partial differential equations, such as (1.11). The transition from the physical law to the differential equation always proceeds along the above lines. In general, a conservation law has the following form. We have some quantity (mass in the example above) which is associated with portions $\mathfrak{D}_1$ of a region $\mathfrak{D}$, the amount of this quantity in $\mathfrak{D}_1$ being determined by the volume integral of some scalar field (density above) over $\mathfrak{D}_1$. The amount of this quantity in $\mathfrak{D}_1$ can change only by its "flow" out across the surface S_1 bounding $\mathfrak{D}_1$.

Then the conservation law states that the *time rate of change* of amount of the quantity in $\mathfrak{D}_1$ equals negative of the *rate of flow* out across S_1. This latter term will be measured by the surface integral over S_1 of the outward normal component of some vector field (the density times the velocity in the above example). One now modifies the law by transforming the surface integral by means of the divergence theorem, so that the law becomes the statement that an integral of something over an *arbitrary* subregion $\mathfrak{D}_1$ is zero [equation (1.9)]. Then by theorem (1.10) the integrand must be identically zero, and this gives a differential equation.

We are going to give here another example of this procedure which leads to one of the equations studied in Chapter 7.

(1.14) Example. Heat Flow. Suppose that the region $\mathfrak{D}$ (Figure 12.5) represents a homogeneous material which is capable of conducting heat. We denote by $u(P, t)$ the temperature of the material at position P at time t. Then u is a scalar field which varies with time.

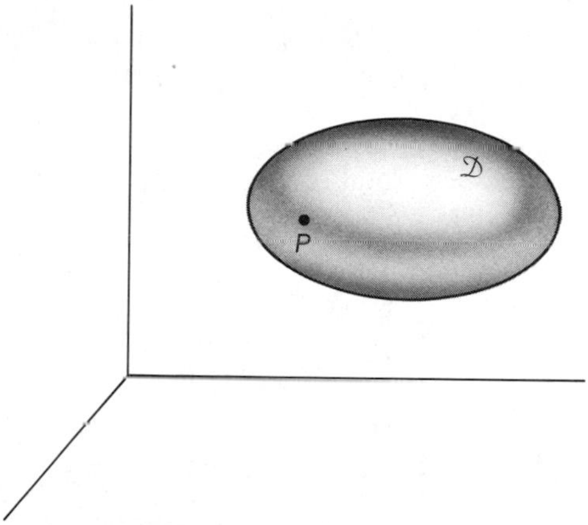

Figure 12.5

We are interested in studying the way in which the temperature at various points of $\mathfrak{D}$ changes with time. Here the quantity which is associated with subregions is what is called the *heat content*. It is defined by the integral

$$\text{(i)} \qquad H_1(t) = \iiint_{\mathfrak{D}_1} \sigma u(P, t)\, dV.$$

In this formula σ is a positive constant† which depends solely on the type of material. We simply state that one can devise experiments to measure σ.

†If the material is nonhomogeneous, then σ may vary from point to point, hence is itself a scalar field, much like the density. See problem 7.

Observe that as the temperature increases in a region its heat content also increases.

Physical experience tells one that there is a tendency of something, which is usually just called *heat*, to flow from hotter to colder places. Experience even indicates that the *rate* at which this flow occurs increases as the temperature difference between the two places increases. The precise mathematical formulation of these principles involves the *gradient* of the temperature.

The physical principle involved here is what we might call *conservation of heat*. It states the following. Let $\mathfrak{D}_1$ be any subregion of $\mathfrak{D}$ and let S_1 be the surface bounding $\mathfrak{D}_1$ (Figure 12.6). Then the rate of change of heat content in $\mathfrak{D}_1$ is equal to the negative of its rate of flow out across S_1. The rate of change of heat content is given by $\dot{H}_1(t)$, where H_1 is defined by (i). The rate of flow out across S_1 is related to the gradient of temperature, as indicated above. It has been found experimentally that this rate is given by the surface integral

$$\text{(ii)} \qquad -\iint_{S_1} \nu \nabla u(P, t) \cdot \mathbf{n}(P)\, dA.$$

Here ν is another positive constant, depending on the material, which can be determined experimentally.

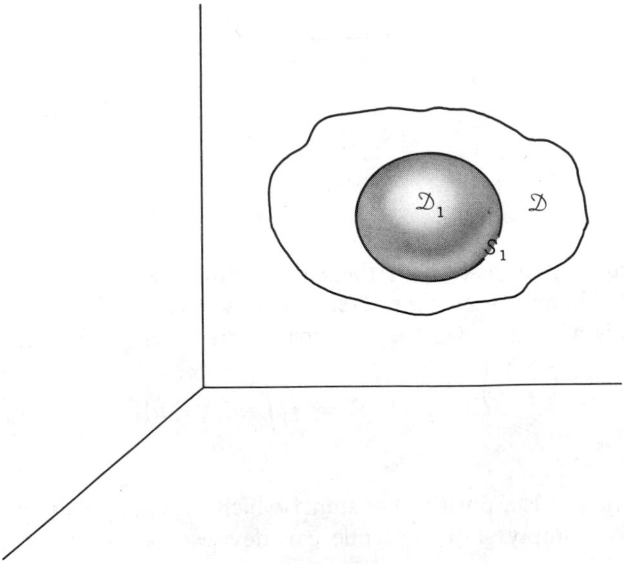

Figure 12.6

The mathematical formulation of the law of conservation of heat is obtained by equating (ii) to $\dot{H}_1(t)$. By (i) this gives

$$\text{(iii)} \qquad \frac{d}{dt}\iiint\limits_{\mathfrak{D}_1} \sigma u(P, t)\, dV = \iint\limits_{S_1} \nu \nabla u(P, t) \cdot \mathbf{n}(P)\, dA \qquad \text{for all } \mathfrak{D}_1.$$

By theorem (1.4) the left side can be written

$$\iiint\limits_{\mathfrak{D}_1} \sigma u_t(P, t)\, dV,$$

while, by the divergence theorem, the right side becomes

$$\iiint\limits_{\mathfrak{D}_1} \nu \operatorname{div}(\nabla u)(P, t)\, dV;$$

thus (iii) yields

$$\text{(iv)} \qquad \iiint\limits_{\mathfrak{D}_1} \big(\sigma u_t - \nu \operatorname{div}(\nabla u)\big)\, dV = 0 \qquad \text{for all } \mathfrak{D}_1.$$

Finally, by theorem 1.10, (iv) yields the equation

$$\text{(v)} \qquad u_t = K \operatorname{div}(\nabla u), \qquad K = \frac{\nu}{\sigma}\cdot$$

We recall that the quantity div (∇u) was discussed in problem 6, §2 of Chapter 11, where we called it the *Laplacian* and denoted it by Δu. If we use the formula for Δu developed in that problem we find that (v) can be written

$$\text{(vi)} \qquad u_t = K(u_{x^1x^1} + u_{x^2x^2} + u_{x^3x^3}), \qquad K = \frac{\nu}{\sigma} > 0.$$

This is called the *three-dimensional heat equation.*

We obtain the heat equation studied in Chapter 7 by considering a very idealized situation—that in which the temperature u does not vary in the x^2 or x^3 directions. Then u is a function only of x^1 and (vi) becomes $u_t = Ku_{x^1x^1}$.

A typical problem in the (three-dimensional) flow of heat is the following. A piece of material, occupying the region $\mathfrak{D}$, has some initial distribution of temperature *at time* $t = 0$. That is, $u(x^1, x^2, x^3, 0)$ is a known function $\varphi(x^1, x^2, x^3)$ in $\mathfrak{D}$. Suppose the material is immersed in an ice bath so that the temperature at its *boundary*, which we denote by S, is always zero. Then we have the two conditions

$$\text{(vii)}\qquad u(x^1, x^2, x^3, 0) = \varphi(x^1, x^2, x^3) \quad \text{in } \mathfrak{D}$$

$$\text{(viii)}\qquad u(x^1, x^2, x^3, t) = 0 \qquad \text{for points } (x^1, x^2, x^3) \text{ on } S.$$

Observe that these are analogous to conditions (1.2) and (1.3) of Chapter 7. One can obtain *exactly* the problem of Chapter 7 if it is assumed that the material is in the form of a slab of thickness L which extends sufficiently far in two directions that the effects from the boundaries of the slab in those directions can be neglected. Then as an approximation one can assume that $\mathfrak{D}$ extends to infinity in the x^2 and x^3 directions and that its boundary S consists just of the two planes $x^1 = 0$, $x^1 = L$. Under these circumstances the assumption that u depends only on x^1 is approximately true. Thus (vi), (vii), and (viii) become exactly (1.1), (1.2), and (1.3) of Chapter 7.

If one assumes that instead of the region being in an ice bath its boundary S is insulated, so that no heat can cross it, then the condition (viii) is replaced by the condition

$$\text{(ix)}\qquad \nabla u \cdot \mathbf{n} = 0 \qquad \text{on } S$$

where $\mathbf{n}$ is the normal to S. (Again, this is simply an empirical fact.) If we specialize to the case of the infinite slab above, this yields the conditions studied in part (1) of example (2.14) of Chapter 7.

Instead of requiring that the temperature at the boundary S always be zero, we could specify it as a function of time; that is, we could heat or cool the outside arbitrarily as time progresses. Then (viii) would be replaced by the condition

$$\text{(x)}\qquad u(x^1, x^2, x^3, t) = k(x^1, x^2, x^3, t) \qquad \text{for } (x^1, x^2, x^3) \text{ on } S.$$

For the infinite slab this becomes (5.17) of Chapter 7.

There is an important kind of problem which arises out of the above example. This idea concerns what are called *steady-state problems*. Suppose that the function k in (x) has a limit $k_0(x^1, x^2, x^3)$, as t tends to infinity, for each (x^1, x^2, x^3) on S. Then what will happen is that, as t tends to infinity, the temperature u at each point (x^1, x^2, x^3) of $\mathfrak{D}$ will tend to a value $u^0(x^1, x^2, x^3)$. Then u^0 is called the *steady-state temperature*. The function u^0 still satisfies (vi), but it is independent of time, so that u_t^0 equals zero. Thus (vi) becomes

$$\text{(1.15a)}\qquad u^0_{x^1x^1} + u^0_{x^2x^2} + u^0_{x^3x^3} = 0 \text{ in } \mathfrak{D}.$$

Also u^0 still satisfies (viii) but for the limiting value of k; that is,

$$u^0(x^1, x^2, x^3) = k^0(x^1, x^2, x^3) \qquad \text{for } (x^1, x^2, x^3) \text{ on } S. \tag{1.15b}$$

Equation (1.15a) is called *Laplace's equation* and the problem of solving (1.15a) subject to (1.15b) is called *Dirichlet's problem.* They are named after mathematicians who studied them. Both the equation and the problem are important in other branches of physics. They are important in heat flow because the transition to steady state ordinarily occurs very rapidly, so that after a very short time the temperature will be essentially equal to u^0. In the following sections we shall establish a uniqueness theorem for Dirichlet's problem.

PROBLEMS

1. For each of the following two-dimensional fluid flows ($v^3 = 0$), find those curves along which the velocity has constant magnitude and those along which it has constant direction, at the times indicated.

(a) $\mathbf{v}(x^1, x^2, t) = x^1\mathbf{e}_1 + x^2\mathbf{e}_2, \ t = 0$

(b) $\mathbf{v}(x^1, x^2, t) = x^1\mathbf{e}_2 - x^2\mathbf{e}_2, \ t = 0$

(c) $\mathbf{v}(x^1, x^2, t) = x^2\mathbf{e}_1 + x^1\mathbf{e}_2, \ t = 0$

(d) $\mathbf{v}(x^1, x^2, t) = 2x^1\mathbf{e}_1 + x^2t\mathbf{e}_2, \ t = 0$

(e) $\mathbf{v}(x^1, x^2, t) = t(x^1)^2\mathbf{e}_1 + t(x^2)^2\mathbf{e}_2, \ t = 1$

2. Determine which, if any, of the flows in problem 1 could satisfy conservation of mass assuming that the density is constant.

3. Given a two-dimensional fluid flow ($v^3 = 0$), a function $\psi(x^1, x^2)$, such that $\psi_{x^1} = v^2$ and $\psi_{x^2} = -v^1$ is called a *stream function.* Show that if such a function exists for an incompressible flow then conservation of mass *must* hold.

4. In a one-dimensional flow, the velocity $\mathbf{v}$ is given by v^1e_1, where $v^1 = xt$. What is the most general form the density can have if conservation of mass is to be satisfied?

5. In a one-dimensional flow, the density has the form $\rho = 1/(1 + t^2)$; that is, it is independent of x^1. What is the most general form the velocity v^1 can have if conservation of mass is satisfied?

6. In example (1.13b) assume that $b_2(t)$, $a_0(t)$, $b_1(t)$, and $b_0(t)$ are identically zero while $a_1(t)$ and $b_2(t)$ are constants. Try to describe geometrically the possible resulting flows which satisfy conservation of mass.

7. A more general problem in heat conduction than that we have discussed occurs if it is assumed that the region is not homogeneous. Then the specific heat and thermal conductivity are themselves scalar fields. What then is the differential equation for conservation of heat?

*8. There are certain chemical reactions in which heat is generated. Suppose the amount of heat generated at a point is proportional to the temperature at that point. Try to formulate a principle of conservation of heat for this situation first as an integral law and then as a differential equation.

9. There is a conservation law in the study of electrostatics called Gauss' law. It states the following. Suppose there exists an electric field $\mathbf{E}$ in a region $\mathfrak{D}$ ($\mathbf{E}$ is a vector field in $\mathfrak{D}$). Then there exist scalar fields σ and K such that for any subregion $\mathfrak{D}_1$ of $\mathfrak{D}$ the following equality holds:

$$\frac{d}{dt}\iiint_{\mathfrak{D}_1} \sigma\, dV = \iint_{S_1} K\mathbf{E}\cdot\mathbf{n}\, dA.$$

Derive a partial differential equation which is equivalent to this statement.

2. Uniqueness Theorems

In this section we are going to illustrate the use of the divergence theorem in the proof of uniqueness theorems for partial differential equations. All these proofs are obtained from a formula discussed in problems 6 and 7, §2 of Chapter 11. This formula was as follows. Given two scalar fields in a region $\mathfrak{D}$ bounded by a surface S, one has

$$\text{(2.1)}\qquad \iiint_{\mathfrak{D}} [f(P)\,\Delta g(P) + \nabla f(P)\cdot\nabla g(P)]\, dV = \iiint_{S} f(P)\nabla g(P)\cdot\mathbf{n}(P)\, dA,$$

where $\mathbf{n}$ is the (outward) normal to the surface. If one chooses the fields f and g in (2.1) to be the same, that is, $g = f$, then one obtains

$$\text{(2.2)}\qquad \iiint_{\mathfrak{D}} [f(P)\,\Delta f(P) + \nabla f(P)\cdot\nabla f(P)]\, dV = \iint_{S} f(P)\nabla f(P)\cdot\mathbf{n}(P)\, dA.$$

We are going to give two different kinds of uniqueness proofs. The first will be analogous to those given in §2 of Chapter 7, while the second refers to the Dirichlet problem introduced in §1. We give examples here and, as in §6 of Chapter 7, illustrate extensions in the problems.

(2.3) The Heat Equation. Here we consider the problem discussed in example (1.14). In particular we consider the problem defined by (iv), (v), and (viii) of that example. Thus we seek a function u of x^1, x^2, x^3, and t

defined for $t \geq 0$ and (x^1, x^2, x^3) in a region $\mathfrak{D}$ such that

$$\text{(i)} \qquad u_t = K\,\Delta u, \qquad K > 0 \text{ in } \mathfrak{D}$$

$$\text{(ii)} \qquad u(x^1, x^2, x^3, 0) = \varphi(x^1, x^2, x^3) \text{ in } \mathfrak{D}$$

$$\text{(iii)} \qquad u(x^1, x^2, x^3, t) = k(x^1, x^2, x^3, t) \text{ on } S,$$

where S is the surface bounding $\mathfrak{D}$.

Our goal is to show that there exists *at most one* solution of this problem. The proof exactly parallels that of example (6.2a) of Chapter 7. The first observation is that (i) is s-linear in the sense of Chapters 4 and 7. This means that if u^1 and u^2 are solutions of (i), then any linear combination,

$$\alpha_1 u^1 + \alpha_2 u^2,$$

where α_1 and α_2 are constants, is also a solution. The reader is asked to verify this in the problems.

Now suppose u^1 and u^2 satisfy (i), (ii), and (iii) and set $u = u^1 - u^2$. Since (i) is s-linear, u is also a solution of (i). Moreover, we have

$$\begin{aligned} \text{(ii}'\text{)} \qquad u(x^1, x^2, x^3, 0) &= u^1(x^1, x^2, x^3, 0) - u^2(x^1, x^2, x^3, 0) \\ &= \varphi(x^1, x^2, x^3) - \varphi(x^1, x^2, x^3) = 0 \text{ in } \mathfrak{D} \end{aligned}$$

$$\begin{aligned} \text{(iii}'\text{)} \qquad u(x^1, x^2, x^3, t) &= u^1(x^1, x^2, x^3, t) - u^2(x^1, x^2, x^3, t) \\ &= k(x^1, x^2, x^3, t) - k(x^1, x^2, x^3, t) = 0 \text{ on } S. \end{aligned}$$

We proceed to show that if u satisfies (i) and (ii′) and (iii′), then it must be identically zero, from which it follows that u^1 and u^2 are identically equal. We use essentially the same trick as in example (6.2a) of Chapter 7. We multiply both sides of equation (i) by u and integrate over $\mathfrak{D}$. Thus we have

$$\text{(iv)} \qquad \iiint_{\mathfrak{D}} u u_t \, dV = K \iiint_{\mathfrak{D}} u\,\Delta u \, dV.$$

In example (6.2a) of Chapter 7 we transformed the right side by integration by parts. Here we accomplish the same end by using (2.2). If we apply (2.2) to the right side of (iv) we have

$$\text{(v)} \qquad \iiint_{\mathfrak{D}} u\,\Delta u \, dV = -\iiint_{\mathfrak{D}} \nabla u \cdot \nabla u \, dV + \iint_S (u \nabla u) \cdot \mathbf{n} \, dA.$$

But by (iii) u is identically zero on S; hence the integral over S in (v) vanishes. Moreover, by theorem (1.4) we have for the term on the left side of (iv),

$$\iiint_{\mathfrak{D}} uu_t\, dV = \iiint_{\mathfrak{D}} \frac{\partial}{\partial t}(\tfrac{1}{2}u^2)\, dV = \frac{1}{2}\frac{d}{dt}\iiint_{\mathfrak{D}} u^2\, dV.$$

Thus (v) yields

$$\text{(vi)} \qquad \frac{1}{2}\frac{d}{dt}\iiint_{\mathfrak{D}} u^2\, dV = -K\iiint_{\mathfrak{D}} \nabla u \cdot \nabla u\, dV.$$

Now we are in the same position we were in example (6.2a) of Chapter 7. Note that $\nabla u \cdot \nabla u = (u_{x1})^2 + (u_{x2})^2 + (u_{x3})^2 \geq 0$; hence the right side of (vi) is less than or equal to zero. We set

$$\text{(vii)} \qquad I(t) = \tfrac{1}{2}\iiint_{\mathfrak{D}} u^2\, dV.$$

Then (vi) implies that

$$\dot{I}(t) \leq 0.$$

On the other hand,

$$I(0) = \tfrac{1}{2}\iiint_{\mathfrak{D}} u^2(P, 0)\, dV$$

and this is zero, since by (ii′) u equals zero at $t = 0$. Hence $I(t)$ is a non-increasing function which is zero at $t = 0$ and can never be negative and thus, as in example (6.2a) of Chapter 7, must be identically zero; that is,

$$\text{(viii)} \qquad \iiint_{\mathfrak{D}} u^2\, dV = 0 \qquad \text{for all } t.$$

Since $u^2 \geq 0$ it follows by proposition (4.4) of Chapter 11 that u must be identically zero.

There is also an analog of example (6.2b) of Chapter 7. This refers to functions satisfying (i) and (ii) but with (iii) replaced by (vii) of example (1.7); that is,

$$\text{(iii}''\text{)} \qquad \nabla u \cdot \mathbf{n} = 0 \text{ on } S.$$

The reader is asked to carry out the proof of the corresponding uniqueness theorem in the problems.

(2.4) The Wave Equation. We present now an analog of example (6.2c) of Chapter 7. We consider functions u of x^1, x^2, x^3, and t defined for $t \geq 0$ and (x^1, x^2, x^3) in a region $\mathfrak{D}$, and satisfying the equations

$$\text{(i)} \qquad u_{tt} = \Delta u \ \text{ in } \mathfrak{D}$$

$$\text{(ii)} \qquad \begin{aligned} u(x^1, x^2, x^3, 0) &= \varphi(x^1, x^2, x^3) \\ u_t(x^1, x^2, x^3, 0) &= \psi(x^1, x^2, x^3) \ \text{ in } \mathfrak{D} \end{aligned}$$

$$\text{(iii)} \qquad u(x^1, x^2, x^3, t) = k(x^1, x^2, x^3, t) \ \text{ on } S.$$

Equation (i) is called the *three-dimensional wave equation*. It arises in various physical situations, for example in the study of sound waves. Conditions (ii) and (iii) are the analogs of conditions for the one-dimensional wave equation, as indicated in example (6.2c) of Chapter 7.

The goal again is to show that the problem (i), (ii), and (iii) has at most one solution. Again the procedure parallels that of example (6.2c) of Chapter 7. First we note that (i) is s-linear (problem 1). Thus if u^1 and u^2 are solutions, and $u = u^1 - u^2$, then u satisfies (i) and the conditions,

$$\text{(ii}'\text{)} \qquad u(x^1, x^2, x^3, 0) = u_t(x^1, x^2, x^3, 0) = 0 \text{ in } \mathfrak{D}$$

$$\text{(iii}'\text{)} \qquad u(x^1, x^2, x^3, t) = 0 \ \text{ on } S.$$

We multiply (i) by u_t and integrate over $\mathfrak{D}$. This gives

$$\text{(iv)} \qquad \iiint_{\mathfrak{D}} u_t u_{tt}\, dV = \iiint_{\mathfrak{D}} u_t\, \Delta u\, dV.$$

We can transform the right side by (2.1) (letting $f = u_t$ and $g = u$) so that we obtain

$$\text{(v)} \qquad \iiint_{\mathfrak{D}} u_t u_{tt}\, dV = -\iiint_{\mathfrak{D}} \nabla u_t \cdot \nabla u\, dV + \iint_{S} (u_t \nabla u) \cdot \mathbf{n}\, dA.$$

The surface integral in (v) is zero by (iii′) ($u \equiv 0$ on S implies $u_t \equiv 0$ on S). We note that

$$\begin{aligned} \nabla u_t \cdot \nabla u &= u_{tx^1} u_{x^1} + u_{tx^2} u_{x^2} + u_{tx^3} u_{x^3} \\ &= \frac{1}{2}\frac{\partial}{\partial t}\left((u_{x^1})^2 + (u_{x^2})^2 + (u_{x^3})^2\right) = \frac{1}{2}\frac{\partial}{\partial t}(\nabla u \cdot \nabla u), \end{aligned}$$

while

$$u_t u_{tt} = \frac{1}{2}\frac{\partial}{\partial t} u_t^2.$$

Thus we can rewrite each of the volume integrals in (v) by using theorem 1.4. When this is done (v) becomes

$$\text{(vi)} \qquad \dot{I}_1(t) + \dot{I}_2(t) = 0,$$

where

$$I_1(t) = \tfrac{1}{2} \iiint_{\mathfrak{D}} u_t^2 \, dV, \qquad I_2(t) = \tfrac{1}{2} \iiint_{\mathfrak{D}} \nabla u \cdot \nabla u \, dV.$$

Equation (vi) yields

$$\text{(vii)} \qquad I_1(t) + I_2(t) = c, \qquad c \text{ a constant.}$$

Moreover, c must be zero, since at $t = 0$ we have, by (ii′),

$$I_1(0) = \tfrac{1}{2} \iiint_{\mathfrak{D}} u_t(P, 0)^2 \, dV = 0$$

$$I_2(0) = \tfrac{1}{2} \iiint_{\mathfrak{D}} \nabla u(P, 0) \cdot \nabla u(P, 0) \, dV = 0$$

($u \equiv 0$ at $t = 0$ implies $u_{x^1} \equiv u_{x^2} \equiv u_{x^2} \equiv 0$ at $t = 0$; hence $\nabla u \equiv \mathbf{0}$ at $t = 0$).

Both I_1 and I_2 are nonnegative and their sum is zero, hence *each* is zero; that is,

$$\text{(viii)} \qquad \iiint_{\mathfrak{D}} u_t^2 \, dV = \iiint_{\mathfrak{D}} (\nabla u \cdot \nabla u) \, dV = 0.$$

Since both the integrands in (viii) are non-negative, (viii) and proposition (4.4) of Chapter 11 imply that u_t and ∇u are both zero; that is,

$$\text{(ix)} \qquad u_t = u_{x^1} = u_{x^2} = u_{x^3} = 0$$

for all (x^1, x^2, x^3) in $\mathfrak{D}$ and *all* $t > 0$. A function of x^1, x^2, x^3, t which has all its partial derivatives zero must be a constant. Hence (ix) implies that u is a constant. But at time $t = 0$, u is zero; hence the constant must be zero. Thus $u \equiv 0$ or $u^1 \equiv u^2$.

(2.5) The Dirichlet Problem. We turn now to a slightly different kind of uniqueness theorem. This is illustrated by the Dirichlet problem [(1.15)]. Recall that this involved finding a function u of (x^1, x^2, x^3) in a region $\mathfrak{D}$ such that

$$\text{(i)} \qquad \Delta u = 0 \text{ in } \mathfrak{D}$$

$$\text{(ii)} \qquad u(x^1, x^2, x^3) = k(x^1, x^2, x^3) \text{ on } S,$$

where S is the surface bounding $\mathfrak{D}$.

Again we want to show that problem (i) and (ii) has at most one solution. The first observation is once more that (i) is s-linear (problem 1). Thus let u^1 and u^2 be solutions and consider $u = u^1 - u^2$. The function u then satisfies (i) and the condition

$$\text{(ii}'\text{)} \qquad u \equiv 0 \text{ on } S.$$

Now we apply equation (2.2) with $f = u$. We obtain

$$\text{(iii)} \qquad \iiint_{\mathfrak{D}} [u\,\Delta u + \nabla u \cdot \nabla u]\,dV = \iint_S (u\nabla u)\cdot \mathbf{n}\,dA.$$

By (i) $\Delta u = 0$, so the first term on the left vanishes, while by (ii′) $u \equiv 0$ on S, so that the term on the right vanishes. Thus (iii) yields

$$\iiint_{\mathfrak{D}} (\nabla u \cdot \nabla u)\,dV = \iiint \left((u_{x^1})^2 + (u_{x^2})^2 + (u_{x^3})^2\right) dV = 0.$$

By proposition (4.4) of Chapter 11 it follows that

$$(u_{x^1})^2 + (u_{x^2})^2 + (u_{x^3})^2 = 0 \text{ in } \mathfrak{D} \qquad \text{or} \qquad u_{x^1} = u_{x^2} = u_{x^3} = 0 \text{ in } \mathfrak{D}.$$

thus u is a function with all its partial derivatives zero in $\mathfrak{D}$; hence it is a constant. But on S it is zero; hence the constant must be zero and $u \equiv 0$ or $u^1 \equiv u^2$.

Various extensions of examples (2.3), (2.4), and (2.5) are given in the problems.

PROBLEMS

1. Show that the differential equations in examples (2.3), (2.4), and (2.5) are all s-linear, that is, that if u^1 and u^2 are solutions, then so is $\alpha_1 u^1 + \alpha_2 u^2$ for any constants α_1 and α_2.
2. Show that the problem defined by (i), (ii), and (iii″) of (2.3) has at most one solution.
3. Show that the problem defined by (i) and (ii) of (2.4), together with the condition $\nabla u \cdot \mathbf{n} = 0$ on S, has at most one solution.
4. Show that in examples (2.3), (2.4), and (2.5) one can replace the given differential equations by the nonhomogeneous ones

$$u_t = \Delta u + f, \qquad u_{tt} = \Delta u + f, \qquad \Delta u = f,$$

and still infer that the problems have at most one solution.

5. The *Neumann problem* is defined as follows. Find a function u of x^1, x^2, x^3 in $\mathfrak{D}$ such that

$$\text{(i)} \qquad \Delta u = 0 \text{ in } \mathfrak{D}$$
$$\text{(ii)} \qquad \nabla u \cdot \mathbf{n} = k \text{ on } S.$$

(a) Show that if u^1 is any solution, then $u^1 + c$, where c is any constant, is also a solution. Thus one *does not* have uniqueness for this problem.

*(b) Show that if u^1 and u^2 are any solutions of (i) and (ii), then there is a constant c such that

$$u^1 = u^2 + c.$$

(c) Show that (i) and (ii) can have a solution *only* if the function k in (ii) satisfies the condition

$$(*) \qquad \iint_S k\, dA = 0.$$

[*Hint:* Use formula (2.1) with $g = u$ and f equal to the function defined by $f(P) = 1$ for all P in $\mathfrak{D}$.]

***6.** Show that the problem

$$\text{(i)} \qquad u_t = \Delta u \text{ in } \mathfrak{D}$$
$$\text{(ii)} \qquad u = \varphi \text{ in } \mathfrak{D} \text{ at } t = 0$$
$$\text{(iii)} \qquad \nabla u \cdot \mathbf{n} = \psi u \text{ on } S,$$

where ψ is a function such that $\psi < 0$, has at most one solution. [Condition (iii) arises in the heat-flow problem of example (3.17) if the boundary of the material is exposed to the atmosphere.]

7. Show that each of the following problems has at most one solution.

(a) $u_t = \Delta u - u$ in $\mathfrak{D}$
$u = \varphi$ in $\mathfrak{D}$ at $t = 0$
$u = k$ on S

(b) $u_{tt} = \Delta u - u$ in $\mathfrak{D}$
$u = \varphi,\ u_t = \psi$ in $\mathfrak{D}$ at $t = 0$
$u = k$ on S

(c) $\Delta u = \psi u,\ \psi > 0$ in $\mathfrak{D}$
$u = k$ on S

8. Show that the methods of this section fail when applied to the following problems:

(a) $u_t = \Delta u + u$ in $\mathfrak{D}$
$u = \varphi$ in $\mathfrak{D}$ at $t = 0$
$u = k$ on S

(b) $\Delta u = -u$ in $\mathfrak{D}$
$u = k$ on S.

3. The Dirichlet Problem

In §§1 and 2 we encountered what we called the Dirichlet problem. In this section we are going to give a very brief indication of some further properties of the solution of this problem.

The Dirichlet problem is the following. Find a function u of x^1, x^2, x^3 in a region $\mathfrak{D}$ such that

$$\Delta u = 0 \text{ in } \mathfrak{D} \tag{3.1}$$

$$u = k \text{ on } S, \tag{3.2}$$

where k is a given function and S is the boundary of $\mathfrak{D}$.

An interesting feature of the Dirichlet problem is that there is a very simple one-dimensional analog of it. We call the following the *one-dimensional Dirichlet problem*. Find a function u of x, $a \leq x \leq b$, such that

$$u''(x) - 0, \qquad a < x < b \tag{3.3}$$

$$u(a) = k_1, \qquad u(b) = k_2. \tag{3.4}$$

It is remarkable that many of the important facts about problem (3.1) and (3.2) are simply generalizations of facts about (3.3) and (3.4).

Problem (3.3) is easy to solve. From (3.3) we deduce that

$$u(x) = Ax + B, \qquad A \text{ and } B \text{ constants.} \tag{3.5}$$

If we substitute (3.5) into (3.4) we obtain

$$Aa + B = k_1, \qquad Ab + B = k_2.$$

Solving for A and B we obtain

$$u = \frac{k_2 - k_1}{b - a} x + \frac{bk_1 - ak_2}{b - a}. \tag{3.6}$$

Formula (3.6) gives a solution of (3.4) and (3.5); hence we have proved an existence theorem for this problem. The reader is asked to provide a uniqueness theorem in problem 1.

Solutions of equation (3.1) are called *harmonic functions*. They have a number of interesting properties which are reflected in the formula (3.5). *All* solutions of (3.3) are necessarily linear functions of x of the form (3.5).

We also note that any linear function of x^1, x^2, x^3, that is,

$$u(x^1, x^2, x^3) = a^1x^1 + a^2x^2 + a^3x^3 + b, \tag{3.7}$$

is a solution of (3.1); however, functions of the form (3.7) by no means constitute all solutions of (3.1). [For example, it is easy to check that the function $2(x^1)^2 - (x^2)^2 - (x^3)^2$ is a solution of (3.1). We indicate others in problems 2 and 3.] Nevertheless all solutions of (3.1) do share with linear functions two properties which we discuss now.

First consider any function of the form (3.5) at some fixed x_0. Observe that

$$\frac{u(x_0 - \delta) + u(x_0 + \delta)}{2} = \frac{A(x_0 - \delta) + B + A(x_0 + \delta) + B}{2}$$
$$= Ax_0 + B = u(x_0).$$

This is called the *mean-value property* and it states that the value of u at the middle of an interval is thc average of the values of u at the end points of the interval. There is a generalization of this property to solutions of (3.1). Instead of considering intervals, though, we have to consider spheres. We state the principle as a theorem.

(3.8) Theorem (Mean-Value property). *Let u be a solution of $\Delta u = 0$ in a region $\mathfrak{D}$. Let P_0 be a point in $\mathfrak{D}$ and let the spherical surface Γ, consisting of points P such that $\|\overrightarrow{P_0P}\| = r$, be in $\mathfrak{D}$ (Figure 12.7). Then if A is the area of Γ we have*

$$u(P_0) = \frac{1}{A} \iint_\Gamma u(P)\, dA.$$

(One calls the integral on the right the *average* of u over Γ, so this theorem does indeed generalize the mean-value property.)

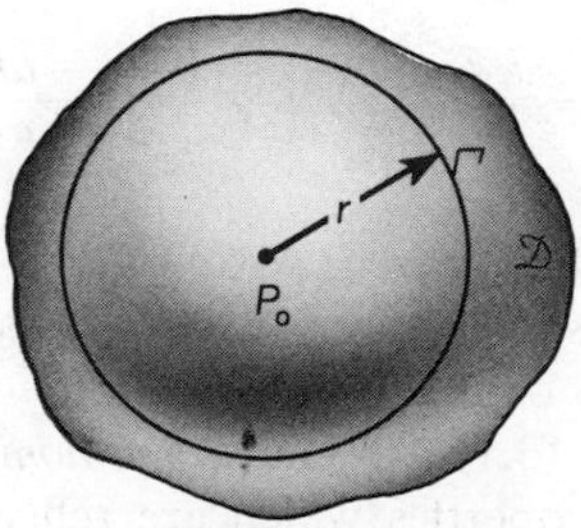

Figure 12.7

A second observation about linear functions of the form (3.5) is that, unless they are constants, that is, $A = 0$, they either always increase or always decrease. Another way of saying the same thing is that they cannot have maxima or minima anywhere inside an interval unless they are constants. This is called the *maximum principle* for (3.3) and is stated more precisely as follows. Let u be a solution of (3.3) on $a < x < b$. Then either

(i) u is a constant, or
(ii) u has its maximum at a and minimum at b, or
(iii) u has its minimum at a and maximum at b.

The reader is asked to prove the maximum principle for (3.3) in the problems. This principle also generalizes to (3.1).

(3.9) Theorem (Maximum Principle). *Let u be a solution of $\Delta u = 0$ in a region $\mathfrak{D}$. Then either*

(i) *u is a constant, or*
(ii) *u assumes both its maximum and minimum values on the boundary S of $\mathfrak{D}$.*

The maximum principle is of great theoretical importance in the study of solutions of (3.1). To illustrate how it is used let us give another proof of the uniqueness of the solution of the Dirichlet problem. We saw in §2 that this can be reduced to showing that if u satisfies

$$\Delta u = 0 \text{ in } \mathfrak{D}, \qquad u = 0 \text{ on } S,$$

then u must be zero in all of $\mathfrak{D}$. But this is an immediate consequence of the maximum principle. If u is a constant, it must be the constant zero, since u is zero on S. If it were not constant it would have both its maximum and minimum on S, and these are both zero, since on S u is identically zero. Thus the maximum and minimum of u are both zero, contradicting the fact that u is assumed to be nonconstant in $\mathfrak{D}$. [An application of a different sort is given in problem 5. We also indicate in problem 6 how the principle can be extended to other equations.]

PROBLEMS

1. Show that there exists at most one solution of the problem (3.3) and (3.4).

2. Determine which of the following are harmonic functions:

(a) $(x^1)^2 + (x^2)^2$

(b) $(x^1)^2 - (x^2)^2$

(c) $\log\left((x^1)^2 + (x^2)^2\right)$, $(x^1, x^2) \neq (0, 0)$

(d) $(x^1)^2 + (x^2)^2 + (x^3)^2$

(e) $[(x^1)^2 + (x^2)^2 + (x^3)^2]^{-1}$, $(x^1, x^2, x^3) \neq (0, 0, 0)$.

3. Determine all functions $X_2(x^2)$ and $X_3(x^3)$ such that

$$u(x^1, x^2, x^3) = e^{x^1} X_2(x^2) X_3(x^3)$$

is a harmonic function.

4. Prove the maximum principle for equation (3.3).

5. AN APPLICATION OF THE MAXIMUM PRINCIPLE. Let u be a solution of the problem indicated in Figure 12.8. Show that $-\frac{4}{3} < u < 0$ in R. [*Hint:* Let

$$v = u - \tfrac{1}{6}(x^1)^3$$

and show that the maximum principle can be applied to v.]

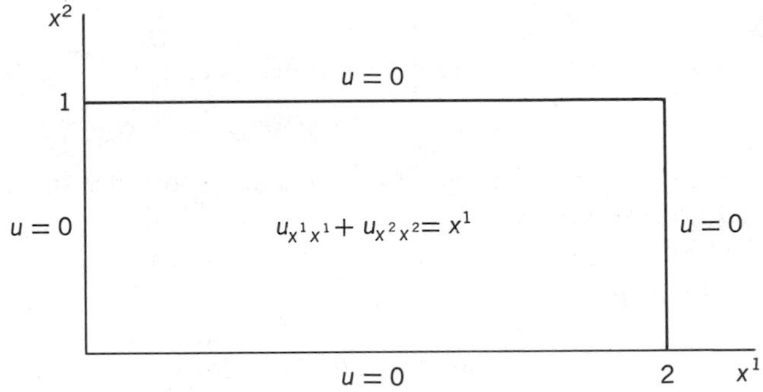

Figure 12.8

6. Consider the equation

$$u''(x^1) - c(x^1)u(x^1),$$

where c is a function which is positive for all x^1. Prove that this equation can never have a positive maximum or a negative minimum. [*Hint:* If a function has a maximum (minimum) at x_0, then its second derivative must be nonpositive (nonnegative) at x_0.]

This result can be generalized to the following theorem about partial differential equations.

Theorem. Let c be a function of (x^1, x^2, x^3) which is positive in $\mathfrak{D}$. Let u be a function of (x^1, x^2, x^3) which satisfies the equation

$$\Delta u - cu = 0 \text{ in } \mathfrak{D}.$$

Then u cannot have a positive maximum or a negative minimum in $\mathfrak{D}$.

Solutions to Selected Problems

CHAPTER 1

Section 1.1

2. (d) $(1 - 2t, -9 - 6t, 2 - 4t, 3 + 3t)$.

5. $\mathbf{0}$ is the constant function $f(t) \equiv 0$.

8. (a) A_1, A_2, M_3 (ii).
(b) M_3 (i), M_3 (ii).
(c) A_2, A_3, A_4, M_3 (ii).
(d) A_3, A_4, M_3 (ii).

9. Yes.

11. Use A_2, A_1, and A_2 in that order.

12. Suppose $\boldsymbol{\alpha}$ and $\boldsymbol{\beta}$ are both zero vectors and consider their sum.

14. [*Hint:* Let P be a reference point and let P_1, P_2 be the midpoints of the two diagonals. Show that $\overrightarrow{PP_1} = \overrightarrow{PP_2}$ and hence $P_1 = P_2$.]

15. Use the same technique as in problem 14.

Section 1.2

1. $\mathcal{R}^2$. (a) $\pi/4$.
$\mathcal{R}^3$. (a) $\pi/2$.
$\mathcal{R}^4$. (b) $\cos\theta = (2 + 6\sqrt{6})/\sqrt{38}$.
$\mathcal{C}[-1, 1]$. (b) $\pi/2$.

2. $\mathcal{R}^2$. (a) Orthogonal (not orthonormal). (d) Orthonormal.
$\mathcal{R}^3$. (a) Orthonormal.
$\mathcal{C}[0, 1]$. Orthogonal.

CHAPTER 2

Section 2.1

1. (a) $\dot{\boldsymbol{\alpha}}(t) = (2t, 6t^2)$; $\dot{\boldsymbol{\alpha}}(-1) = (-2, 6)$.
(b) $\dot{\boldsymbol{\alpha}}(t) = (\cos t, -\sin t, 0)$; $\dot{\boldsymbol{\alpha}}(\pi) = (-1, 0, 0)$.
(c) $\dot{\boldsymbol{\alpha}}(t) = e^t(1, -1, 1)$, $\dot{\boldsymbol{\alpha}}(0) = (1, -1, 1)$.

2. $\boldsymbol{\alpha}(t) = (t, -2t)$, $\boldsymbol{\alpha}(1) = (1, -2)$

$\|\boldsymbol{\alpha}(t) - \boldsymbol{\alpha}(1)\| = \|(t - 1, -2t + 2)\| = \sqrt{(t-1)^2 + (-2t+2)^2}$.

$\sqrt{(t-1)^2 + (-2t+2)^2} < \varepsilon \Rightarrow (t-1)^2 + (-2t+2)^2 < \varepsilon^2$

$\Rightarrow t^2 - 2t + 1 + 4t^2 - 8t + 4 < \varepsilon^2$
$\Rightarrow 5t^2 - 10t + 5 < \varepsilon^2$
$\Rightarrow 5(t^2 - 2t + 1) < \varepsilon^2$
$\Rightarrow 5(t-1)^2 < \varepsilon^2 \Rightarrow (t-1)^2 < \varepsilon^2/5$
$\Rightarrow |t-1| < \varepsilon/\sqrt{5} = \delta.$
(a) if $\varepsilon = 1$, then $\delta = 1/\sqrt{5}$.
(b) if $\varepsilon = \frac{1}{10}$, then $\delta = \frac{1}{10}\sqrt{5}$.

3. $\boldsymbol{\alpha}(t) = tx$, $\boldsymbol{\alpha}(1) = x$

$$\|\boldsymbol{\alpha}(t) - \boldsymbol{\alpha}(1)\| = \|tx - x\| = \|(t-1)x\| = \sqrt{\int_0^1 (t-1)^2 x^2\,dx}$$
$$= \sqrt{(t-1)^2 \int_0^1 x^2\,dx} = \sqrt{(t-1)^2 x^3/3|_0^1} = \sqrt{(t-1)^2/3}.$$

$\sqrt{(t-1)^2/3} < \varepsilon \Rightarrow (t-1)^2/3 < \varepsilon^2$
$\Rightarrow (t-1)^2 < 3\varepsilon^2 \Rightarrow |t-1| < \sqrt{3}\,\varepsilon = \delta$. If $\varepsilon = 1$, then $\delta = \sqrt{3}$.

5. $\dot{\boldsymbol{\alpha}}(t) = f(t)\boldsymbol{\alpha}_0$.

6. $\boldsymbol{\alpha}(t) = e^{t+x} = e^t e^x$, so $\dot{\boldsymbol{\alpha}}(t) = e^t e^x$, $\dot{\boldsymbol{\alpha}}(0) = e^x$.

8. (a) $\dot{a}(t) = (\boldsymbol{\alpha}(t) \cdot \dot{\boldsymbol{\alpha}}(t))/\|\boldsymbol{\alpha}(t)\|$.
(b) $\dot{a}(t) = \cos \|\boldsymbol{\alpha}(t)\| (\boldsymbol{\alpha}(t) \cdot \dot{\boldsymbol{\alpha}}(t))/\|\boldsymbol{\alpha}(t)\|$.

9. (a) $\boldsymbol{\alpha}(t) = (c_1, c_2)$, c_1, c_2 any constants.
(b) $\boldsymbol{\alpha}(t) = (t^2/2 + c_1, e^t + c_2)$, c_1, c_2 any constants.
(c) $\boldsymbol{\alpha}(t) = (t^3/3 + c_1)\sin x + (e^t + c_2)x$, c_1, c_2 any constants.

11. $\overrightarrow{P_0Q} = \overrightarrow{P_0P} + \overrightarrow{P_1Q}$
$\overrightarrow{P_0P} = \mathbf{r}_1(t)$, $\overrightarrow{P_1Q} = \frac{1}{2}\overrightarrow{P_1P_2} = \frac{1}{2}(\mathbf{r}_2(t) - \mathbf{r}_1(t))$
$\therefore\ \mathbf{r}(t) = \mathbf{r}_1(t) + \frac{1}{2}(\mathbf{r}_2(t) - \mathbf{r}_1(t))$
$\mathbf{r}(t) = \frac{1}{2}(\mathbf{r}_1(t) + \mathbf{r}_2(t))$
$\dot{\mathbf{r}}(t) = \frac{1}{2}(\dot{\mathbf{r}}_1(t) + \dot{\mathbf{r}}_2(t))$
$\dot{\mathbf{r}}(t) = \frac{1}{2}(\mathbf{v}_1(t) + \mathbf{v}_2(t))$.

14. (a) $$\left.\begin{aligned} a(t)x_1 + b(t)x_2 &= f(t) \\ c(t)x_1 + d(t)x_2 &= g(t) \end{aligned}\right\} \Rightarrow x_1 = \frac{\begin{vmatrix} f(t) & b(t) \\ g(t) & d(t) \end{vmatrix}}{\begin{vmatrix} a & b \\ c & d \end{vmatrix}},\quad x_2 = \frac{\begin{vmatrix} a & f \\ c & g \end{vmatrix}}{\begin{vmatrix} a & b \\ c & d \end{vmatrix}},\ \textit{i.e.},$$

$$x_1 = \frac{fd - bg}{ad - bc}, \qquad x_2 = \frac{ag - cf}{ad - bc}.$$

If a, b, c, d, e, f are differentiable on some interval and $ad - bc \neq 0$ for any t_0 in that interval then x_1 and x_2 differentiable $\Rightarrow$ $\mathbf{x}$ is differentiable in the interval.

Section 2.2

1. $\overrightarrow{OP} + \overrightarrow{PP'} = \overrightarrow{OO'} + \overrightarrow{O'P'}$
$t\mathbf{a} + \overrightarrow{PP'} = \overrightarrow{OO'} + t^2\mathbf{a}$
$\overrightarrow{PP'} = (t^2 - t)\mathbf{a} + \overrightarrow{OO'}$.
$\overrightarrow{PP'}$ is differentiable, since it is the sum of fixed vectors multiplied by differentiable functions of t:

$$\frac{d}{dt}\overrightarrow{PP'} = (2t - 1)\mathbf{a}.$$

2. (a) $\overrightarrow{PP'} = \overrightarrow{OP'} - \overrightarrow{OP} = t^2/\sqrt{2}\,(\mathbf{a} + \mathbf{b}) - t\mathbf{a} = ((t^2/\sqrt{2}) - t)\mathbf{a} + (t^2/\sqrt{2})\mathbf{b}$.
(b) $\overrightarrow{PP'}$ is differentiable since it is a sum of fixed vectors multiplied by differentiable functions of t and $(d/dt)\overrightarrow{PP'} = (\sqrt{2}\,t - 1)\mathbf{a} + \sqrt{2}\,t\mathbf{b}$.

3. $\mathbf{r}(t) = |t|\mathbf{a}$. Since $|t|$ is not differentiable at $t = 0$, neither is $\mathbf{r}$.

4. $\mathbf{r}(t) = \mathbf{r}_P - \mathbf{r}_{P_0}$, $\dot{\mathbf{r}}(t) = \mathbf{v}_P(t) - \mathbf{v}_{P_0}(t)$.

5. $\|\boldsymbol{\alpha} \times \boldsymbol{\beta}\| = \sqrt{2}/2$, $\boldsymbol{\alpha} \times \boldsymbol{\beta}$ points upward from paper.
$\boldsymbol{\alpha} \times -\boldsymbol{\beta}$ points downward from paper.
$-\boldsymbol{\alpha} \times 2\boldsymbol{\beta}$ points downward from paper with length $= \sqrt{2}$.

6. $2\boldsymbol{\alpha} \times \boldsymbol{\beta} = 2\boldsymbol{\gamma}$
$\boldsymbol{\alpha} \times 2\boldsymbol{\beta} = 2\boldsymbol{\gamma}$
$-\boldsymbol{\alpha} \times \boldsymbol{\beta} = -\boldsymbol{\gamma}$
$c_1\boldsymbol{\alpha} \times c_2\boldsymbol{\beta} = (c_1c_2)\boldsymbol{\alpha} \times \boldsymbol{\beta}$.

7. (b) $A(t) = \|\mathbf{a} \times \mathbf{b}\| = \|\mathbf{a}\|\,\|\mathbf{b}\| \sin\theta = (2t + 1)t^2 \sin\pi/4 = (\sqrt{2}/2)(2t + 1)t^2$

$$A(1) = \frac{3\sqrt{2}}{2}.$$

8. [*Hint:* If $\boldsymbol{\alpha} \times \boldsymbol{\beta} = \mathbf{0}$ for all vectors $\boldsymbol{\beta}$, then $\|\boldsymbol{\alpha} \times \boldsymbol{\beta}\| = 0$. Since $\boldsymbol{\alpha}$ is fixed, choose $\boldsymbol{\beta}$ such that $\boldsymbol{\alpha}$ is not parallel to $\boldsymbol{\beta}$ and $\|\boldsymbol{\beta}\| \neq 0$ and compute $\|\boldsymbol{\alpha} \times \boldsymbol{\beta}\|$.]

9.
$$\left.\begin{aligned} tx_1 + 3x_2 &= t \\ 3x_1 + tx_2 &= |t + 1| \end{aligned}\right\} \Rightarrow \begin{aligned} 3tx_1 + 9x_2 &= 3t \\ -3tx_1 - t^2x_2 &= -t|t + 1| \end{aligned}$$

$$\Rightarrow (9 - t^2)x_2 = 3t - t|t + 1|$$

$$\Rightarrow x_2 = \frac{t(3 - |t + 1|)}{9 - t^2}.$$

$$\text{Then } x_1 = \frac{t - 3x_2}{t} = \frac{t - \dfrac{3t(3 - |t + 1|)}{9 - t^2}}{t}$$

$$= \frac{3t|t + 1| - t^3}{t(9 - t^2)} = \frac{3|t + 1| - t^2}{9 - t^2}$$

$\boldsymbol{\alpha}$ is continuous at all points except $t = \pm 3$;
$\boldsymbol{\alpha}$ is differentiable at all points except $t = -1, \pm 3$.

10. [*Hint:* Recall that if a real-valued function $u(t)$ has a maximum or minimum at $t = t_0$, then $(d/dt)u(t_0) = 0$.]

12. $\dot{\mathbf{r}}(t) = \mathbf{v}_0$. But $(d/dt)(t\mathbf{v}_0) = \mathbf{v}_0$. Consider $\mathbf{r}(t) - t\mathbf{v}_0$.
$(d/dt)[\mathbf{r}(t) - t\mathbf{v}_0] = \dot{\mathbf{r}}(t) - (d/dt)(t\mathbf{v}_0) = \mathbf{v}_0 - \mathbf{v}_0 = \mathbf{0}$
$\therefore\ \mathbf{r}(t) - t\mathbf{v}_0 = \boldsymbol{\alpha}$, $\boldsymbol{\alpha}$ a constant vector, so $\mathbf{r}(t) = t\mathbf{v}_0 + \boldsymbol{\alpha}$.

Section 2.3

2. (a) $\displaystyle\int_0^{\pi} \sin t\,dt = -\cos t\big|_0^{\pi} = 2.$

$\displaystyle\int_0^{\pi} \cos t\,dt = \sin t\big|_0^{\pi} = 0$, hence answer is $(2, 0)$.

(b) $\int_0^1 (2t - 1)\,dt = t^2 - t|_0^1 = 0$

$$\int_0^1 t^2\,dt = \frac{t^3}{3}\bigg|_0^1 = \frac{1}{3}$$

$\int_0^1 0\,dt = 0$, hence answer is $(0, \frac{1}{3}, 0)$.

3. (a) $\varphi(t) = (t + c_1, (t^2/2) + c_2)$, $\varphi(0) = \mathbf{0} \Rightarrow c_1 = c_2 = 0$.
Thus $\varphi(t) = (t, t^2/2)$.
(b) $\varphi(t) = ((t^2/2) - t + c_1, c_2, (t^2/2) - t + c_3)$
$\varphi(1) = (-2, 0, 1) = (-\frac{1}{2} + c_1, c_2, -\frac{1}{2} + c_3) \Rightarrow c_1 = -\frac{3}{2}, c_2 = 0, c_3 = \frac{3}{2}$.

$$\text{Thus } \varphi(t) = \left(\frac{t^2}{2} - t - \frac{3}{2}, 0, \frac{t^2}{2} - t + \frac{3}{2}\right).$$

(c) $\varphi(t) = \left(\int_0^t e^{\tau^2}\,d\tau + c_1, \int_0^t c^{-\tau^2}\,d\tau + c_2\right)$

$\varphi(0) = \mathbf{0} \Rightarrow c_1 = 0, c_2 = 0$.

Thus $\varphi(t) = \left(\int_0^t e^{\tau^2}\,d\tau, \int_0^t e^{-\tau^2}\,d\tau\right)$.

5. (a) $$\int_0^1 (te^x + (t - 1)x)\,dt = \left[\frac{t^2}{2}e^x + \left(\frac{t^2}{2} - t\right)x\right]_0^1 = \tfrac{1}{2}e^x - \tfrac{1}{2}x.$$

(b) $$\int_0^\pi \sin(x + 2t)\,dt = \int_0^\pi (\sin x \cos 2t + \cos x \sin 2t)\,dt$$
$$= \left[\frac{\sin 2t}{2}\sin x - \frac{\cos 2t}{2}\cos x\right]_0^\pi$$
$$= -\tfrac{1}{2}\cos x + \tfrac{1}{2}\cos x = 0.$$

7. Let $\boldsymbol{\beta}(t) = \cos(t^2)\mathbf{e}_1 + \sin(t^2)\mathbf{e}_2$
$\|\boldsymbol{\beta}\|^2 = \cos^2(t^2) + \sin^2(t^2) = 1$.
Thus $\cos(t^2)\mathbf{e}_1 + \sin(t^2)\mathbf{e}_2$ is a unit vector in the direction $\boldsymbol{\alpha}(t)$.
(a) $\boldsymbol{\alpha}(t) = 2(\cos(t^2)\mathbf{e}_1 + \sin(t^2)\mathbf{e}_2)$

$$\int_0^1 \boldsymbol{\alpha}(t)\,dt = 2\left(\int_0^1 \cos(t^2)\,dt\right)\mathbf{e}_1 + 2\left(\int_0^1 \sin(t^2)\,dt\right)\mathbf{e}_2.$$

(b) $\boldsymbol{\alpha}(t) = t(\cos(t^2)\mathbf{e}_1 + \sin(t^2)\mathbf{e}_2)$

$$\int_0^1 \boldsymbol{\alpha}(t)\,dt = \left(\tfrac{1}{2}\int_0^1 2\cos(t^2)t\,dt\right)\mathbf{e}_1 + \tfrac{1}{2}\left(\int_0^1 2\sin(t^2)t\,dt\right)\mathbf{e}_2$$
$$= \tfrac{1}{2}\sin(t^2)|_0^2\mathbf{e}_1 - \tfrac{1}{2}\cos(t^2)|_0^1\mathbf{e}_2$$
$$= \frac{\sin 1}{2}\mathbf{e}_1 - \tfrac{1}{2}(\cos 1 - 1)\mathbf{e}_2.$$

8. (a) $\mathbf{v}(t) = t^2\mathbf{v}_0$. Thus $\mathbf{r}(t) = (t^3/3)\mathbf{v}_0 + \boldsymbol{\alpha}$, $\boldsymbol{\alpha}$ a constant vector. Since particle starts from 0 at $t = 0$, $\mathbf{r}(0) = \mathbf{0} = 0\mathbf{v}_0 + \boldsymbol{\alpha} \Rightarrow \boldsymbol{\alpha} = \mathbf{0}$. Thus $\mathbf{r}(t) = (t^3/3)\mathbf{v}_0$. At $t = 1$, $\mathbf{r}(1) = \frac{1}{3}\mathbf{v}_0$.

CHAPTER 3

Section 3.1

1. (a) $\mathbf{r}(t) = (-t^3/6 + 3/2t - \frac{1}{3})\boldsymbol{\alpha}$.
(c) $\mathbf{r}(t) = (-\frac{1}{4}\cos 2t + \frac{5}{4})\boldsymbol{\alpha}$.

2. $\sqrt{3}$ units from time $t = 0$ to time it stops.

3. [*Hint:* One wants max $\|\mathbf{r}(t_2) - \mathbf{r}(t_1)\|$ for arbitrary t_1, t_2.]

4. 4 seconds.

5. [*Hint:* Use the formulas in Chapter 3, §2.]

6. (a) One.
(b) None.
(c) Many.
(d) One.

Section 3.2

2. (d) $\dot{\mathbf{v}}(t) = -\cos\theta(t)\mathbf{e}_1 - \sin\theta(t)\mathbf{e}_2$.

3. [*Hint:* Consider the equations at the end of example (2.15).]

6. [*Hint:* Use equations (2.2), (2.3), and (2.4).]

7. (b) $\frac{1}{4}gt^2\mathbf{e}_1 = \mathbf{r}(t)$.

Section 3.3

1. Solve for $\mathbf{v}$ as in example (1.5), Chapter 3, §1.

3. (b) First component equation is $m\ddot{x}_1 = \dfrac{\|F_0\|x_1}{(x_1^2 + x_2^2 + x_3^2)^{1/2}}$.

5. $\mathbf{F}(t) = \dfrac{-k\|\mathbf{v}(t)\|^2\mathbf{r}(t)}{\|\mathbf{r}(t)\|}$.

6. $\mathbf{F} = ((mg/\sqrt{2}) - k\|\mathbf{r}\|)\mathbf{e}_2$.

7. (a) [*Hint:* Write out Newton's law and take scalar product of both sides with $\mathbf{v}$.]

Section 3.4

1. [*Hint:* Consider $\mathbf{F} \cdot \mathbf{v}$.]

5. [*Hint:* Use Newton's law and the principle of work and energy.]

8. [*Hint:* Use Newton's law, take inner product of both sides with $\dot{\mathbf{r}}_2$ and integrate.]

CHAPTER 4

Section 4.0

1. (a) $f(t) = 0$.
(b) $f(t) = -\cos t + 2$.
(c) $f(t) = (t^2/2) + t - \frac{3}{2}$.
(d) $f(t) = e^t + \sin t - 1$.
(e) $f(t) = t^2 - e^t - 3\cos t + 3$.

Section 4.1

1. (a) $y = 2e^{3t^2/2}$.
(b) $y = e^{\cos t + 1}$.
(c) $y = e^{-1/3e^{-3t}+1/3}$.
(e) $y = e^{-t} + \dfrac{(1-e)}{e^2}e^{-2t}$.

4. Distance $= \dfrac{m}{k^2}\left[kv_0 + mg\log\dfrac{mg}{v_0k + mg}\right]$.

6. (a) $y = -\frac{1}{2}t + \frac{3}{4}$.
(b) $y = -\frac{1}{2}t^2 - 1$.
(c) $y = e^{2t}$.
(d) $y = \frac{1}{10}\cos 3t + \frac{3}{10}\sin 3t + \frac{1}{2}\cos t - \frac{1}{2}\sin t$.
(e) $y = (t-1)e^{2t}$.

8. (a) $y = e^{1/\pi - 1/t}$.
(b) $y = (t - \pi/4)\sin t$.
(c) $y = \sin t\,(\log\sqrt{2}\sin t)$.

Section 4.2

1. (a) Linear. (b) Not linear. (c) Not linear. (d) Not linear. (e) Linear. (f) Not linear.

3. (a) $y = \log(t+1)$, solution exists for $t > -1$.
(b) $y = 1/(1-t)$, solution exists for all $t < 1$.
(c) $y = \dfrac{1}{\sqrt{1-2t}}$, solution exists for all $t < \frac{1}{2}$.
(d) $y = \sqrt{\log(2t+e)}$, solution exists for all $t \geq (1-e)/2$.
(e) $y = \sqrt[3]{\dfrac{3t^2}{2} - \dfrac{79}{54}}$, solution exists for all t.
(f) $y = \sqrt{1 - \left(\dfrac{\sqrt{3}}{2} - t\right)^2}$, solution exists for $(\sqrt{3}/2) - 1 < t < (\sqrt{3}/2) + 1$; if $y(0) = 2$, there is no solution.

7. (a) $y \equiv 1$, $y = 1 - \left(\dfrac{1-t}{2}\right)^2$
(b) $y \equiv 0$, $y = \sin^{-1}(t^2/4)$
(c) $y \equiv -2$, $y = (\frac{3}{4}(t+1))^{4/3} - 2$.

8. (a) Can solve for all $t = t_0$ such that $t_0 < \log 2$.
(b) Can solve for all $t = t_0$ such that $t_0 \geq -\frac{1}{e}$.

Section 4.3

1. (a) $y_1(t) = 1 - 2t$, $y_2(t) = 1 - 2t - 2t^2$.
(b) $y_1(t) = \dfrac{1 + t^2}{2}$, $y_2(t) = \dfrac{2t^2 + t^4 + 5}{8}$.
(c) $y_1(t) = t$, $y_2(t) = t + \dfrac{t^2}{3}$.
(d) $y_1(t) = e^t$, $y_2(t) = \dfrac{e^{2t} + 1}{2}$.

2. (a) $y_1(t) = \frac{1}{2}\left[\sin^{-1} t + t\sqrt{1 - t^2} - \dfrac{\pi}{6} - \dfrac{\sqrt{3}}{4}\right]$.
(b) $y_1(t)$ is defined for $-1 \leq t \leq 1$.

3. (a) $y_1(t) = 1 + t$, $y_2(t) = 1 + \log(1 + t)$.
(b) $y_1(t)$ is defined for all t, $y_2(t)$ is defined for $t > -1$.

4. (a) $y_1(t) = 2 - \dfrac{1}{t}$, $y_2(t) = \dfrac{5}{2} + \dfrac{2}{t} + \dfrac{1}{2t^2}$.
$y_1(t)$ and $y_2(t)$ are defined for all t except $t = 0$.

6. (b) Part (a) applies to $\dot{y}(t) = e^t \sin y(t)$ and $\dot{y}(t) = p(t)y(t)^3$.

Section 4.4

1. (a) Let $y_1 = y$, $y_2 = \dot{y}_1$. Then $\dot{y}_1 = y_2$, $\dot{y}_2 + k^2 y_1 = 0$.
(c) Let $y_1 = y$, $y_2 = \dot{y}_1$, $y_3 = \dot{y}_2$. Then $\dot{y}_1 = y_2$, $\dot{y}_2 = y_3$, $\dot{y}_3 + y_3 y_2 y_1 = 0$.

2. (b) Let $z_1 = y_1$, $z_2 = \dot{z}_1$, $z_3 = \dot{z}_2$, $z_4 = y_2$, $z_5 = \dot{z}_4$. Then $\dot{z}_1 = z_2$, $\dot{z}_2 = z_3$, $\dot{z}_4 = z_5$, $\dot{z}_3 + z_4^2 = 1$, $\dot{z}_5 - z_1 = 0$.

3. (a) Let $z_1 = y_1$, $z_2 = \dot{z}_1$, $z_3 = y_2$, $z_4 = \dot{z}_3$, $z_5 = y_3$, $z_6 = \dot{z}_5$. Then $\dot{z}_1 = z_2$, $\dot{z}_3 = z_4$, $\dot{z}_5 = z_6$, $\dot{z}_2 = z_3$, $\dot{z}_4 = z_5$, $\dot{z}_6 = z_1$.
(c) Let $z_1 = y_1$, $z_2 = \dot{z}_1$, $z_3 = \dot{z}_2$, $z_4 = y_2$, $z_5 = \dot{z}_4$. Then $\dot{z}_1 = z_2$, $\dot{z}_2 = z_3$, $\dot{z}_4 = z_5$, $\dot{z}_3 - z_2 z_4 = 0$, $\dot{z}_5 + z_3 z_1 = 0$.

4. Newton's Law is $f(\rho(t), \dot{\rho}(t)) = m\dot{\rho}(t)$. Let $y_1 = \rho$, $y_2 = \dot{y}_1$. Then system is $\dot{y}_1 = y_2$, $m\dot{y}_2 = f(y_1, y_2)$.

7. (a) $(y_1^1(t), y_2^1(t)) = (1, t)$; $(y_1^2(t), y_2^2(t)) = (1 + t^2, t)$.
(b) $(y_1^1(t), y_2^1(t)) = (t, 1)$, $(y_1^2(t), y_2^2(t)) = (t, 1 + t^3/3)$.
(c) $(y_1^2(t), y_2^1(t)) = \left(1, \dfrac{1 - t^2}{2}\right)$,
$(y_1^2(t), y_2^2(t)) = \left(\dfrac{3 - 2\log + t^2}{4}, \dfrac{1 - t^2}{2}\right)$.

8. (a) $y = \frac{1}{2}\sin 2t$.
(b) Let $y_1 = y$, $y_2 = \dot{y}_1$. Then $\dot{y}_1 = y_2$, $\dot{y}_2 + 4y_1 = 0$.
(c) $(y_1^1(t), y_2^1(t)) = (t, 1)$, $(y_1^2(t), y_2^2(t)) = (t, 1 - 2t^2)$.

9. $y_1 \equiv 1$, $y_2 \equiv 0$, $y_1(t) = t + 1$, $y_2(t) = -t$.

Section 4.5

1. (a) $y(t) = e^t$.
(b) $y(0) = 1$, $y(1) \approx 2$.
(c) $y(0) = 1$, $y(1) \approx 2.25$.

2. Exact calculation is $y(t) = \dfrac{1}{1 - t}$; for a single interval $y(\frac{1}{2}) \approx 1.5$; for two intervals $y(\frac{1}{2}) \approx 1.64$; $y(1) \approx 2.62$.

CHAPTER 5

Section 5.1

1. (a) No. (b) Yes. (c) No. (d) Yes.

2. (b) dim $= 2$, basis $= (1, 0, 0), (0, 0, 1)$.
(d) dim $= 2$, basis $= (1, 1, 0, 0), (1, 0, 0, 1)$.

3. S_2 is a subspace with basis $1, t$.

4. (a) Subspace. (b) Subspace. (c) Not a subspace. (d) Subspace. (e) Not a subspace.

5. (a) dim $= 1$, basis: 1.
(b) dim $= 2$, basis: $1, t$.
(d) dim $= 1$, basis: e^{-t}.

6. Solutions are of form $y(t) = ct^2 + bt + a$. A subspace if and only if $a = b = 0$; basis is: t^2.

7. Subspace if $a = b = 0$.

10. (c) Is a subspace.

14. $\mathcal{R}^2$. (a) All vectors of the form $(a, 2a)$.
(b) All of $\mathcal{R}^2$.
$\mathcal{R}^3$. (a) All vectors of form $(a, b, -b)$.
$\mathcal{P}^4$. (a) All polynomials of form $at^3 + bt$.

16. None, if S_2 is to be a subspace of $\mathcal{R}^3$, then $(0, 0, 0) \in S_2$. But then $d_1 = d_2 = 0$.

17. Any two of the three form a basis for their span.

18. (a) $(1, 0, 1), (0, 1, 0)$.
(b) $(1, 0, -1, 1), (0, 1, 0, 1)$.
(c) $1, t, t^2$.
(d) $\sin t, \sin 2t, \sin 3t$.

Section 5.2

2. (a) $\begin{bmatrix} \cos b \\ \sin b \end{bmatrix}$.

(b) $\begin{bmatrix} \dfrac{1}{\sqrt{2}}(\cos b - \sin b) \\ \dfrac{1}{\sqrt{2}}(\cos b + \sin b) \end{bmatrix}$.

3. $B_3 = (0, 0, 1)$.

4. A and A'' are bases

$$[(1, 1, 1)]_B = \begin{bmatrix} \frac{1}{2} \\ \frac{1}{2} \\ \frac{1}{2} \end{bmatrix} \text{ (for } A\text{)}, \begin{bmatrix} 0 \\ -1 \\ 1 \end{bmatrix} \text{ (for } A''\text{)}.$$

5. (a) Yes. (b) Yes. (c) Yes.

6. (a) No. (b) No. (c) Yes.

7. $\mathcal{R}^2$. A: Independent. B: Dependent (can express any of the vectors in terms of the others). C: Dependent $((0, 0) = 0(1, 1))$.
$\mathcal{R}^3$. D: Dependent (every vector can be expressed in terms of the others). E: Independent.
$\mathcal{C}(-\infty, \infty)$. F: Independent. G: Independent.

9. dim = 3.

10. (a) No. (b) No. (c) Yes.

11. (a) dim = 3. (b) dim = 3. (c) dim = 4.

Section 5.3

1. (a) $y(t) = c_1e^{4t} + c_2e^{-4t}$.
(b) $y(t) = c_1 \cos 2t + c_2 \sin 2t$.
(c) $y(t) = c_1 \cos 3t + c_2 \sin 3t$.
(d) $y(t) = c_1e^{2t} + c_2$.
(e) $y(t) = c_1t + c_2$.
(f) $y(t) = c_1e^{2t} + c_2e^{-t}$.
(g) $y(t) = e^{2t}(c_1 \cos t + c_2 \sin t)$.
(h) $y(t) = c_1e^{2t} + c_2te^{2t}$.

2. (a) $y(t) = -\cos 3t + \frac{1}{3} \sin 3t$.
(b) $y(t) \equiv 1$.
(d) $y(t) = -(1/\sqrt{5})(\sin \sqrt{5}\, t)e^{-t}$.
(e) $y(t) = te^{-3t}$.
(f) $y(t) = \frac{4}{5}e^{2t} + \frac{1}{5}e^{-3t}$.

4. As $t \to \infty$, charge $\to cE_0$.

Section 5.4

1. (a) $y(t) = -\frac{1}{3}te^t - \frac{2}{9}e^t + c_1e^{2t} + c_2e^{-2t}$.

(b) $y(t) = \dfrac{t}{2} + \dfrac{3}{4} + c_1e^t + c_2e^{2t}$.

(c) $y(t) = (-2 \log t + c_1)e^{-t} + \left(\dfrac{-2}{t} + c_2\right) te^{-t}$.

(d) $y(t) = \dfrac{\sin t - \cos t}{2} + c_1 + c_2e^{-t}$.

2. (a) $y(t) = (\log \cos t + 1) \cos t + t \sin t$.

(b) $y(t) = \displaystyle\int_1^t \log \tau \, d\tau - e^{-t} \int_1^t e^\tau \log \tau \, d\tau$.

3. (a) $y_0(t) = 2 - 2t.$
(b) $y_0(t) = -4 - 2t - t^2.$
(c) $y_0(t) = \dfrac{1}{\alpha^2 + \alpha + 2} e^{\alpha t}.$
(e) $y_0(t) = \left(\dfrac{-3}{4} + \dfrac{1}{2}t\right) e^t.$
(f) $y_0(t) = -\frac{1}{5}t \cos 2t + \frac{4}{25} \sin 2t.$

4. (a) $y(t) = -t^3 - 6t - 1.$
(b) $y(t) = (\frac{1}{2} - t + \frac{1}{2}t^2)e^t.$
(c) $y(t) = \frac{1}{5}e^t \sin t - \frac{2}{5}e^t \cos t.$

5. (a) $y(t) = c_1 \cos t + c_2 \sin t + \frac{1}{2}t \sin t.$
(b) $y(t) = c_1 e^t + c_2 e^{-t} + \frac{1}{2}te^t.$
(c) $y(t) = c_1 e^{-3t} + c_2 e^t - \frac{1}{4}te^{-3t}.$

6. (a) $y(t) = -2e^{-t} + \frac{3}{4}e^{-2t} - \frac{1}{2}t + \frac{5}{4}.$
(b) $y(t) = e^{2t} + \frac{2}{9} - \frac{2}{9}e^{3t} - \frac{4}{9}te^{3t}.$
(c) $y(t) = e^t(\frac{13}{10} \sin t - \frac{2}{5} \cos t) - \frac{1}{10} \cos 2t - \frac{1}{5} \sin 2t + \frac{1}{2}t + \frac{1}{2}.$

7. $\omega = \dfrac{1}{\sqrt{LC}}.$

8. (b) As $t \to \infty$, charge $\to cE_0$.

9. (c) $y(t) = c_1 e^{e^t} + c_2 e^{-e^t} - e^{2t} - 2.$
(d) $y(t) = (5/2e)e^{e^t} + (e/2)e^{-e^t} - e^{2t} - 2.$

CHAPTER 6

Section 6.1

2. $\mathcal{R}^2$. (a) $(1, 0), (0, 1).$
(b) $(1/\sqrt{2}, 1/\sqrt{2}), (1/\sqrt{2}, -1/\sqrt{2}).$
(c) $(-1, 0). (0, 1).$
$\mathcal{R}^3$. (a) $(1/\sqrt{3})(1, 1, 1), (1/\sqrt{6})(-2, 1, 1).$
(b) $(1/\sqrt{2})(0, 1, 1), (1, 0, 0).$
$\mathcal{R}^4$. (b) $(1/\sqrt{6})(1, 2, 0, 1), (1/\sqrt{498})(17, -8, 12, -1).$
$\mathcal{C}[-1, 1]$. (a) $1/\sqrt{2}, \sqrt{3/2}\, t, \sqrt{45/8}\,(t^2 - \frac{1}{3}).$

3. (a) $(1/\sqrt{21})(1, 2, 0, 4), (1/\sqrt{42})(2, 1, -6, -1), (1/\sqrt{77})(-3, -2, 8, 0).$

4. $(\frac{7}{3}, -\frac{2}{3}, 1, -2).$

5. [*Hint:* Choose a vector f not in $\langle 1, t, \sin \pi t\rangle$ and use Gram-Schmidt on $1, t, \sin \pi t, f$.]

13. (a) [*Hint:* Consider $\|P^{\perp}\beta + P\beta\|^2$ and use problem 12.]
(c) [*Hint:* Decompose $\boldsymbol{\alpha} + \boldsymbol{\beta}$ as in problem 11 and use problem 12.]

Section 6.2

1. $c = \frac{7}{3}.$

2. (a) $(x_1, x_2) = (2, \frac{3}{2}).$

3. (a) (i) $y = \frac{3}{5}x + \frac{3}{2}$.
(ii) $y = \frac{1}{3}x^2 + \frac{3}{5}x + \frac{2}{3}$.
(iii) $y = \frac{4}{3}x + \frac{3}{2} - \frac{1}{3}x$.

4. (a) $H(t) = \frac{3}{5}t$.
(b) $H(t) = (\pi/2) + \frac{1}{2}\sin t$.
(c) $H(t) = \frac{3}{5}t$.

Section 6.3

1. (a) $f(t) \sim \frac{1}{2} + 2\sum_{m=1}^{\infty} \frac{(-1)^m - 1}{m^2} \cos \pi mt.$

(b) $f(t) \sim 1 + \frac{4}{\pi^2}\sum_{m=1}^{\infty} \frac{(-1)^m - 1}{m^2} \cos \frac{\pi mt}{2}.$

(c) $f(t) \sim 1 + \cos t.$

(d) $f(t) \sim \frac{-2}{\pi} + \frac{2}{\pi}\sum_{m=2}^{\infty} \frac{1}{1 - m^2}[(-1)^m + 1]\cos mt.$

(e) $a_0 = \frac{1}{4}$; $a_m = \frac{4}{\pi^2 m^2}(1 - (-1)^{m/2})$, m even; $a_m = -\frac{4}{\pi^2 m^2}$, m odd.

(f) $a_0 = \frac{1}{2}$; $a_m = 0$, m even, $a_m = -\frac{8}{\pi^2 m^2}$, m odd.

2. (a) $f(t) \sim \frac{2}{\pi}\sum_{m=1}^{\infty} \frac{(-1)^{m+1}}{m} \sin \pi mt.$

(b) $f(t) \sim \frac{2}{\pi}\sum_{m=1}^{\infty} \frac{(-1)^{m+1}}{m} \sin \frac{\pi m}{2} t.$

(c) $f(t) \sim \frac{2}{\pi}\sum_{m=1}^{\infty} a_m \sin mt$; $a_m = \frac{2}{m}$, m odd; $a_m = \frac{2m}{m^2 - 1}$, m even.

(d) $f(t) \sim \sin t.$

(e) $f(t) \sim \sum_{m=1}^{\infty} a_m \sin \frac{\pi mt}{2}$; $a_m = \frac{-2}{\pi m}$, m even; $a_m = \frac{2}{\pi m} + \frac{4}{\pi^2 m^2}(-1)^m$, m odd.

(f) $f(t) \sim \sum_{m=1}^{\infty} a_m \sin \frac{\pi mt}{2}$; $a_m = 0$, m even, $a_m = \frac{4}{\pi m}$, m odd.

3. (a) $f(t) \sim \frac{2}{\pi}\sum_{m=1}^{\infty} \frac{1}{m}(-1)^{m+1} \sin \pi mt.$

(b) $f(t) \sim \frac{4}{\pi}\sum_{m=1}^{\infty} \frac{1}{m}(-1)^{m+1} \sin \frac{\pi mt}{2}.$

(c) $f(t) \sim 1 + \cos t.$

(d) $f(t) \sim \frac{1}{2\pi}\sum_{m=1}^{\infty} (-1)^{m+1}\left(\frac{m}{m^2 - \frac{1}{4}}\right) \sin mt.$

(e) $f(t) \sim \frac{\pi}{4} + \frac{1}{\pi} \sum_{m=1}^{\infty} \left[\frac{(-1)^m - 1}{m} \cos 2\pi m + \frac{(-1)^{m+1}}{m} \sin 2\pi m \right].$

(f) $f(t) \sim -\frac{1}{2} + \sum_{m=1}^{\infty} \left[\frac{2}{\pi^2 m^2} (1 + (-1)^{m+1}) \cos \frac{\pi m t}{2} \right.$

$\left. + \frac{2}{\pi m} (-1)^{m+1} \sin \frac{\pi m t}{2} \right].$

6. (a) [*Hint:* Use identities in problem 5.]

7. [*Hint:* Use the identity $\sin \alpha \cos \beta = \frac{1}{2} [\sin (\alpha + \beta) + \sin (\alpha - \beta)]$.]

10. $f(t) \sim \frac{2}{\pi} \sum_{m=1}^{\infty} (-1)^{m+1} \sin \pi m t.$

11. $f(t) \sim \sum_{m=1}^{\infty} a_m \sin \frac{m}{2} t$; $a_m = 0$, m odd; $a_m = \frac{-4}{\pi m} (-1)^{m/2}$, m even.

12. [*Hint:* Use induction to show the last part.]

15. $f(t) = 1 - 2 \sum_{m=1}^{\infty} \frac{(-1)^m + 1}{m} \sin mt.$

17. [*Hint:* Examine $f(t) = \cos t - \cos 2t$ and get a result similar to that in (3.11).]

Section 6.4

1. (a) $f(t) \sim \frac{\pi}{2} + \frac{2}{\pi} \sum_{m=1}^{\infty} \frac{(-1)^m - 1}{m^2} \cos mt.$

(c) $f(t) \sim \sin \pi t.$

(e) $f(t) \sim \frac{2}{\pi} \sum_{m \text{ odd}} \frac{(-1)^{(m+1)/2}}{m} \sin \frac{\pi m t}{2}.$

(g) $f(t) = \cos 1 \sin t - \sin 1 \cos t.$

2. (a) $f(t) = \sin t.$
(c) $f(t) = \frac{1}{2} - \frac{1}{2} \cos 2t.$
(e) $f(t) = \frac{1}{2} + \frac{1}{2} \cos 2t.$

3. (b), (c), (d), (f).

6. $y(t) \sim a_0 + \sum_{m=1}^{\infty} \left[\frac{4a_m}{(4 + \pi^2 m^2)} \cos \frac{\pi m t}{2} - \frac{4b_m}{(4 + \pi^2 m^2)} \sin \frac{\pi m t}{2} \right]$ where a_m and b_m are the Fourier coefficients of f.

7. $y(t) \sim -a_0 + \sum_{m=1}^{\infty} \left[\frac{-a_m}{1 + m^2} \cos mt + \frac{-b_m}{1 + m^2} \sin mt \right]$ where a_m and b_m are the Fourier coefficients of f.

8. $y(t) = a_0 + \sum_{m=1}^{\infty} \left[\frac{a_m}{k - \pi^2 m^2} \cos \pi m t + \frac{b_m}{k - \pi^2 m^2} \sin \pi m t \right]$ where a_m, b_m are the Fourier coefficients of f.

Section 6.5

1. (a) $S_1(\omega) = \dfrac{-\omega}{1+\omega^2}$, $S_2(\omega) = \dfrac{-1}{\omega^2+1}$;

$C_1(\omega) = \dfrac{-1}{\omega^2+1}$, $C_2(\omega) = \dfrac{\omega}{1+\omega^2}$.

(b) $S_1(\omega) = \dfrac{-\omega}{4+\omega^2}$, $S_2(\omega) = \dfrac{2}{4+\omega^2}$;

$C_1(\omega) = \dfrac{2}{4+\omega^2}$, $C_2(\omega) = \dfrac{\omega}{4+\omega^2}$.

(c) $C_1(\omega) = \dfrac{1-\omega^2}{(1+\omega^2)^2}$, $C_2(\omega) = \dfrac{2\omega}{(1+\omega^2)^2}$;

$S_1(\omega) = \dfrac{-2\omega}{(1+\omega^2)^2}$, $S_2(\omega) = \dfrac{1-\omega^2}{(1+\omega^2)^2}$.

(d) $C_1(\omega) = \dfrac{-1}{\omega^2+1}$, $C_2(\omega) = 0$; $\quad S_1(\omega) = 0$, $S_2(\omega) = \dfrac{-1}{\omega^2+1}$.

3. (a) $y = -\dfrac{\pi}{8} - \dfrac{1}{\pi}\cos t - \dfrac{1}{\pi}\sin t.$

(b) $y = \dfrac{\pi}{16} - \dfrac{2}{5\pi}\cos t + \dfrac{4}{5\pi}\sin t.$

(c) $y = \dfrac{\pi}{8} - \dfrac{1}{\pi}\cos t.$

(d) $y = -\dfrac{\pi}{8} - \dfrac{1}{\pi}\sin t.$

4. (a) $y_1 = -\dfrac{2}{5\pi}\cos t - \dfrac{4}{5\pi}\sin t.$

5. $y_1 = \dfrac{\pi}{2} - \dfrac{4}{\pi}\sin t.$

6. $y_1 = -\dfrac{16}{\pi^2}\cos t.$

CHAPTER 7

Section 7.0

1. (a) $u(x, t) = f(t).$
(c) $u(x, t) = f(t) + g(x).$

2. (a) $u(x, t) = tx + f(t).$

(c) $u(x, t) = \dfrac{t^2}{2}x + \dfrac{x^2}{2}t + f(t) + g(x).$

3. (c) $u(x, t) = \dfrac{tx^3}{6} - \dfrac{t}{2}x + \frac{4}{3}t.$

4. Try $u(x, t) = f(x - t)$. Then $u(x, -x) = f(x - (-x)) = f(2x) = 2x$. Hence can choose $f(w) = w$ so that $u(x, t) = x - t$ is the desired solution.

6. $u(x, t) = f\left(\frac{x}{t}\right)$. Let $f'(w)$ be the value at w of the derivative of f with respect to w. Then by (0.1.4):

$$u_x(x, t) = f'\left(\frac{x}{t}\right)\frac{\partial}{\partial x}\left(\frac{x}{t}\right) = f'\left(\frac{x}{t}\right)\cdot\frac{1}{t},$$

$$u_t(x, t) = f'\left(\frac{x}{t}\right)\frac{\partial}{\partial t}\left(\frac{x}{t}\right) = f'\left(\frac{x}{t}\right)\left(-\frac{x}{t^2}\right).$$

Hence $xu_x(x, t) + tu_t(x, t) = f'\left(\frac{x}{t}\right)\frac{x}{t} - f'\left(\frac{x}{t}\right)\frac{x}{t} = 0.$

8. $f(x) = \frac{1 + L}{2}x + c$, $g(x) = \frac{1 - L}{2}x - c$ where c is any constant.

9. (a), (b), (d).

Section 7.1

1. (a) $u(x, t) = e^{-4t}\sin 2x$.
(b) $u(x, t) = e^{-8t}\sin 2x$.
(c) $u(x, t) = e^{-\pi^2 t}\sin \pi x$.
(f) $\sin 3x \cos x + \cos 3x \sin x = \sin(3x + x) = \sin 4x$ so solution is $u(x, t) = e^{-16t}\sin 4x$.

2. (a) $\varphi(x) = \alpha_1 \sin\frac{\pi}{2}x + \alpha_2 \sin \pi x + \alpha_3 \sin\frac{3\pi x}{2} + \cdots + \alpha_n \sin\frac{n\pi x}{2}$.

(b) $\varphi(x) = \alpha_1 \sin\frac{1}{2}x + \alpha_2 \sin x + \alpha_3 \sin\frac{3x}{2} + \cdots + \alpha_n \sin\frac{nx}{2}$.

(c) $\varphi(x) = \alpha_1 \sin\frac{\pi}{3}x + \alpha_2 \sin\frac{2\pi}{3}x + \alpha_3 \sin \pi x + \cdots + \alpha_n \sin\frac{n\pi x}{3}$.

4. Equation 1.6 must be replaced by:

$$\dot{a}_m(t) + K\frac{m^2\pi^2}{L^2}ta_m(t) = 0.$$

Section 7.2

1.

(a) $e^{-n^2\pi^2 t}\sin n\pi x$	$n = 1, 2, \ldots$
(c) $e^{n^2 t}\sin nx$	$n = 1, 2, \ldots$
(d) $e^{n^2 t}\cos nx$	$n = 0, 1, 2, \ldots$
(f) $e^{-2(n+1/2)^2\pi^2 t}\cos(n + \frac{1}{2})\pi x$	$n = 0, 1, 2, \ldots$
(g) $e^{-(n^2+1/4)t}e^{-x/2}\sin nx$	$n = 1, 2, \ldots$
(i) $e^{-n^2 \arctan t}\sin nx$	$n = 1, 2, \ldots$

2. (a) $Ce^{at}e^{-ax}$, C and a constants.
(c) $Ct^a x^{-a}$, C and a constants.
(e) $Ce^{ae^{-t}}e^{ae^x}$, C and a constants.
(h) No product solutions except constants.

Section 7.3

1. X: $\sqrt{2/\pi}\cos(n+\frac{1}{2})x \qquad n = 0, 1, 2, \ldots.$
$u(x, t) \sim 4/\pi(\pi - 2)e^{-t/2}\cos x/2 - 4/3\pi(\pi + \frac{2}{3})e^{-9t/2}\cos 3x/2 + \cdots.$

3. X: $1, 1/\sqrt{2}\cos n\pi x \qquad n = 1, 2, \ldots.$
$u(x, t) = 1 + 2t$ (exact solution).

4. X: $\sqrt{2/\pi}\sin nx \qquad n = 1, 2, \ldots.$
$\sin 2x\cos x + \cos 2x\sin x + \sin 3x\cos 2x + \cos 3x\sin 2x = \sin 3x + \sin 5x.$
Hence problem has the *exact* solution

$$u(x, t) = e^{9t}\sin 3x + e^{-25t}\sin 5x.$$

6. X: $\sqrt{2}\cos(n+\frac{1}{2})\pi x \qquad n = 0, 1, 2, \ldots.$

$$u(x, t) \sim 4/\pi(1 - 2/\pi)e^{t(1+\pi^2/4)}\cos \pi x/2 - 4/3\pi(1 + 2/3\pi)e^{t(1+9\pi^2/4)}\cos 3\pi x/2$$

8. X: $\sin n\pi x/2 \qquad n = 1, 2, \ldots.$
$u(x, t) \sim e^{\pi^2(1+e^t)/4}\sin \pi x/2 + e^{9\pi^2(1+e^t)/4}\sin 3\pi x/2 + \cdots.$

10. Let $u(x, t) = e^{-3x/4}\gamma(x, t)$. Then:
$u_t(x, t) = e^{-3x/4}\gamma_t(x, t)$
$u_x(x, t) = -\frac{3}{4}e^{-3x/4}\gamma(x, t) + e^{-3x/4}\gamma_x(x, t)$
$u_{xx}(x, t) = \frac{9}{16}e^{-3x/4}\gamma(x, t) - \frac{3}{2}e^{-3x/4}\gamma_x(x, t) + e^{-3x/4}\gamma_{xx}(x, t).$
Hence:
$u_t - 2u_{xx} - 3u_x = e^{-3x/4}\{\gamma_t(x, t) - 2\gamma_{xx}(x, t) - (\frac{9}{8} - \frac{9}{4})\gamma(x, t)\} = 0$
or:
(i) $\gamma_t = 2\gamma_{xx} + \frac{9}{8}\gamma,$
(ii) $\gamma(x, 0) = 1,$
(iii) $\gamma(0, t) = \gamma(\pi, t) = 0.$
The problem for γ is of the standard form (3.2)–(3.4) with

$$r(t) = 1,\ K = 2,\ M = \tfrac{9}{8}.$$

The functions $X_m(x)$ are

$$X_m(x) = \sqrt{2/\pi}\sin mx \qquad m = 1, 2, \ldots,$$

and the numbers α_m are

$$\alpha_m = \tfrac{9}{8} - 2m^2 \qquad m = 1, 2, \ldots.$$

According to Example (1.16)(3) we have for the function $\varphi \equiv 1$,

$$\varphi(x) \sim 4/\pi\sin x + 4/3\pi\sin 3x + \cdots.$$

The functions $T_m(t)$ are given by

$$T_m(t) = e^{\alpha_m t} = e^{(9/8-2m^2)t} \qquad m = 1, 2, \ldots.$$

Hence the Fourier series for γ is,
(iv) $\gamma(x, t) \sim 4/\pi e^{-7t/8}\sin x + 4/3\pi e^{-55t/8}\sin 2x + \cdots.$
[*Note:* The Fourier series for u is *not* obtained by simply multiplying the terms on the right side of (iv) by $e^{-3x/4}$. Explain.]

Section 7.4

1. (a) $A \cos \sqrt{2}\, nt \sin nx$, $B \sin \sqrt{2}\, nt \sin nx$; A, B constants, $n = 1, 2, \ldots$.
(c) $A \cos nt \cos nx$, $B \sin nt \cos nx$; A, B constants, $n = 0, 1, 2, \ldots$.
(e) $A \cos (n + \frac{1}{2})t \sin (n + \frac{1}{2})x$, $A \sin (n + \frac{1}{2})t \sin (n + \frac{1}{2})x$; A, B constants, $n = 0, 1, 2, \ldots$.
(f) $A \sin x$, $Bt \sin x$, $C \cos \sqrt{n^2 - 1}\, t \sin nx$, $D \sin \sqrt{n^2 - 1}\, t \sin nx$, A, B, C, D constants $\quad n = 2, 3, \ldots$.

2. (a)
$$u(x, t) = \left(-\cos \frac{\pi}{\sqrt{2}} t + \frac{4\sqrt{2}}{\pi} \sin \frac{\pi}{\sqrt{2}} t\right) \sin \frac{\pi}{2} x + \left(2 \cos \sqrt{2}\,\pi t - \frac{3}{\sqrt{2}\,\pi} \sin \sqrt{2}\,\pi t\right) \sin \pi x.$$

(c) $u(x, t) = \cos t \sin x - \cos \sqrt{17}\, t \sin 3x.$

(e)
$$u(x, t) = \frac{1}{\sqrt{1 + (\pi^2/4)}} \sin \sqrt{1 + \frac{\pi^2}{4}}\, t \cos \frac{\pi}{4} x + \left(\cos \sqrt{1 + \frac{9\pi^2}{4}}\, t - \frac{2}{\sqrt{1 + (9\pi^2/4)}} \sin \sqrt{1 + \frac{9\pi^2}{4}}\, t\right) \cos \frac{3\pi x}{4}.$$

3. (a) $u(x, t) \sim (2 \cos t + 4/\pi \sin t) \sin x - \cos 2t \sin 2x + \cdots$.
(b) $u(x, t) \sim -1/\pi^3 \sin 2\pi t \cos \pi x - 1/27\pi^3 \sin 6\pi t \cos 3\pi x + \cdots$.

(d)
$$\begin{aligned} u(x, t) \sim &\left(\frac{8}{\pi}\left(1 - \frac{2}{\pi}\right) \cos \sqrt{1 + \frac{9\pi^2}{16}}\, t \right.\\ &+ \left.\frac{8}{\pi\sqrt{1 + (9\pi^2/16)}}\left(1 - \frac{2}{\pi}\right) \sin \sqrt{1 + \frac{9\pi^2}{16}}\, t\right) \cos \frac{\pi x}{4}\\ &- \left(\frac{8}{3\pi}\left(1 + \frac{2}{3\pi}\right) \cos \sqrt{1 + \frac{81\pi^2}{16}}\, t \right.\\ &+ \left.\frac{8}{3\pi\sqrt{1 + (81\pi^2/16)}}\left(1 + \frac{2}{3\pi}\right) \sin \sqrt{1 + \frac{81\pi^2}{16}}\, t\right) \cos \frac{3\pi x}{4} + \cdots. \end{aligned}$$

5. $u_{tt}(x, t) = v_{ttt}(x, t)$ and $u_{xx}(x, t) = v_{txx}(x, t)$. But $v_{tt}(x, t) = v_{xx}(x, t)$ hence differentiation with respect to t yields,

$$v_{ttt}(x, t) = v_{txx}(x, t).$$

Thus u satisfies $u_{tt} = u_{xx}$. Since $v(0, t) = 0$ for all t differentiation with respect to t yields $v_t(0, t) = u(0, t) = 0$. Similarly $v(L, t) = 0$. Since $v(x, 0) = 0$ two differentiations with respect to x yield $v_{xx}(x, 0) = 0$. But $v_{xx} = v_{tt}$ hence $v_{tt}(x, 0) = u_t(x, 0) = 0$. Finally $u(x, 0) = v_t(x, 0) = \varphi(x)$.

Section 7.5

1. (a) $u(x, t) = (-\frac{1}{2}t + \frac{1}{8} - \frac{1}{8}e^{-4t}) \sin x + 2/\pi e^{-t} \sin x - 6/\pi e^{-9t} \sin 3x$.
(c) $u(x, t) = (-\frac{1}{2}t + \frac{1}{8} - \frac{1}{8}e^{-4t}) \cos x + 2/\pi e^{-t} \cos x - 6/\pi e^{-9t} \cos 3x$.
(f) $u(x, t) = (1 - \cos t) \sin x + 2 \sin t \sin x + \cos 2t \sin 2x$.

2. (a) $u(x, t) \sim \frac{4}{\pi} \sin x + \left(\frac{4}{27\pi} + \frac{32}{27\pi} e^{-9t}\right) \sin 3x + \cdots.$

(c) $u(x, t) \sim \frac{t^2}{2} + \frac{\pi}{2} - \frac{4}{\pi} \cos x + \cdots.$

(e) $$u(x, t) \sim \frac{2}{\pi(1 + \pi^2)} \left[e^t - \cos \pi t - \frac{1}{\pi} \sin \pi t\right] \sin \pi x$$
$$+ \frac{2}{3\pi(1 + \pi^2)} \left[e^t - \cos 3\pi t - \frac{1}{3\pi} \sin 3\pi t\right] \sin 3\pi x$$
$$+ \frac{1}{\pi} \cos \pi t \sin \pi x - \frac{1}{2\pi} \cos 2\pi t \sin 2\pi x + \cdots.$$

3. (a) Let $u_0(x, t) = t(1 - x)$ and $v(x, t) = u(x, t) - u_0(x, t)$. Then $v(0, t) = t - t = 0$ and $v(1, t) = 0$. Also,

$$v_t(x, t) = u_t(x, t) - (1 - x),$$
$$v_{xx}(x, t) = u_{xx}(x, t),$$

so that

$$v_t(x, t) = u_t(x, t) - (1 - x) = u_{xx}(x, t) + x - (1 - x)$$
$$= v_{xx}(x, t) - 1 + 2x.$$

Finally,

$$v(x, 0) = u(x, 0) = x.$$

(c) Let $u_0(x, t) = t(1 + x)$ and $v(x, t) = u(x, t) - u_0(x, t)$. Then $v(0, t) = t - t = 0$ and $v_x(\pi, t) = u_x(\pi, t) - t = t - t = 0$. Also,

$$v_{tt}(x, t) = u_{tt}(x, t) \quad \text{and} \quad v_{xx}(x, t) = u_{xx}(x, t),$$

hence $v_{tt} = v_{xx}$. Finally

$$v(x, 0) = u(x, 0) = 0, v_t(x, 0) = u_t(x, 0) - (1 + x) = 1 - (1 + x) = -x.$$

Section 7.6

1. (a) (i) $u^1_t = u^1_{xx} + xt; \quad u^1(x, 0) = x; \quad u^1_x(0, t) = u^1_x(L, t) = 0.$
(ii) $u^2_t = u^2_{xx} + xt; \quad u^2(x, 0) = x; \quad u^2_x(0, t) = u^2_x(L, t) = 0.$
Hence if $u = u^1 - u^2$ then subtraction of (i) and (ii) yields,
(iii) $u_t = u_{xx}; \quad u(x, 0) = 0; \quad u_x(0, t) = u_x(L, t) = 0.$
Multiply by u and integrate from 0 to L. This gives

$$\frac{1}{2} \frac{d}{dt} \int_0^L u^2\, dx = \int_0^L uu_t\, dx = \int_0^L uu_{xx}\, dx = u(L, t)u_x(L, t)$$
$$- u(0, t)u_x(0, t) - \int_0^L u_x^2\, dx.$$

Since $u_x(L, t) = u_x(0, t) = 0$ the result is

$$\frac{d}{dt}\int_0^L u^2\,dx = -\int_0^L u_x^2\,dx \le 0,$$

with $\int_0^L u^2(x, 0)\,dx = 0$. It follows that $u(x, t) \equiv 0$.

(d) (i) $u_t^1 = u_{xx}^1 - u^1$; $u^1(x, 0) = x$; $u^1(0, t) = u^1(L, t) = 0$.
(ii) $u_t^2 = u_{xx}^2 - u^2$; $u^2(x, 0) = x$; $u^2(0, t) = u^2(L, t) = 0$.
Hence if $u = u^1 - u^2$ then subtraction of (i) and (ii) yields
(iii) $u_t = u_{xx} - u$; $u(x, 0) = 0$; $u(0, t) = u(L, t) = 0$.
Multiply by u and integrate from 0 to L. This gives

$$\frac{1}{2}\frac{d}{dt}\int_0^L u^2\,dx = \int_0^L uu_t\,dx = \int_0^L uu_{xx}\,d_x - \int_0^L u^2\,dx$$

$$= u(L, t)u_x(L, t) - u(0, t)u_x(0, t) - \int_0^L (u_x^2 + u^2)\,dx.$$

Since $u(L, t) = u(0, t) = 0$ the result is,

$$\frac{d}{dt}\int_0^L u^2\,dx = -\int_0^L (u_x^2 + u^2)\,dx \le 0,$$

with $\int_0^L u^2(x, 0)\,dx = 0$. It follows that $u(x, t) \equiv 0$.

(f) (i) $u_t^1 = u_{xx}^1 + u_x^1$; $u^1(x, 0) = 1$; $u^1(0, t) = u^1(L, t) = 0$.
(ii) $u_t^2 = u_{xx}^2 + u_x^2$; $u^2(x, 0) = 1$; $u^2(0, t) = u^2(L, t) = 0$.
Hence if $u = u^1 - u^2$ then subtraction if (i) and (ii) yields,
(iii) $u_t = u_{xx} + u_x$; $u(x, 0) = 0$; $u(0, t) = u(L, t) = 0$.
Multiply by u and integrate from 0 to L. This gives

$$\text{(iv)}\quad \frac{1}{2}\frac{d}{dt}\int_0^L u_t^2\,dx = \int_0^L uu_t\,dx = \int_0^L (uu_{xx} + uu_x)\,dx.$$

Now $uu_x = \dfrac{1}{2}\dfrac{\partial}{\partial x}u^2$ hence

$$\int_0^L uu_x\,dx = \frac{1}{2}\int_0^L \frac{\partial}{\partial x}u^2\,dx = \frac{1}{2}\left(u(L, t)^2 - u^2(0, t)\right).$$

Thus (iv) yields,

$$\frac{1}{2}\frac{d}{dt}\int_0^L u^2\,dx = u(L, t)u_x(L_0, t) - u(0, t)u_x(0, t)$$

$$+ \tfrac{1}{2}\left(u^2(L, t) - u^2(0, t)\right) - \int_0^L u_x^2\,dx.$$

Since $u(0, t) = u(L, t) = 0$ this gives

$$\frac{1}{2}\frac{d}{dt}\int_0^L u^2\,dx = -\int_0^L u_x^2\,dx \le 0,$$

with $\int_0^L u^2(x, 0)\,dx = 0$. It follows that $u(x, t) \equiv 0$.

2. Let u be the difference of two solutions. Then

$$u_t = u_{xx} + au; \qquad u(x, 0) = 0; \qquad u(0, t) = u(L, t) = 0.$$

Multiply by u and integrate from 0 to L. This gives

$$\frac{1}{2}\frac{d}{dt}\int_0^L u^2\,dx = \int_0^L uu_t = \int_0^L (uu_{xx} + au^2)\,dx$$

$$= u(L, t)u_x(L, t) - u(0, t)u_x(0, t) + a\int_0^L u^2\,dx.$$

Since $u(L, t) = u(0, t) = 0$ the result is,

(i) $\displaystyle \frac{d}{dt}\int_0^L u^2\,dx = 2a\int_0^L u^2\,dx.$

Since $a > 0$ the right side is ≥ 0 so that the proof used before cannot be applied.

Note: A more sophisticated proof can be given as follows. Let

$$I(t) = \int_0^L u^2\,dx.$$

Then (i) can be written,

(ii) $\dot{I}(t) = 2aI(t)$.

Moreover $I(0) = \int_0^1 u^2(x, 0)\,dx = 0$. $I(t)$ is thus a solution of the ordinary differential equation (ii) with value zero at $t = 0$. But then it follows from Proposition 4.1.10 that $I(t) \equiv 0$ from which it follows that $u(x, t) \equiv 0$.

4. (a) (i) $\overset{1}{u}_{tt} = \overset{1}{u}_{xx}$; $\quad \overset{1}{u}(x, 0) = 1, \overset{1}{u}_t(x, 0) = 0$; $\quad \overset{1}{u}_x(0, t) = \overset{1}{u}_x(L, t) = 0$.

(ii) $\overset{2}{u}_{tt} = \overset{2}{u}_{xx}$; $\quad \overset{2}{u}(x, 0) = L, \overset{2}{u}_t(x, 0) = 0$; $\quad \overset{2}{u}_x(0, t) = \overset{2}{u}_x(L, t) = 0$.

Hence if $u = u^1 - u^2$ then subtraction of (i) and (ii) yields

(iii) $u_{tt} = u_{xx}$; $\quad u(x, 0) = 0, u_t(x, 0) = 0$; $\quad u_x(0, t) = u_x(L, t) = 0$.

Multiply by u_t and integrate from 0 to L. This gives,

$$\frac{1}{2}\frac{d}{dt}\int_0^L u_t^2\,dx = \int_0^L u_t u_{tt} = \int_0^L u_t u_{xx}\,dx$$

$$= u_t(L, t)u_x(L, t) - u_t(0, t)u_x(0, t) - \int_0^L u_{tx}u_x\,dx.$$

Since $u(L, t) \equiv 0$ and $u(0, t) \equiv 0$, it follows by differentiation with respect to t that $u_t(L, t) = u_t(0, t) = 0$. Hence

$$\frac{1}{2}\frac{d}{dt}\int_0^L u_t^2\,dx = -\int_0^L u_{tx}u_x\,dx = -\frac{1}{2}\frac{d}{dt}\int_0^L u_x^2\,dx.$$

Hence if $I_1(t) = \int_0^L u_t^2\,dx$ and $I_2(t) = \int_0^L u_x^2\,dx$ then $\dot{I}_1(t) + \dot{I}_2(t) = 0$ or $I_1(t) + I_2(t)$ is a constant. $I_1(0) = I_2(0) = 0$ hence the constant is zero and

$$I_1(t) + I_2(t) \equiv 0 \qquad \text{or} \qquad I_1(t) \equiv I_2(t) \equiv 0.$$

Thus $u_t(x, t) \equiv u_x(x, t) \equiv 0$ and u is a constant. But $u(x, 0) \equiv 0$ hence $u(x, t) \equiv 0$.

CHAPTER 8

Section 8.1

1. (a) $\mathcal{W} = (-\infty, \infty)$, nonlinear; one-to-one; $T(A) = [0, 1]$.
(b) $\mathcal{W} = (-\infty, \infty)$, nonlinear for $n \neq 1$; one-to-one for n odd, many-to-one for n even; $T(A) = [-2^n, 2^n]$ for n odd, $T(A) = [0, 2^n]$ for n even.
(c) $\mathcal{W} = (-\infty, \infty)$, linear; many-to-one; $T(A) = (-\infty, \infty)$.

2. (a) $\mathcal{W} = \mathcal{R}^2$, nonlinear; $T(A) =$ line segment joining $(1, 0)$ and $(0, 1)$; $R_T =$ first quadrant (including edges).
(b) $\mathcal{W} = \mathcal{R}^2$, linear; $T(A) =$ the line $(3m + 1)x_1 - (m + 3)x_2 + 8b = 0$; $R_T = \mathcal{R}^2$, $\dim R_T = 2$. [Express x_1 and x_2 as functions of $u = 3x_1 - x_2$ and $v = x_1 - 3x_2$].
(c) $\mathcal{W} = \mathcal{R}^3$, linear; $T(A) =$ the plane $2x_1 - x_2 - x_3 = 0$; $R_T = \langle(1, 1, 1), (-1, 2, -4), (2, -1, 5)\rangle$, $\dim R_T = 2$.
(d) $\mathcal{W} = \langle \sin t, \cos t\rangle$, linear; $T(A) =$ the set of vectors $c_1 \sin t + c_2 \cos t$ such that $c_1^2 + c_2^2 \leq \pi/2$; $R_T = \mathcal{W}$, $\dim R_T = 2$.
[Express $f = a \cos t + b \sin t + g$ where $g \in \mathcal{W}^{\perp}$].
(e) $\mathcal{W} = \mathcal{C}^1[0, \pi]$, linear; $T(A) =$ the set of all $g \in \mathcal{W}$ having $g(0) = \dot{g}(0) = 0$; $R_T =$ the set of all $g \in \mathcal{W}$ having $g(0) = 0$.
(f) $\mathcal{W} = \mathcal{C}[0, \pi]$, linear; $T(A) = \mathcal{W}$; $R_T = \mathcal{W}$. [Given $g \in C[0, \pi]$ find a solution of $\dot{f} = g$ satisfying $\int_0^\pi f(t)\,dt = 0$.]

7. (a) $\mathbf{y}_S$ is the S-approximator to $\mathbf{y}$ and $\mathbf{y}'_S$ is the S-approximator to $\mathbf{y}'$ if and only if $\mathbf{y} = \mathbf{y}_S + \mathbf{z}$, $\mathbf{y}' = \mathbf{y}'_S + \mathbf{z}'$ where $\mathbf{z}, \mathbf{z}' \in S^{\perp}$. But $\mathbf{y} + \mathbf{y}' = \mathbf{y}_S + \mathbf{y}'_S + (\mathbf{z} + \mathbf{z}')$ is the corresponding decomposition of $\mathbf{y} + \mathbf{y}'$. Similarly for $c\mathbf{y}$.

12. $T(x + y) = (x + y)(t_0) = x(t_0) + y(t_0) = Tx + Ty$. Similarly for $T(cx)$.

18. (a) $(T_1 + T_2)\mathbf{x} = (2x_1, 2x_1, 3x_1 + 3x_2)$.

(b) $$(-T_1 + T_2)f = tf(t) - \int_0^t f(s)\,ds, \qquad T_1T_2f = \int_0^t sf(s)\,ds,$$

$$T_2T_1f = t\int_0^t f(s)\,ds.$$

Section 8.2

1. (a) $P = (1, 1, 0) + \langle(-\frac{3}{2}, \frac{1}{2}, 1)\rangle$ (for all c) (line through $(1, 1, 0)$).
(b) $P = -1 + \frac{1}{2}\sin t + \langle e^t, e^{-t}\rangle$.

(d) $$P = \frac{1}{e^\pi - 1} + \langle e^t\rangle^{\perp}.$$

(g) $P = 2$.

3. (a) $P = 1 + \langle t, t^2\rangle$.
(c) $P = 1 - t + \langle t - t^2\rangle$.

5. (a) $P = 4(\frac{2}{5}, \frac{1}{5}, 0, 0) - 3(-\frac{1}{5}, -\frac{3}{5}, 0, 0) + \langle(-\frac{3}{5}, -\frac{4}{5}, 0, 1), (0, 1, 1, 0)\rangle$.
(b) None of the w's are in the subspace $\langle(3, 1, 3), (-1, -2, 4), (1, 2, -4), (1, -1, 5)\rangle$.
(c) $P = 2(-(t+1)) - 3(-\frac{1}{2}(\sin t + \cos t)) + 5te^t + \langle e^t\rangle$.
(e) $P = 1(t/2 + \frac{1}{4} - (\frac{1}{4})e^{2t}) + 10e^{2t} + \langle e^{2t} - e^{-t}\rangle$.
(i) $P = -3((-1 + \cos t)\sin x) + 2(\cos 2t \sin 2x)$
$+ \langle \sin t \sin x, \sin 2t \sin 2x, \sin 3t \sin 3x, \ldots\rangle$.

9. $y(t) = 2 + 2t^3$.

Section 8.3

1. (a) $\lambda_1 = 3$, $\mathbf{y} = k(1, 2)$; $\lambda_2 = -1$, $\mathbf{y} = k(1, -2)$.
(b) None.
(d) λ = any real number, $y(t) = ke^{(2+\lambda)t}$.
(f) $\lambda = -n^2$, $y(t) = k \sin nt$, $n = 1, 2, \ldots$.
(g) $\lambda = -4n^2$, $y(t) = k \sin 2nt + m \cos 2nt$, $n = 1, 2, \ldots$.

2. $\lambda_1 = 1$, $\mathbf{y}$ any vector in S; $\lambda_2 = 0$, $\mathbf{y}$ any vector in S.

6. (a) $T^{-1}(w_1, w_2) = (-(\frac{1}{3})w_1 + (\frac{1}{3})w_2, (\frac{4}{3})w_1 - (\frac{1}{3})w_2)$.
(b) $T^{-1}(w_1, w_2) = ((\frac{2}{3})w_1 + (\frac{1}{3})w_2, -(\frac{1}{3})w_1 + (\frac{1}{3})w_2)$.

7. $T^{-1}f = g$, where $g(t) = f(t) - e^{-t}\int_0^t e^s f(s)\, ds$.

9. (a) $y(t) = 2(\frac{1}{10}e^{3t}) - 3(\frac{1}{5}e^{2t}) + 5(\frac{1}{2}e^{-t})$.

11. $\mathbf{y} = 1(1 \cdot \frac{1}{2}, 1)) - 3(-\frac{1}{5}(-\frac{1}{2}, 1))$.

Section 8.4

1. (a) $\begin{pmatrix} \frac{1}{2} & -\frac{3}{2} \\ \frac{3}{2} & \frac{1}{2} \end{pmatrix}$

(c) $\begin{pmatrix} 1 & 0 \\ 1 & 0 \end{pmatrix}$

(f) $\begin{pmatrix} 1 & 0 & 0 \\ 1 & 0 & 0 \\ 1 & 0 & 0 \end{pmatrix}$

2. (a) $T = \begin{pmatrix} c & d \\ e & f \end{pmatrix}$ where $c - 2d = 3$, $e - 2f = 1$.

4. (a) $\begin{pmatrix} 0 & 1 \\ 1 & 0 \end{pmatrix}$

(d) $\begin{pmatrix} -\frac{1}{3} & \frac{2}{3} & 0 \\ \frac{2}{3} & -\frac{1}{3} & 0 \\ 0 & 0 & 1 \end{pmatrix}$

(e) $\begin{pmatrix} -\frac{1}{3} & \frac{2}{3} & 0 & 0 \\ \frac{2}{3} & -\frac{1}{3} & 0 & 0 \\ 0 & 0 & \frac{3}{7} & -\frac{1}{7} \\ 0 & 0 & -\frac{2}{7} & \frac{3}{7} \end{pmatrix}$

6. (a) $\lambda_1 = 1$, $\gamma_1 = \begin{pmatrix}1\\1\end{pmatrix}$; $\lambda_1 = -1$, $\gamma_2 = \begin{pmatrix}1\\-1\end{pmatrix}$; symmetric; eigenvectors form a basis.

(c) $\lambda_1 = \dfrac{1+\sqrt{17}}{2}$, $\gamma_1 = \begin{pmatrix}1\\ \dfrac{-1+\sqrt{17}}{4}\end{pmatrix}$; $\lambda_2 = \dfrac{1-\sqrt{17}}{2}$,

$\gamma_2 = \begin{pmatrix}1\\ \dfrac{-1-\sqrt{17}}{4}\end{pmatrix}$; not symmetric; eigenvectors form a basis.

(g) $\lambda_1 = 0$, $\gamma_1 = \begin{pmatrix}-2\\-1\\1\end{pmatrix}$; $\lambda_2 = 2+\sqrt{5}$, $\gamma_2 = \begin{pmatrix}1\\0\\ \dfrac{1+\sqrt{5}}{2}\end{pmatrix}$;

$\lambda_3 = 2-\sqrt{5}$, $\gamma_3 = \begin{pmatrix}1\\0\\ \dfrac{1-\sqrt{5}}{2}\end{pmatrix}$; not symmetric; eigenvectors form a basis.

7. (a) $\lambda_1 = 1+\sqrt{6}$, $\gamma_1 = \begin{pmatrix}1\\ \dfrac{\sqrt{6}}{2}\end{pmatrix}$; $\lambda_2 = 1-\sqrt{6}$, $\gamma_2 = \begin{pmatrix}1\\ \dfrac{-\sqrt{6}}{2}\end{pmatrix}$; a basis.

(e) $\lambda_1 = 1+\sqrt{6}$, $\gamma_1 = \begin{pmatrix}0\\1\\ \dfrac{\sqrt{6}}{2}\end{pmatrix}$; $\lambda_2 = 1-\sqrt{6}$, $\gamma_2 = \begin{pmatrix}0\\1\\ \dfrac{-\sqrt{6}}{2}\end{pmatrix}$;

$\lambda_3 = -1$, $\gamma_3 = \begin{pmatrix}1\\0\\0\end{pmatrix}$; a basis.

8. (a) Not symmetric. $\left[\begin{pmatrix}1\\-1\end{pmatrix}\cdot T\begin{pmatrix}1\\1\end{pmatrix} \neq T\begin{pmatrix}1\\-1\end{pmatrix}\cdot\begin{pmatrix}1\\1\end{pmatrix}\right]$.
(b) Symmetric.
(c) Not symmetric.

11. (a) $X \cdot CY = \int_0^L X(x)Y''(x)\,dx = X(x)Y'(x)|_0^L - \int_0^L X'(x)Y'(x)\,dx$

$X(x)Y'(x)|_0^L X'(x)Y(x)|_0^L + \int_0^L X''(x)Y(x)\,dx = 0 - 0 + CX \cdot Y.$

14. (a) $n = 3$, $m = 2$; not one-to-one.
(b) $n = 2$, $m = 3$; one-to-one.
(c) $n = 3$, $m = 4$; one-to-one.

15. (a) $S = \begin{pmatrix} -2 & 17 \\ 11 & -6 \end{pmatrix}.$

(b) $S = \begin{pmatrix} 15 & 13 & 11 \\ 1 & 2 & 1 \\ -18 & -1 & -6 \end{pmatrix}.$

CHAPTER 9

Section 9.1

1. (a) $B\dot{\mathbf{y}}(t) + C\mathbf{y}(t) = \mathbf{w}(t)$, $B = \begin{pmatrix} 1 & 0 \\ 0 & 1 \end{pmatrix}$; $C = \begin{pmatrix} 0 & 1 \\ 1 & 0 \end{pmatrix}$ $\mathbf{w}(t) = \begin{pmatrix} 0 \\ 0 \end{pmatrix}.$

(c) $A\ddot{\mathbf{y}}(t) + B\dot{\mathbf{y}}(t) + \mathbf{y}(t) = \mathbf{w}(t)$,

$$A = \begin{pmatrix} 2 & -1 \\ 1 & 1 \end{pmatrix};\ B = \begin{pmatrix} 3 & 0 \\ 0 & -4 \end{pmatrix};\ C = \begin{pmatrix} 2 & -1 \\ 1 & -1 \end{pmatrix};\ \mathbf{w}(t) = \begin{pmatrix} -1 \\ 1 \end{pmatrix}.$$

(e) $A\ddot{\mathbf{y}}(t) + B\dot{\mathbf{y}}(t) + C\mathbf{y}(t) = \mathbf{w}(t)$,

$$A = \begin{pmatrix} 0 & 1 \\ 1 & 1 \end{pmatrix};\ B = \begin{pmatrix} -1 & 1 \\ 0 & -1 \end{pmatrix};\ C = \begin{pmatrix} 0 & 0 \\ 0 & 0 \end{pmatrix};\ \mathbf{w}(t) = \begin{pmatrix} t \\ 4 \end{pmatrix}.$$

2. (b) This is of the form $B\dot{\mathbf{y}}(t) + C\mathbf{y}(t) = \mathbf{w}(t)$,

$$B = \begin{pmatrix} 1 & 1 \\ 1 & -1 \end{pmatrix};\ C = \begin{pmatrix} 1 & -1 \\ -1 & -1 \end{pmatrix};\ \mathbf{w}(t) = \begin{pmatrix} 0 \\ 1 \end{pmatrix}.$$

The matrix of the inverse transformation for B is given by,

$$B^{-1} = \begin{pmatrix} \frac{1}{2} & \frac{1}{2} \\ \frac{1}{2} & -\frac{1}{2} \end{pmatrix}.$$

The matrix of the product transformation $B^{-1}C$ is given by the procedure of problem (4.16) of Chapter 8. It is

$$B^{-1}C = \begin{pmatrix} 0 & -1 \\ 1 & 0 \end{pmatrix}.$$

The effect of B^{-1} on $\mathbf{w}$ is,

$$B^{-1}\mathbf{w}(t) = \begin{pmatrix} \frac{1}{2} & \frac{1}{2} \\ \frac{1}{2} & -\frac{1}{2} \end{pmatrix}\begin{pmatrix} 0 \\ 1 \end{pmatrix} = \begin{pmatrix} \frac{1}{2} \\ -\frac{1}{2} \end{pmatrix}.$$

Thus the equation can be written as $\dot{\mathbf{y}}(t) + \hat{C}\mathbf{y}(t) = \hat{\mathbf{w}}(t)$,

$$\hat{C} = \begin{pmatrix} 0 & -1 \\ 1 & 0 \end{pmatrix};\ \hat{\mathbf{w}}(t) = \begin{pmatrix} \frac{1}{2} \\ -\frac{1}{2} \end{pmatrix}.$$

(d) The equation can be written as $\ddot{\mathbf{y}}(t) + \hat{B}\dot{\mathbf{y}}(t) + \hat{C}\mathbf{y}(t) = \hat{\mathbf{w}}(t)$,

$$\hat{B} = \begin{pmatrix} 0 & -1 \\ 1 & 0 \end{pmatrix};\ \hat{C} = \begin{pmatrix} 0 & 0 \\ 0 & 1 \end{pmatrix};\ \hat{\mathbf{w}}(t) = \begin{pmatrix} t \\ 1 \end{pmatrix}.$$

4.
$$\begin{aligned} m_1\ddot{z}_1(t) &= k(z_2(t) - 2z_1(t)) \\ m_2\ddot{z}_2(t) &= k(z_1(t) - 2z_2(t) + z_3(t)) \\ m_3\ddot{z}_3(t) &= -k(z_3(t) - z_2(t) - L) \end{aligned}$$

or if $y_1 = z_1 - L$, $y_2 = z_2 - 2L$, $y_3 = z_3 - 3L$,

$$\begin{aligned} m_1\ddot{y}_1(t) &= k(y_2(t) - 2y_1(t)) \\ m_2\ddot{y}_2(t) &= k(y_1(t) - 2y_2(t) + y_3(t)) \\ m_3\ddot{y}_3(t) &= -k(y_3(t) - y_2(t)). \end{aligned}$$

6. (a) The conditional equation $T\mathbf{x} = \mathbf{y}$ becomes

$$\begin{pmatrix} t_{11} & 0 & 0 \\ 0 & t_{22} & 0 \\ 0 & 0 & t_{33} \end{pmatrix} \begin{pmatrix} x_1 \\ x_2 \\ x_3 \end{pmatrix} = \begin{pmatrix} y_1 \\ y_2 \\ y_3 \end{pmatrix}$$

or $t_{11}x_1 = y_1$, $t_{22}x_2 = y_2$; $t_{33}x_3 = y_3$.
For these equations to have solutions for *arbitrary* y_1, y_2 and y_3 it is necessary and sufficient that $t_{11} \neq 0$, $t_{22} \neq 0$, and $t_{33} \neq 0$. Then the inverse is

$$\begin{pmatrix} 1/t_{11} & 0 & 0 \\ 0 & 1/t_{22} & 0 \\ 0 & 0 & 1/t_{33} \end{pmatrix}.$$

(b) The equation $B\dot{\mathbf{y}}(t) + C\mathbf{y}(t) = \mathbf{w}(t)$ becomes, when B and C are diagonal

$$\begin{pmatrix} b_{11} & 0 & 0 \\ 0 & b_{22} & 0 \\ 0 & 0 & b_{33} \end{pmatrix} \begin{pmatrix} \dot{y}_1(t) \\ \dot{y}_2(t) \\ \dot{y}_3(t) \end{pmatrix} + \begin{pmatrix} c_{11} & 0 & 0 \\ 0 & c_{22} & 0 \\ 0 & 0 & c_{33} \end{pmatrix} \begin{pmatrix} y_1(t) \\ y_3(t) \\ y_3(t) \end{pmatrix} = \begin{pmatrix} w_1(t) \\ w_2(t) \\ w_3(t) \end{pmatrix}$$

or

$b_{11}\dot{y}_1(t) + c_{11}y_1(t) = w_1(t)$
$b_{22}\dot{y}_2(t) + c_{22}y_2(t) = w_2(t)$
$b_{33}\dot{y}_3(t) + c_{33}y_3(t) = w_3(t)$.

If b_{11}, b_{22}, and b_{33} are nonzero, one can divide these equations by b_{11}, b_{22}, and b_{33}, respectively, and obtain three separate first order linear non-homogeneous equations which can be solved by the methods of Chapter 4.

Section 9.2

1. $y_1(t) = e^t; y_2(t) = e^{-t}$.

3. $y_1(t) = \frac{2}{3}e^{5t} + \frac{1}{3}e^{2t}; y_2(t) = -\frac{1}{3}e^{5t} + \frac{1}{3}e^{2t}$.

4. $y_1(t) = \frac{1}{6}t + \frac{7}{36} - \frac{4}{9}e^{-3t} + \frac{1}{4}e^{-2t}; y_2(t) = -\frac{1}{3}t + \frac{17}{18} - \frac{4}{9}e^{-3t} + \frac{1}{2}e^{-2t}$.

6. $y_1(t) = -\frac{1}{26}\sin t - \frac{5}{26}\cos t + \frac{1}{6}e^t + \frac{1}{39}e^{-5t}$;
$y_2(t) = \frac{6}{13}\sin t + \frac{4}{13}\cos t - \frac{1}{3}e^t + \frac{1}{39}e^{-5t}$.

8. $y_1(t) = \frac{1}{5}e^{3t} + e^{-t} - \frac{6}{5}e^{-2t}; y_2(t) = \frac{1}{2}e^{3t} - \frac{1}{2}e^{-t}; y_3(t) = -\frac{1}{2}e^{3t} + \frac{1}{2}e^{-t}$.

10. (a) Try $y^*(t) = \beta e^{-bt}$.
$\dot{\mathbf{y}}^*(t) = -b\beta e^{-bt}$ hence substitution into (2.1) gives
$-b\beta e^{-bt} + \beta e^{-bt} = (-b\beta + \beta)e^{-bt} = \omega e^{-bt}$.
This will be satisfied if
(i) $-b\beta + C\beta = \omega$.
(i) is a conditional equation on $\mathcal{R}^n$. It will have a unique solution, for any ω, unless the homogeneous equation,
(ii) $-b\beta + C\beta = 0$ or $C\beta = b\beta$
has nonzero solutions. But if (ii) had nonzero solutions β then b would be an eigenvalue of C.

(b) The equations in problem (8) have the form $\dot{\mathbf{y}}(t) + C\mathbf{y}(t) = \omega e^{3t}$ where,

$$C = \begin{pmatrix} 2 & 2 & 0 \\ 0 & 0 & 1 \\ 0 & 1 & 0 \end{pmatrix}; \omega = \begin{pmatrix} 2 \\ 1 \\ -1 \end{pmatrix}.$$

The eigenvalues of C are 2, 1, and -1 hence $b = -3$ is not an eigenvalue. Equation (i) becomes

$$C\beta + 3\beta = \omega$$

or

$$\begin{pmatrix} 5 & 2 & 0 \\ 0 & 3 & 1 \\ 0 & 1 & 3 \end{pmatrix} \begin{pmatrix} \beta_1 \\ \beta_2 \\ \beta_3 \end{pmatrix} = \begin{pmatrix} 2 \\ 1 \\ -1 \end{pmatrix},$$

or

$$\begin{aligned} 5\beta_1 + 2\beta_2 &= 2 \\ 3\beta_2 + \beta_3 &= 1 \\ \beta_2 + 3\beta_3 &= 1. \end{aligned}$$

The solution is $\beta_1 = \frac{1}{5}, \beta_2 = \frac{1}{2}, \beta_3 = -\frac{1}{2}$. Hence a solution is

$$\mathbf{y}^* = e^{3t}\begin{pmatrix} \frac{1}{5} \\ \frac{1}{2} \\ -\frac{1}{2} \end{pmatrix} \quad \text{or} \quad \begin{aligned} y_1^* &= \tfrac{1}{5}e^{3t} \\ y_2^* &= \tfrac{1}{2}e^{3t} \\ y_3^* &= -\tfrac{1}{2}e^{3t}. \end{aligned}$$

11. These equations have the form $\dot{\mathbf{y}}(t) + C\mathbf{y}(t) = \boldsymbol{\omega}e^{-bt}$ where

$$C = \begin{pmatrix} 0 & 1 \\ 1 & 0 \end{pmatrix}, \mathbf{w} = \begin{pmatrix} 1 \\ 2 \end{pmatrix} b = -1.$$

The eigenvalues of C are ± 1 hence b is an eigenvalue. Try $\mathbf{y}^*(t) = \boldsymbol{\beta}e^{-bt} = \boldsymbol{\beta}e^{t}$. Then

$$\boldsymbol{\beta} + C\boldsymbol{\beta} = \boldsymbol{\omega}$$

or

$$\begin{pmatrix} 1 & 1 \\ 1 & 1 \end{pmatrix}\begin{pmatrix} \beta_1 \\ \beta_2 \end{pmatrix} = \begin{pmatrix} 1 \\ 2 \end{pmatrix},$$

or

$$\begin{aligned} \beta_1 + \beta_2 &= 1 \\ \beta_1 + \beta_2 &= 2. \end{aligned}$$

These equations clearly have *no* solutions.

15. Any solution $\mathbf{y}(t)$ can be written in the form,

$$y(t) = u_1(t)\Upsilon_1 + \cdots + u_n(t)\Upsilon_n$$

where the u_k's are solutions of the equations,

$$\dot{u}_k(t) + a_k u_k(t) = 0.$$

Hence $u_k(t) = u_k(t_0)e^{-a_k(t-t_0)}$. If some a_k is zero then the corresponding u_k is a constant. Then *that* u_k does not, in general, tend to zero at t tends to infinity.

17. [*Hint:* The system can be reduced to a set of first order equations of the form $\dot{u}_k(t) + a_k p(t)u_k(t) = w_k(t)$.]

Section 9.3

1. (b) $\dot{\mathbf{y}}(t) + C\mathbf{y}(t) = 0$ where

$$C = \begin{pmatrix} -4 & 2 \\ 1 & -3 \end{pmatrix}.$$

The eigenvectors γ_1 and γ_2 of C are

$$\gamma_1 = \begin{pmatrix} -2 \\ 1 \end{pmatrix}, \text{ corresponding to } a_1 = -5, \gamma_2 = \begin{pmatrix} 1 \\ 1 \end{pmatrix}, \text{ corresponding to } a_2 = -2.$$

Hence

$$\mathbf{Y}_1(t) = e^{5t}\begin{pmatrix} -2 \\ 1 \end{pmatrix}, \qquad \mathbf{Y}_2(t) = e^{2t}\begin{pmatrix} 1 \\ 1 \end{pmatrix}$$

and the basis is

$$y_1^1(t) = -2e^{5t}, \qquad y_2^1(t) = e^{5t}, \qquad y_1^2(t) = e^{2t}, \qquad y_2^2(t) = e^{2t}.$$

(d) $\dot{\mathbf{y}}(t) + C\mathbf{y}(t) = 0$ where

$$C = \begin{pmatrix} 3 & 2 \\ 4 & 1 \end{pmatrix}.$$

The eigenvectors are,

$$\gamma_1 = \begin{pmatrix} 1 \\ -2 \end{pmatrix}, \text{ corresponding to } a_1 = -1; \gamma_2 = \begin{pmatrix} 1 \\ 1 \end{pmatrix}, \text{ corresponding to } a_2 = 5.$$

Hence

$$\mathbf{Y}_1(t) = e^{t}\begin{pmatrix} 1 \\ -2 \end{pmatrix}, \qquad \mathbf{Y}_2(t) = e^{-5t}\begin{pmatrix} 1 \\ 1 \end{pmatrix}$$

and the basis is,

$$y_1^1(t) = e^{t}, \qquad y_2^1(t) = -2e^{t}, \qquad y_1^2(t) = e^{-5t}, \qquad y_2^2(t) = e^{-5t}.$$

3. (a) $y_1(t) = \frac{5}{3}e^{2t} + \frac{1}{3}e^{-2t}$, $y_2(t) = -\frac{4}{3}e^{2t} - \frac{1}{3}e^{-2t}$.
(d) $y_1(t) \equiv 0$, $y_2(t) = -\frac{1}{2}t - \frac{1}{4}$, $y_3(t) \equiv -1$.

4. (a) $y_1(t) = A_1e^{-t} + A_2e^{t} + \frac{5}{3}e^{2t} + \frac{1}{3}e^{-2t}$,
$y_2(t) = A_1e^{-t} - A_2e^{t} - \frac{4}{3}e^{2t} - \frac{1}{3}e^{-2t}$.
(d) $y_1(t) = A_1e^{t} + A_3e^{-t}$, $y_2(t) = A_2e^{2t} - \frac{1}{2}t - \frac{1}{4}$,
$y_3(t) = A_1e^{t} - A_3e^{-t} - 1$.

Section 9.4

2. $y_1(t) = \frac{17}{80}e^{3t} + \frac{1}{80}e^{-3t} - \frac{1}{10}\cos t - \frac{3}{5}\sin t - \frac{1}{16}e^{t} - \frac{1}{16}e^{-t}$,
$y_2(t) = \frac{7}{80}e^{3t} - \frac{9}{80}e^{-3t} - \frac{1}{10}\cos t - \frac{3}{5}\sin t + \frac{1}{16}e^{t} + \frac{1}{16}e^{-t}$.

4. $y_1(t) = \frac{1}{6}t + \frac{1}{6} - \frac{2}{3}\cos\sqrt{3}\,t + \dfrac{4}{3\sqrt{3}}\sin\sqrt{3}\,t + \frac{1}{2}\cos\sqrt{2}\,t - \dfrac{1}{2\sqrt{2}}\sin\sqrt{2}\,t$,

$y_2(t) = -\frac{1}{3}t + \frac{2}{3} - \frac{2}{3}\cos\sqrt{3}\,t + \dfrac{4}{3\sqrt{3}}\sin 3t + \cos\sqrt{2}\,t - \dfrac{1}{\sqrt{2}}\sin\sqrt{2}\,t$.

6. $y_1(t) = \frac{1}{12}e^{t} - \frac{1}{12}e^{-t} - \dfrac{1}{6\sqrt{5}}\sin\sqrt{5}\,t$,

$y_2(t) = -\frac{1}{6}e^{t} + \frac{1}{6}e^{-t} - \dfrac{1}{6\sqrt{5}}\sin\sqrt{5}\,t + \frac{1}{2}\sin t$.

8. $y_1(t) = \frac{1}{5}e^{3t} + 2 - \frac{1}{2}e^t - \frac{1}{2}e^{-t} - \frac{6}{5}\cos t - \frac{3}{5}\sin t,$
$y_2(t) = -1 + \frac{1}{2}e^t + \frac{1}{2}e^{-t},$
$y_3(t) = 1 - \frac{1}{2}e^t - \frac{1}{2}e^{-t}.$

11. (a) We have $\ddot{\mathbf{y}}^*(t) = -b^2\boldsymbol{\beta}\sin bt$. Substitution into (4.2) yields

$$-b^2\boldsymbol{\beta}\sin bt + C\boldsymbol{\beta}\sin bt = \boldsymbol{\omega}\sin bt$$

or
(i) $-b^2\boldsymbol{\beta} + C\boldsymbol{\beta} = \omega.$
(i) has a unique solution unless
(ii) $-b^2\beta + C\beta = 0 \quad$ or $\quad C\beta = b^2\beta$
has a nonzero solution. But if (ii) had a nonzero solution then b^2 would be an eigenvalue of C, contrary to assumption.

(b) The equation in (6) is $\dot{\mathbf{y}}(t) + C\mathbf{y}(t) = \boldsymbol{\omega}\sin bt$ where,

$$C = \begin{pmatrix} 3 & 2 \\ 4 & 1 \end{pmatrix}, \qquad \boldsymbol{\omega} = \begin{pmatrix} 1 \\ 0 \end{pmatrix}, \qquad b = 1.$$

The eigenvalues of C are -1 and 5, hence $b^2 = 1$ is not an eigenvalue of C. Equations (ii) are,

$$\begin{pmatrix} 3 & 2 \\ 4 & 1 \end{pmatrix}\begin{pmatrix} \beta_1 \\ \beta_2 \end{pmatrix} + \begin{pmatrix} -\beta_1 \\ -\beta_2 \end{pmatrix} = \begin{pmatrix} 1 \\ 0 \end{pmatrix}$$

or $2\beta_1 - 2\beta_2 = 1$, $4\beta_1 = 0$
hence $\beta_1 = 0$, $\beta_2 = -\frac{1}{2}$ and the solution is,

$$\mathbf{y}^*(t) = \begin{pmatrix} 0 \\ -\frac{1}{2} \end{pmatrix}\sin t \qquad \text{or} \qquad y_1^*(t) = 0,\ y_2^*(t) = -\tfrac{1}{2}\sin t.$$

12. (a) Substitute

$$\mathbf{y}^*(t) = \boldsymbol{\beta}\sin\sqrt{6}\,t \qquad \text{or} \qquad y_1^* = \beta_1\sin\sqrt{6}\,t,\ y_2^* = \beta_2\sin\sqrt{6}\,t$$

into (i). This yields,

$$(-6\beta_1 + 6\beta_1)\sin\sqrt{6}\,t = \sin\sqrt{6}\,t,\ (-6\beta_2 + \beta_2)\sin\sqrt{6}\,t = 2\sin\sqrt{6}\,t.$$

The first of these equations cannot be satisfied for any β_1.

(b) Solution of (i) is

$$y_1(t) = -\frac{1}{2\sqrt{6}}\,t\cos\sqrt{6}\,t + A\sin\sqrt{6}\,t + B\cos\sqrt{6}\,t,$$

$$y_2(t) = -\tfrac{2}{5}\sin\sqrt{6}\,t + C\cos t + D\sin t.$$

CHAPTER 10

Section 10.1

1. (e) 2. (g) $\frac{3}{2} - \frac{1}{2}i$. (j) -1.
2. (c) $\sqrt{2}\,i$, $-\sqrt{2}\,i$.
6. (b) $1, -1, i, -i$.
8. (b) $y(t) = c_1e^t\cos 3t + c_2e^t\sin 3t$.

Section 10.2

1. (a) Not a subspace. (b) Subspace; $\boldsymbol{\beta} = (0, 1)$ is basis; $\dim S = 1$.

2. (b) Subspace; $\boldsymbol{\beta}_1 = (0, 0, 1), \boldsymbol{\beta}_2 = (2i, 1, 0)$; $\dim S = 2$.

3. $\begin{pmatrix} 1-i & 1 \\ 1 & 0 \end{pmatrix}$.

4. (a) $\lambda = 1, \boldsymbol{\gamma} = \begin{pmatrix} 1 \\ 0 \end{pmatrix}$.

8. Eigenvalues are solutions of $-\lambda^3 + a\lambda^2 + 6\lambda + c = 0$ (a, b, c real), and every real cubic has at least one real root.

11. (b) With f_m as indicated we have

$$\begin{aligned}
&\|f - (d_0e_0 + d_1e_1 + d_1e_1 + \cdots + d_me_m + d_{-m}e_{-m})\|^2 \\
&= \|(f - f_m) - ((d_0 - c_0)e_0 + (d_1 - c_1)e_1 + \cdots + (d_{-m} - c_m)e_m)\|^2 \\
&= [(f - f_m) - ((d_0 - c_0)e_0 + \cdots + (d_{-m} - c_m)e_{-m})] \cdot [(f - f_m) \\
&\quad - ((d_0 - c_0)e_0 + \cdots + (d_{-m} - c_{-m})e_{-m})] = \|f - f_m\|^2 \\
&\quad - [(f - f_m) \cdot ((d_0 - c_0)e_0 + \cdots + (d_{-m} - c_{-m})e_{-m})] \\
&\quad - [((d_0 - c_0)e_0 + \cdots + (d_{-m} - c_{-m})e_{-m}) \cdot (f - f_m)] \\
&\quad + |d_0 - c_0|^2 + \cdots + |d_{-m} - c_{-m}|^2.
\end{aligned}$$

Now the bracketed terms are both zero (by the formulas for the c's and the orthonormality of the e's) so the choice $d_0 = c_0, \ldots, d_{-m} = c_{-m}$ minimizes $\|f - (d_0e_0 + \cdots + d_{-m}e_{-m})\|^2$.

Section 10.3

1. (a) $y_1(t) = \sin t, y_2(t) = \cos t$.
(b) $y_1(t) = \frac{1}{2}e^t - \frac{1}{2}(\cos t - \sin t), y_2(t) = -\frac{1}{2}e^t + \frac{1}{2}(\cos t + \sin t)$.
(f) $y_1(t) = -\frac{11}{10}e^t \cos 2t - \frac{3}{10} \sin t + \frac{11}{10} \cos t$,
$y_2(t) = \frac{9}{10}e^t \cos 2t + \frac{2}{10}e^t \sin 2t - \frac{3}{10} \sin t - \frac{9}{10} \cos t$.
(g) $y_1(t) = \cos t, y_2(t) = -\sin t, y_3(t) = -\frac{2}{5}e^{-4t} - \frac{3}{5}e^t$,
$y_4(t) = -\frac{2}{5}e^{-4t} + \frac{2}{5}e^t$.

6. Any $\boldsymbol{\delta} = \begin{pmatrix} d_1 \\ d_2 \end{pmatrix}$ where $d_1 + d_2 = -1$.

CHAPTER 11

Section 11.1

2. (i) $\tilde{f}(x^1, x^2, x^3) = \dfrac{k}{(x^1)^2 + (x^2)^2 + (x^3)^2}$.

(ii) $\tilde{f}(x^1, x^2, x^3) = c_1x^1 + c_2x^2 + c_3x^3$ where $\boldsymbol{\gamma} = c_1\mathbf{e}_1 + c_2\mathbf{e}_2 + c_3\mathbf{e}_3$.
(iv) $\tilde{f}(x^1, x^2) = x^1(x^1 - c_1) + x^2(x^2 - c_2)$ where $\overrightarrow{P_0P_1} = c_1\mathbf{e}_1 + c_2\mathbf{e}_2$.

3. (i) $\tilde{f}(x^1, x^2, x^3) = \dfrac{k}{(x^1 - b_1)^2 + (x^2 - b_2)^2 + (x^3 - b_3)^2}$ where

$\boldsymbol{\beta} = b_1\mathbf{e}_1 + b_2\mathbf{e}_2 + b_3\mathbf{e}_3$.

4. (i) $$\tilde{\mathbf{F}}(x^1, x^2, x^3) = \frac{kx^1}{(x^1)^2 + (x^2)^2 + (x^3)^2}\mathbf{e}_1 + \frac{kx^2}{(x^1)^2 + (x^2)^2 + (x^3)^2}\mathbf{e}_2 + \frac{kx^3}{(x^1)^2 + (x^2)^2 + (x^3)^2}\mathbf{e}_3.$$

(ii) $\tilde{\mathbf{F}}(x^1, x^2, x^3) = [(c_1x^1 + c_2x^2 + c_3x^3)\,d_1]\mathbf{e}_1 + [(c_1x^1 + c_2x^2 + c_2x^3)\,d_2]\mathbf{e}_2 + [(c_1x^1 + c_2x^2 + c_3x^3)\,d_3]\mathbf{e}_3$ where $\boldsymbol{\gamma} = c_1\mathbf{e}_1 + c_2\mathbf{e}_2 + c_3\mathbf{e}_3$, $\boldsymbol{\delta} = d_1\mathbf{e}_1 + d_2\mathbf{e}_2 + d_3\mathbf{e}_3$.

8. $\varphi(s) = h(P + s\boldsymbol{\alpha}) = f(P + s\boldsymbol{\alpha}) + g(P + s\boldsymbol{\alpha}) = \varphi_1(s) + \varphi_2(s)$, so $\delta h(P; \boldsymbol{\alpha}) = \dot{\varphi}(0) = \dot{\varphi}_1(0) + \dot{\varphi}_2(0) = \delta f(P; \boldsymbol{\alpha}) + \delta g(P; \boldsymbol{\alpha})$.

11. $\varphi(s) = f(g(P(s))) = f(\varphi_1(s))$, so $\delta h(P; \boldsymbol{\alpha}) = \dot{\varphi}(0) = f'(\varphi_1(0))\dot{\varphi}_1(0) = f'(g(P))\,\delta g(P; \boldsymbol{\alpha})$.

12. $\delta f(P; \boldsymbol{\alpha}) = x^2a_1 + x^2a_2 \quad \boldsymbol{\alpha} = a_1\mathbf{e}_1 + a_2\mathbf{e}_2$, so $\varphi(s) = f(P + s\boldsymbol{\alpha})$ is an *increasing* function (for small s) if $\boldsymbol{\alpha}$ is chosen so that $x^2a_1 + x^1a_2 > 0$.

Section 11.2

1. (i) $\varphi(s) = \mathbf{F}(P + s\boldsymbol{\alpha}) = [x^1 + sa_1 + x^2 + sa_2 + x^3 + sa_3]\mathbf{e}_1 + [(x^1 + sa_1)^2 + (x^2 + sa_2)^2 + (x^3 + sa_3)^2]\mathbf{e}_2 + [(x^1 + sa_1)(x^2 + sa_2)(x^3 + sa_3)]\mathbf{e}_3$,
$\delta\mathbf{F}(P; \boldsymbol{\alpha}) = \dot{\varphi}(0) = (a_1 + a_2 + a_3)\mathbf{e}_1 + 2(x^1a_1 + x^2a_2 + x^3a_3)\mathbf{e}_2 + (x^2x^3a_1 + x^1x^3a_2 + x^1x^2a_3)\mathbf{e}_3$ for $\boldsymbol{\alpha} = a_1\mathbf{e}_1 + a_2\mathbf{e}_2 + a_3\mathbf{e}_3$.

(iv) $$\varphi(s) = \mathbf{F}(P + s\boldsymbol{\alpha}) = \frac{x^1 + sa_1}{\sqrt{(x^1 + sa_1)^2 + (x^2 + sa_2)^2}}\mathbf{e}_1 - \frac{x^2 + sa_2}{\sqrt{(x^1 + sa_1)^2 + (x^2 + sa_2)^2}}\mathbf{e}_2,$$

$$\delta\mathbf{F}(P; \boldsymbol{\alpha}) = \dot{\varphi}(0) = \left[\frac{a_1}{\sqrt{(x^1)^2 + (x^2)^2}} - \frac{(x^1)^2a_1 + x^1x^2a_2}{(\sqrt{(x^1)^2 + (x^2)^2})^3}\right]\mathbf{e}_1 + \left[\frac{-a_2}{\sqrt{(x^1)^2 + (x^2)^2}} + \frac{x^2x^1a_1 + (x^2)^2a_2}{(\sqrt{(x^1) + (x^2)^2})^3}\right]\mathbf{e}_2 \text{ for } \boldsymbol{\alpha} = a_1\mathbf{e}_1 + a_2\mathbf{e}_2.$$

2. (i) $\varphi(s) = \mathbf{F}(P + s\boldsymbol{\alpha}) = [(\overrightarrow{P_0P})\cdot\boldsymbol{\gamma} + s\boldsymbol{\alpha}\cdot\boldsymbol{\gamma}]\boldsymbol{\delta}$,
$\delta\mathbf{F}(P; \boldsymbol{\alpha}) = \dot{\varphi}(0) = (\boldsymbol{\alpha}\cdot\boldsymbol{\gamma})\boldsymbol{\delta}$.

(ii) $\varphi(s) = F(P + s\boldsymbol{\alpha}) = [\|\overrightarrow{P_0P}\|^2 + 2s(\overrightarrow{P_0P})\cdot\boldsymbol{\alpha} + s^2\|\alpha\|^2(\overrightarrow{P_0P} + \boldsymbol{\beta} + s\boldsymbol{\alpha})$,
$\delta\mathbf{F}(P; \boldsymbol{\alpha}) = [2(\overrightarrow{P_0P})\cdot\boldsymbol{\alpha}]\overrightarrow{P_0P} + \|\overrightarrow{P_0P}\|^2\boldsymbol{\alpha}$.

3. (i) $$\operatorname{grad}\mathbf{F}(P) \sim \begin{pmatrix} 1 & 1 & 1 \\ 2x^1 & 2x^2 & 2x^3 \\ x^2x^3 & x^1x^3 & x^1x^2 \end{pmatrix}.$$

5. $$L'_p = \begin{pmatrix} \tilde{f}_{x^1x^1} & \tilde{f}_{x^1x^2} & \tilde{f}_{x^1x^3} \\ \tilde{f}_{x^2x^1} & \tilde{f}_{x^2x^2} & \tilde{f}_{x^2x^3} \\ \tilde{f}_{x^3x^1} & \tilde{f}_{x^3x^2} & \tilde{f}_{x^3x^3} \end{pmatrix}.$$

9. (i) $\operatorname{div}\mathbf{F}(P) = 1 + 2x^2 + x^1x^2$,
$\operatorname{curl}\mathbf{F}(P) = (x^1x^3 - 2x^3)\mathbf{e}_1 + (1 - x^2x^3)\mathbf{e}_2 + (2x^1 - 1)\mathbf{e}_3$.

10. (i) All $P \sim (x^1, x^2, x^3)$ for which
$(x^2 - x^1)x^2x^2 + (x^3 - x^2)x^2x^3 + (x^1 - x^3)x^3x^1 \neq 0$.

Section 11.3

1. (a) (i) $\frac{3}{2}$; (ii) $\frac{3}{2}$; (iv) 72; (v) $\frac{2}{3}$.
   (b) (i) 8; (iii) $-\pi/2$; (iv) $3\pi/2$.
2. (a) (i) π; (ii) $-\pi$; (iv) 0.
   (b) (i) 0; (ii) 6.
3. (c) $\tilde{f}(x, y) = \frac{1}{3}(x^2 + y^2)^{3/2}$.
   (e) $\tilde{f}(x^1, x^2, x^3) = x^1e^{x^2} + x^2e^{x^3}$.
4. (a) Not P.I.
   (b) P.I.
   (c) Not P.I.
   (d) Not P.I.

CHAPTER 12

Section 12.1

1. (a) Constant magnitude along circles with center at (0, 0) and constant direction along lines through (0, 0).
   (c) Constant magnitude and direction along circles with centers at (0, 0).
   (d) Constant magnitude along vertical lines, direction constant everywhere.
2. Only (b) and (c).
4. $\rho(x^1, x^2, x^3, t) = c/x^1$ where c is a constant.
5. $v^1(x^1, t) = -\dfrac{t}{(1 + t^2)}x^1 + f(t)$, where f is an arbitrary function of t.
7. $\sigma u_t = \operatorname{div} \nabla(\nu u)$.
8. $\sigma u_t = \nu \operatorname{div}(\nabla u) - Lu$ where L is a constant.
9. $\sigma_t = K \operatorname{div} \mathbf{E}$.

Section 12.2

2. In (v) of example (2.3) the integral over S vanishes because $\nabla u \cdot \mathbf{n} = 0$ on S.
3. Same comment as in problem 2.
4. In each case form the difference of two solutions and show that it satisfies a problem treated before.
6. Equation (vi) of example (2.3) is replaced by [*see* (v)],

$$\frac{1}{2}\frac{d}{dt}\iiint_{\mathfrak{D}} u^2\,dV = -K\iiint_{\mathfrak{D}} \nabla u \cdot \nabla u\,dV - \iint_S \psi u^2\,dS.$$

   The rest of the argument proceeds as in example 2.3.
7. (a) Let u be the difference of two solutions. Multiply the equation by u, integrate over $\mathfrak{D}$ and show that

$$\frac{1}{2}\frac{d}{dt}\iiint_{\mathfrak{D}} u^2\,dV = -\iiint_{\mathfrak{D}} \nabla u \cdot \nabla u\,dV - \iiint_{\mathfrak{D}} u^2\,dV.$$

   Then proceed as in example (2.3).

(c) Let u be the difference of two solutions. Apply (2.2) and deduce that,

$$\iiint_{\mathfrak{D}} (\nabla u \cdot \nabla u)\, dV + \iiint_{\mathfrak{D}} u^2\, dV = 0.$$

Then proceed as in example (2.5).

8. Compare with problem 7. Show that if u is the difference of two solutions, then

$$\frac{1}{2}\frac{d}{dt}\iiint_{\mathfrak{D}} u^2\, dV = -\iiint_{\mathfrak{D}} \nabla u \cdot \nabla u\, dV + \iiint_{\mathfrak{D}} u^2\, dV.$$

Show that the further steps used in problem 7 do not work now. (*See* problem 2 of §6, Chapter 7. That method can also be applied here.)

Section 12.3

1. Let u^1 and u^2 be two solutions and set $u = u^1 - u^2$. Then

$$u''(x) = 0 \qquad u(a) = u(b) = 0.$$

$u'' = 0$ implies that $u(x) = Ax + B$. Then

$$0 = Aa + B, \qquad 0 = Ab + B, \qquad \text{hence } A = B = 0.$$

2. (b), (c), and (e) are harmonic functions.

3. $X_2(x^3)$ and $X_3(x^3)$ must satisfy the differential equations,

$$X_2''(x^2) = \alpha X_2(x^2), \qquad X_3''(x^3) = -(1 + \alpha)X_3(x^3)$$

where α is a constant. There are several cases corresponding to the signs of α and $1 + \alpha$.

4. Solutions of (3.3) have the form $u(x) = Ax + B$.

(i) If $A = 0$, u is a constant.

(ii) If $A > 0$ $u'(x) = A > 0$ and u is increasing, it has its minimum at a and maximum at b.

(iii) If $A < 0$ $u'(x) = A < 0$ and u is decreasing, it has its maximum at a and minimum at b.

6. Suppose u has a maximum u^0 at x_0^1. Then by the given equation

$$u''(x_0^1) = c(x_0^1)u_0.$$

By the hint $u''(x_0^1) \leq 0$ hence $c(x_0^1)u_0 \leq 0$ or, since $c(x_0^1) > 0$, $u_0 \leq 0$. A similar proof applies for a minimum.

Index